Harden's

In association with

RÉMY MARTIN
FINE CHAMPAGNE COGNAC

Restaurant Guide
2008

"Restaurant lovers bible" Daily Mail

HARDEN'S RESTAURANT GUIDE

10
Years

1,800 independently reviewed pubs, cafés & restaurants

A golden age of dining dawns

Whilst culinary excellence has always been taken for granted in France, the restaurant scene in the UK has undergone what can only be described as a revolution over the past decade. Richard Harden has described this as a 'golden age' for the British restaurant scene, and Rémy Martin are proud to be involved with this bible for people who enjoy the finer things in life. Like Rémy Martin, the Harden's guide has a proud history. Now in its tenth year, Harden's is perhaps the UK's leading upmarket restaurant guide.

The Harden's guide is unique because it is perhaps the only 'democratic' restaurant guide where reviews are almost entirely provided by the general public rather than so called experts. In its own way, Rémy Martin also strives to be different: by only selecting eaux-de-vie from the two finest crus regions in Cognac – Grande Champagne and Petite Champagne – and through superior ageing and blending processes, we ensure our Cognacs have an aromatic profile and depth of flavour that exceed every expectation. Our revolutionary new Coeur de Cognac adds further weight to our epicurean philosophy.

What unites Rémy Martin and Harden's is a passion for great food, drink and for shared experience. Through these awards Rémy Martin and Harden's are committed to highlighting and developing the new talent emerging from the thriving UK restaurant scene whilst bringing you the highest quality restaurant information. We raise a glass of our finest – be it V.S.O.P, XO or Coeur de Cognac – to the UK restaurant scene and to the golden age of UK restaurants. Long may it continue.

RÉMY MARTIN
FINE CHAMPAGNE COGNAC

The Heart of Cognac

Rémy Martin is passionate about creating cognac of exceptional quality and taste.

From the Heart of the Cognac region

Rémy Martin only selects grapes from vineyards in the two finest crus in the heart of the Cognac region – Grande Champagne and Petite Champagne in the South-West of France. This outstanding chalky terroir brings out the best in the ugni blanc, colombard and folle blanche grapes that are used in the production of cognac. Blends of eaux-de-vie from these crus are known as Fine Champagne Cognac, an appellation protected by law since 1938.

From the Heart of tradition

Thanks to its indisputable know-how, Rémy Martin has been producing the finest cognacs since 1724. Rémy Martin remains committed to traditional methods of distillation on the lees, in small copper stills, to capture all the flavours and aromas at the heart of the grapes. Our eaux-de-vie are aged for much longer than the minimum required by law, in the highest quality Limousin oak barrels, to reveal a greater aromatic breadth and intensity.

From the Heart of the cellar master

Once distilled, the eaux-de-vie are nurtured with the great expertise and passion of our cellar master Pierette Trichet. She uses her vast experience and skill to select the perfect eaux-de-vie for our inimitable blends, which show perfect balance and an exceptional spectrum of aromas and flavours.

New Coeur de Cognac

Through expert blending Rémy Martin has created an innovative, succulent, fruity spirit – Coeur de Cognac. The first taste is like the first bite into a ripe peach. The nose bursts with ripe summer fruits and the palate is rich and soft – without the fiery finish usually associated with cognac.

Coeur de Cognac is intended for sheer drinking pleasure to be enjoyed anytime, anywhere: try it over a little crushed ice as an aperitif or neat as the perfect end to your meal. So the next time you feel like treating your taste buds try a drop from our heart. You never know, you might fall in love with it.

RÉMY MAR

FINE CHAMPAGNE C

V.S.O

Fondée en 1724

PRODUCT OF FRA

CHAMPAGNE C

RÉMY MARTIN
FINE CHAMPAGNE COGNAC

V.S.O.P

This is the world's favourite V.S.O.P (Very Superior Old Pale) cognac and the benchmark by which all other V.S.O.Ps are measured. Rémy Martin V.S.O.P shows near perfect balance of the three cornerstones of great cognac: floral, fruity and spice. Blended from over 240 eaux-de-vie and aged in cask for up to 14 years, the result is wonderfully balanced and smooth, with a unique aromatic intensity.

A glass of V.S.O.P is the perfect way to end an excellent dinner, or why not kick-start a party with a VSOP cocktail muddled with ginger ale and orange zest? Rémy Martin V.S.O.P is a special cognac for every occasion.

RÉMY MARTIN
FINE CHAMPAGNE COGNAC

XO

Sophisticated and beautifully balanced, Rémy Martin XO Excellence (Extra Old) combines aromatic richness and complexity with a wonderful velvety texture. The nose yields hints of jasmine, ripe fig and candied orange, and the palate shows notes of cinnamon and freshly baked brioche.

Remy Martin XO is aged for up to 37 years in Limousin oak cask to achieve its maturity and balance.

XO is a wonderful digestif and the perfect partner for a rich chocolate dessert. Rémy Martin XO is truly the taste of extravagance.

Enjoying Rémy Martin

Not only are Rémy cognacs the ideal choice to round off a wonderful meal, but Rémy Martin can also be enjoyed as a long drink before dinner or as the perfect accompaniment to fine food.

Coeur de Cognac Flash Tea Infusion
Elderflower and Peppermint infusion

1 x peppermint tea bag
2 tea spoons elderflower cordial
50ml Rémy Martin Coeur de Cognac

Method:

Place tea bag in mixing glass
Add Rémy Martin Coeur de Cognac and stir gently for 5 seconds, then leave to stand for another 20
Add elderflower cordial and fill with ice and stir briskly for another 15 seconds
Fill tumbler with crushed ice then strain infused Coeur de Cognac into tumbler
Serve with 2 short straws

Centaur Spice

A refreshing long drink, combining Rémy Martin V.S.O.P with a hint of orange and bitters, lengthened with ginger ale. A simple but stunning drink – ideal for dinner parties.

Method:

Fill a glass with ice
Add 2 dashes of Angostura bitters
Twist a sliver of orange peel over ice and drop into glass
Add a shot of Rémy Martin V.S.O.P
Top with ginger ale
Gently stir

RÉMY MARTIN
FINE CHAMPAGNE COGNAC

2008 Rémy Martin Restaurant Awards

Now in its sixth year, the Rémy Martin Restaurant Awards recognise the new restaurants across the UK which have achieved outstanding levels of excellence. This award will help you to recognise food and service quality.

There are six regional awards, and five for the capital. The UK is divided as follows:

- Scotland
- North East England
- Central England
- South West England
- South East England

One restaurant has additionally been awarded the ultimate accolade – the Rémy Martin Excellence Award. This award is given to the restaurant which has shown itself as the true outstanding rising star of the UK restaurant scene.

WINNER 2008

RÉMY MARTIN
FINE CHAMPAGNE COGNAC

Winner Of The Excellence Award

The Westerly, Reigate, Surrey

Jon and Cynthia Coomb are old hands when it comes to running great restaurants, having previously managed Michelin rated Stephan Langton in nearby Dorking. It was there that they mastered fundamental basics of the restaurant business – great food at reasonable prices keeps the customers coming back time and again.

The Westerly marks a move by the Coombs into a more streamlined operation, where a fantastic atmosphere and décor complements the outstanding food. However, The Westerly has hit the nail on the head, combining fantastic food, fair pricing, and elegant decoration.

Rustic but refined, cooking is the order of the day here, with a selection of dishes that, while simple in execution, offer deep and satisfying flavours, and signature dishes include salt cod and potato ravioli, tomatoes, olives and capers and croquette of pig's head, sauce Gribiche.

The wine list is as carefully sourced as the cooking ingredients, and many of the wines are available in half litre carafes. It is helpfully grouped by specific styles such as 'fleshy & fruity', 'ripe, savoury & spicy' and 'dry, crisp & mineral'. Service is friendly and utterly professional.

Acorn House, Bloomsbury

Co-launched by Arthur Potts Dawson and James Grainger Smith (with help from the Shoreditch Trust), this King's Cross establishment is London's first premium eco-friendly training restaurant. Every aspect of Acorn House aims to be environmentally aware or sustainable. Not only does the restaurant offer vegetables, meat and fish from sustainable sources and local farmers, but it purifies its water on site and uses 'green electricity'. Takeaway packaging is biodegradable, and all kitchen waste is recycled or composted.

Barrafina, Soho

Sam and Eddie Hart credit the famous Cal Pep Tapas bar in Barcelona as the inspiration for their new Soho eatery. Indeed, the resemblance to the Barcelona operation is striking. Customers sit at high stools eating at a single L-shaped, marble-topped bar counter, creating a social eating experience.

Barrafina serves tapas which are, in the best sense, simple and traditional. The nibbles include almonds, olives and pan

con tomate (tomato-rubbed bread), but many diners are keen to move on swiftly to the cold meats, such as slivers of cured jabugo ham cut from a whole leg behind the counter. A mound of crushed ice displays the fresh seafood: three types of huge prawns, clams, mussels, and a vast chunk of raw tuna used to make tuna tartare.

Barrafina is as Spanish as Spanish gets in London.

El Faro, Isle of Dogs

El Faro (Spanish for lighthouse) looks out over the tranquil scenery of Crossharbour dock, and is only 10 minutes from bustling Canary Wharf. There is a large terrace and on the first floor, a private area. Head Chef Edward Guttierez trained with Ferran Adrià of El Bulli fame, and it shows. He claims to make some of the most authentic tapas in London. However El Faro's particular claim to fame is that a whole suckling pig is flown in weekly from Segovia, just outside Madrid.

152

Magdalen Restaurant, Southwark

Magdalen is owned by father-and-son duo Roger and James Faulks. James and his wife Emma (the pastry chef) run the

restaurant along with sous chef, David Abbott James. Their impressive, collective CV includes The Fat Duck, La Trompette, Le Manoir aux Quat'Saisons and The Anchor and Hope. This two-storey restaurant is traditionally decorated with bentwood chairs, aubergine walls, big mirrors and beautiful chandeliers. The restaurant serves the best of British food with a French twist. Emphasis is on simplicity and quality of ingredients which are seasonal and sourced locally wherever possible.

Scott's, Mayfair

Scott's, from the same stable as such legends as The Ivy and J Sheekey, is a restaurant with great heritage. After its total recent refurbishment, however, it's effectively a completely new restaurant, albeit in a grand and essentially traditional clubby style.

The menu is a sublime, fish-heavy affair, with signature dishes such as Cornish stargazy pie (served with sardines poking their heads out through pastry), or rack of Shetland lamb with pan haggerty (a Northumberland dish of potato, cheese and onion). But there are modern European notes too, like hake with pork belly and braised arrocino (haricot) beans – a meaty, savoury dish of Iberian inspiration.

UK

The Glasshouse at Eskmills, Musselburgh

The Glasshouse at Eskmills in Musselburgh is owned by one of Scotland's most creative and passionate chefs, Steve Adair. The former mill has been transformed to create a welcoming

neighbourhood restaurant where the original architecture blends with stunning contemporary features.

The Glasshouse is passionate about uncomplicated food, and this is clearly reflected in the menus. Locally-grown seasonal produce and local suppliers are the basis for all dishes. Signature dishes include pan-fried seabream with carrots, leek, spring onions and chive beurre blanc, and fillet steak with smoked bacon and tarragon risotto and balsamic jus.

Zutshi's at The Toll Bar, Fowey, Cornwall

After garnering a reputation for excellent outside events, Alison Zutschi has taken on the popular Toll Bar, which enjoys commanding views of the water (and boats). During the day fresh home-made cakes, puddings, and lattes feature alongside great sandwiches, salads and specials of the day. For the evenings, there is a cosy lounge area and the menu features an eclectic mix of food. Signature dishes include goat's cheese feta salad with roasted peppers and balsamic dressing, salt and pepper calamari with sweet chilli, moules marinières with bread for dipping, salmon and tiger prawns in a coriander sauce with saffron rice, and carbonnade of beef with crushed garlic root vegetables and

creamy leeks. All are home-made and prepared with the care of someone who loves to cook.

El Gato Negro, Ripponden, W Yorks.

Chef Simon Shaw has extensive experience of being involved with professional restaurant operators, having formerly worked within a top London restaurant group, along with his restaurant manager Chris Williams. Here in an old pub, they have introduced a touch of Spain to Yorkshire with their convincing tapas menu. The restaurant is remarkably authentic and signature dishes include scallops served with a light chickpea puree and chorizo sausages, fried bread layered with anchovies both salted and marinated, and monkfish served on the bone with crisped pancetta and a stew of tomatoes, olives and white beans, all of which display a precise understanding of Spanish cuisine.

Hipping Hall, Kirkby Lonsdale, Cumbria

The Wildsmith family opened the door on Hipping Hall in its present guise in June 2005, after an extensive six month refurbishment. Andrew Wildsmith spotted the hall for sale and has been responsible for the general concept,

refurbishment and now the day-to-day management. The Head Chef, Jason (Bruno) Birkbeck has been at Hipping Hall from the outset. He has quite a pedigree, having worked at The Samling and Northcote Manor. His style is Modern British using classical French techniques.

Wherever possible, ingredients are found locally. Hipping Hall sources all their lamb, pork and beef from a local farm, and it is this close relationship with suppliers which allows them to maintain consistency and a high standard of cuisine.

Shanghai 30's, Oxford

Situated in a beautiful 15th-century building, Shanghai 30's is bursting with character and warmth. The cuisine is based on both the classic and contemporary dishes of Shanghai. Fresh, delicious, and beautifully presented, the menu includes the more standard dishes like beef with broccoli as well as some unique finds, like Shanghai 30's seafood deluxe, a melange of seafood in abalone sauce. Aside from the food, the real joy is in the restaurant ambience and the dining experience. Upon ascending the stairs after going through a short tunnel, you are transported back to 1930's Shanghai, where you can imagine that you have been welcomed into the parlour of a successful merchant.

Search online
www.hardens.com

© **Harden's Limited 2007**

ISBN 978-1-873721-79-7

British Library Cataloguing-in-Publication data: a catalogue record for this book is available from the British Library.

Underlying UK map images © MAPS IN MINUTES™ 2004.
© Crown Copyright, Ordnance Survey & Ordnance Survey Northern Ireland 2004 Permit No. NI 1675 & © Government of Ireland, Ordnance Survey Ireland.

Printed in Finland by WS Bookwell

Research assistants: Marc McDermott, Elizabeth Koslov, Brian Cameron, Jack Fenton

Harden's Limited
14 Buckingham Street
London WC2N 6DF

The views expressed in the editorial section of this guide are exclusively those of Harden's Limited

Would restaurateurs (and PRs) please address communications to 'Editorial' at the above address, or ideally by email to: editorial@hardens.com

The contents of this book are believed correct at the time of printing. Nevertheless, the publisher can accept no responsibility for errors or changes in or omissions from the details given.

CONTENTS

Fishers Bistro 241

Pétrus 88

RATINGS & PRICES

We see little point in traditional rating systems, which generally tell you nothing more than that expensive restaurants are 'better' than cheap ones, as they use costlier ingredients and attempt more ambitious dishes. You probably knew that already. Our system assumes that, as prices rise, so do diners' expectations.

£ Price
The cost of a three-course dinner for one person. We include half a bottle of house wine, coffee and service (or a 10% tip if there is no service charge).

Food
The following symbols indicate that, *in comparison with other restaurants in the same price-bracket*, the cooking at the establishment is:

 Exceptional

 Very good

Some restaurants are worth a mention but, for some reason (typically low feedback) we do not think a rating is appropriate. These are indicated as follows:

 Tip

We also have a category for places which attract a notably high proportion of adverse comment:

 Disappointing

Ambience
Restaurants which provide a setting which is very charming, stylish or 'buzzy' are indicated as follows:

 Particularly atmospheric

Restaurant Rémy awards
 A bold Restaurant Rémy symbol signifies this year's winners — see front colour section

Small print
Telephone number – All numbers in the London section are (020) numbers.
Sample dishes – these dishes exemplify the style of cooking at a particular establishment. They are merely samples - it is unlikely that these specific dishes will be available at the time of your visit.
Details – the following information is given where relevant:
Directions – to help you find the establishment.
Website – if applicable.
Last orders time – at dinner (Sun may be up to 90 mins earlier).
Opening hours – unless otherwise stated, restaurants are open for lunch and dinner seven days a week.
Credit and debit cards – unless otherwise stated, Mastercard, Visa, Amex and Maestro are accepted.
Dress – where appropriate, the management's preferences concerning patrons' dress are given.
Children – if we know of a specified minimum age for children, we note this.
Accommodation – if an establishment has rooms, we list how many and the minimum price for a double.

FROM THE EDITORS

To an extent we believe to be unique, this guide is written 'from the bottom up'. That is to say, its composition reflects the restaurants, pubs and cafés which people across the country – as represented by our diverse reporter base – talk about. It does not, therefore, concentrate on hotel restaurants (as does one of the major 'independent' guides whose publisher also does big business in paid-for hotel inspections). Nor does it 'overweight' European cuisines. Most restaurants in this country fall in the category usually called 'ethnic', but most guidebooks would lead you to think that such places are generally unworthy of serious commentary. It seems to us that this approach is positively wrong-headed in a country where the diversity of restaurant types is one of the most notable (and positive) features.

The effects of London's restaurant revolution of the '90s are now apparent across the whole of the UK. Most major conurbations, for example, now have several ambitious restaurants good enough to be of note to visitors. The areas that are still truly 'culinary deserts' are becoming both smaller and more dispersed. Much as this is to be applauded, it does not make our task any easier, and we are keenly aware – as any honest publisher must acknowledge – that all guide books are imperfect. There will be deserving places missing, and opinions will be repeated that the passing of time has rendered redundant. However, we believe that our system – involving the careful processing of tens of thousands of reports – is the best available.

We are very grateful to each of our thousands of reporters, without whose input this guide could simply not have been written. Many of our reporters express views about a number of restaurants at some length, knowing full well that – given the concise format of the guide – we can seemingly never 'do justice' to their observations. We must assume that they do so in the confidence that the short – and we hope snappy – summaries we produce are as fair and as well-informed as possible. You, the reader, must judge – restaurant guides are not works of literature, and should be assessed on the basis of utility. This is a case where the proof of the pudding really is in the eating.

Given the growing scale of our task, we are particularly grateful for the continuing support we have received from Rémy Martin Fine Champagne Cognac in the publication of this guide. With their help, this is now well on the way to becoming the most comprehensive – as well as the most democratic and diverse – guide available to the restaurants of the UK.

All restaurant guides are the subject of continual revision. This is especially true when the restaurant scene is undergoing a period of rapid change, as at present. **Please help us to make the next edition even more comprehensive and accurate: sign up to join the survey by following the instructions overleaf.**

Richard Harden   Peter Harden

How This Book Is Organised

This guide begins in London, which, in recognition of the scale and diversity of its restaurant scene, has an extensive introduction and indexes, as well as its own maps. Thereafter, the guide is organised strictly alphabetically, without regard to national divisions – Ballater, Beaumaris, Belfast and Birmingham appear together under 'B'.

For cities and larger towns, you should therefore be able to turn straight to the relevant section. Cities which have significant numbers of restaurants also have a brief introductory overview, as well as entries for the restaurants themselves.

In less densely populated areas, you will generally find it easiest to start with the map of the relevant area at the back of the book, which will guide you to the appropriate place names.

How This Book Is Researched

This book is the result of a research effort involving thousands of 'reporters'. These are 'ordinary' members of the public who share with us summary reviews of the best and the worst of their annual dining experiences. This year, more than 8,000 people gave us over 90,000 reviews in total.

The density of the feedback on London (where many of the top places attract several hundred reviews each) is such that the ratings for the restaurants in the capital included in this edition are almost exclusively statistical in derivation. We have, as it happens, visited almost all the restaurants in the London section, anonymously, and at our own expense, but we use our personal experiences only to inform the standpoint from which to interpret the consensus opinion.

In the case of the more commented-upon restaurants away from the capital, we have adopted an approach very similar to London. In the case of less-visited provincial establishments, however, the interpretation of survey results owes as much to art as it does to science.

In our experience, smaller establishments are – for better or worse – generally quite consistent, and we have therefore felt able to place a relatively high level of confidence in a lower level of commentary. Conservatism on our part, however, may have led to some smaller places being underrated compared to their more visited peers.

How You Can Join The Survey

Register on our mailing list at www.hardens.com and you will be invited, in the spring of 2008, to participate in our next survey. **If you take part you will, on publication, receive a complimentary copy of Harden's Restaurant Guide 2009.**

LONDON INTRODUCTION & SURVEY RESULTS

LONDON INTRODUCTION

What makes London special?

London is not Paris, Rome or Madrid, which are mainly of note for their French, Italian and Spanish restaurants respectively. Although there is some sign of a resurgence of interest in a cuisine which may be said to be genuinely British, it is still fair to say that British cuisine is still generally perceived to have lost its way over 200 years ago.

Like New York, London's real strength has always been its cosmopolitanism. Perhaps for the first time, though, the city has now reached the stage where it can really be said to offer a good range of restaurants offering all of the world's major cuisines (and many minor ones too).

The greatest weakness nowadays is probably in the cuisines of China. The greatest strength is as a centre – arguably the leading centre worldwide – of Indian restaurants. 'Indian' cooking is now available at every price-level, in every part of town, in eating-places of every style and level of grandeur, and with a vast range of different regional influences.

Which is London's best restaurant?

Gordon Ramsay is the biggest name in UK gastronomy, and his Royal Hospital Road flagship remains one of London's best restaurants. In terms of overall experience, however, it lost out in this year's survey to its stablemate Pétrus, and in culinary terms it is almost equalled by both Pétrus and Aubergine. For a grand, old-fashioned dinner, Le Gavroche – London's original grand stand-alone French restaurant – remains hard to beat. The survey found the very best food of all at Chez Bruce – a grand 'local' restaurant whose stellar standards belie its distant Wandsworth location.

For further 'best' restaurant suggestions, consult the double-page spread on pp 32 and 33.

What's 'in' at the moment?

The all-purpose answer to that question in recent times has been the famous Ivy, but it is no longer the must-have table it once was. Some lower-profile names – such as at Ivy stablemates Le Caprice and J Sheekey – are more sought-after by those in the know. The larger and more obvious Wolseley also makes a good all-purpose fashionable destination (especially for business). The new St Alban seems to have something of an instant thespian/media following, but nothing much broader. Also new, L'Atelier de Joel Robuchon combines high chic with good and interesting Gallic cooking.

Mayfair has very much re-established itself as a key see-and-be-seen destination of late, thanks to such arrivals as the trashy-but-fun Cipriani, and the re-launch of the all-purpose success-story of the moment, Scott's. At the younger, more fashion-driven end of the Mayfair market, Mourad Mazouz's Sketch retains quite a following.

For younger City and international types, Nobu-imitator Zuma has become, and remains, the destination of choice – even in preference to the two West End Nobus. Other oriental restaurants with a fashionable following include Roka, Hakkasan and Yauatacha.

I'm not fussed about 'scenes' – where can I get a good meal at reasonable cost?

The best tip of all, if you have the choice, is to lunch, rather than dine. If you do that, you can experience some of London's very grandest restaurants – for example, Le Gavroche – for less than many lesser restaurants charge for dinner.

One of the greatest successes of recent times has been Arbutus – right in the heart of Soho – which has always put offering value right at the heart of the package offered. Its recent offshoot Wild Honey offers a broadly similar approach, but in a more comfortable Mayfair setting. Galvin Bistro de Luxe and Racine are in some ways similar, but their prices are pitched a notch higher.

At the top end of the middle market, the restaurant portfolio assembled by Nigel Platts-Martin has an unparalleled reputation. The stellar Chez Bruce is the one people tend to talk about, but The Glasshouse, The Ledbury and La Trompette are all very impressive too. Another top value suggestion, down south London way, is Lambert's.

The names above, however, are just the beginning. Look through the Area Overviews beginning on page 116. These should quickly enable you to find value – wherever in town you're looking and whatever your budget – for any particular occasion.

And for the best of British tradition?

There are few long-established British restaurants of any note. Of these the most recommendable are Rules and – only if money is no object – Wilton's. Most people will probably find the former more fun. For a very British meal, the clubby St James's restaurant Green's is also well worth considering.

Most of the grand hotel dining rooms nowadays are not of particular interest. The grandest of the traditional experiences – albeit in a style which owes as much to France as it does to Britain – is to be had at the Ritz, where the cooking seems, after decades in the doldrums, to be on themend. The overall experience in the room usually hailed as London's prettiest is certainly memorable. For a truly British experience, the outstanding hotel is the Goring.

The City preserves some extraordinary olde-worlde places such as Sweetings and Simpson's Tavern. Ancient taverns worth seeking out on grounds of charm alone include the Grenadier, the Windsor Castle and Ye Olde Cheshire Cheese.

The Smithfield restaurant St John has for many years pioneered a rebirth of English cooking. For some reason this 'new-traditional'-style of St John cooking (or, usually a slightly less offal-rich version of it) seems to have become largely the province of gastropubs – most obviously the Anchor & Hope – but a few pure restaurants, such as Magdalen have recently picked up the baton.

The new eco-restaurants – such as Acorn House and Konstam at the Prince Albert – which particularly prize locality of supply also, of necessity, explore some dishes from the truly English canon in a way that has not been the fashion for some decades.

Isn't London supposed to be a top place for curry?

As noted above, London is arguably the world's leading Indian restaurant city. At the top end, names such as Rasoi Vineet Bhatia, and then the likes of Amaya, The Cinnamon Club, Tamarind, Vama and Zaika are pushing back the frontiers.

If you want to eat the best-value food you will ever find in London, however, you need to avoid the obvious postcodes (in which all of the fashionable Indian mentioned above are located)

Two of the most accessible of the quality budget subcontinentals are the East End duo – which are strictly speaking Pakistani not Indian – New Tayyabs and the Lahore Kebab House. But these are just examples of the many brilliant options

You said diverse: what about other cuisines?

A major hit of recent times has been the cuisines of North Africa and the Eastern Mediterranean. These cuisines lend themselves well to good budget experiences. London was traditionally notably deficient in Mexican (and Latin American) restaurants, but this has been something of a buzz area in the last few years, with openings such as Crazy Homies, Green & Red Bar & Cantina.

SURVEY MOST MENTIONED

These are the restaurants which were most frequently mentioned by reporters. (Last year's position is given in brackets.) An asterisk* indicates the first appearance in the list of a recently-opened restaurant.

1   J Sheekey (1)
2   Chez Bruce (4)
3   The Wolseley (5)
4   Bleeding Heart (6)
5   Hakkasan (2)
6   Gordon Ramsay (3)
7   The Ivy (7)
8   Oxo Tower (11)
9   La Poule au Pot (9)
10 Andrew Edmunds (10)

The Wolseley

11 Le Gavroche (12)
12 Pétrus (24)
13 Arbutus*
14 Gordon Ramsay at Claridge's (8)
15 Le Caprice (21)
16 Galvin Bistrot de Luxe (22)
17 Nobu (13)
18 La Trompette (16)
19 Yauatcha (19)
20 Locanda Locatelli (20)

Le Caprice

21 maze (14)
22 Zuma (15)
23 The Cinnamon Club (17)
24 Scott's*
25 Tom Aikens (18)
26 The Square (22)
27 The Anchor & Hope (28)
28 Amaya (27)
29 Moro (32)
30= The Don (36)

Tom Aikens

30= Savoy Grill (-)
32= L'Atelier de Joel Robuchon*
32= The River Café (30)
32= Bentley's (40)
35 St Alban*
36= Racine (29)
36= St John (36)
38 Coq d'Argent (-)
39 Blue Elephant (33)
40 Roussillon (-)

St John

LONDON - HIGHEST RATINGS

These are the restaurants which received the best average food ratings (excluding establishments with a small or notably local following).

Where the most common types of cuisine are concerned, we present the results in two price-brackets. For less common cuisines, we list the top three, regardless of price.

British, Modern

£45 and over	**Under £45**
1 Chez Bruce	1 Inside
2 The Glasshouse	2 Lamberts
3 Notting Hill Brasserie	3 Emile's
4 Lindsay House	4 Ottolenghi
5 Le Caprice	5 The Anglesea Arms

French

£45 and over	**Under £45**
1 Gordon Ramsay	1 Comptoir Gascon
2 Aubergine	2 Galvin Bistrot de Luxe
3 Pétrus	3 Magdalen
4 La Trompette	4 Le Cercle
5 Le Gavroche	5 The Food Room

Italian/Mediterranean

£45 and over	**Under £45**
1 Assaggi	1 Pizza Metro
2 Quirinale	2 Latium
3 Zafferano	3 Sarracino
4 Locanda Locatelli	4 Salt Yard
5 Theo Randall	5 Il Bordello

Indian

£45 and over	**Under £45**
1 Rasoi Vineet Bhatia	1 Lahore Kebab House
2 The Painted Heron	2 Kastoori
3 Amaya	3 Hot Stuff
4 The Cinnamon Club	4 New Tayyabs
5 Benares	5 Mirch Masala

Chinese

£45 and over

1 Yauatcha
2 Hunan
3 Ken Lo's Memories
4 Hakkasan
5 Kai Mayfair

Under £45

1 Mandarin Kitchen
2 Royal China
3 Four Seasons
4 Good Earth
5 Singapore Garden

Japanese

£45 and over

1 Zuma
2 Roka
3 Umu
4 Nobu
5 Nobu Berkeley

Under £45

1 Tsunami
2 Edoko
3 Café Japan
4 Pham Sushi
5 Chisou

British, Traditional

1 Fuzzy's Grub
2 The Anchor & Hope
3 St John Bread & Wine

Vegetarian

1 Mildred's
2 Food for Thought
3 The Gate

Burgers, etc

1 Lucky Seven
2 Haché
3 Gourmet Burger Kitch.

Pizza

1 Pizza Metro
2 Il Bordello
3 Oliveto

Fish & Chips

1 Golden Hind
2 Nautilus
3 Fish Club

Thai

1 Sukho Thai Cuisine
2 Amaranth
3 Patara

Fusion

1 Tsunami
2 Nobu
3 Ubon

Fish & Seafood

1 One-O-One
2 J Sheekey
3 Mandarin Kitchen

Greek

1 The Real Greek
2 Daphne
3 Costa's Grill

Spanish

1 Barrafina
2 Moro
3 Fino

Turkish

1 Kazan
2 Haz
3 Ev

Lebanese

1 Ranoush
2 Maroush
3 Noura

SURVEY - NOMINATIONS

Ranked by the number of reporters' votes.

Top gastronomic experience

Pétrus

1   Gordon Ramsay (1)
2   Chez Bruce (2)
3   Le Gavroche (5)
4   Pétrus (6)
5   Tom Aikens (5)
6   L'Atelier de Joel Robuchon*
7   maze (7)
8   Gordon Ramsay at Claridge's (4)
9   La Trompette (8)
10 Locanda Locatelli (-)

Favourite

Andrew Edmunds

1   Chez Bruce (1)
2   The Wolseley (4)
3   J Sheekey (2)
4   The Ivy (2)
5   Le Caprice (5)
6   La Trompette (6)
7   Moro (9)
8   Gordon Ramsay (7)
9   Galvin Bistrot de Luxe (-)
10 Andrew Edmunds (-)

Best for business

The Don

1   The Wolseley (3)
2   Bleeding Heart (1)
3   The Don (3)
4   Coq d'Argent (6)
5   1 Lombard Street (2)
6   The Square (5)
7   Savoy Grill (7)
8   Smiths (Top Floor) (-)
9= The Ivy (10)
9= Rhodes 24 (8)

Best for romance

Bleeding Heart

1   La Poule au Pot (1)
2   Andrew Edmunds (2)
3   Bleeding Heart (3)
4   Chez Bruce (4)
5   Le Caprice (6)
6   Café du Marché (8)
7   Clos Maggiore
8   The Ivy (5)
9   Oxo Tower (9)
10 Blue Elephant (-)

OPENINGS AND CLOSURES

Restaurants in bold are included in the London section of this guide – for the full selection, see Harden's London Restaurants 2008 (£11.99), available in all good bookshops.

Openings

Acorn House
**Alain Ducasse
  at the Dorchester**
The Albion
Alisan
All Star Lanes
Angelus
The Arbiter
Atami
Atma
Aubaine *W1*
Bacchus
Barrafina
Bartego Carcoco
Beach Blanket Babylon *E1*
Beirut Express *SW7*
Benja
Benugo (BFI Southbank)
Bincho Yakitori
Bodeguita del Medio
Bowler Bar & Grill
Brasserie Pierre
Brompton Quarter Café
The Brown Dog
Brumus
Bumpkin
C Garden
Le Café Anglais
Café RED
Café Vergnano *SE1*
Camden Bar & Kitchen
Camino
Canteen
Cape Town Fish Market
Caricatura
Chelsea Brasserie
Chez Patrick
Crescent House
Daylesford Organics
dim T
Diner
Dinings
Dish Dash
Duke on the Green
The Duke's Head
Emni
Empress of India
Eriki *NW8*
Fat Badger
The Forge
Four O Nine
Franklins
Gail's Bread *W11*
Gazette
Goldfish
Goodness
Grazing
Great Queen Street
Green Chilli
Ground

Haiku
Harrison's
Hat & Feathers
Haz *EC3*
Hereford Road
Herne Tavern
Hibiscus
Hokkien Chan
The Horseshoe
The Hoxton Grille
Hummus Bros *WC1*
Las Iguanas
Jerk City
Just Falafs
Kensington Square Kitchen
Kenza
Kiasu
Kicca
Kobe Jones
Kruger
Ladurée *W1*
Langtry's
The Larder
**Leadenhall Italian
   Restaurant**
Lola Rojo
Luc's Brasserie
Magdalen
Molloy's
Mugen
Mulberry Street
Nagomi
The Napket
The Narrow
National Gallery Café Natural
Burger Co & Grill
Nordic Bakery
Norfolk Arms
Northbank
Olivomare
The Only Running Footman
Ooze
Ortega
Pacific Oriental
Le Pain Quotidien *various*
Pearl Liang
La Petite Maison
The Phoenix *SW1*
Piccolino *W1*
Prima
The Prince Arthur
The Queen's Arms
Le Querce
Rajasthan, *Houndsditch*
Raviolo
Rhodes W1 Restaurant
Ristorante Semplice
Rocket *EC2*
The Roebuck
Rooburoo
The Rosendale

Openings cont'd

Rossopomodoro *W11*
Rotisserie *N20, NW6*
St Alban
St Germain
Sake No Hana
Salaam Namaste
Salade
Santa Maria del Sur
La Saveur
Seabass *W2*
Seaport
Shimo
Sitaaray
Skylon
Snazz Sichuan
So
Square Pie Co *WC1*
Stanza
The Stonhouse

Suka
Suzie Wong
Texture
Three Crowns
Tiffinbites
Tom's Place
Trenta
2 Amici
2 Veneti
Vino Rosso
Vivezza
Wahaca
The Wallace
The Warrington
Wild Honey
Wood Street
Yumenoki
Zaffrani
Zaytouna

Closures

Abbey *EC1*
Armadillo
Astor Bar & Grill
Babes 'n' Burgers
Balham Kitchen & Bar
Barcelona Tapas *Bell Ln E1*
Base *SW3*
Bank *Aldwych*
Ben's Thai (see The Warrington)
Berkeley Square Cafe
Blue Kangaroo
Bluebird Club
Café Bagatelle
Café Fish
Calabash
Canyon
Chelsea Kitchen
Christophers in the City
Circus
Les Coulisses
Cristini *Seymour Pl W2*
CVO Firevault
Deya
Dine
Eddalino
Entrecôte Café de Paris
Est, Est, Est
L'Estaminet
Exotika
Fairuz *W2*
Fina Estampa
Fiore
1492
Gabrielle's
Ghillies *SW18*
Ginger
Glas
Globe
Gravy
Harlem *SW9*
The Han of Nazz
Harry Ramsden's *W1*
Hosteria del Pesce
The Ifield

Just Gladwin's
Just the Bridge
Lightship
Lillo e Franco
Little Earth Café
Luigi's
Maison Blanc Vite
Manzi's
Mawar
Matilda's
Mocotó
Mr Jerk
Nathalie
Neal Street
Noto *EC4*
Origin
The Painted Heron *SE11*
The Penthouse
The People's Palace
La Perla *SW6*
Pescador Too
Le Petit Train
Pizzeria Castello *SE1*
Rocco
Sabai Sabai
Sabras
Sarkhels
Satu
Savarona
The Sea Cow *SW6*
Siam Central
La Spighetta
Spoon+
Sri Siam City
Sri Siam Soho
Stratfords
Teca
Ultimate Burger *N10*
Tugga
W'sens
Winkles
Wizzy
Xich-lo
Zim Zum
Zinc

LONDON DIRECTORY

A Cena TW1 £42 Ⓐ⭐
418 Richmond Rd 8288 0108
*Just over Richmond Bridge, this "very friendly" modern Italian,
in St Margarets, is one of the brightest sparks in the area, offering
a "simple" menu and an "interesting wine list". / Details: 10.30 pm;
closed Mon L & Sun D; booking: max 6, Fri & Sat.*

Abeno Too WC2 £31 ⭐
17-18 Great Newport St 7379 1160 3–3B
*"Having the food cooked in front of you adds to the fun", at this
"homely" Japanese, whose "cheap" and "interesting" Osaka-style
omelettes make an ideal Theatreland snack. / Details: 11 pm;
no booking.*

The Abingdon W8 £43 Ⓐ
54 Abingdon Rd 7937 3339 4–2A
*This "upscale gastropub" is probably the most "reliable", "friendly"
and "buzzing" spot for "a good bite" near Kensington High Street,
and the "booths in the back are great" (if you can get one).
/ Details: www.theabingdonrestaurant.com; 11 pm, Mon 10.30 pm.*

Acorn House WC1 £40
69 SwintonSt 7812 1842 8–3D
*A "worthy" (low-carbon) King's Cross newcomer,which impresses
many reporters with its "fresh", "seasonal" and "locally-sourced"
dishes, and – given that this is a training restaurant – by the
standard of service too; a Hackney offshot opens in late-
2007./ Details: www.acornhouserestaurant.com; 10 pm.*

Adams Café W12 £25 Ⓐ
77 Askew Rd 8743 0572 6–1B
*"The owners are like old friends", to regulars at this "bright and
friendly" Shepherd's Bush BYO caff; by day it's a greasy spoon,
but by night it offers "generous" tagines, cous-cous and the like.
/ Details: 11 pm; closed Sun.*

Addie's Thai Café SW5 £26 ⭐
121 Earl's Court Rd 7259 2620 4–2A
*Handily-located (by Earl's Court tube), this "cheap, cheerful and
reliable" oriental caff is "a regular haunt for locals".
/ Details: www.addiesthaicafe.co.uk; 11 pm; closed Sat L & Sun L.*

Agni W6 £26 ⭐
160 King St 8846 9191 6–2C
*It's "not on the nicest part of King Street" and a bit "cramped" and
"basic", but this Hammersmith two-year-old is "a wonderful find" –
it offers "fresh and exciting" cooking ("a spin on Indian street food")
and "impeccable" service. / Details: www.agnirestaurant.com; 11 pm;
Mon-Thu D only, Fri-Sun open L & D.*

Al Sultan W1 £38 ⭐
51-52 Hertford St 7408 1155 2–4B
*"Amazing mezze" steal the show at this "usually very good"
Shepherd Market Lebanese; arguably, though, its low-key premises
could use a "face lift". / Details: www.alsultan.co.uk; 11 pm.*

Alain Ducasse
Dorchester W1 £100
53 Park Ln   7629 8888   2–3A
*International superstar-chef Alain Ducasse is finally set to open
a London outpost in late-2007; his New York venture (at the Essex
House Hotel) was never the success which might have been
expected – let's hope he's learned from the experience...
/ **Details:** www.thedorchester.com.*

Alisan HA9 £29 ⭐⭐
The Junction, Engineers Way, Wembley   8903 3888
*"Outstanding" dim sum (from an ex-Yauatcha chef) wins praise for
this "futuristic" but "soulless" Cantonese newcomer beside the new
Wembley Stadium; "the other food is good, but not world-beating".
/ **Details:** www.alisan.co.uk; Mon-Thu 11 pm, Fri & Sat 11.30 pm,
Sun 10.30 pm.*

Alloro W1 £49 ⭐
19-20 Dover St   7495 4768   2–3C
*"A good all-rounder, especially for a business lunch" –
this "very slick" and "spacious" Mayfair Italian serves up "fantastic"
food (and a "huge" wine list) to a largely besuited clientele.
/ **Details:** 10.30 pm; closed Sat L & Sun.*

Amaya SW1 £54 Ⓐ⭐⭐
Halkin Arc, 19 Motcomb St   7823 1166   4–1D

*This sleek and "classy" Belgravia subcontinental wins many rave
reviews for its innovative "grazing" formula (which incorporates
"light" and "exciting" dishes from an open grill); service, though,
can sometimes come "with attitude". / **Details:** www.amaya.biz; 11 pm.*

The Anchor & Hope SE1 £35 Ⓐ⭐⭐
36 The Cut   7928 9898
*"You have to camp out for days for a table", at this "chaotic", no-
bookings legend near Waterloo; again the survey's No. 1 gastropub,
it has won a huge reputation for its "amazing" and "gutsy" British
fare. / **Details:** 10.30 pm; closed Mon L & Sun D; no Amex; no booking.*

Andrew Edmunds W1 £34 Ⓐ
46 Lexington St   7437 5708   2–2D
*It may be small and "cramped", but this "eternally popular" Soho
townhouse – with its "quirky", "snug" and "Bohemian" charm –
remains many a Londoner's "No. 1 choice for romance"; its "lovely"
staff serve up "simple", "straight-up" food, plus an "exceptional-
value" wine list. / **Details:** 10.30 pm; no Amex; booking: max 6.*

The Connaught W1 £84
Carlos Pl 7592 1222 2–3B
Shortly before this guide went to press, it was announced that the Ramsay group and Angela Hartnett, would no longer be involved with this legendary panelled chamber; it is rumoured that the new incumbent will be star Parisian chef Alain Passard of Arpège fame, / **Value tip:** *set weekday L £51 (FP).* **Details:** *11 pm; jacket; booking: max 8.*

The Anglesea Arms W6 £38 Ⓐ ★ ★
35 Wingate Rd 8749 1291 6–1B
Near the top of London's "gastropub premier league" – this "brilliant" boozer, near Ravenscourt Park, serves up "incredibly flavourful" cooking at very "reasonable prices" in a "relaxed" (if "cramped") setting; service – traditionally "slow" – "has got better" under a new owner. / **Details:** *Tue-Sat 10.30 pm, Sun & Mon 10 pm; no Amex; no booking.*

Anglo Asian Tandoori N16 £24
60-62 Stoke Newington Church St 7254 3633
"It's been around for yonks", but this "Stoke Newington staple" is still "always a winner", thanks to its "reliable" food and its "smiling" staff ("who deliver a plethora of freebies"). / **Details:** *www.angloasian.co.uk; 11.45 pm.*

Annie's £35 Ⓐ
162 Thames Rd, W4 8994 9080
36-38 White Hart Ln, SW13 8878 2020
"Mismatched furniture and heavy drapes" help create a "very romantic", "front-room" feeling at these "friendly" neighbourhood spots (in Strand on the Green and Mortlake); their "generous", "comfort" food helps make them a "favourite weekend brunch haunt". / **Details:** *W4 10 pm, SW13 11 pm.*

Arancia SE16 £28 Ⓐ ★
52 Southwark Park Rd 7394 1751
"Still going strong" – after a decade in business, this "delightful find", in deepest Bermondsey, continues to offer "simple" but "well prepared" Italian dishes, in a homely setting. / **Details:** *11 pm; closed Mon & Sun.*

Arbutus W1 £44 ★
63-64 Frith St 7734 4545 3–2A
"Gastronomic finesse, but without a fine-dining price-tag", has made a smash foodie hit of this "spectacular" Soho yearling, where "unfussy" (but "intriguing") dishes are complemented by "exceptional-quality" wines (available by the carafe); the setting, though, strikes some reporters as rather "cramped" or "canteen-like". / **Details:** *www.arbutusrestaurant.co.uk; 10.30 pm.*

Archipelago W1 — £49 Ⓐ
110 Whitfield St   7383 3346   1–1B
"Like a cross between a harem and a junk shop", this "ultra-quirky" venue in the shadow of the Telecom Tower makes "a great place for a date", and its "fascinating" and "exotic" menu "turns out better than you'd expect". / Details: www.archipelago-restaurant.co.uk; 10.30 pm; closed Sat L & Sun.

L'Artiste Musclé W1 — £34 Ⓐ
1 Shepherd Mkt   7493 6150   2–4B
The "spitting image of a slightly shabby Parisian bistro" – this Shepherd Market fixture may serve "basic" fare, but it has a wonderfully "convivial" atmosphere. / Details: 11 pm.

Asia de Cuba
St Martin's Lane Hotel WC2 — £66 Ⓐ
45 St Martin's Ln   7300 5588   3–4C
It may be "full of itself" – and charge "shocking" prices – but this "eccentric" style-scene, on the fringe of Covent Garden, still offers "a fun night out"; on the food front, its "far-out" fusion sharing plates are "surprisingly OK" (and "great for group dining"). / Details: www.morganshotelgroup.com; midnight, Thu-Sat 12.30 am, Sun 10.30 pm.

Assaggi W2 — £59 ★★
39 Chepstow Pl   7792 5501   5–1B
"For great produce, simply and beautifully cooked, Nino Sassu is the man"; his food yet again won this unlikely venture – a Spartan room over a Bayswater pub – the survey's vote as London's top Italian; "passionate" staff play a "theatrical" supporting rôle. / Details: 11 pm; closed Sun; no Amex.

L'Atelier de Joel Robuchon WC2 — £70 Ⓐ★★
13-15 West St   7010 8600   3–2B

Who cares if it's "outrageously pricey"? – this "exquisite" Parisian import has been an "awesome" addition to London, offering a "bite-size" cuisine that's "so good it should be illegal"; the "beautiful", "dark" and "sophisticated" ground floor is usually tipped over the "more conventional" dining room upstairs. / Details: 10.30 pm.

The Atlas SW6 — £34 Ⓐ★
16 Seagrave Rd   7385 9129   4–3A
"Fresh and flavoursome" Mediterranean cooking has made quite a name for this "cosy" gastropub near Earl's Court 2; such is its popularity, though, that "it can get uncomfortably crowded". / Details: www.theatlaspub.co.uk; 10.30 pm; no Amex; no booking.

Atma NW3 £34 ⭐

106c Finchley Rd 7431 9487

*"Interesting" dishes – especially from south India – are winning a strong local following for this "reasonably-priced" Belsize Park newcomer; service is "warm" and "attentive" too. / **Details:** 11.30 pm.*

Aubergine SW10 £88 ⭐⭐

11 Park Wk 7352 3449 4–3B

*Though he works "in the shadow of Ramsay" (who kicked off his own solo career at this Chelsea dining room), William Drabble's "divine" cuisine was – to within a thousandth of a point – rated the equal of his predecessor's this year; "they sure know how to charge" for it, of course (but there's an "exceptional"-value lunch menu). / **Value tip:** set weekday L £38 (FP). **Details:** www.auberginerestaurant.co.uk; 11 pm; closed Sat L & Sun.*

Aurora W1 £38 🅐

49 Lexington St 7494 0514 2–2D

*A "chilled" vibe and "friendly" service help make this Soho "gem" a "really intimate" West End haven ("particularly in summer, thanks to its courtyard"); its "tasty" food "won't break the bank" either. / **Details:** 10.30 pm; closed Sun.*

L'Aventure NW8 £50 🅐⭐

3 Blenheim Ter 7624 6232

*Catherine is a "wonderful hostess", and helps create a "very French" and "romantic" atmosphere at this "tucked-away" St John's Wood favourite, which has a "brilliant summer terrace"; the Gallic menu is "not adventurous", but it "really works". / **Details:** 11 pm; closed Sat L & Sun.*

Awana SW3 £46 ⭐

85 Sloane Ave 7584 8880 4–2C

*"Seriously good" Malaysian cooking (not least, "amazing satay") is winning greater acclaim for this smart Chelsea yearling; it's "at the top end of its price scale", though, so "frequent online offers are worth seeking out". / **Details:** www.awana.co.uk; 11.30 pm.*

Azou W6 £27

375 King St 8563 7266 6–2B

*A "friendly", family-run North African café in Hammersmith; fans say it's "fantastic" – with "good-value" tagines and so on – and even less-enthusiastic reporters consider it "a handy stand-by". / **Details:** www.azou.co.uk; 11 pm; closed Sat L & Sun L.*

Babur Brasserie SE23 £32 🅐⭐⭐

119 Brockley Rise 8291 2400

*This "haute" Indian "transcends" its "unlikely" Honor Oak Park location, and is "really worth a detour"; it offers "exceptional" food ("regularly showcasing the cuisines of different regions") and "utterly attentive" service, in a "classy" modern setting. / **Details:** www.babur.info; 11.30 pm.*

Back to Basics W1   **£42**   ⭐⭐

21a Foley St   7436 2181   1–1B

"Small, cramped, noisy and quite splendid" – this Fitzrovia bistro
offers an *"amazing choice"* of *"really fresh fish"* (and seafood)
at *"superb"* prices. / **Details:** www.backtobasics.uk.com; 10.30 pm;
closed Sun.

Balans   **£34**   ❌

34 Old Compton St, W1   7439 3309   3–2A
60 Old Compton St, W1   7439 2183   3–3A
239 Old Brompton Rd, SW5   7244 8838   4–3A
214 Chiswick High Rd, W4   8742 1435   6–2A
187 Kensington High St, W8   7376 0115   4–1A

The *"buzzy, young atmosphere"* is all there is to shout about
nowadays, at these *"mostly gay"* diners – the food *"just gets worse
and worse"*; people of all persuasions, though, find them *"good for
a quick brunch"*. / **Details:** www.balans.co.uk; varies from midnight to 6 am,
34 Old Compton St 24 hrs; some booking restrictions apply.

Bam-Bou W1   **£41**   Ⓐ

1 Percy St   7323 9130   1–1C

"Beautiful, colonial Franco/Vietnamese décor" and *"fabulous"*
cocktails contribute to a *"seductive"* ambience at this *"buzzing"*
Fitzrovia townhouse; the oriental fare is usually *"delicious"* too,
but service can be *"erratic"*, and critics find bills excessive.
/ **Details:** www.bam-bou.co.uk; 11 pm; closed Sat L & Sun; booking: max 6.

Banners N8   **£32**   Ⓐ

21 Park Rd   8348 2930

Brunch here may be *"a bit of a local cliché"*, but Crouch End's
"perennial" favourite *"still rocks"* – the *"buzzy"* vibe is the
highpoint, but the *"comfort food with a twist"* is certainly
"very solid". / **Details:** 11.30 pm, Fri midnight; no Amex.

Bar Italia W1   **£18**   Ⓐ

22 Frith St   7437 4520   3–2A

"First choice for a shot of espresso", with some *"great people-
watching"* on the side – this *"fantastic"* 24/7 veteran remains
a linchpin of Soho life: *"it's always fab, but especially late-night"*.
/ **Details:** open 24 hours, Sun 3 am; no booking.

Barrafina W1   **£49**

54 Frith St   7813 8016   3–2A

"Tapas the way they should be" – *"as good as Barcelona"* –
have instantly made the Hart brothers' *"slick and cool"* new 27-
seater, in the heart of Soho, a raging success (even if it is *"a tad
pricey"*); *"arrive early, or you'll have to queue"*.
/ **Details:** www.barrafina.co.uk; 11 pm; closed Sun; no booking.

Beach Blanket Babylon   £65   A X
45 Ledbury Rd, W11   7229 2907   5–1B
19-23 Bethnal Green Rd, E1   awaiting tel
*"You don't go for the food or service" ("appalling"), but "great
cocktails" and a "beautiful" Gothic interior can still make this
(once groundbreaking) Notting Hill hang-out a "very romantic"
destination; an offshoot is to open in Shoreditch around the
publication date of this guide. / Details: 11.30 pm.*

Belvedere W8   £50   A
Holland Pk, off Abbotsbury Rd   7602 1238   6–1D
*This landmark in the very heart of Holland Park offers
"the complete package" – not just a "beautiful" location, but also
"gorgeous" Art Deco styling, "attentive" service and "well-cooked"
("straight-down-the-middle") cuisine; summer Sunday lunches are
a particular highlight. / **Value tip:** set dinner £29
(FP). Details: www.belvedererestaurant.co.uk; 10 pm; closed Sun D.*

Benares W1   £63   ★
12 Berkeley Hs, Berkeley Sq   7629 8886   2–3B
*Thanks to his "fabulous, subtle and exotic" modern Indian cuisine,
Atul Kochar's "ultra-modern" (if "slightly cold") Mayfair venture has
earned many accolades; service can be "erratic", though, and prices
sometimes seem "horrendous". / Details: www.benaresrestaurant.com;
10.30 pm; closed Sat L.*

Bengal Clipper SE1   £34   A ★
Shad Thames   7357 9001
*This "well-spaced" South Bank Indian has "impeccable" service,
and offers a "delicious" and "slightly different" menu, often to the
"relaxed sound of a live pianist". / Details: www.bengalclipper.co.uk;
11.30 pm.*

Benja W1   £39   ★
17 Beak Street   7287 0555   2–2D
*Just off Regent Street, a "cramped" but lavishly-decorated Thai
newcomer, praised by all early-days reporters for its "nice food and
good service". / Details: 10.45 pm; closed Sun.*

The Bentley Hotel SW7   £78
27-33 Harrington Gdns   7244 5555   4–2B
*After Andrew Turner's departure from the 1880 restaurant at this
"elaborate" South Kensington hotel, "it all went downhill";
the management seems to be aware of this, and a total re-jig of the
dining facilities – including shifting the main room to the ground
floor – is mooted for some point in late-2007.
/ Details: www.thebentley-hotel.com; 10 pm; D only, closed Mon & Sun; booking:
max 8.*

Bentley's W1   £58
11-15 Swallow St   7734 4756   2–3D
*Richard Corrigan's "elegant" transformation of this WWI-era
dowager, just off Piccadilly, again wins torrents of praise for its
"classic" seafood; the "fun" downstairs oyster bar outscores the
"more formal" restaurant upstairs, though, and there have been
growing gripes about "average" food and "amateurish" service.
/ Details: www.bentleysoysterbarandgrill.co.uk; midnight; booking: max 12.*

Benugo
BFI Southbank SE1 £34 Ⓐ⭐
Belvedere Rd   7401 9000   1–3D
"Perfect for a pre-movie date"; this stylish new South Bank arts-venue café – which has *"no menu similarities to the eponymous sandwich chain"* – offers *"straightforward"* and *"well-priced"* brasserie fare in a *"really relaxing"* setting. / **Details:** www.benugo.com; 11 pm.

Best Mangal W14 £24 ⭐
104 North End Rd   7610 1050   6–2D
"Great properly char-grilled meat" is the highlight at this small and *"efficient"* Turkish outfit, near West Kensington tube. / **Details:** midnight; no Amex.

Bevis Marks EC3 £47
4 Heneage Ln   7283 2220
"Still the best kosher restaurant in London" – this *"unique"* (*"lean-to"*) annex, joined to an ancient City synagogue, offers very *"decent"* cuisine in a *"calming"* and *"sophisticated"* setting. / **Details:** www.bevismarkstherestaurant.com; 8 pm; closed Fri D, Sat & Sun.

Bibendum SW3 £67 Ⓐ
81 Fulham Rd   7581 5817   4–2C
"The most splendid setting, especially on a sunny lunchtime" – plus *"one of the best wine lists in town"* – makes the airy first-floor dining room of this *"heart-of-Chelsea"* landmark a firm favourite for many reporters; the food is *"nothing exceptional"* though, and *"very expensive"* for what it is. / **Details:** www.bibendum.co.uk; Mon-Fri 11 pm, Sat 11.30 pm, Sun 10.30 pm; booking: max 12.

Bincho Yakitori
Oxo Tower SE1 £31 Ⓐ⭐
2nd Floor, Barge House St   7803 0858
Adjoining Tamesa@Oxo, this second-floor South Bank yakitori (Japanese skewer) parlour opened in mid-2007; a visit here offers a rare combination of interesting food, friendly service and a view – and all at reasonable prices! / **Details:** www.bincho.co.uk; 11.30 pm.

Blakes
Blakes Hotel SW7 £101 Ⓐ
33 Roland Gdns   7370 6701   4–2B
"For a dinner with romantic promise", fans find this datedly-glamorous South Kensington basement *"unbeatable"*; the object of your affections better be worth it, though – the food can be *"dire"*, and prices are *"unbelievably high"*. / **Details:** www.blakeshotel.uk.com; 10.45 pm.

Bleeding Heart EC1 £46 Ⓐ⭐
Bleeding Heart Yd, Greville St   7242 8238
It's "bleedin' hard to find", but this *"top-class"* Holborn *"gem"* is as mega-popular for business entertaining as it is for *"intimate dîners-à-deux"*; *"top-notch"* Gallic food (and a *"head-spinning"* wine list) are served in an *"unusually cosy"* (and historic) setting. / **Details:** www.bleedingheart.co.uk; 10 pm; closed Sat & Sun.

Blue Elephant SW6 £51 Ⓐ
3-6 Fulham Broadway   7385 6595   4–4A
*"Pagodas, bridges, streams, fish and foliage" create a "magical" and
"truly stunning" vista at this "jungle-oasis", in deepest Fulham; critics
have always found the place "a bit of a theme-park", though,
and the once-excellent Thai food has seemed more "incidental"
in recent years. / Details: www.blueelephant.com; midnight, Sun 10.30 pm;
closed Sat L (except Stamford Bridge match days).*

Blue Jade SW1 £29
44 Hugh St   7828 0321   1–4B
*"It doesn't spring many surprises", but this "staple" Thai, in a
Pimlico back street, is "a handy stand-by in a culinary desert",
and offers a "warm" welcome. / Details: 11 pm; closed Sat L & Sun.*

Bluebird SW3 £56 Ⓐ
350 King's Rd   7559 1000   4–3C
*The re-named Conran empire (D&D London) relaunched this huge
Chelsea hangar in mid-2007; pre-revamp, the survey had found
"remarkably indifferent" standards – in the early days of the new
régime, the straightforward British menu was of high quality,
but prices were lofty too. / Details: www.bluebird-restaurant.co.uk;
10.30 pm.*

Boisdale SW1 £52 Ⓐ
13-15 Eccleston St   7730 6922   1–4B
*The "completely non-PC" charms of this perennially "buzzing"
Belgravia bar/restaurant (decked out "Scottish hunting lodge" style)
win many fans – "serious steaks" are a lead attraction, as is the
"wonderful range of whiskies" (plus jazz at the weekends); critics,
though, find it "overpriced". / Details: www.boisdale.co.uk; 11.15 pm;
closed Sat L & Sun.*

Bombay Brasserie SW7 £50 Ⓐ✪
Courtfield Close, Gloucester Rd   7370 4040   4–2B
*Some reporters say it's "tired", but – for its many devotees –
this "posh" Indian "old-favourite", by Gloucester Road tube, is still
"a total winner", with "tasty" food and a "loud" and "jolly"
atmosphere (especially in the conservatory); "the Sunday buffet is a
must". / Details: www.bombaybrasserielondon.com; 11.30 pm.*

Bombay Palace W2 £38 ✪✪
50 Connaught St   7723 8855   5–1D
*It has a "nondescript" setting north of Hyde Park, but this low-
profile Indian (part of an international chain) is "one of London's
best-kept secrets" – the "extraordinarily good" food "has few rivals
in town", and service is extremely "pleasant and professional".
/ Details: www.bombay-palace.co.uk; 11.30 pm.*

Il Bordello E1 £39 Ⓐ✪
75-81 Wapping High St   7481 9950
*"Supersize me!", say fans of the "pizzas-like-bicycle-wheels",
and other "hearty" fare, offered by this "ever-popular" Wapping
Italian; you may have to sit "elbow-to-elbow" with other guests,
but service is "outstanding". / Details: 11 pm; closed Sat L.*

La Bouchée SW7 £42
56 Old Brompton Rd   7589 1929   4–2B
Offering "splendid" food at "good-value" prices, this "dark" and "characterful" South Kensington bistro has a candlelit interior which manages to "feel just like Paris"; "don't go if you're claustrophobic", though. / **Details:** www.boudinblanc.co.uk; 11 pm.

(Grill)
Brown's Hotel W1 £68
Albemarle St   7493 6020   2–3C
With its "quiet and spacious" setting and its "traditional British" menu, this "club-like" Mayfair dining room is perfect "for great aunts and important business deals"; the atmosphere "lacks sparkle", though, as does the food. / **Details:** www.roccofortehotels.com; 10.30 pm; no booking at weekends.

Brula TW1 £38
43 Crown Rd   8892 0602
A "cosy interior" – "like someone's front room" – and "polite" and "attentive" staff set the scene at this "charming St Margarets bistro", where "straightforward" Gallic fare comes at "good-value" prices. / **Details:** www.brula.co.uk; 10.30 pm.

Brunello
Baglioni Hotel SW7 £75
60 Hyde Park Gate   7368 5700   4–1B
It's the "really decadent" ambience (and, perhaps, the wine list) which makes this Kensington design-hotel dining room of note – the Italian cooking is "good, but in no way as good as the price level suggests". / **Value tip:** set pre theatre £48
(FP). **Details:** www.baglionihotellondon.com; 10.45 pm.

Busaba Eathai £27
106-110 Wardour St, W1   7255 8686   2–2D
8-13 Bird St, W1   7518 8080   2–1A
22 Store St, WC1   7299 7900   1–1C
"Much better than Wagamama" – Alan Yau's "inviting", communal-seating cafés offer a "fantastic-value" formula of "cheap" and "punchy" Thai dishes, served in a "classy", dark-wood setting; the Soho branch is "always crowded (expect to queue)". / **Details:** 11 pm, Fri & Sat 11.30 pm, Sun 10 pm; W1 no booking; WC1 need 12+ to book .

C Garden SW3 £44
119 Sydney St   7352 2718   4–3C
"The garden is unbeatable in summer", say fans of this "friendly" new Italian (on the venerable Chelsea site that was long Dan's, RIP); there's the odd "dreadful" report, but we had an enjoyable meal here, and most of the (few) initial reports are upbeat. / **Details:** www.cgarden.co.uk; 11 pm; closed Sun D.

The Cabin SW6 £38
125 Dawes Rd   7385 8936
"Amazing burgers" and "great steaks" win local raves for this "cheap and cheerful" yearling, in deepest Fulham. / **Details:** www.thecabinbarandgrill.co.uk; 10.30 pm; D only, ex Sun open L & D.

Café 209 SW6 £20 Ⓐ
209 Munster Rd   7385 3625
Joy, the owner, is "a brilliant comedy act in her own right", and helps ensure a visit to this "buzzy" BYO Fulham Thai is "a complete laugh"; for the money, "the food is pretty good too".
/ **Details:** 10.30 pm; D only, closed Sun, closed Dec; no credit cards.

Café du Marché EC1 £42 Ⓐ⭐
22 Charterhouse Sq   7608 1609
"Very Frenchly-romantic" – and also "just far enough from the Square Mile to be good for business" – this "secluded" Clerkenwell stalwart is an "excellent all-rounder", offering "top-quality" bourgeois cuisine and "discreet and friendly" service.
/ **Details:** www.cafedumarche.co.uk; 10 pm; closed Sat L & Sun; no Amex.

Café Japan NW11 £28 ⭐⭐
626 Finchley Rd   8455 6854
"Nothing beats the sushi", at this "friendly" and "inspired" (but "scruffy") café opposite Golder's Green station; "it is telling that most of the menu is in Japanese, and that most of the diners ARE Japanese". / **Details:** www.cafejapan.co.uk; 10 pm; closed Mon, Tue, & Wed L-Fri L; no Amex.

Café Spice Namaste E1 £41 ⭐
16 Prescot St   7488 9242
Cyrus Todiwala's "slightly out-of-the-way", east-City Indian is "as different as you can imagine from the dross in nearby Brick Lane"; its "friendly" staff deliver "outstanding" and "original" (going-on "eccentric") dishes in a setting that's "part hippie, part Salvation Army Hall". / **Details:** www.cafespice.co.uk; 10.30 pm; closed Sat L & Sun.

La Cage Imaginaire NW3 £34 Ⓐ
16 Flask Walk   7794 6674
The "lovely" setting of this "cosy" Hampstead spot is straight out of a picture-book; the food may be "a blast from the past", but it's "amazingly well-priced". / **Value tip:** set weekday L £20 (FP). **Details:** 11 pm.

Cambio de Tercio SW5 £48 Ⓐ⭐
163 Old Brompton Rd   7244 8970   4–2B
For "a great take on modern Spanish food" – "made even better by now offering smaller dishes" – it's hard to beat this "terribly noisy" Earl's Court spot; its wine list is "better than many in Spain!" / **Details:** 11.30 pm.

Cantina Italia N1 £32 Ⓐ⭐
19 Canonbury Ln   7226 9791
A "regular-haunt", for some locals – this Islington spot may be "noisy", but it serves "generous" pizza and pasta in "friendly" style. / **Details:** www.cantinaitalia.co.uk; 11 pm, Fri & Sat 11.30 pm; D only, ex Sun open L & D; no Amex.

Il Cantuccio di Pulcinella SW11 £29
143 St John's Hill   7924 5588
Wandsworth locals are divided over this "very friendly" Italian – fans say it's "reliable" and sometimes "spectacular", but critics say they "won't be rushing back". / **Details:** www.ilcantucciodipulcinella.co.uk; 11.30 pm; closed Tue L; no Amex.

The Capital Restaurant
Capital Hotel SW3   £82
22-24 Basil St   7591 1202   4–1D
*Eric Chavot's "faultless" cuisine maintains the first-rank position
of this long-established Knightsbridge hotel dining room (where the
"fantastic" set lunch is particularly worth seeking out); the setting,
though, can seem a trifle "dull". / **Value tip:** set weekday L £53
(FP). **Details:** www.capitalhotel.co.uk; 10 pm.*

Le Caprice SW1   £55
Arlington Hs, Arlington St   7629 2239   2–4C

*"Lower-key than the Ivy, but far classier" – this "slick" '80s
brasserie, behind the Ritz, remains an "all-time favourite" for many
reporters; "take your date here to show them you've got style,
but don't need to show off". / **Details:** www.caprice-holdings.co.uk;
midnight.*

Caraffini SW1   £42
61-63 Lower Sloane St   7259 0235   4–2D
*It's "unbeatable", say fans of this "warm and buzzy" Sloane Square
veteran, which "hits the 'classic Italian' nail right on the head";
if there is a criticism, it's that the cuisine "lacks wow-factor".
/ **Details:** 11.30 pm; closed Sun.*

Carluccio's Caffè   £28
*Quality is still "slipping" at this hugely successful Italian deli-café
chain, whose "faux-foodie vibe" is increasingly at odds with the often
"slapdash" standards; "decent coffee", though.
/ **Details:** www.carluccios.com; 11 pm; no booking weekday L.*

Le Cercle SW1   £40
1-5 Wilbraham Pl   7901 9999   4–2D
*"Truly exceptional French tapas" and "carefully chosen" wines-by-
the-glass "encourage gastronomic adventure" at Club Gascon's
Belgravia offshoot; the "ethereal" décor – complete with "intimate
booths" – manages to make this a "most unbasement-y" basement.
/ **Details:** www.lecercle.co.uk; 11 pm; closed Mon & Sun.*

Champor-Champor SE1 £45 Ⓐ☆

62 Weston St   7403 4600

*"Zany" décor and "exciting" Malay/fusion fare help create
"an intriguing and romantic experience" at this "really unusual" and
"fun" hide-away, in a Borough backstreet.*
/ **Details:** www.champor-champor.com; 10.15 pm; closed L, closed Sun; booking:
max 12.

The Chancery EC4 £45 ☆

9 Cursitor St   7831 4000

*"An out-of-the-way back alley" provides the site for this "wonderful"
Clerkenwell "find" – "a perfect business lunch spot", thanks to its
"very high standard of cooking", and "speedy" and "charming"
service; "some art on the wall", though, "would not go amiss".*
/ **Details:** www.thechancery.co.uk; 10.30 pm; closed Sat & Sun.

Chapter Two SE3 £40 ☆

43-45 Montpelier Vale   8333 2666

*"By far the best place in Blackheath" – this "great local" (sibling
to Chapter One, in Bromley) offers "well-composed" food,
"consistently good" service and a "buzzy" atmosphere.*
/ **Details:** www.chaptersrestaurants.co.uk; 10.30 pm, Fri-Sat 11 pm.

Chez Bruce SW17 £56 Ⓐ☆☆

2 Bellevue Rd   8672 0114

*"It's a true local with no airs and graces", but Bruce Poole's
"peerless" venture, by Wandsworth Common, is again voted
Londoners' favourite, thanks to its "superlative" food (this year,
the best-rated in the capital bar none), its "unrivalled" wine and its
"awesome" service; can an expansion in early-2008 make it even
better?* / **Details:** www.chezbruce.co.uk; 10.30 pm; booking: max 6 at D.

Chez Liline N4 £41 ☆☆

101 Stroud Green Rd   7263 6550

*Its location is "not the most stylish", and the exterior "may not fill
you with confidence" (nor the "bleak" interior, come to that),
but this "surprising" Finsbury Park veteran is still well worth truffling
out for its "ridiculously fresh" and "excitingly-spiced" Mauritian fish
cooking.* / **Details:** 11 pm; closed Sun L.

Chez Marcelle W14 £25 ☆☆

34 Blythe Rd   7603 3241   6–1D

*Marcelle is "cook, greeter, hostess, and friend", at this "anomalous"
Lebanese institution, in Olympia, which "doesn't seem to be run
on commercial grounds"; a recent revamp has left the infamously
"drab" décor more "welcoming".* / **Details:** 10 pm; closed Mon,
Tue-Thu D only; no credit cards.

China Tang
Dorchester Hotel W1 £75 ✕

53 Park Ln   7629 9988   2–3A

*"Are they kidding?" – HK style guru David Tang's "'30s Shanghai"-
style basement "promises much", but takes a major beating from
reporters for its "dull" food, "cramped" tables, "clunky" service and
"scary" prices; "loved the bar", though.* / **Value tip:** set weekday L £21
(FP). **Details:** 11.30 pm.

Chisou W1   £40

4 Princes St   7629 3931   2–1C

"Popularity amongst the Japanese community" attests to the "excellent" quality of the sushi and other dishes (particularly seafood) at this "elegantly utilitarian" (and "speedy") café, near Oxford Circus. / **Value tip:** *set weekday L £21 (FP).* **Details:** *www.chisou.co.uk; 10.15 pm; closed Sun.*

Chor Bizarre W1   £42

16 Albemarle St   7629 9802   2–3C

"Eclectic" décor sets the scene for some "good food" (and at "sensible prices" too), at this "OTT" Mayfair Indian; it's never won the following it deserves – perhaps a recent refurb' will broaden its appeal. / **Details:** *www.chorbizarre.com; 11.30 pm; closed Sun L.*

Churchill Arms W8   £17

119 Kensington Church St   7792 1246   5–2B

"An old favourite still knocking out top-quality Thai cuisine at amazing prices" – the "pretty" ("butterfly-themed") rear annex of this "cluttered" traditional boozer, off Notting Hill Gate, is "so wildly popular, it's hard to book". / **Details:** *10 pm; closed Sun D.*

Chutney SW18   £27

11 Alma Rd   8870 4588

"A real find" – this recently-revamped Indian is beginning to make quite a name for itself down Wandsworth way, thanks to its "very friendly" staff and its "scrumptious" cooking. / **Details:** *11.30 pm; D only.*

Chutney Mary SW10   £54

535 King's Rd   7351 3113   4–4B

"Still going strong", this "very pleasant" contemporary Indian on the Chelsea/Fulham border continues to please most reporters with its "imaginative" (and "sometimes sublime") cuisine; if you get a table in the conservatory, it can be quite "romantic" too. / **Details:** *www.realindianfood.com; 11.15 pm, Sun 10 pm; closed weekday L; booking: max 12.*

Ciao Bella WC1   £31

90 Lamb's Conduit St   7242 4119   1–1D

There's "always a queue" for entry to this "old-fashioned" Bloomsbury favourite – a "heaving" place, where "wonderful" staff serve up "quick, cheap and traditional Italian scoff". / **Details:** *www.ciaobellarestaurant.co.uk; 11.30 pm.*

Cibo W14   £41

3 Russell Gdns   7371 6271   6–1D

This once-celebrated Italian in an Olympia backstreet goes largely unnoticed nowadays; fans insist it's "still performing so well", though, and all of the (few) reports it inspires say the cooking is "delicious". / **Details:** *www.ciborestaurant.net; 11 pm; closed Sat L & Sun D.*

Cicada EC1   £39

132-136 St John St   7608 1550

"Trendy" for longer than is reasonable, Will Ricker's "casual", "noisy" and "bustling" Clerkenwell bar/diner still offers "interesting" (and sometimes "amazing") Asian-Fusion fare. / **Details:** *www.rickerrestaurants.com; 11 pm; closed Sat L & Sun.*

The Cinnamon Club SW1   **£57**   Ⓐ ✪

Old Westminster Library, Great Smith St   7222 2555   1–4C

"Zingy" cuisine (with much "delicate use of spices") has made this "elegant" Westminster restaurant — with its "interesting" setting in a former library — one of London's foremost 'nouvelle Indians'; at lunch, it is a notably "suit-y" destination. / **Value tip:** set pre theatre £38 (FP). **Details:** www.cinnamonclub.com; 10.45 pm; closed Sun.

Cipriani W1   **£70**   ⊗

25 Davies Street   7399 0500   2–2B

"The best people-watching in town" — a mêlée of "aspiring supermodels", "oligarchs" and "Eastern European beauties on a mission" — draws a "vibrant" throng to this Mayfair Venetian; well, it can't be the "dull" food, the "hilarious" prices, or the too-often-"contemptuous" service. / **Details:** www.cipriani.com; 11.45 pm.

Clarke's W8   **£52**   ✪

124 Kensington Church St   7221 9225   5–2B

"Memorable" meals using "wonderful, seasonal ingredients" inspire the usual glowing accounts of Sally Clarke's California-inspired Kensington "classic"; even fans say you "must sit upstairs", though, and this year has seen the emergence of a few claims that it has "has lost its way". / **Details:** www.sallyclarke.com; 10 pm; closed Mon D & Sun; booking: max 14.

Clos Maggiore WC2   **£55**   Ⓐ

33 King St   7379 9696   3–3C

With its "romantic" conservatory, this "beautiful" — "magical", even — fixture makes an unexpected "find" amidst the hurly-burly of Covent Garden; the food is "decent" too, but "totally overshadowed by the awesome wine list".

/ **Details:** www.closmaggiore.com; 10.30 pm, Sat 11 pm; closed Sat L & Sun.

Club Gascon EC1   **£70**   ✪

57 West Smithfield   7796 0600

Still "the place to go for foie gras" — it pops up time and again in the "intriguing", "tapas-style" Gascon dishes at this foodie Mecca, near Smithfield Market, and the wines from SW France are "wonderful", too; "rocketing" prices, however, are a cause of growing concern. / **Details:** www.clubgascon.com; 10 pm; closed Sat L & Sun.

Club Mangia
The Punch Tavern EC4   **£20**   Ⓐ ✪

99 Fleet St   7353 6658

The "chilled" approach of this "very friendly" pub is at odds with its setting in a beautiful old City tavern; at lunch, it serves a "winning buffet" of "home-cooked" food — there's also an evening menu — all at "reasonable prices". / **Details:** www.punchtavern.com; 11.45 pm; closed Sat & Sun.

Le Colombier SW3   **£47**   Ⓐ

145 Dovehouse St   7351 1155   4–2C

"You don't have to be of a certain age, but it helps", best to enjoy a visit to this "civilised" and "quintessentially French" bistro on a quiet Chelsea backstreet; the "classic" fare, though, is arguably an attraction secondary to those of the "welcoming" service and the "superlative" terrace. / **Details:** www.lecolombier-sw3.co.uk; 10.30 pm.

Comptoir Gascon EC1 £37 A✰✰
61-63 Charterhouse St 7608 0851
"Don't take the Eurostar to Paris, take the Circle Line to Farringdon", say fans of this *"genius"* spin-off from the swankier *Club Gascon*; it serves *"outstanding versions of French rustic classics"* and *"fantastic"* wine – all at *"sensible"* prices.
/ ***Details:*** www.comptoirgascon.com; 10 pm; closed Mon & Sun; booking essential.

Il Convivio SW1 £47
143 Ebury St 7730 4099 1–4A
This *"serene"* Belgravia Italian offers an impressive combination of *"good"* food, an *"exceptional"* wine list, an *"airy"* setting, and *"immaculate"* service; even some fans, though, feel it curiously *"lacks wow-factor"*. / ***Details:*** www.etruscarestaurants.com; 10.45 pm; closed Sun.

Coq d'Argent EC3 £56
1 Poultry 7395 5000
An *"unbeatable"* 6th-floor location – with *"lovely"* terraces and *"stunning"* views – is the star feature of this D&D London (fka Conran) operation, by Bank; it's *"a predictable and expensive, if reliable, pit stop for City deal-makers"*.
/ ***Details:*** www.coqdargent.co.uk; 10 pm; closed Sat L.

Cork & Bottle WC2 £33 A✗
44-46 Cranbourn St 7734 7807 3–3B
Despite its *"bonkers"* location – next to a sex shop, off Leicester Square – this *"secret"* basement wine bar has long offered *"a marvellous escape from the West End crowds"*; the dated menu *"is only a sideline"* to a wine list that's *"one of the best in town"*.
/ ***Details:*** www.donhewitson.com; 11.30 pm; no booking after 6.30 pm.

Costa's Fish Restaurant W8 £21 ✰
18 Hillgate St 7727 4310 5–2B
On a good day, you still get *"brilliant fish 'n' chips"* at this venerable Greek-run chippy, near Notting Hill Gate. / ***Details:*** 10 pm; closed Mon & Sun; no credit cards.

Crazy Bear W1 £46 A✰
26 Whitfield St 7631 0088 1–1C
From its *"ultra-cool bar"* to its *"magical loos"*, this *"funky"* Fitzrovia oriental feels simply *"amazing"*, and it's *"definitely one for a date"*; the Thai food is *"unexpectedly good"* too, making the place a real *"all-round winner"*. / ***Details:*** www.crazybeargroup.co.uk; 10.30 pm; closed Sat L & Sun.

Crazy Homies W2 £31 A✰
127 Westbourne Park Rd 7727 6771 5–1B
Tom Conran's *"hectic"* Notting Hill hang-out is *"one of the best Mexicans in London"*, offering *"excellent"* grub and *"top margaritas too"*; on a bad day, though, service can be the *"worst ever"*. / ***Details:*** 10.30 pm; closed weekday L; no Amex.

Crussh £11 ⭐

1 Curzon St, W1 7629 2554 2–3B
BBC Media Village, Wood Ln, W12 8746 7916 5–2A
27 Kensington High St, W8 7376 9786 4–1A
One Canada Sq, E14 7513 0076
Unit 21 Jubilee Pl, E14 7519 6427
48 Cornhill, EC3 7626 2175
6 Farringdon St, EC4 7489 5916

*"All the goodness you need during a day in the office" – "fabulous smoothies", "wholesome soups" and "unusual sandwiches" – is on offer at this health-conscious chain. / **Details:** www.crussh.com; 4.30 pm-7 pm; some branches closed all or part of weekend; no credit cards.*

The Cuckoo Club W1 £75 ❌

99-101 Regent St, Victory Hs 7287 4300 2–3D

*You'd have to be cuckoo to seek out this Mayfair supper club for its food ("awful") or its service ("terrible"); "watching the Eurotrash-wannabes is interesting", though. / **Details:** www.thecuckooclub.com; 10 pm; D only, closed Sun-Tue.*

Cyprus Mangal SW1 £24 ⭐⭐

45 Warwick Way 7828 5940 1–4B

*A Pimlico pit stop, where "you walk through the kebab shop to get to the restaurant at the back" – it serves "enormous portions" of "explosively fresh" grills, at "unbeatable" prices. / **Details:** Sun-Thu midnight, Fri & Sat 1 am; no Amex.*

Dans le Noir EC1 £49 Ⓐ❌

29 Clerkenwell Grn 7253 1100

*"You'll probably only go once", but this gimmicky Clerkenwell yearling – where "you eat in the dark, and the staff are blind" – can still be "a brilliant experience"; the food, though, is somewhere round the level of "school dinners". / **Details:** www.danslenoir.com; 9.30 pm; D only.*

Daylesford Organics SW1 £35 Ⓐ

44B Pimlico Rd 7881 8060 4–2D

*"A welcome addition to Pimlico" – this "luxuriously organic" ("is that an oxymoron?") diner/food store has instantly established itself as a "stylish" local rendezvous for breakfast, coffee or a light bite. / **Details:** www.daylesfordorganic.com; 8 pm, Sun 5 pm.*

Defune W1 £64 ⭐⭐

34 George St 7935 8311 2–1A

*Arguably, "the sushi is the best in town", at this Japanese stalwart in Marylebone; "there's not much atmosphere", though, and "do they have to charge quite so much?" / **Value tip:** set always available £39 (FP). **Details:** 11 pm.*

Delfina Studio Café SE1 £39 ⭐⭐

50 Bermondsey St 7357 0244

*"Wonderful", "innovative" food and "brilliant" service again win strong acclaim for this "really cool" venture, in an "airy warehouse" space, in Bermondsey; "shame it's open for dinner only on Fridays". / **Details:** www.delfina.org.uk; 10 pm; L only, except Fri when open L&D, closed Sat & Sun.*

Diner £26

18 Ganton St, W1 7287 8962 2–2C

128 Curtain Rd, EC2 7729 4452

*You get the "authentic US diner experience", at this Shoreditch spot – now with a larger offshoot, just off Carnaby Street – which does "excellent" burgers, "awesome" chilli fries and "great" breakfasts. / **Details:** W1 12.30 am, Sun midnight - EC2 midnight, Sun & Mon 10.30 pm.*

Dinings W1 £30

22 Harcourt St 7723 0666

*"A marvel of minimalism"; ex-Nobu chef Tomonari Chiba's "brilliant", if "tiny" and basic, Marylebone newcomer serves some "heavenly" Japanese dishes (including notably "delicious sushi and sashimi") at "good prices". / **Details:** 10.30 pm; closed Sat L & Sun.*

The Don EC4 £49

20 St Swithin's Ln 7626 2606

*"A real gem in the Square Mile"; this "slick" but "unstarchy" business favourite – "hidden"-away near Bank – offers "very satisfactory" Gallic cuisine and a "totally pornographic" wine list; if you're in the mood for a "less fancy" feel, head for the "crowded" cellar. / **Details:** www.thedonrestaurant.com; 10 pm; closed Sat & Sun.*

Don Pepe NW8 £32

99 Frampton St 7262 3834

*This "little hide-away" – London's oldest tapas bar – is "not something you expect to find", near Lords; it offers "the full Spanish experience", with "a warm welcome", "good tapas", "unbeatable prices"... "and lots of Spaniards". / **Details:** 11.30 pm; closed Sun.*

Dorchester Grill

Dorchester Hotel W1 £75

53 Park Ln 7629 8888 2–3A

*A "camp" Scottish revamp has made this (once-lovely) grand hotel dining room a "hideous" disaster-zone in recent times; newspaper reports, however, suggest it may be on the mend under new chef Aiden Byrne / **Value tip:** set Sun L £50 (FP). **Details:** www.thedorchester.com; 11 pm.*

Dragon Castle SE17 £29

114 Walworth Rd 7277 3388

*"Incredibly welcome" in "the desert around Elephant & Castle", this surprising yearling offers "the best dim sum south of the river", and other "very fresh" and "distinctive" Chinese dishes, in a "spacious" setting. / **Details:** 11 pm.*

The Duke's Head SW15 £30

8 Lower Richmond Rd 8788 2552

*"A wonderful location" by the Thames is a highpoint of this newly-revamped landmark pub, near Putney Bridge; other plusses include "simple, tasty food", and – for parents – an "impressively child-friendly" attitude. / **Details:** www.dukesheadputney.co.uk; 10.30 pm.*

E&O W11 £43 Ⓐ✪
14 Blenheim Cr 7229 5454 5–1A
*For "smashing fusion tapas" and "cool people", it's still hard to beat
this eternally-"buzzy" Notting Hill pan-Asian – "the best branch"
of Will Ricker's mini-'chain', and a London "benchmark".*
/ **Details:** www.rickerrestaurants.com; 11 pm; booking: max 6.

The Eagle EC1 £25 Ⓐ✪
159 Farringdon Rd 7837 1353
*"The original gastropub, and still the best", say the many loyal fans
of this "crushed" and "loud" Clerkenwell "institution" (est 1992);
despite some "ups and downs in recent years", its "simple"
Mediterranean cooking "hasn't lost its touch".* / **Details:** 11 pm,
Sun 5 pm; closed Sun D; no Amex; no booking.

Ealing Park Tavern W5 £37 Ⓐ✪
222 South Ealing Rd 8758 1879
*A "standard-bearer" in the ranks of "classy" gastropubs; with its
"hearty fare", "reliably good" service and "simple, Victorian, wood-
panelled interior", this South Ealing favourite is "always busy".*
/ **Details:** 10 pm; closed Mon L; booking: max 10.

Earl Spencer SW18 £32 Ⓐ✪
260-262 Merton Rd 8870 9244
*"There are no duds on the menu", at this large and "lovely" pub-
conversion; its "extremely fresh and tasty" food makes it "an oasis
of gastronomy in sunny Southfields".* / **Details:** www.theearlspencer.co.uk;
10 pm; no booking.

The Easton WC1 £29 Ⓐ✪
22 Easton St 7278 7608
*A "perfect gastropub", say fans of this "spacious" hang-out,
near Exmouth Market, which serves food that's almost invariably
"well-executed".* / **Details:** 10 pm; closed Sat L; no Amex.

Edokko WC1 £36 ✪✪
50 Red Lion St 7242 3490 1–1D
*It looks "unassuming", but this "very authentic" Japanese, by Gray's
Inn, elicits a hymns of praise from reporters for its "outstanding-
value" cooking (including the "exceptional" set lunch); service
is "lovely" and "efficient" too.* / **Details:** 11 pm; closed Sat D & Sun;
no Amex.

Eight Over Eight SW3 £45 Ⓐ✪
392 King's Rd 7349 9934 4–3B
*"Sleek" and "very buzzy" – this Chelsea hang-out is very like its
sibling E&O, offering a "healthy and delicious" menu of oriental
"fusion" fare to a similarly "glam" crowd.*
/ **Details:** www.rickerrestaurants.com; 11 pm; closed Sun L.

Electric Brasserie W11   **£43**
191 Portobello Rd   7908 9696   5–1A

There's "top people-watching" to be had at this "loud", "see-and-be-seen" brasserie, beloved of the "Notting Hill set"; to fans, the food is "appealing in a simple kind of way" (especially for a burger or brunch) – to cynics, it's just "unimpressive".
/ **Details:** www.the-electric.co.uk; 10.45 pm.

Elena's L'Etoile W1   **£51**
30 Charlotte St   7636 7189   1–1C
Elena Salvoni – octogenarian doyenne of maîtresses d' – oversees the "stalwart professional service" at this "timeless" Fitzrovia "favourite"; its "old-world charm" and "old-school French" food provide "a solid foundation for a lost afternoon".
/ **Details:** www.elenasletoile.co.uk; 10.30 pm; closed Sat L & Sun.

Emile's SW15   **£31**
96-98 Felsham Rd   8789 3323
This Putney backstreet "gem" has been on cracking form of late, with "delicious" food and a "really great little wine list", all at notably "reasonable" prices; part of its charm used to be "old-fashioned" approach – let's hope a recent minimalist revamp doesn't wreck it! / **Details:** www.emilesrestaurant.co.uk; 11 pm; D only, closed Sun; no Amex.

The Engineer NW1   **£42**
65 Gloucester Ave   7722 0950
Crammed with "effortlessly-cool locals", this "bubbly" Primrose Hill "stalwart" serves "good" gastro-grub in an "erratic but friendly" style; "booking is essential for the garden".
/ **Details:** www.the-engineer.com; 11 pm; no Amex.

Enoteca Turi SW15   **£46**
28 Putney High St   8785 4449
It may seem "unpretentious", but this family-run Putney Italian can be quite a "memorable" destination; the "enormous" wine list is a major plus, but the "rustic" cooking is "bursting with flavour" too, and service "really goes the extra mile". / **Value tip:** set weekday L £29 (FP). **Details:** www.enotecaturi.com; 11 pm; closed Sun.

The Enterprise SW3   **£42**
35 Walton St   7584 3148   4–2C
The bar scene can be "like a grown-up meat-market", but that only adds to the "fun" and "very buzzy" atmosphere at this "welcoming" and (surprisingly) "unpretentious" Chelsea hang-out; the food's "not bad" either. / **Details:** www.theenterprise.com; 10.30 pm; no booking, except weekday L.

Eriki £37

4-6 Northways Pde, Finchley Rd, NW3   7722 0606

122 Boundary Rd, NW8   7372 2255

"An unusual menu" is "cooked to perfection", at this "friendly" Indian that's "quite glam… for Finchley Road"; together with its new St John's Wood offshoot, it's winning an impressive following. / **Details:** NW3 & NW8 10.45 pm; NW3 Sat L - NW8 Sun, Mon L.

Esarn Kheaw W12 £25

314 Uxbridge Rd   8743 8930   6–1B

"I thought it was a myth that it was London's best Thai… after four months in Thailand, I can say it really is the best and most authentic in town…" – one reporter says it all regarding this "unspectacular"-looking stalwart in "deepest Shepherd's Bush". / **Details:** www.esarnkheaw.co.uk; 11 pm; closed Sat L & Sun L.

L'Escargot W1 £48

48 Greek St   7437 2679   3–2A

It's perhaps a bit "forgotten" these days, but MPW's "classy" Soho "classic" still serves up a brilliant all-round experience – the "traditional" setting is "spacious" and "comfortable", service is "helpful without being intrusive", and the Gallic cuisine is "consistently good" and "inventive". / **Details:** www.whitestarline.org.uk; 11.30 pm; closed Sat L & Sun.

L'Escargot (Picasso Room) W1 £62

48 Greek St   7437 2679   3–2A

Above the main brasserie, this "lovely" room offers a "luxurious" combination of "sophisticated" cuisine, "great" wine and "wonderful" service. / **Value tip:** set weekday L £39 (FP). **Details:** www.whitestarline.org.uk; 11.30 pm; closed Mon, Sat L & Sun.

The Farm SW6 £39

18 Farm Ln   7381 3331   4–3A

New owners have made this stylish Fulham spot the "great local gastropub" that – on launch – it never was; now it's a "cosy" and "relaxing" place (with a "light" and "restaurant-like" dining room) serving "super" food at "reasonable" prices. / **Details:** www.thefarmfulham.co.uk; 11 pm.

El Faro E14 £34

3 Turnberry Quay   7987 5511

It may be "stuck in the middle of nowhere", but "brilliant-quality" dishes (plus "impressive" wine) make it "worth the trek" to this ace new waterside tapas bar/restaurant, near Crossharbour DLR. / **Details:** www.el-faro.co.uk; 11 pm.

Ffiona's W8 £42

51 Kensington Church St   7937 4152   4–1A

"Ffiona is on hand to offer tips and advice", at her "friendly", "front room-style", candlelit bistro, in Kensington; even though the food can be "hit-and-miss", fans say the overall experience is a "joy". / **Details:** www.ffionas.com; 11 pm; D only, closed Mon.

Fifteen Restaurant N1 £81

15 Westland Pl 7251 1515

There are reporters who "go cynical" to Jamie Oliver's charitable Hoxton project but still "leave happy"; for many, though, it's just "a disaster" – a "depressed" basement with "indifferent" service, charging "shocking" prices for food that's "at best average". / **Value tip:** *set always available £43 (FP).* **Details:** *www.fifteenrestaurant.com; 9.30 pm; booking: max 6.*

Fifteen Trattoria N1 £54

15 Westland Pl 7251 1515

"The best cooked breakfast in town" (with "everything organic, and done to a turn") is the highlight of Jamie's (somewhat) less expensive ground-floor operation; otherwise, "the prices and the reputation seem unjustified". / **Details:** *www.fifteenrestaurant.com; 10 pm; booking: max 12.*

Fig N1 £39

169 Hemingford Rd 7609 3009

"Tucked-away in a small terraced house, in the back streets of Barnsbury", this "welcoming bolt-hole" makes a good "romantic hide-away", with "very personal" service and "adventurous" food. / **Details:** *www.fig-restaurant.co.uk; 10 pm; closed Mon, Tue-Sat D only, closed Sun D; no Amex.*

La Figa E14 £33

45 Narrow St 7790 0077

"Unbeatable pizzas" and other "realistically priced", "traditional" dishes come in "massive" portions, at this "always-busy" Docklands favourite – "a great all-rounder". / **Details:** *10.30 pm.*

Fino W1 £50

33 Charlotte St 7813 8010 1–1C

The "stunning" tapas at the Hart brothers's "slick" (and "pricey") Fitzrovian are an "eye-opener", and it is again tipped by some reporters as "London's best Spanish restaurant"; the "simple but stylish" basement setting is invariably "buzzing". / **Details:** *www.finorestaurant.com; 10.30 pm; closed Sat L & Sun; booking: max 12.*

First Floor W11 £39

186 Portobello Rd 7243 0072 5–1A

This "OTT" room – "at the centre of Portobello Market" – is "magical" (in a shabby-chic sort of way); if only the the same could be said for the "really disappointing" food… / **Details:** *www.firstfloorportobello.co.uk; 11 pm; closed Mon & Sun D.*

Fish Club SW11 £29

189 St John's Hill 7978 7115

"The chippy goes upmarket, but stays true to its roots", say fans of this "incredibly welcoming", "no-frills" Battersea two-year-old, which serves up "fabulous" fish (including some "alternative options"), with "fantastic chips" and "very good mushy peas"; (option to BYO at £2.50 corkage). / **Details:** *www.thefishclub.com; 10 pm; closed Mon.*

Fish Hook W4 £46 ⭐
6-8 Elliott Rd   8742 0766   6–2A
Michael Nadra's "brilliantly-prepared" fish ("ordered in full or half portions") "maintains the high standards set by the South African predecessor" on this Chiswick site; it's still "way too cramped, though". / **Value tip:** *set weekday L £27 (FP).* **Details:** *www.fishhook.co.uk; 10.30 pm.*

Five Hot Chillies HA0 £20 ⭐
875 Harrow Rd   8908 5900
It's "worth the trek" to Sudbury, to seek out this "basic" but "bustling" BYO canteen, which serves "real" Indian dishes "extremely cheap". / **Details:** *11.30 pm; no Amex.*

The Flask N6 £25 Ⓐ
77 Highgate West Hill   8348 7346
"Don't want to leave London for authentic country pub atmosphere?" – this ancient and "lovely" Highgate coaching inn is "perfect", even if its "good, no-fuss grub" only plays a minor rôle in the experience. / **Details:** *10pm.*

Flat White W1 £ 9 ⭐
17 Berwick St   7734 0370   2–2D
"It's all about the coffee" – "these guys are wild-eyed and intense about it" – at this Kiwi-run café in Soho; some of the snacks, though, are "delectable" too. / **Details:** *www.flat-white.co.uk; L only; no credit cards.*

Foliage
Mandarin Oriental SW1 £72 Ⓐ⭐⭐
66 Knightsbridge   7201 3723   4–1D
This "understated" and "well-spaced" Knightsbridge dining room is currently on top form, with its "enthusiastic" staff serving up Chris Staines's "sublime" dishes; lunch is "unbeatable value" too, especially if you bag a table with a park-view. / **Value tip:** *set weekday L £44 (FP).* **Details:** *www.mandarinoriental.com; 10.30 pm; booking: max 6.*

The Food Room SW8 £39 ⭐⭐
123 Queenstown Rd   7622 0555
"The prices are a real bonus", at this "excellent neighbourhood place", in Battersea; its "interesting" Gallic-inspired cooking is served by "knowledgeable" staff, but the ambience "needs lightening up". / **Details:** *www.thefoodroom.com; 10.30 pm; D only, closed Sun-Tue.*

The Forge WC2 £43
14 Garrick St   7379 1531   3–3C
"Exemplary" service features in most reports on this new occupant of the interesting Covent Garden site that was L'Estaminet (RIP); as at its siblings, Café du Jardin and Deuxième, however, reactions to the cooking are muted. / **Value tip:** *set weekday L £27 (FP).* **Details:** *midnight.*

Four O Nine SW9 £42 Ⓐ⭐
409 Clapham Rd   7737 0722
"A great addition to Clapham" – at this dining room above a pub, an ex-Chez Bruce chef offers some "good-value" cooking in "cool" surroundings. / **Details:** *www.fouronine.co.uk; 10.30 pm; closed Mon L, Tue L & Thu L.*

The Fox & Hounds SW11 £33 **A ★**
66 Latchmere Rd   7924 5483
"It retains a fun and casual pub atmosphere" (complete with "well-kept beer"), but this Battersea boozer is every bit a "first-class" gastropub, and serves "an inventive and frequently-changing blackboard menu". / Details: 10.30 pm; Mon-Thu D only, Fri-Sun open L & D; no Amex.

Frantoio SW10 £40 **A**
397 King's Rd   7352 4146   4–3B
It's taken a while, but this family-run Italian at World's End is "now firmly established in the area", thanks not least to its "very helpful" staff and its "realistic" prices. / Value tip: set weekday L £26 (FP). Details: 11.15 pm.

Frederick's N1 £48 **A**
106 Camden Pas   7359 2888
Some still say it "needs a make-over", but this "lovely" Islington "old favourite" made something of a ratings comeback this year; particular attractions include an "airy" and "romantic" conservatory, and a "fairly-priced" wine list. / Value tip: set pre theatre £28 (FP). Details: www.fredericks.co.uk; 11 pm; closed Sun; no Amex.

The Freemasons SW18 £35 **A**
2 Wandsworth Common Northside   7326 8580
An "ideal" gastropub, in Wandsworth – the atmosphere is "chilled", the staff are "friendly" and the "hearty" food is "done really well". / Details: www.freemasonspub.com; 10 pm.

Fresco W2 £15 **★**
25 Westbourne Grove   7221 2355   5–1C
"Awesome juices", "fantastic falafel wraps" and "very fresh" mezze make this "good-natured" Bayswater pit stop quite a "cheap and cheerful" favourite. / Details: 11 pm.

La Fromagerie Café W1 £25 **A ★★**
2-4 Moxon St   7935 0341   2–1A
"A magnificent cheese shop, offering delicious lunch bites and fabulous salads" (and "really imaginative breakfasts" too); "the only complaint about this Marylebone deli is that the capacity isn't larger"! / Details: www.lafromagerie.co.uk; 7pm; L only; no booking.

Fuzzy's Grub £13 **★★**
6 Crown Pas, SW1   7925 2791   2–4D
15 Basinghall St, Unit 1 Mason's Ave, EC2   7726 6771
56-57 Cornhill, EC3   7621 0555
10 Well Ct, EC4   7236 8400
62 Fleet St, EC4   7583 6060
A "simple concept, brilliantly executed"; "sandwiches don't come better" than the "monster" "Sunday-roasts-in-a-bap" which are charmingly served at these "upmarket greasy spoons" – "the queues are getting longer as word gets out".
/ Details: www.fuzzysgrub.com; 3 pm-4 pm; closed Sat & Sun; no credit cards; no booking.

Gail's Bread   £14

138 Portobello Rd, W11   7460 0766   5–1B
64 Hampstead High St, NW3   7794 5700
"Sublime" bread and pastries have carved out an ardent (if still small) fanclub for this growing bakery/café mini-chain; "everyone loves the new one in Portobello". / **Details:** W11 8 pm - NW3 9 pm.

Galvin at Windows
Park Lane London Hilton Hotel W1   £68

22 Park Ln, 28th Floor   7208 4021   2–4A
"The restaurant is now as impressive as the views", say fans of the Galvin brothers' "elegant" year-old relaunch of this 28th-floor Mayfair eyrie; given the location, though, it's perhaps no surprise that it can seem "painfully overpriced".
/ **Details:** www.hilton.co.uk/londonparklane; 10.30 pm; closed Sat L & Sun D.

Galvin Bistrot de Luxe W1   £44

66 Baker St   7935 4007   1–1A

Chris & Jeff Galvin's "slick", year-old 'Bistrot de luxe', in Marylebone, is rapidly emerging as a modern classic – "cuisine bourgeoise" is "beautifully executed" and "professionally" served, in a "classy" and "club-like" setting. / **Value tip:** set weekday L £28
(FP). **Details:** www.galvinbistrotdeluxe.co.uk; 10.45 pm.

Ganapati SE15   £26

38 Holly Grove   7277 2928
An "unexpected" Peckham Rye spot that's developing quite a following, thanks to its "welcoming" style and its "tasty" and "interesting" south Indian cuisine. / **Details:** www.ganapatirestaurant.com; 10.45 pm; closed Mon; no Amex.

Garrison SE1   £38

99-101 Bermondsey St   7089 9355
A "funky" make-over of this boozer near Bermondsey Market has created a "buzzing" – if "crowded" – setting, where the "modern-style pub food" is usually "spot-on". / **Details:** www.thegarrison.com; 10.30 pm.

Le Gavroche W1   £123

43 Upper Brook St   7408 0881   2–2A
"Old-school in the best possible way" – Michael Roux Jr's Mayfair institution of 40 years' standing still offers "sensational" Gallic cooking, "legendary" service and a "definitive" wine list; prices, of course, are "extra-terrestrial". / **Value tip:** set weekday L £54
(FP). **Details:** www.le-gavroche.co.uk; 10.45 pm; closed Sat L & Sun; jacket required.

Gem N1 £21

265 Upper St   7359 0405

*"Paradise for both veggies and carnivores" – this "very friendly" Kurdish restaurant in Islington offers "fantastic" mezze and "succulent" grills, at "ludicrously cheap" prices. / **Details:** midnight.*

George & Vulture EC3 £39

3 Castle Ct   7626 9710

*"You can almost imagine Pepys walking in to grab a quick bite", at this "atmospheric" City chophouse; even after making due historical allowances, though, its "school dinners" fare could be "a lot better". / **Details:** L only, closed Sat & Sun.*

Giraffe £33

6-8 Blandford St, W1   7935 2333   1–1A
270 Chiswick High Rd, W4   8995 2100   6–2A
7 Kensington High St, W8   7938 1221   4–1A
29-31 Essex Rd, N1   7359 5999
46 Rosslyn Hill, NW3   7435 0343
Royal Festival Hall, Riverside, SE1   7928 2004   1–3D
27 Battersea Rise, SW11   7223 0933

*"So long as you don't mind kids", brunch is the "top attraction" at this "jolly" and "hectic" world-food chain – more generally, however, drifting survey ratings support those who say it's "not as good as it was". / **Value tip:** set dinner £22 (FP). **Details:** www.giraffe.net; 10.45 pm; no booking at weekends.*

The Glasshouse TW9 £52

14 Station Pde   8940 6777

*"A worthy sibling to Chez Bruce" – this "light and airy" (if somewhat "squashed-in and noisy") "neighbourhood gem", by Kew Gardens station, once again wins all-round raves for its "superb" and "unfussy" cuisine and its "charming" and "efficient" service; "excellent" wine too. / **Details:** www.glasshouserestaurant.co.uk; 10.30 pm.*

Golden Hind W1 £18

73 Marylebone Ln   7486 3644   1–1A

*"The best fish 'n' chips in London" – bar none – are to be had at this "traditional" Marylebone chippy; "arrive early if you want a table". / **Details:** 10 pm; closed Sat L & Sun.*

Good Earth £40

233 Brompton Rd, SW3   7584 3658   4–2C
143-145 The Broadway, NW7   8959 7011

*This "civilised" and "professional" Chinese mini-chain is (practically) "always dependable"; "outstanding" veggie dishes attract particular praise. / **Details:** 10.45 pm.*

Gordon Ramsay SW3 £109 Ⓐ ✪✪

68-69 Royal Hospital Rd   7352 4441   4–3D

*Mark Askew's cuisine may still be "flawless" and Jean-Claude's service "unrivalled" but – following a rather "anaemic" revamp, and with ever more "exorbitant" prices – Ramsay's Chelsea HQ is now at risk of losing its customary pre-eminence; despite (for the 12th year) topping reporters' nominations as London's 'top gastronomic experience', it failed – for the first time this decade – to achieve either the best survey rating for its food, or for the overall experience offered. / **Value tip:** set weekday L £61*
(FP). **Details:** *www.gordonramsay.com; 11 pm; closed Sat & Sun; no jeans or trainers; booking: max 8.*

Gordon Ramsay at Claridge's
Claridge's Hotel W1 £87 Ⓐ

55 Brook St   7499 0099   2–2B

*"Capitalising on Ramsay's name"; this Art Deco-style Mayfair chamber may look "impressive", but the cooking too often seems "conservative, going-on boring" nowadays – by a growing margin, reporters find it "nothing like as good as in Royal Hospital Road", and "ludicrously" pricey too. / **Value tip:** set weekday L £44*
(FP). **Details:** *www.gordonramsay.com; 11 pm; no jeans or trainers; booking: max 8.*

Gordon's Wine Bar WC2 £22 Ⓐ ⊗

47 Villiers St   7930 1408   3–4D

"It's got to be Gordon's!"; nothing to do with the "overpriced" food, though – "it's the ambience" of this "secret", "dark" and "dingy" cellar, near Embankment tube, which makes it a sure-fire "winner" (and, for the summer, there's a huge terrace).
*/ **Details:** www.gordonswinebar.com; 11 pm; no booking.*

The Goring Hotel SW1 £68 Ⓐ

15 Beeston Pl   7396 9000   1–4B

*"Dignified, discreet and quintessentially English" – the "grown-up" dining room of this "charming", family-owned hotel, near Victoria, is a "virtually flawless oasis" of "old-fashioned" values; its food is "absolutely reliable" (and includes, of course, the "best civilised breakfast"). / **Details:** www.goringhotel.co.uk; 10 pm; closed Sat L; booking: max 12.*

The Grapes E14 £40 Ⓐ ✪

76 Narrow St   7987 4396

*"A great little find in the East End" – this ancient Thameside pub serves "cracking fish" (and "the best Sunday roasts"); you can eat in the bar, but the main menu is served in the "smarter" and "cosier" upstairs room, which has "great views". / **Details:** 11 pm; closed Sun D.*

Great Eastern Dining Room EC2 £40 Ⓐ ✪

54 Gt Eastern St   7613 4545

"In a sea of trendy bars", Will Ricker's "funky hotspot", in "the heart of Shoreditch", still stands out, thanks to its "fantastic Pan-Asian food" and its "superb cocktail list".
*/ **Details:** www.rickerrestaurants.com; 11 pm; closed Sat L & Sun.*

Green & Red Bar & Cantina E1 £38 A ✪ ✪
51 Bethnal Green Rd   7749 9670
"1,000,000 miles away from Tex-Mex yukiness" – this "cool"
cantina, near Brick Lane, serves Mexican food that's the "real thing"
(and better than anything else in town); there's also "an amazing
selection of tequilas" – "it's worth a visit for that alone".
/ **Details:** www.greenred.co.uk; 11 pm; Mon-Fri closed L, Sat & Sun closed D.

Green's SW1 £55 A
36 Duke St   7930 4566   2–3D
"Expense be damned!", say fans of Simon Parker Bowles's "club-like
but unstuffy" bastion of St James's – a "charming", "old-school"
fixture that promises "no surprises", just "marvellous fish and
nursery food", "professionally" served. / **Details:** www.greens.org.uk;
11 pm, Sun 9 pm; May-Sep closed Sun.

The Greenhouse W1 £87
27a Hays Mews   7499 3331   2–3B
The "tucked-away" location is "lovely", the food can be "stunning"
and the wine list is "immense", yet the "staid" régime at Marlon
Abela's Mayfair mews spot does not invariably please reporters;
perhaps it would help if prices weren't so "extortionate". / **Value
tip:** set weekday L £53 (FP). **Details:** www.greenhouserestaurant.co.uk; 11 pm;
closed Sat L & Sun; booking: max 6-10.

Grenadier SW1 £37 A
18 Wilton Row   7235 3074   4–1D
This "hidden jewel" of a pub, in a Belgravia mews, is in every
tourist guide, and you pay accordingly if you want to eat in its "cosy"
dining room; those in the know opt for a sausage and a Bloody
Mary – both house specialities – at the bar. / **Details:** 9.30 pm.

Ground W4 £26 ✪
217-221 Chiswick High Rd   8747 9113   6–2A
"It thrashes GBK", say fans of this Chiswick "newcomer to the
upmarket burger scene", where "great courgette fries" are a top tip
from the "fantastic" menu; it's certainly more "atmospheric".
/ **Details:** Mon-Sat 11 pm.

(Ground Floor)
Smiths of Smithfield EC1 £23 A
67-77 Charterhouse St   7251 7950
Weekend mornings "can't start better", than by "lounging" around
in the "cool and fun" ground floor bar of this large warehouse-
conversion, enjoying the "great and varied" brunch selection;
"too bad the service doesn't live up".
/ **Details:** www.smithsofsmithfield.co.uk; L only.

The Guinea Grill W1 £52 ✪
30 Bruton Pl   7409 1728   2–3B
"Great steaks" and "brilliant pies" ("with crust to die for, and rich
gravy") fly the flag for traditional British cuisine at this "squashed"
but "cosy" pub-cum-grill, hidden-away in Mayfair; all this,
and "a very decent pint" in the bar too. / **Details:** www.theguinea.co.uk;
10.30 pm; closed Sat L & Sun; booking: max 8.

The Gun E14 £42 Ⓐ★

27 Coldharbour Ln 7515 5222
This "brilliant", "chilled-out" Thames-side boozer may be "wretched to get to", but it's worth the trek for its "fabulous comfort food" and the "great views of the Dome"; there's also a terrace for the summer, and "roaring fires" in winter.
/ **Details:** *www.thegundocklands.com; 10.30 pm.*

Haandi SW7 £36 ★

7 Cheval Pl 7823 7373 4–1C
"Shame they lost the front door" (almost opposite Harrods), but last year's refurb has really perked up this "reasonably-priced" Indian – its back (mews) entrance is well worth finding!
/ **Details:** *www.haandi-restaurant.com; 11 pm, Fri-Sat 11.30 pm.*

Haché NW1 £24 Ⓐ★

24 Inverness St 7485 9100
"Eclipsing the various gastro-burger chains", this "cosy" Camden Town two-year-old boasts, for many reporters, "the best burgers in London", and "brisk but friendly" service too.
/ **Details:** *www.hacheburgers.co.uk; 10.30 pm.*

Hakkasan W1 £76 Ⓐ

8 Hanway Pl 7927 7000 3–1A

"For sheer WOW! factor", it's hard to beat Alan Yau's "sexy", "dark" and "moody" West End basement-oriental, and the cuisine (especially dim sum) is "incredible" too; on the downside, the location is "grim", prices are "astronomical", and service is definitely "cooler-than-thou". / **Details:** *11.30 pm, Fri-Sat 12.30 pm.*

Hara The Circle Bar SE1 £40 ★★

Queen Elizabeth St 0845 226 9411
"Wow!", the food is "stunning", at this "inventive" Indian bar (downstairs)/restaurant (upstairs), hidden-away near Tower Bridge; its location "doesn't do it justice", though, and it's too often "empty".
/ **Details:** *www.hararara.co.uk; midnight.*

The Havelock Tavern W14 £35 ★

57 Masbro Rd 7603 5374 6–1C
"Back with a vengeance" – post-fire, this famous Olympia backstreet gastropub is again dishing up some "fantastic" and "innovative" dishes; even if the food is perhaps a touch more "hit-and-miss" than it was, the service – "rudeness elevated to a fine art" – provides reassuring continuity.
/ **Details:** *www.thehavelocktavern.co.uk; 10 pm; no credit cards; no booking.*

The Haven N20 £36 Ⓐ
1363 High Rd 8445 7419
*Despite an unlikely Whetstone location, this "excellent" five-year-old draws fans from across north London with its "interesting" cuisine and its "ebullient" atmosphere. / **Value tip:** set weekday L £23 (FP). **Details:** www.haven-bistro.co.uk; 10.30 pm; no Amex.*

Hawksmoor E1 £52 ✪
157 Commercial St 7247 7392
*"Brilliant", "man-sized" steaks, "truly award-winning chips", and cocktails that are the "real thing" have won instant acclaim for this "loud" yearling, just north of Spitalfields. / **Details:** www.thehawksmoor.co.uk; 10.30 pm; closed Sat L & Sun.*

Hellenik W1 £31
30 Thayer St 7935 1257 1–1A
*"The world moves on, leaving the odd gem like this in its wake…"; it may be an "anachronism", but this veteran Marylebone Greek offers retro-charm of a sort it's "pitifully hard to find" nowadays, and "you eat well for a good price". / **Details:** 10.45 pm; closed Sun; no Amex.*

Hibiscus W1 £65
29 Maddox St 7629 2999 2–2C
Claude Bosi is very close to the pinnacle of UK gastronomy , and – though little-known in the capital – achieved survey ratings among the country's very best when he was cooking in Ludlow; in late-2007, he opens in Mayfair with the same team (and same prices!) that won him fame in Shropshire – could be the début of the year. /

High Road Brasserie W4 £44 Ⓐ
162-166 Chiswick High Rd 8742 7474 6–2A
*This "cool" and "buzzy" new member of Nick 'Soho House' Jones's empire has proved "an excellent addition to Chiswick"; the brasserie fare "isn't going to win any Michelin stars", but it is "well-prepared and thought-out" (and brunch is "fabulous"). / **Value tip:** set weekday L £28 (FP). **Details:** www.highroadhouse.co.uk; 10.45 pm, Fri & Sat 11.45 pm.*

Hilliard EC4 £24 ✪✪
26a Tudor St 7353 8150
*"It's odd to see barristers polishing off bottles of claret in a sandwich shop!", but this "gastro-café", by Inner Temple, is a "magnificent" place, which uses "fantastic" ingredients to create some "top-class" bites. / **Details:** www.hilliardfood.co.uk; 6 pm; closed Sat & Sun.*

Holly Bush NW3 £35 Ⓐ
22 Holly Mount 7435 2892
*A "fabulous old-world" interior ensures that this countrified boozer, just 100 yards from Hampstead tube, is often "crowded" (so "get there early"); it serves a hearty menu of "better-than-basic" pub fare". / **Details:** www.hollybushpub.com; 10 pm; no Amex.*

The Horseshoe NW3 £32 🅰⭐

28 Heath St   7431 7206

*You get "simple" British food "served with flair" at this new heart-of-Hampstead gastropub; "there are so few good places roundabouts", though, that it's "constantly rammed", and service can be "erratic". / **Value tip:** set weekday L £18 (FP). **Details:** www.thehorseshoehampstead.com; 10 pm; no Amex.*

Hot Stuff SW8 £20 ⭐⭐

19 Wilcox Rd   7720 1480

*"Sensational" curries, "astoundingly cheap" prices, and "the friendliest" service – a formula that wins adulation for this "crowded, downmarket and wonderful" South Lambeth Indian; BYO. / **Details:** www.eathotstuff.com; 10 pm; closed Sun.*

Hunan SW1 £46 ⭐⭐

51 Pimlico Rd   7730 5712   4–2D

*"Do as you're told, and eat what you're given" – that's the way to get the best out of Mr Peng's "stellar", but "unpretentious" and "friendly", Pimlico Chinese, which remains among "the best in London". / **Details:** 11.30 pm; closed Sun.*

Ikeda W1 £68 ⭐⭐

30 Brook St   7629 2730   2–2B

*Mrs Ikeda's stalwart Mayfair Japanese doesn't look much, and provokes little feedback nowadays, but its fans "are happy for others to nominate lesser places" – "it makes it easier to get a table here", to enjoy the "extraordinary sushi". / **Value tip:** set weekday L £31 (FP). **Details:** 10.15 pm; closed Sat L & Sun.*

Imperial China WC2 £37 ⭐

25a Lisle St   7734 3388   3–3B

*A large but "hidden-away" Chinatown "oasis" that's "a bit smarter than average", and offers food that's "reliable and fairly-priced"; "superb dim sum" too. / **Details:** 11.30 pm.*

Inaho W2 £31 ⭐⭐

4 Hereford Rd   7221 8495   5–1B

*"Tiny" and "eccentric", this "Swiss chalet"-style shack in Bayswater is the unlikely venue for some of "the best sushi in town"; be prepared for "very long waits" for service, though. / **Details:** 11 pm; closed Sat L & Sun L; no Amex or Maestro.*

Indian Ocean SW17   £25   ⭐
216 Trinity Rd   8672 7740
"Consistently good" and *"well-priced"* cooking (with fish a speciality) makes this *"welcoming"* and *"lavishly-staffed"* Indian very popular, down Wandsworth way; *"they also have a super take-away service"*. / **Details:** 11.30 pm.

Indian Zing W6   £29   ⭐
236 King St   8748 5959   6–2B
The *"fantastic"* food is full of *"fresh, crisp flavours"*, at Manog Vasaikar's *"classy"* (if unglamorously-located) and *"personable"* Hammersmith yearling – *"a modern take on the traditional neighbourhood Indian"*. / **Details:** www.indianzing.co.uk; 10.30 pm.

Indigo
One Aldwych WC2   £55   Ⓐ
1 Aldwych   7300 0400   1–2D
"Overlooking a buzzing bar", this *"smart"* and *"spacious"* mezzanine restaurant – part of a *"hip hotel"* near Covent Garden – is a *"classy"* venue with *"attentive"* service and *"reliable"* cuisine; it's most popular for business and pre-theatre. / **Details:** 11.15 pm.

Inside SE10   £38   ⭐⭐
19 Greenwich South St   8265 5060
The settling may be *"like someone's front room"*, and service can get *"confused"*, but the food at Guy Awford's *"unassuming"* Greenwich gaff is *"phenomenally good"* – possibly *"the best in South East London"*. / **Details:** www.insiderestaurant.co.uk; 10.30 pm, Fri-Sat 11pm; closed Mon & Sun D.

Isarn N1   £34   Ⓐ⭐
119 Upper St   7424 5153
With its *"careful cooking"*, this Islington two-year-old, *"stands apart from your run-of-the-mill Thais"*; it's a *"stylish"* place, too, with notably accomplished and *"friendly"* service. / **Details:** www.isarn.co.uk; 11 pm.

Ishbilia SW1   £38   ⭐
9 William St   7235 7788   4–1D
"As you can see from the number of Arabs who dine here", this *"oasis among the Knightsbridge shops"* is *"authentically Lebanese"*; *"wonderful mezze"* is a highlight. / **Details:** www.ishbilia.com; 11.30 pm.

Isola del Sole SW15   £38   ⭐
16 Lacy Rd   8785 9962
"A lovely, cosy Sicilian restaurant, in the heart of Putney", where *"very friendly and laid-back"* staff serve up *"good and original"* cooking. / **Details:** www.isoladelsole.co.uk; 10.30 pm; closed Sun; no Amex.

The Ivy WC2   £54   Ⓐ
1 West St   7836 4751   3–3B
"For a touch of glamour and a damn good time", this world-famous Theatreland icon is still a *"classic"* destination; but for how much longer? – realisation of its *"comfort food"* menu seems ever-more *"average"*, and some reporters feel the place is now *"best left to the WAGs"*. / **Details:** www.the-ivy.co.uk; midnight; booking: max 6.

Izgara N3 £24 ★

11 Hendon Lane   8371 8282

"A local Godsend" – this "genuine" Turkish café/take-away, in Finchley, offers some "wonderfully tasty" food, and maintains a "thoughtful" level of service, even though it's often "packed".
/ **Details:** midnight; no Amex.

Jaan
The Howard WC2 £59 ★

12 Temple Pl   7300 1700   1–2D

"Hints of the Fat Duck" permeate the "bizarre" but interesting menu at this "smart" and "competent" – and often-overlooked – dining room, in a hotel by Temple tube; it also boasts an unexpected courtyard, which is "great in summer".
/ **Details:** www.swissotel.com; 10.30 pm; closed Sat L & Sun.

Jashan £21 ★★

1-2 Coronet Pde, Ealing Rd, HA0   8900 9800
19 Turnpike Ln, N8   8340 9880

For an exotic meal that's truly "cheap and cheerful", these friendly south Indian canteens are very hard to beat. / **Value tip:** set weekday L £7 (FP). **Details:** www.jashanrestaurants.co.uk; 10.45 pm; N8 D only, closed Mon; no Amex; no weekend bookings.

Jenny Lo's Tea House SW1 £25 ★

14 Eccleston St   7259 0399   1–4B

"Steaming noodles and stir-frys" that taste "fresh! fresh! fresh!" are the sort of "easy, fun and quick" sustenance you find at this "loud and hectic" Belgravia canteen. / **Details:** 10 pm; closed Sat L & Sun; no credit cards; no booking.

Jin Kichi NW3 £35 ★★

73 Heath St   7794 6158

It feels "just like being in Tokyo", at this "very cramped" Hampstead "hide-away", which is "packed nightly", thanks to its "simple" but "fantastic" yakitori and sushi, at great prices.
/ **Details:** www.jinkichi.com; 11 pm; closed Mon, Tue-Fri D only, Sat & Sun open L & D.

Joanna's SE19 £34 Ⓐ

56 Westow Hill   8670 4052

"A winner every time" – that's the local verdict on this low-lit Crystal Palace "favourite", which boasts a "lovely" atmosphere, "really friendly" service and "consistently good" food.
/ **Details:** www.joannas.uk.com; 11 pm.

Joe Allen WC2 £40 Ⓐ

13 Exeter St   7836 0651   3–3D

It's the "light-hearted Theatreland vibe" that makes this Covent Garden basement such an enduring favourite, and (especially late-night) it's "still frequented by the odd celeb" – the American food can be "truly awful", but the off-menu burgers have their fans.
/ **Details:** www.joeallen.co.uk; 12.45 am.

Joe's Brasserie SW6 £33 Ⓐ
130 Wandsworth Bridge Rd 7731 7835
"The best-value wine in London" (from merchant/restaurateur John Brinkley) is the special plus-point of this "buzzing" brasserie, in deepest Fulham, but the food is often surprisingly "tasty" too.
/ **Details:** www.brinkleys.com; 11 pm.

Julie's W11 £46 ⒶⓍ
135 Portland Rd 7229 8331 5–2A
This "inventively-decorated" Holland Park survivor – a maze of "wonderful, romantic nooks and crannies" – holds fond memories for many reporters; it's a shame, then, that service is "amateurish", and the food is sometimes plain "rubbish".
/ **Details:** www.juliesrestaurant.com; 11pm.

The Junction Tavern NW5 £34 Ⓐ
101 Fortess Rd 7485 9400
"Good beers", "extremely friendly service", a "great garden" and "uncomplicated", filling food – these are the virtues of this "airy" Kentish Town gastropub "favourite". / **Details:** www.junctiontavern.co.uk; 10.30 pm; no Amex.

Just Falafs £16 ★
155 Wardour St, W1 7734 1914 2–1D
27b Covent Garden Piazza, WC2 7240 3838 3–3D
"Superb" falafel (and "great coffee" too) wins raves for this "miniscule" Covent Garden newcomer – on the edge of the Market, and with outside tables, it's much better than most of the tourist traps nearby; there is also now a branch in Soho.
/ **Details:** www.justfalafs.com; WC2 9 pm, W1 10 pm, Fri & Sat 11 pm; W1 closed Sun; no credit cards.

Kai Mayfair W1 £57 ★
65 South Audley St 7493 8988 2–3A
The "de luxe" décor may not be to all tastes, but this "formal" Mayfair oriental continues to impress reporters with its "excellent" (if "slightly precious") Chinese fare; "make sure you sit upstairs".
/ **Details:** www.kaimayfair.com; 10.45 pm.

kare kare SW5 £34 ★
152 Old Brompton Rd 7373 0024 4–2B
"The unsung hero of the Brompton Road Indians"; though overshadowed by the famous 'Star', it's consistently praised for its "refreshingly different" cuisine and "good service". / **Value tip:** set weekday L £17 (FP). **Details:** www.karekare.co.uk; 11 pm.

Karma W14 £27 ★
44 Blythe Rd 7602 9333 6–1D
The "refreshing" cooking at this year-old Olympia Indian is often "very impressive indeed", so it's a shame that, like its predecessor Cotto (long RIP), it "suffers from its out-of-the-way location and thus poor ambience". / **Details:** www.k-a-r-m-a.co.uk; 11.30 pm.

Kastoori SW17 £22 ⭐⭐
188 Upper Tooting Rd   8767 7027
Don't be fooled by the "dingy" decor or the "cr*p" location – they're "more than offset" by the "incredible-value" "voyage of discovery" offered by the menu of this family-run Tooting veteran, where the "ever-changing" east African/south Indian cuisine is nothing short of "sublime". / **Details:** *10.30 pm; closed Mon L & Tue L; no Amex or Maestro; booking: max 12.*

Kasturi EC3 £32 ⭐
57 Aldgate High St   7480 7402
"A little different in style from the operations in nearby Brick Lane" – this well-presented contemporary City Indian is a good all-rounder. / **Details:** *www.kasturi-restaurant.co.uk; 11 pm, Sat 9.30 pm; closed Sun L.*

Kazan SW1 £34 Ⓐ⭐
93-94 Wilton Rd   7233 7100   1–4B
Cleaning up at the Victoria end of Pimlico – this "invaluable" Turkish restaurant is a "buzzy" sort of place with notably "pleasant" service; the food (including "brilliant" mezze) is "delicious" and "reasonably-priced" too. / **Details:** *11.45 pm, Sun-Tue 10.30 pm; no Amex.*

Ken Lo's Memories of China W8 £48 ⭐⭐
353 Kensington High St   7603 6951   6–1D
"All-round excellent food and service" win many fans for this "dependable" and "understated" fixture, near Olympia; it "beats many more high-profile Chinese places" (including its Belgravia parent). / **Details:** *www.memories-of-china.co.uk; 11 pm; closed Sun L.*

(Brew House)
Kenwood House NW3 £24 Ⓐ
Hampstead Heath   8341 5384
"Unbeatable on a fine day" – the superb garden of this café by Hampstead Heath is ideal for brunch, Sunday lunch or afternoon tea; "a walk afterwards is obligatory". / **Details:** *www.companyofcooks.com; 6 pm (summer), 4 pm (winter).*

Koba W1 £44 ⭐
11 Rathbone St   7580 8825   1–1C
"Unlike many Koreans", this Fitzrovia yearling is decked out in a "trendy" style; "brilliant young staff" guide you through the "interesting" BBQ dishes, which are "impressively cooked at your table". / **Details:** *11 pm; closed Sun L.*

Kolossi Grill EC1 £24 Ⓐ
56-60 Rosebery Ave   7278 5758
"A throwback, but none the worse for that" – this "basic", "honest" and "consistently friendly" Clerkenwell Greek veteran is a "reliable" sort of place (and it can be "great fun" too). / **Value tip:** *set weekday L £14 (FP).* **Details:** *www.kolossigrill.com; 11 pm; closed Sat L & Sun.*

Konditor & Cook £19

Curzon Soho, 99 Shaftesbury Ave, W1   7292 1684   3–3A
46 Gray's Inn Rd, WC1   7404 6300
10 Stoney St, SE1   7407 5100
22 Cornwall Rd, SE1   7261 0456

"Terrifyingly tempting" snacks – from "decadent cakes" to "fantastic soups" – inspire many ecstatic reports on this "wonderful" chain of café/take-aways. / *Details:* www.konditorandcook.com; W1 11 pm; SE1 closed Sun; no Amex; no booking.

Konstam at the Prince Albert WC1   £38

2 Acton St   7833 5040

This "wacky" King's Cross outfit has made quite a name with its "valiant efforts to utilise local produce" (from within the M25); results are a bit hit-and-miss, but, for most reporters, this is "a great idea, fantastically delivered". / *Details:* www.konstam.co.uk; 10.30 pm; closed Sat L & Sun.

Kovalam NW6   £21

12 Willesden Ln   7625 4761

It "may not look that inviting", but this Kilburn-fringe spot is universally tipped for its "tasty and authentic" south Indian food. / *Details:* www.kovalamrestaurant.co.uk; 11 pm.

The Ladbroke Arms W11   £37

54 Ladbroke Rd   7727 6648   5–2B

It may be "frustratingly full" (and "a bit squished"), but that's only because this "really cosy" Notting Hill boozer offers "top-quality" grub, and the terrace is nice too. / *Details:* www.thecapitalpubcompany.com; 9.45 pm; no booking after 7.30 pm.

Lahore Kebab House E1   £22

2-4 Umberston St   7488 2551

"A dive, but a must-try!"; this "not-for-the-faint-hearted" East End "institution" may have all the ambience of a "transport caff" (refurb notwithstanding), but it serves "stunningly authentic" Pakistani scoff at "unbelievable" prices; BYO. / *Details:* midnight; need 8+ to book.

Lamberts SW12   £42

2 Station Pde   8675 2233

"An excellent alternative to Chez Bruce" – this "chic", "friendly" and "imaginative" Balham spot is an "unbeatable" local, whose standards, say fans, are "not far behind" those of its legendary rival; perhaps its recent refurbishment will draw even wider acclaim. / *Details:* www.lambertsrestaurant.com; 10.30 pm, Sun 9 pm; closed Mon; no Amex.

(The Conservatory)
The Lanesborough Hotel SW1 £79 Ⓐ
Hyde Park Corner   7259 5599   4–1D
"There's nothing actually wrong with the food", in the grand
conservatory of this OTT hotel, but "it's just eye-wateringly expensive
for what it is"; for a "decadent brunch" or a "fabulous afternoon
tea", however, "you feel special just sitting there". / **Value tip:** set
dinner £51 (FP). **Details:** www.lanesborough.com; 11 pm.

Langan's Bistro W1 £34 Ⓐ
26 Devonshire St   7935 4531   1–1A
This pint-sized bistro was here long before Marylebone became
trendy; its "straightforward" cuisine can seem "tired" nowadays,
but its "cosy" ambience and "charming" service are still going
strong. / **Details:** www.langansrestaurants.co.uk; 11 pm; closed Sat L & Sun.

La Lanterna SE1 £32 Ⓐ
6-8 Mill St   7252 2420
Just over Tower Bridge, this "very pleasant" backstreet Italian is well
worth knowing about – the cooking is "good" (or better), and on
a summer evening the courtyard is "wonderful".
/ **Details:** www.pizzeriadelanterna.co.uk; 11 pm; closed Sat L.

Latium W1 £43 Ⓐ⭐⭐
21 Berners St   7323 9123   2–1D
An "all-round-great Italian experience", north of Oxford Street,
where "delightful" staff serve up some "wonderfully seasonal"
cooking; if it has a flaw, it's that the "elegant" interior can seem
a trifle "austere". / **Details:** www.latiumrestaurant.com; 10.30 pm, Fri-Sat
11pm; closed Sat L & Sun.

Leadenhall Italian Restaurant EC3 £45
48-52 Leadenhall Mkt   7621 0709
"Unfussy but well-executed Italian food" (and "reasonably-priced"
wine) make this "handily-located" and "friendly" City basement,
recently re-branded, a stand-by that's well worth knowing about.
/ **Details:** www.leadenhallitalianrestaurant.co.uk; 9.30 pm; closed Sat & Sun.

The Ledbury W11 £69 Ⓐ⭐⭐
127 Ledbury Rd   7792 9090   5–1B
"Elegant and restrained", this Notting Hill sibling of Chez Bruce and
The Square is a "superb" all-rounder, where Brett Graham's
"terrific" and "inventive" dishes are complemented by an
"outstanding" wine list; service is "impeccable" too. / **Value tip:** set
weekday L £40 (FP). **Details:** www.theledbury.com; 10.30 pm.

Lemonia NW1 £31 Ⓐ
89 Regent's Park Rd   7586 7454
"A very special place" – this Primrose Hill landmark is "always
busy", thanks to the "buzzy" and "cheerful" ambience created
by its long-serving staff; the "classic Greek fare" is "nothing special"
(but lunches offer "astonishing value"). / **Value tip:** set weekday L £17
(FP). **Details:** 11.30 pm; closed Sat L & Sun D; no Amex.

74

Levant W1 £46 Ⓐ
Jason Ct, 76 Wigmore St 7224 1111 2–1A
A "loud" and "highly entertaining" Lebanese den, near the Wigmore
Hall, that's "fun for a group outing" (or "for a date"); the food
is "enjoyable", but hardly the point. / **Details:** www.levant.co.uk;
11.30 pm.

Lindsay House W1 £76 Ⓐ
11-15 Swallow St 7439 0450 3–3A
Richard Corrigan's "elegant" Soho townhouse still divides opinion;
for its many ardent fans, it offers "a wonderful experience",
with "impeccable cuisine" and its own "unique" and "cosy" charm –
to a disappointed minority, though, it's just a "hushed" place, where
the cooking is "ho-hum". / **Value tip:** set pre theatre £51
(FP). **Details:** www.lindsayhouse.co.uk; 10.30 pm; closed Sat L & Sun.

Lisboa Pâtisserie W10 £ 5 ⭐⭐
57 Golborne Rd 8968 5242 5–1A
"The best coffee" and "delicious" Portuguese pastries – sweet and
savoury – win ongoing raves for this "authentic" and ever-crowded
North Kensington café. / **Details:** 8 pm; L & early evening only; no booking.

LMNT E8 £25 Ⓐ
316 Queensbridge Rd 7249 6727
"Bliss out like an Egyptian", at this "surreal" Hackney pub-
conversion; the food is "not the star of the show", but then – given
the "bizarre" décor – how could it be? / **Details:** www.lmnt.co.uk;
10.45 pm; no Amex.

Lobster Pot SE11 £43 Ⓐ⭐
3 Kennington Ln 7582 5556
"It's worth the trek to deepest Kennington", to seek out the Régent
family's "so-kitsch-it's-cool" fixture, which mixes "bizarre ship's cabin
décor" with surprisingly "excellent" (but "pricey") Gallic seafood;
before too long, though, it's going to need a "facelift". / **Value tip:** set
weekday L £27 (FP). **Details:** www.lobsterpotrestaurant.co.uk; 10.30 pm; closed
Mon & Sun; booking: max 8.

Locanda Locatelli
Churchill InterCont'l W1 £57 Ⓐ⭐
8 Seymour St 7935 9088 1–2A
With its "wonderfully fresh" Italian cuisine, its "professional" service
and its "cool but unobtrusive modern setting", Giorgio Locatelli's
Marylebone "all-rounder" is the "crème de la crème of the cat's
whiskers" for most reporters; disappointments are not unknown,
though, and a fair few find it "over-rated".
/ **Details:** www.locandalocatelli.com; 11 pm, Fri & Sat 11.30 pm; booking: max 8.

The Lock Dining Bar N17 £40 ⭐
Heron Hs, Hale Wharf, Ferry Ln 8885 2829
With its "unexpectedly good" food and "efficient" service,
this Tottenham yearling is maintaining the standards of its
predecessor on this obscure site (Mosaica at the Lock, RIP). / **Value
tip:** set weekday L £20 (FP). **Details:** www.thelock-diningbar.com; 10.30 pm;
closed Mon D, Sat L & Sun D; no Amex.

Love India SW3 £37 ⭐

153 Fulham Rd 7589 7749 4–2C
Near pricey Brompton Cross, this basement Indian (long called the Tandoori of Chelsea) deserves to be better known; service can be a touch "eccentric", but some of the "spicy" dishes are "particularly fine". / Details: 11.30 pm.

Lucky Seven
Tom Conran Restaurants W2 £33 Ⓐ⭐

127 Westbourne Park Rd 7727 6771 5–1B
"If you like American diners", Tom Conran's "tiny", "'50s-style" re-creation looks like "the real McCoy", and serves "great burgers, pancakes and shakes". / Details: www.tomconranrestaurants.com; 11 pm; no Amex; no booking.

Lundum's SW7 £46 Ⓐ⭐

119 Old Brompton Rd 7373 7774 4–2B
This "civilised" (and "very romantic") spot in South Kensington offers an "utterly reliable" mix of "warm yet unfussy" service and "refreshingly different" Danish food (including some "excellent fish"); tips includes its "fantastic Sunday brunch buffet", and particularly nice "semi-private rooms". / Details: www.lundum.com; 10.30 pm; closed Sun D.

Ma Cuisine £36 ⭐

6 Whitton Rd, TW1 8607 9849
9 Station Approach, TW9 8332 1923
John McClements's wilfully retro "neighbourhood bistros" (in Kew and Twickenham) offer "a reliable nostalgia trip for anyone who was around in the '60s" — fortunately, "genial" staff and "good food at sensible prices" have a "timeless" appeal.
/ Details: www.macuisinegroup.co.uk; 10.30 pm; TW1 closed Sun; no Amex.

Ma Goa £31 ⭐⭐

194 Wandsworth Bridge Rd, SW6 7384 2122
244 Upper Richmond Rd, SW15 8780 1767
"Exciting Goan cooking" and "brilliant" service combine to make this family-run Putney fixture not just a "lovely local" but also one of London's more interesting Indians; its deepest-Fulham spin-off is less well-known, but equally highly rated. / Details: www.ma-goa.com; 11 pm; SW15 closed Mon & Sat L, SW6 closed Mon; SW6 no Amex.

Made in China SW10 £36 ⭐

351 Fulham Rd 7351 2939 4–3B
"Meals always seem to have been prepared individually", at this "very useful" Chelsea Chinese; staff are "friendly" too, though the design is not about to win any awards. / Details: 11.30 pm.

Madhu's UB1 £34 Ⓐ⭐⭐

39 South Rd 8574 1897
"I live in India, and this is where I eat when I'm back in London" — this Southall subcontinental offers "excellent" food (with "some dishes showing the owners' East African roots").
/ Details: www.madhusonline.com; 11.30 pm; closed Tue, Sat L & Sun L.

Magdalen SE1

£40

152 Tooley St 7403 1342

This "stonking" newcomer (on the site of Fina Estampa, RIP) is "a dream come true", in the thin area near Tower Bridge; its "solid" but "beautiful-tasting" English food – "like the Anchor & Hope, but a bit grander" – is served by "dedicated" staff in a "convivial" setting. / **Details:** 10.30 pm; closed Mon L & Sun.

Maggie Jones's W8

£44

6 Old Court Pl 7937 6462 4–1A

With its "cosy" and "country kitchen-ish" interior, this candlelit, "70s rustic" joint, near Kensington Palace, "oozes warmth and romance"; its "stodgy" comfort fare "won't win any awards" but "does the job". / **Details:** 11 pm.

Maison Bertaux W1

£9

28 Greek St 7437 6007 3–2A

"Anachronistic" but "very special" – this endearingly "grotty" Soho "institution" (est 1871) is still very popular for its "lovely" cakes, and "the best croissants in London". / **Details:** 11 pm, Sun 7 pm; no credit cards; no booking.

Malabar W8

£31

27 Uxbridge St 7727 8800 5–2B

"High standards have been maintained over many years", at this "low-key" Indian veteran, "tucked-away" off Notting Hill Gate; the "inventive" food is "far from bog-standard", staff are "very charming", and the setting is "relaxed but chic". / **Details:** www.malabar-restaurant.co.uk; 11.30 pm.

Malabar Junction WC1

£40

107 Gt Russell St 7580 5230 1–1C

"No rush and plenty of space" ("a refreshing change in central London") – that's much of the appeal of this "large, light and airy" Bloomsbury fixture; "reliable" south Indian food is an added bonus. / **Value tip:** set weekday L £13 (FP). **Details:** 11 pm.

Malmaison Brasserie EC1

£42

18-21 Charterhouse St 7012 3700

Surprisingly "pleasant" all-round for an hotel dining room – this Clerkenwell basement makes a "buzzy", "friendly" and "discreet" rendezvous, where the food doesn't usually let the side down. / **Details:** www.malmaison.com; 10.30 pm.

Mandarin Kitchen W2 £33 ✪✪
14-16 Queensway   7727 9012   5–2C
*"You just can't beat the lobster noodles", at this "frenetic" and
fantastically grungy Bayswater veteran, which is known for its
"amazing" Chinese seafood; waits can be "dreadful", though, even if
you've booked.* / **Details:** *11.30 pm.*

Mao Tai SW6 £42 ✪
58 New King's Rd   7731 2520
*The revamp "has made it a little more trendy", but "prices are up"
at this long-established Fulham oriental; fans insist that the
impressively "consistent" – if not especially authentic – pan-Asian
fare is still "worth it".* / **Details:** *11.30 pm.*

The Marquess Tavern N1 £38 ✪
32 Canonbury St   7354 2975
*An "always-welcoming" gastropub "gem", "in the heart
of Canonbury"; it offers an unusually "delicious" menu, which
is "heavy on meat and traditional British fare".* / **Value tip:** *set always
available £24 (FP).* **Details:** *www.marquesstavern.co.uk; 10.30 pm; closed Sun D.*

The Mason's Arms SW8 £35 ✪
169 Battersea Park Rd   7622 2007
*A "noisy" Battersea boozer whose "busy" kitchen is once again
turning out "modern basics" with "above-average success".* / **Value
tip:** *set Sun L £22 (FP).* **Details:** *www.london-gastros.co.uk; 10 pm.*

Matsuba TW9 £43 ✪
10 Red Lion St   8605 3513
*"The best sushi to the west of London" is to be had, say fans, at this
"simple but effective" restaurant, on the edge of Richmond town-
centre; it offers "an excellent range of Japanese and Korean dishes".*
/ **Details:** *11 pm; closed Sun.*

Matsuri £60 ✪
15 Bury St, SW1   7839 1101   2–3D
Mid City Place, 71 High Holborn, WC1   7430 1970   1–1D
*"High-quality sushi" and "attentive" service have helped win a big
following for these Japanese establishments in St James's and
Holborn; their interiors can seem a touch "sterile" (but, in SW1,
the teppan-yaki offers "great theatre").*
/ **Details:** *www.matsuri-restaurant.com; SW1 10.30 pm, WC1 10 pm;
WC1 closed Sun.*

maze W1 £55 ✪
10-13 Grosvenor Sq   7107 0000   2–2A
*Jason Atherton's "fabulous", "creative" food – served tapas-style –
helps make this "hip" Ramsay-group Mayfair dining room
an "amazing" destination for most reporters; service is a bit
"patchy", though, and prices can seem "outrageous".*
/ **Details:** *www.gordonramsay.com/maze; 10.30 pm.*

Memsaheb on Thames E14 £28 ✪
65/67 Amsterdam Rd   7538 3008
*A "great riverside location" boosts the appeal of this "excellent" –
if little-known – Indian, on the Isle of Dogs.* / **Value tip:** *set weekday L
£15 (FP).* **Details:** *www.memsaheb.com; 11.30 pm; closed Sat L.*

Meson don Felipe SE1 £26 Ⓐ
53 The Cut   7928 3237
*"It looks Spanish, and it feels Spanish", at this "totally reliable" and
"hard-to-get-into" tapas bar, near the Old Vic, which remains
"as crowded and frantic as ever"; NB: "the guitarist can be very
loud". / **Details:** 11 pm; closed Sun; no Amex; no booking after 8 pm.*

Mildred's W1 £30 Ⓐ⭐
45 Lexington St   7494 1634   2–2D
*"Who needs meat?", when you can eat at this "inspiring" Soho
"veggie stronghold"; "get there early", as there's no booking, and it
can get "ultra-crowded". / **Details:** www.mildreds.co.uk; 11 pm; closed Sun;
only Maestro; no booking.*

Mini Mundus SW17 £34 Ⓐ
218 Trinity Rd   8767 5810
*A "great local", in Wandsworth, where the "authentic" Gallic
cooking includes "melt-in-the-mouth" steaks. / **Details:** 10.30 pm;
closed Mon L.*

Mirch Masala £21 ⭐⭐
171-173 The Broadway, UB1   8867 9222
1416 London Rd, SW16   8679 1828
213 Upper Tooting Rd, SW17   8767 8638
111 Commercial Rd, E1   7247 9992
*"Forget the drab surroundings" – you get "astonishing food"
at "unbelievable" prices at these "bustling" Pakistani "caffs"; BYO.
/ **Details:** midnight.*

Miyama W1 £60 ⭐
38 Clarges St   7499 2443   2–4B
*Its ambience is "dire", but this Japanese veteran, in Mayfair, offers
"delicious and subtle" food and "helpful and courteous" service
(plus "one of the best-value lunches in the West End").
/ **Details:** www.miyama.co.uk; 10.30 pm; closed Sat L & Sun L.*

Mohsen W14 £26 ⭐
152 Warwick Rd   7602 9888   6–1D
*For "good-quality, simple Persian cuisine" (including "delicious
freshly-made flat-breads"), it's worth seeking out this "welcoming"
and "inexpensive" family-run spot, opposite the Olympia branch
of Homebase; BYO. / **Details:** midnight; no credit cards.*

Monmouth Coffee Company £10 Ⓐ⭐⭐
27 Monmouth St, WC2   7379 3516   3–2B
2 Park St, SE1   7645 3585
*"What more could you want?" ("apart from a few more branches"),
say fans of these "enthusiastic" pit stops, which offer "world-class"
coffee and "tempting" pastries; at Borough Market, "you can sit
around eating bread and jam" too – more popular than you might
think! / **Details:** www.monmouthcoffee.co.uk; L & afternoon tea only; closed Sun;
no Amex; no booking.*

The Morgan Arms E3 £40

43 Morgan St   8980 6389

"Always-interesting" food draws crowds to this "lively" Bow boozer; fans say it's "perfect" — well, it would be if it weren't getting "too popular with the locals". / **Details:** *www.geronimo-inns.co.uk; 10 pm; closed Sun D; no Amex; booking: max 10.*

Morgan M N7 £50

489 Liverpool Rd   7609 3560

Morgan Meunier's "inspired" Gallic venture offers "ravishing" cuisine at "unbeatable" prices; his north-Islington premises are "miles from anywhere", but have recently (too late to be reflected in the survey) been given a "warmer look". / **Details:** *www.morganm.com; 9.30 pm; closed Mon, Tue L, Sat L & Sun D; no Amex; booking: max 6.*

Moro EC1 £42

34-36 Exmouth Mkt   7833 8336

Sam and Samantha Clark's "stunning" and "interestingly different" (Spanish/North African) cuisine helps maintain their "seriously buzzing" Clerkenwell "canteen" as a perennial favourite; the noise level, though, can be "unbearable". / **Details:** *www.moro.co.uk; 10.30 pm; closed Sun; booking essential.*

Mosaica
The Chocolate Factory N22 £37

Unit C005, Clarendon Rd   8889 2400

"It's always worth the trek", say fans of this stylish — if "very noisy" — factory-conversion, whose location is obscure even by Wood Green standards. / **Details:** *www.mosaicarestaurants.com; 9.30 pm; closed Mon, Sat L & Sun D.*

Mr Wing SW5 £42

242-244 Old Brompton Rd   7370 4450   4–2A

"Get a seat downstairs" — "with tropical fish swimming by" — best to enjoy this atmospheric and "very romantic" Earl's Court "old favourite"; the "fairly traditional Chinese" food is "reliable", if arguably "rather pricey" for what it is. / **Details:** *www.mrwing.com; midnight.*

Nahm
Halkin Hotel SW1 £77

5 Halkin St   7333 1234   1–3A

Fans of David Thompson's much-fêted Belgravia Thai rave about his "wonderful" cooking, and its "mind-blowing textures and tastes"; far too many reporters, though, find a meal here to be a total turn-off — a "cold" place with "snooty" service, serving "pretentious" fare that's "grossly overpriced". / **Value tip:** *set always available £48 (FP).* **Details:** *www.nahm.como.bz; 10.30 pm; closed Sat L & Sun L.*

Nanglo SW12   £26   ⭐
88 Balham High Rd   8673 4160
*"Much better than your average local", this "pleasant" Balham Nepalese offers some "interesting" dishes, and the staff "couldn't be more charming". / **Details:** 11.30 pm; D only.*

Napket SW3   £35   ⭐
342 King's Rd   7352 9832   4–3C
*The "super-stylish" surroundings aren't to all tastes, but early reporters praise the "amazing bread and sandwiches" and "superb coffee" at this self-consciously hip new café, in Chelsea.
/ **Details:** www.napket.com; 9 pm, Fri-Sun 10 pm.*

Nautilus NW6   £25   ⭐⭐
27-29 Fortune Green Rd   7435 2532
*A "crowded" kosher chippy in West Hampstead, which fans tip as "the best in North London"; "portions are huge"; BYO.
/ **Details:** 10 pm; closed Sun L; no Amex.*

New Tayyabs E1   £20   ⭐⭐
83 Fieldgate St   7247 9543
*"Absolutely astounding" Pakistani food ensures this "cheap-as-chips" (and BYO) Whitechapel canteen is always "rammed full"; indeed, the only real criticism is that it's "too popular"!
/ **Details:** www.tayyabs.co.uk; 11.30 pm.*

Nobu
Metropolitan Hotel W1   £88   ⭐
Old Park Ln   7447 4747   2–4A
*For its army of fans, the "sensational" dishes at this legendary Mayfair Japanese/Latin American still make it the "Gold Standard" for oriental-fusion cuisine; its ratings are "fading", though, and it's "sooooooo expensive" that doubters feel it's plain "lost it".
/ **Details:** 10.15 pm; booking: max 12.*

Nobu Berkeley W1   £88   ⭐
15-16 Berkeley St   7290 9222   2–3C

*With its "fun and trashy" crowd, the newer of the Mayfair Nobus is "much the more happening of the two", and its "gorgeous" but "outrageously pricey" oriental fare now risks overhauling that at the original. / **Details:** www.noburestaurants.com; 1.30 am; D only, closed Sun.*

La Noisette SW1 £76 ✖
164 Sloane St 7750 5000 4–1D
"What a disaster!"; Bjorn van Der Horst's food at the latest addition to Ramsay's London empire may sometimes be "superb", but it's too often "hit-and-miss" – this might not be so bad if it were not for the "brown and forgettable" décor and the sometimes "non-existent" service, and all at "eye-watering" prices. / **Value tip:** *set weekday L £38 (FP).* **Details:** *10.30 pm; closed Sat L & Sun.*

Noor Jahan £33 ⭐
2a Bina Gdns, SW5 7373 6522 4–2B
26 Sussex Pl, W2 7402 2332 5–1D
"Seriously good" Indian food – "nothing fancy or trendy", mind – has long made this "reliable" curry house an Earl's Court institution; its Bayswater spin-off is less known, but even better. / **Details:** *11.30 pm.*

Nordic Bakery W1 £12 ⭐
14 Golden Sq 3230 1077 2–2D
An impressively spacious and airy new café, with a calming view of Soho's Golden Square; service is charming, and the short menu of Scandinavian snacks is realised to a high standard. / **Details:** *www.nordicbakery.com; 10 pm, Sat 7 pm; closed Sat D & Sun; no booking.*

North China W3 £25 ⭐
305 Uxbridge Rd 8992 9183 6–1A
"Hidden-away in Acton", this long-established, family-owned oriental has earned a very "loyal clientele", thanks to its "unfailing" service and its "high-quality" Chinese cooking. / **Value tip:** *set dinner £16 (FP).* **Details:** *www.northchina.co.uk; 11 pm.*

North Sea Fish WC1 £28 ⭐
7-8 Leigh St 7387 5892
"Exemplary" fish 'n' chips draw many admirers to this "old-style" chippy, hidden away in Bloomsbury. / **Details:** *10.30 pm; closed Sun.*

Notting Hill Brasserie W11 £53 🅐⭐⭐
92 Kensington Park Rd 7229 4481 5–2B
"Romantic... special... gorgeous"; this "highly polished" restaurant (not brasserie) offers a "really lovely", "all-round" experience – Mark Jenkel's "very accomplished" food is served by "slick" staff, in a townhouse setting that's "elegant but not stuffy"; "great live jazz" too. / **Details:** *11 pm; closed Sun D.*

Nozomi SW3 £66
15 Beauchamp Pl 7838 1500 4–1C
A "very self-conscious" Japanese for Knightsbridge "beautiful people"; it's sometimes "fun", but even fans concede it's "overpriced", and critics would settle for nothing less than "a massive overhaul of the kitchen". / **Details:** *www.nozomi.co.uk; 11.30 pm; closed Sun L.*

Numero Uno SW11 £33 🅐
139 Northcote Rd 7978 5837
"Always full, and deservedly so", this "very friendly" and "buzzy" family-run Battersea Italian pleases many fans with its "consistently good" food; "good value" too. / **Details:** *11.30 pm; no Amex.*

Nuovi Sapori SW6　　　　　　　**£38**　　　⭐

295 New King's Rd　7736 3363
*"Passionate" cooking and "chatty" service have established this "buzzy" Fulham two-year-old as a "proper neighbourhood Italian"; it is "cramped", though, and the occasional reporter feels it's "over-rated". / **Details:** 11 pm; closed Sun.*

Nutmeg SW1　　　　　　　　**£24**　　　⭐

147 Lupus St　7233 9828　4–3D
*"Trying really hard in an awkward location" – this year-old Pimlico spot offers some "unusual" Bangladeshi dishes, realised to "above-average" standards. / **Details:** www.nutmegbarrestaurant.co.uk; 11 pm.*

O'Zon TW1　　　　　　　　**£24**

33-35 London Rd　8891 3611
*A supremely friendly pan-Asian restaurant in downtown Twickenham, where the "eat-all-you-like menu" is "really good value". / **Details:** www.ozon.co.uk; 11 pm.*

The Oak W2　　　　　　　　**£35**　　🅐⭐

137 Westbourne Park Rd　7221 3355　5–1B
*"Finally re-opened after the fire", this "well-loved" Notting Hill pub-conversion has made a "welcome return" – its "relaxed" ambience still "can't be beaten" and the pizza is "even better than before". / **Details:** www.theoaklondon.com; 10.30 pm, Sun 9 pm; Mon-Thu closed L; no booking.*

Odette's NW1　　　　　　　**£68**

130 Regent's Park Rd　7586 8569
*Ex-rock promoter Vince Power's re-launch (without the trademark mirrors) of this "romantic" Primrose Hill classic divides opinion – fans acclaim a "lovely refurbishment" that's "impossible to fault", but critics find the wallpaper "scary", and think that, given the "high" prices, the food is rather "pedestrian". / **Value tip:** set weekday L £42 (FP). **Details:** 10.30 pm; closed Mon & Sun D.*

Odin's W1　　　　　　　　**£47**　　🅐

27 Devonshire St　7935 7296　1–1A
*"Beautiful art" (the late Peter Langan's collection) and "unruffled" service add to the "classy" charm of this "dignified" Marylebone "old favourite"; it makes a good choice for business or romance... "so long as you are happy with old-school British cooking". / **Details:** www.langansrestaurant.co.uk; 11 pm; closed Sat L & Sun; booking: max 10.*

(Ognisko Polskie)
The Polish Club SW7　　　**£39**　　🅐

55 Prince's Gate, Exhibition Rd　7589 4635　4–1C
*The "unique" atmosphere offers "reason enough to visit" this "time-warp" émigrés' club, which benefits from "gracious" South Kensington premises (and a "wonderful balcony" for the summer); the hearty Polish fare, though, is "undistinguished". / **Details:** www.ognisko.com; 11 pm.*

Ye Olde Cheshire Cheese EC4 £32 A X
145 Fleet St 7353 6170
*"The cosy coal fire and Dickensian setting here is very romantic...
if you like that kind of thing!"; the food at this wonderful old City
tavern can be "awful", though – "I feel sorry for the tourists!"
/ **Details:** www.yeoldecheshirecheese.com; 9.30 pm; closed Sun D; no booking,
Sat & Sun.*

Olivo SW1 £44 ☆
21 Eccleston St 7730 2505 1–4B
*It's "cramped and noisy", but this "long-time favourite" attracts
a "very smart" Belgravia crowd, and it's always "buzzing", thanks
to its "consistently fresh" Sardinian cooking and "very friendly"
service. / **Details:** 11 pm; closed Sat L & Sun L.*

Olivomare SW1 £47 ☆
10-12 Lower Belgrave St 7730 9022 1–4B
*This summer-2007 spin-off from Olivo, also of Belgravia, has been
hailed in the press as one of the best openings of recent times,
and we see no reason to disagree – a chic Italian seafood specialist,
it scores across the board. / **Details:** 11 pm; closed Sun.*

Olley's SE24 £31 ☆
67-69 Norwood Rd 8671 8259
*"South London's finest chippy" – occupying a railway arch
overlooking Brockwell Park. / **Details:** www.olleys.info; 10.30 pm; closed
Mon L.*

1 Lombard Street EC3 £75
1 Lombard St 7929 6611
*A location in the very heart of the City makes this "cavernous"
classic – a former banking hall – "an archetypal choice for
a business lunch" (and so, of course, "totally over-priced"); those
paying their own way may wish to head for the "noisy" but
(somewhat) cheaper brasserie area. / **Details:** www.1lombardstreet.com;
9.45 pm; closed Sat & Sun; no trainers; booking essential.*

One-O-One
Sheraton Park Tower SW1 £75
101 Knightsbridge 7290 7101 4–1D
*Pascal Proyart's cooking of fish is often reckoned
"the best in London", but the design of this Knightsbridge dining
room has infamously never lived up – it was re-opening, after
a major shake-up, as this guide went to press.
/ **Details:** www.oneoone.com; 10 pm.*

L'Oranger SW1 £80 A
5 St James's St 7839 3774 2–4D
*This "elegant" and "welcoming" St James's fixture offers a "really
classy" all-round experience; its "classic" cuisine is "a notch below
the Ramsays of the world", but typically inspires "few complaints".
/ **Value tip:** set weekday L £48 (FP). **Details:** www.loranger.co.uk; 11 pm; closed
Sat L & Sun; booking: max 8.*

Origin Asia TW9   **£35** ★

100 Kew Rd   8958 0509

"Imaginative", "Indian-with-a-twist" cuisine wins rave reviews from local fans of this bright and "friendly" Richmond spot.

/ *Details: www.originasia.co.uk; 11 pm.*

Orrery W1   **£68**

55 Marylebone High St   7616 8000   1–1A

"The best Conran by far" (even if the group is now officially called 'D&D London'), offering "pricey" modern French cooking that's often "surprisingly good"; the interior can seem "sterile", but some of the larger tables – overlooking a churchyard – are "lovely".

/ *Details: www.orreryrestaurant.co.uk; 10.30 pm, Thu-Sat 11 pm; booking: max 12.*

Oslo Court NW8   **£46** Ⓐ★

Charlbert St, off Prince Albert Rd   7722 8795

To the delight of its many mature patrons (and the odd young whippersnapper too), "old-fashioned" dishes come in "epic" portions (especially puds, from the trolley) at this "bizarre" time warp, at the foot of a Regent's Park apartment block; it's "the most endearing waiters ever", though, who really make the occasion. / *Details: 11 pm; closed Sun.*

Osteria Basilico W11   **£40** Ⓐ★

29 Kensington Park Rd   7727 9957   5–1A

"Fun", "noisy" and "crowded" – this rustic Italian has been a linchpin of Notting Hill life for 15 years, thanks not least to its "great pasta" and "lovely pizza"; sometimes, though, the "truly Italian" staff "could be friendlier". / *Details: www.osteriabasilico.co.uk; 11.30 pm; no booking, Sat L.*

Ottolenghi   **£37** ★★

63 Ledbury Rd, W11   7727 1121   5–1B

1 Holland St, W8   7937 0003   4–1A

287 Upper St, N1   7288 1454

"You're tantalised the moment you enter" these "über-trendy" cafés, which offer a "vibrant" selection of salads, and "stunningly beautiful cakes and confections"; the food can initially seem "vastly overpriced", but fortunately it's all just as "scrummy" as it looks.

/ *Details: www.ottolenghi.co.uk; 10.15 pm; W11 8pm, Sun 6 pm; N1 closed Sun D, Holland St takeaway only; W11 no booking, N1 booking for D only.*

Le Pain Quotidien   **£23** Ⓐ

18 Great Marlborough St, Turner Bdg, W1   7486 6154   2–2C

72-75 Marylebone High St, W1   7486 6154   1–1A

201-203A Kings Rd, SW3   7486 6154   4–3C

9 Young St, W8   7486 6154   4–1A

Royal Festival Hall, Belvedere Rd, SE1   7486 6154   1–3D

The arrival of these "top communal-tables Belgian bakeries" is universally welcomed by reporters – attractions include "wholesome" bread and pastries, "lovely" coffee and a "great range of breakfast and brunch dishes". / *Details: W1U 9 pm, Sun 8 pm; SW3 10 pm, Sun 7 pm; W8 8 pm, Sun & Mon 7 pm; SE1 11 pm, Sun 10 pm; W1F 10 pm, Sun 7 pm.*

The Painted Heron SW10 £45 ★★
112 Cheyne Walk   7351 5232   4–3B
*"Unique" cuisine that's "as good as you'll find in London" makes
it worth seeking out this "posh Indian", tucked-away by the Chelsea
Embankment; it deserves to be better known.*
/ **Details:** www.thepaintedheron.com; 11 pm; closed Sat L.

Pampa £40 ★
4 Northcote Rd, SW11   7924 1167
60 Battersea Rise, SW11   7924 4774
*The "exquisite steaks" are "the best in South West London, if not
the whole of town", at these "friendly" Battersea Argentineans.*
/ **Details:** 11 pm; D only; Battersea Rise closed Sun.

Paolina Café WC1 £16 ★
181 Kings Cross Rd   7278 8176
*"Very tasty Thai food at incredibly cheap prices" and
"the friendliest" service commend this small BYO oriental caff,
in King's Cross, to reporters.* / **Details:** 10 pm; closed Sun; no credit cards.

Papillon SW3 £50 Ⓐ
96 Draycott Ave   7225 2555   4–2C
*Soren Jessen's "sophisticated but friendly" Belle Epoque-style
yearling has been "a happy addition to the Chelsea scene"; it offers
"competent" Gallic fare, plus an "overwhelming" (and, perhaps,
"overpriced") wine list.* / **Value tip:** set weekday L £30
(FP). **Details:** www.papillonchelsea.co.uk; midnight, Sun 10 pm.

Pappa Ciccia £27 Ⓐ★
105-107 Munster Rd, SW6   7384 1884
41 Fulham High St, SW6   7736 0900
90 Lower Richmond Rd, SW15   8789 9040
*These "great-value, local pizza places" are "fun" and "lively"
destinations with a strong regular following; you can BYO too
(Fulham High St, wine only).* / **Details:** www.pappaciccia.com; 11 pm;
no Amex.

**Paradise by Way of
Kensal Green W10** £35 Ⓐ★
19 Kilburn Ln   8969 0098

*A "characterful building" is the star of the show at this long-running
favourite; the food is still consistently "good", though, and service
is "attentive" too; major changes are afoot for 2008.*
/ **Details:** www.theparadise.co.uk; 10.30 pm, 9pm; no Amex.

El Parador NW1   **£26** ★
245 Eversholt St   7387 2789
*"If it wasn't in a grotty part of town, it would be impossible to get
a table", at this "shabby" but "cheerful" Spanish veteran,
near Euston – the food is "basic", but it's "cheap" and "full of
taste". / Details: www.elparadorlondon.com; Mon-Sat 11 pm, Sun 9.30 pm;
closed Sat L & Sun L; no Amex.*

Pasha SW7   **£48** Ⓐ
1 Gloucester Rd   7589 7969   4–1B
*A "sexy and sultry" atmosphere pervades the "numerous nooks and
crannies" of this South Kensington Moroccan; new management,
though, has yet to pep up its food and service, which are still
sometimes "terrible". / Details: www.pasha-restaurant.co.uk; midnight,
Thu-Sat 1 am; booking: max 10 at weekends.*

Patara   **£45** ★
15 Greek St, W1   7437 1071   3–2A
3-7 Maddox St, W1   7499 6008   2–2C
181 Fulham Rd, SW3   7351 5692   4–2C
9 Beauchamp Pl, SW3   7581 8820   4–1C
*"Stunningly-presented and delicious" dishes, "very polite and
professional" staff, and "calm" and "comfortable" branches – that's
the formula which has created a large fan club for these "elegant"
Thai oases. / Details: www.pataralondon.com; 10.30 pm.*

Patio W12   **£26** Ⓐ
5 Goldhawk Rd   8743 5194   6–1C
*"Solid, stodgy, Polish fare is served with enthusiasm" (and free
vodka!) at this "eccentric" and "entertaining" venture by Shepherd's
Bush Green; it's all a bit "hit-and-miss", but prices are "very fair".
/ Details: 11.30 pm; closed Sat L.*

Pâtisserie Valerie   **£28**
17 Motcomb St, SW1   7245 6161   4–1D
Hans Cr, SW1   7590 0905   4–1D
105 Marylebone High St, W1   7935 6240   1–1A
162 Piccadilly, W1   7491 1717   2–3C
44 Old Compton St, W1   7437 3466   3–2A
215 Brompton Rd, SW3   7823 9971   4–1C
Duke of York Sq, SW3   7730 7094   4–2D
27 Kensington Church St, W8   7937 9574   4–1A
37 Brushfield St, E1   7247 4906
*This "cosmopolitan"-feeling chain was sold to ex-PizzaExpress
entrepreneur Luke Johnson in late-2006; its "fail-safe" breakfasts,
"gorgeous cakes" and "dependable" other bites have won it many
fans – let's hope the formula survives the dreaded 'roll-out' (coming
soon to a high street near you). / Details: www.patisserie-valerie.co.uk;
7 pm, Old Compton St 7.30 pm, 10.30 pm Wed-Sat, Brushfield St 8 pm, Hans Cr
11.30 pm; minimum £5 using Amex; no booking.*

Patterson's W1   **£60** ★
4 Mill St   7499 1308   2–2C
*"You get very good value, especially for Mayfair", at this
"very sound" family-run venture – "warm and personal" service
helps offset the rather "bland" and "crowded" interior, and the
cuisine is sometimes "outstanding".
/ Details: www.pattersonsrestaurant.com; 11 pm; closed Sat L & Sun.*

Pearl WC1   **£70**

252 High Holborn   7829 7000   1–1D

"Airy" and *"well-spaced"*, this former Holborn banking hall is ideal for a *"glamorous"* business dinner (and also tipped for romance), thanks not least to Jan Tanaka's *"classy"* cuisine and the *"superb"* wine list; it's *"expensive"*, though, and the *"beautiful"* décor can sometimes seem *"cold"*. / **Details:** www.pearl-restaurant.com; 10 pm; closed Sat L & Sun.

Pearl Liang W2   **£35**   ⭐

8 Sheldon Sq   7289 7000   5–1C

"Delicate and divine dim sum" – and other *"very authentic"* Chinese cooking – has carved out an instant reputation for this opium den-style newcomer, *"hidden-away"* in the bowels of the huge new Paddington Basin development. / **Details:** www.pearlliang.co.uk; 11 pm.

Pellicano SW3   **£44**   ⭐

19-21 Elystan St   7589 3718   4–2C

"Very much back on form" – this *"friendly"* Chelsea backstreet Italian is an *"attentive"* sort of place, offering *"attractively-presented"* dishes. / **Details:** 11 pm.

E Pellicci E2   **£14**   🅐

332 Bethnal Green Rd   7739 4873

A *"stunning"* Art Deco interior would make this landmark East End greasy spoon notable, irrespective of any other virtues; however, its *"brilliant Full English breakfasts"* – served with *"passion"* – are *"worth crossing town for"*. / **Details:** 5pm; L only, closed Sun; no credit cards.

Père Michel W2   **£42**   ⭐

11 Bathurst St   7723 5431   5–2D

"Good quality" – *"if uninspired"* – Gallic dishes win a loyal older following for this *"unchanging"* Bayswater bistro, where fish and seafood are specialities. / **Details:** 11 pm; closed Sat L & Sun.

Petek N4   **£25**   🅐⭐

96 Stroud Green Rd   7619 3933

"More than your bog-standard Turkish café" – this Finsbury Park yearling is a *"friendly"* place, offering a good *"cheap and cheerful"* experience. / **Details:** 11 pm; closed Sun.

Pétrus
The Berkeley SW1   **£89**   🅐⭐⭐

Wilton Pl   7235 1200   4–1D

How long before Marcus Wareing's *"brilliant"* cuisine overtakes that at his boss Gordon Ramsay's Royal Hospital Road flagship?; looking at the whole experience – and factoring in the charm of the *"classy, plush and opulent"* surroundings – this Knightsbridge dining room is already rated by the survey as the better all-round choice; the wine list is *"simply astounding"* too. / **Value tip:** set always available £50 (FP). **Details:** www.marcuswareing.com; 10.45 pm; closed Sat L & Sun; no jeans or trainers; booking: max 10.

Pham Sushie EC1 £23 ⓒⓒ
155 Whitecross St   7251 6336
*Some of "the best-value-for-money sushi" in town — "superbly fresh
every time" — draws many fans to this "basic" spot, in a
"backwater" near the Barbican. / **Details:** 10 pm; closed Sat L & Sun.*

Phoenix Bar & Grill SW15 £43 Ⓐⓒ
162-164 Lower Richmond Rd   8780 3131
*"Very good in recent times" — this "buzzy" Putney brasserie serves
up some "high-quality" Mediterranean dishes (not least "the best-
ever pasta"); "nice terrace" too. / **Details:** www.sonnys.co.uk; 10.30 pm,
11 pm.*

Pick More Daisies N8 £30 Ⓐⓒ
12 Crouch End Hill   8340 2288
*"Fantastic all-American breakfasts", "serious salads" and "succulent
burgers to die for" are among features that make this "chilled" and
"child-friendly" hang-out a smash hit, up Crouch End way.
/ **Details:** www.pickmoredaisies.com; 10 pm; no Amex.*

Pied à Terre W1 £84 ⓒ
34 Charlotte St   7636 1178   1–1C
*Shane Osborn's "magnificent" cuisine and an "astonishing" wine
list maintain David Moore's Fitzrovia townhouse as a Mecca for
serious foodies; its "relaxed and informal" style, though,
can sometimes give a rather "uneventful" impression. / **Value tip:** set
weekday L £53 (FP). **Details:** www.pied-a-terre.co.uk; 11 pm; closed Sat L & Sun;
booking: max 6.*

The Pig's Ear SW3 £39 Ⓐ
35 Old Church St   7352 2908   4–3C
*A "very buzzy" and "very Chelsea" pub, with a "crammed"
downstairs bar, and a more "civilised" dining room upstairs;
its combination of a "cosy" British ambience with "Frenchified" fare
is making it very popular. / **Details:** www.thepigsear.co.uk; 10 pm.*

La Piragua N1 £26 Ⓐⓒ
176 Upper St   7354 2843
*"A true Latin American experience in the heart of Islington" —
highlights include "fantastic Argentinian steaks, and real salsa
dancing after 11pm". / **Details:** 11.30 pm (Fri club till 6 am); no Amex.*

Pissarro's W4 £41 Ⓐ
Corney Reach Way   8994 3111
*This "relaxed" Thames-side spot, near Chiswick House, doesn't
just rely on the "lovely" charms of its "conservatory overlooking the
river" — it serves "surprisingly good" traditional scoff.
/ **Details:** www.pissarro.co.uk; 10.30 pm.*

Pizza Metro SW11 £32 Ⓐⓒⓒ
64 Battersea Rise   7228 3812
*"Is it the best pizza in London?" — this "really authentic" and "good-
value" Neapolitan joint, in Battersea, has a better claim than most;
it's "really fun and buzzy" too. / **Details:** www.pizzametro.com; 11 pm;
closed Mon, Tue-Fri D only, Sat & Sun open L & D; no Amex.*

Plateau E14 £69
Canada Pl 7715 7100
With its "great location, and view of Canary Wharf", this fourth-floor vantage point is "one of the few real choices" for business entertaining in the area; it's "strictly for expense-accounts", though, and can seem "uninspiring", "snotty" and "overpriced" – the brasserie (price £53) is probably a better bet. / **Value tip:** set dinner £45 (FP). **Details:** www.plateaurestaurant.co.uk; 10 pm; closed Sat L & Sun D.

Poissonnerie de l'Avenue SW3 £57 ★
82 Sloane Ave 7589 2457 4–2C
"An old-fashioned fish restaurant, in the best sense" – this "grown-up" Brompton Cross "institution" is notable for its "consistent quality" over many years; younger bloods, though, may find its clientele a touch "geriatric". / **Details:** www.poissonneriedelavenue.co.uk; 11.15 pm; closed Sun.

Pomegranates SW1 £50 Ⓐ
94 Grosvenor Rd 7828 6560 1–4C
"Eccentric, '70s décor" adds to the "quirky" charm of Patrick Wynn Jones's "clubby" Pimlico basement; the "eclectic" menu is similarly a "throwback" – part of an overall experience that's "enjoyable, if pricey". / **Details:** 11.15 pm; closed Sat L & Sun.

Le Pont de la Tour SE1 £66
36d Shad Thames 7403 8403
"Only for the view of Tower Bridge"; otherwise, this D&D London (formerly Conran) veteran – with its "bored" staff and its "boring" food – often seems "a bit of a rip-off"; optimists insist it's "getting better", though, and they have (modest) support from the ratings. / **Details:** www.danddlondon.com; 11 pm; closed Sat L.

La Porte des Indes W1 £56 Ⓐ
32 Bryanston St 7224 0055 1–2A
"You'd never guess you're only a block from Marble Arch", at this "dramatic", "tropical-themed" basement, which comes complete with waterfall; it can seem "overpriced", but its "eclectic, French-Indian fusion" fare is usually "very enjoyable" (and the Sunday buffet is "splendid"). / **Details:** www.pilondon.net; 11.30 pm; closed Sat L.

Il Portico W8 £42 Ⓐ
277 Kensington High St 7602 6262 6–1D
A "homely" Kensington Italian "staple" – now run by the third generation of the Chiavarini family – to which "the faithful return time-after-time". / **Details:** www.ilportico.co.uk; 11.15 pm; closed Sun, & Bank Holidays.

La Poule au Pot SW1 £50 Ⓐ
231 Ebury St 7730 7763 4–2D
"Take someone you love" to this "quirky" and "romantically dark" candlelit bit of "rustic France", in Pimlico – yet again, the survey's top tip for a date; the cuisine is "simple" and generally "well-cooked", but the "idiosyncratic" service has sometimes seemed "arrogant" of late. / **Value tip:** set weekday L £32 (FP). **Details:** 11 pm.

The Princess EC2 £40 ⭐

76 Paul St   7729 9270

This Shoreditch two-year-old (sibling to Farringdon's Easton) wins nothing but praise for its "sophisticated gastropub fare"; the stylish small dining room is up a spiral staircase, over the main bar.
/ *Details: 10 pm; closed Sat L & Sun.*

Princess Garden W1 £50 ⭐

8 North Audley St   7493 3223   2–2A

For an "upmarket" (if slightly "sterile") Chinese experience, this "comfortable" Mayfair spot – with its "remarkably helpful" service and its "consistently good" food – is often tipped as "pricy but worth it". / **Value tip:** *set weekday L £29*
(FP). Details: www.princessgardenofmayfair.com; 11.15 pm.

Prism EC3 £70

147 Leadenhall St   7256 3888

Some reporters do tip Harvey Nics's City outpost as a "decent" business venue; prices for the "formulaic" cuisine are "outrageous", though, and the setting – a converted banking hall – can seem "stilted" and "echoey". / **Details:** *www.harveynichols.com; 10 pm; closed Sat & Sun.*

The Providores W1 £55 ⭐

109 Marylebone High St   7935 6175   1–1A

Peter Gordon's "wacky combinations of ingredients" and some "great Kiwi wines" make this "unusual" (and "cramped") first-floor Marylebone dining room something of a foodie Mecca; for critics, though, the food can be "rich and overcomplicated".
/ **Details:** *www.providores.co.uk; 10.30 pm; booking: max 12.*

(Tapa Room)
The Providores W1 £35 ⭐

109 Marylebone High St   7935 6175   1–1A

"Unusual combos that work really well" create a "yummy" choice of "imaginative" tapas at this popular Marylebone hang-out, where "unbeatable Kiwi brunches" and "splendid NZ wines" are highlights; it's "a tight squeeze", though, and "mad" when busy.
/ **Details:** *www.theprovidores.co.uk; 10.30 pm.*

The Pumphouse N8 £42 Ⓐ

1 New River Ave   8340 0400

"The location is the star", at this "funky" converted pumping station, in Hornsey; not infrequently, though, the food "fails to live up to the interesting setting". / **Details:** *www.phn8.co.uk; 9.30 pm; closed Mon.*

Queen's Head W6 £30 Ⓐ

13 Brook Grn   7603 3174   6–1C

A huge, "charming" tavern on Brook Green, with a "fantastic" rear garden – "it's such a pity that the gigantic menu is stuck in the '70s". / **Details:** *10 pm; no booking.*

Le Querce SE23 £29 ⭐⭐
66-68 Brockley Rise   8690 3761
"Well worth the trip to SE23" — this totally unexpected (and very modest) newcomer, in the backwoods of Lewisham, serves "the best" Italian food you'll find for the money, including some "excellent home-made pasta"; (option to BYO for £2 corkage). / **Value tip:** set weekday L £18 (FP). **Details:** 10.30 pm; no Amex.

Quilon SW1 £47 ⭐
41 Buckingham Gate   7821 1899   1–4B
It's worth braving the "slightly cold" setting of this subcontinental in the "barren" area near Buckingham Palace — service is "courteous" and the south Indian cuisine shows "great subtlety and lightness of touch". / **Value tip:** set Sun L £20 (FP). **Details:** www.thequilonrestaurant.com; 11 pm; closed Sat L & Sun.

Quirinale SW1 £55 ⭐
North Ct, 1 Gt Peter St   7222 7080   1–4C
"Plenty of rotund MPs" add to the businesslike vibe of this "discreet" Westminster basement; it's a shame the setting can seem rather "characterless" — the service is "slick", and Stefano Favio's Italian cooking is often "superb". / **Details:** www.quirinale.co.uk; 10.30 pm; closed Sat L & Sun.

Racine SW3 £48 ⭐
239 Brompton Rd   7584 4477   4–2C
"Just sit back and pretend you're in Paris", at this "wonderful" (if "very crowded and noisy") Knightsbridge brasserie, where Henry Harris is in charge of the "particularly well-executed" cuisine, and Eric Garnier oversees "attentive but unobtrusive" service that's "close to perfect". / **Details:** 10.30 pm.

Ragam W1 £30 ⭐⭐
57 Cleveland St   7636 9098   1–1B
Forget the "grotty" décor and the "crowded and noisy" conditions — this "low-key Fitzrovia classic" delivers "astoundingly good" South Indian dishes (mostly veggie) at prices that "can't be beaten"; BYO at modest corkage. / **Value tip:** set weekday L £13 (FP). **Details:** www.mcdosa.co.uk; 11 pm.

Rasa N16 £24 ⭐⭐
55 Stoke Newington Church St   7249 0344
The "Stokey original" is "still the best" of this superb Indian group; its "passionate" staff are "exceptionally friendly", and its veggie Keralan fare is "superlative" — so "fresh", so "interesting", and at such "incredibly low" prices. / **Details:** www.rasarestaurants.com; 10.30 pm; closed weekday L.

Rasa £35 ⭐⭐
5 Charlotte St, W1   7637 0222   1–1C
6 Dering St, W1   7629 1346   2–2B
Holiday Inn Hotel, 1 Kings Cross, WC1   7833 9787
56 Stoke Newington Church St, N16   7249 1340
With its "wonderful South Indian cuisine" at "incredibly low prices", this Keralan mini-chain stands in "a class apart"; Dering Street and N16 (Travancore) serve meat, while the Charlotte Street branch (Samudra) offers "amazing seafood curries" and the like; (see also Rasa N16). / **Details:** www.rasarestaurants.com; 10.45 pm; N16 Mon-Fri closed L, Dering St W1 closed Sun, N16 D only Mon-Sat, N1 L only Mon-Fri.

Rasoi Vineet Bhatia SW3 £74
10 Lincoln St   7225 1881   4–2D
Vineet Bhatia's "incredible" cuisine – "a superb synthesis
of traditional and modern styles" – makes this Chelsea townhouse
"arguably the best Indian restaurant in the world"; its interior can
"lack buzz", but this year it has seemed more "intimate" and
"elegant". / **Value tip:** set weekday L £42 (FP). **Details:** www.vineetbhatia.com;
11 pm; closed Sat L & Sun.

Rebato's SW8 £30
169 South Lambeth Rd   7735 6388
"As if by magic, you're transported to Seville", at this "comforting"
and "old-fashioned" Vauxhall veteran, where "great" staff oversee
the "buzzing" tapas bar, and an amiably "cheesy" restaurant.
/ **Details:** www.rebatos.com; 10.45 pm; closed Sat L & Sun.

Red Fort W1 £60
77 Dean St   7437 2525   3–2A
"An interesting slant on Indian cooking of the highest quality"
retains quite a following for this grand and slightly "staid" Soho
veteran. / **Details:** www.redfort.co.uk; 11.15 pm; closed Sat L & Sun L.

(Restaurant)
Oxo Tower SE1 £72
Barge House St   7803 3888
"Pound-for-pound, is this the worst restaurant in the world?";
"even the view cannot make up for the poor and pricey food",
on the 8th floor of this South Bank landmark – yet again the
survey's top nomination for both overpricing and disappointment.
/ **Details:** www.harveynichols.com; 11 pm; booking: max 14.

Rhodes 24 EC2 £62
25 Old Broad St   7877 7703
"If conversation flags, you can always discuss the view", at Gary
Rhodes's 24th-floor City eyrie, which "hits all the right spots for
business entertaining"; fans say his trademark "English staples with
a twist" are equally "fabulous", but others have found them
increasingly "pedestrian" of late. / **Details:** www.rhodes24.co.uk; 9 pm;
closed Sat & Sun; booking essential.

Rhodes W1 Restaurant W1 £71
Gt Cumberland Pl   7479 3737   1–2A

We sadly didn't get to visit Gary Rhodes's new (mid-2007) fine
dining room, near Marble Arch, before this guide went to press;
newspaper reviews have hailed the very high quality of its Gallic
cuisine, but commentary on the décor is more mixed.
/ **Details:** www.rhodesw1.com; 10.30 pm; closed Mon, Sat L & Sun; no trainers.

Rib Room
Jumeirah Carlton Tower Hotel SW1   **£80**
2 Cadogan Pl   7858 7251   4–1D
It's a shame about the "greatly inflated prices" of this "luxurious"
(but staid) Knightsbridge grill room, as – on a good day – it offers
"the best thick-cut roast beef in town", and very good oysters and
fowl too. / **Details:** www.jumeirah.com; 10.30 pm.

RIBA Café   Ⓐ
Royal Ass'n of Brit' Architects W1   **£34**
66 Portland Pl   7631 0467   1–1B
A "soaring" Art Deco interior, and one of the
best (and least discovered) terraces in London dominate
commentary on this Marylebone café; "you hardly notice the food".
/ **Details:** www.riba-venues.com; L only, closed Sun.

El Rincón Latino SW4   **£28**   Ⓐ
148 Clapham Manor St   7622 0599
"Incredibly friendly" service, and "wonderful" tapas make this
family-fun Clapham stalwart "extremely popular" – "visit during the
day if you want to avoid the noise". / **Details:** 11.30 pm; closed Mon,
Tue-Fri D only, Sat & Sun open L & D.

The Ritz W1   **£93**   Ⓐ
150 Piccadilly   7493 8181   2–4C
"There is no more romantic room in London" than this "ornate,
Louis XVI-style" chamber; unless you're looking for the "ne plus ultra
of formal breakfasts", the food has generally been lacklustre for
decades, but better survey ratings are – at last! – beginning
to support those who say it's "improved" of late. / **Value tip:** set
weekday L £53 (FP). **Details:** www.theritzlondon.com; 10.30 pm; jacket & tie
required.

Riva SW13   **£48**   ★
169 Church Rd   8748 0434
Fans find "no gimmicks, just unpretentious and perfectly-cooked
dishes", at Andreas Riva's "outstanding" Barnes Venetian; it's a
pretty "basic" place, though, and some reporters feel it's "better for
those who know the patron". / **Details:** 10.30 pm; closed Sat L.

The River Café W6   **£64**   ★
Thames Wharf, Rainville Rd   7386 4200   6–2C
"Still a winner after all these years" – this "casual" Hammersmith
legend is still the "epitome" of haute-rustic Italian style (and its
hard-to-find riverside location can be "inspirational" on a summer's
day); prices, though, can seem "obscene". / **Details:** www.rivercafe.co.uk;
9 pm; closed Sun D.

Roka W1 £51 Ⓐ★★★
37 Charlotte St   7580 6464   1–1C

With its "non-stop buzz", its "sexy" bar and its "brilliant" Japanese
fare – largely from the central robata grill – this Fitzrovia "goldfish
bowl" arouses almost as much excitement as its grander sibling
Zuma; portions, though, "suit size-zero supermodels".
/ **Details:** www.rokarestaurant.com; 11.15 pm; booking: max 8.

Ronnie Scott's W1 £45 Ⓐ✖
47 Frith St   7439 0747   3–2A
"You don't go to Ronnie Scott's for the food", which is just as well –
"it's all about the jazz", and the "superb" atmosphere.
/ **Details:** www.ronniescotts.co.uk; 3 am, Sun midnight; D only.

Rooburoo N1 £27 ★
21 Chapel Mkt   7278 8100
"More-imaginative-than-usual dishes" make it "worth the trek"
to this new modern-Indian, rather "rough" Islington location
notwithstanding. / **Details:** www.rooburoo.com; 11 pm; closed Mon L.

Rosemary Lane E1 £44 ★
61 Royal Mint St   7481 2602
"A hidden gem on the fringes of the City" (in an "unpromising"-
looking ex-boozer, near the DLR track, a few minutes' walk
east of Tower Hill); staff are extremely "friendly" and the cooking
is "surprisingly good". / **Value tip:** set always available £28
(FP). **Details:** www.rosemarylane.btinternet.co.uk; 10 pm; closed Sat L & Sun.

Roussillon SW1 £68 ★★
16 St Barnabas St   7730 5550   4–2D
A "classy" Pimlico "hidden gem" that's "not to be missed";
few places can match its "elegant and interesting" Gallic cuisine,
its "outstanding" wine list (with "very knowledgeable" selections
from SW France) or its "superb" service. / **Value tip:** set weekday L £39
(FP). **Details:** www.roussillon.co.uk; 10.30 pm; closed Mon L, Sat L & Sun;
booking: max 11.

Royal China £37 ⭐⭐
24-26 Baker St, W1   7487 4688   1–1A
805 Fulham Rd, SW6   7731 0081
13 Queensway, W2   7221 2535   5–2C
68 Queen's Grove, NW8   7586 4280
30 Westferry Circus, E14   7719 0888
"Stunning" dim sum – and other "authentic" Chinese dishes –
make this "consistent" chain a true culinary benchmark; "only lovers
of '70s clubbing will like the décor", though (and beware "shocking"
Sunday queues, especially at the Bayswater branch).
/ **Details:** 10.45 pm, Fri & Sat 11.15 pm; E14 no bookings Sat & Sun L;
SW6 no bookings Sat & Sun L.

Royal Oak E2 £37 Ⓐ
73 Columbia Rd   7729 2220
"A lovely buzz" permeates this characterful East End boozer, where
you can eat in the "attractive" upstairs room (overlooking Columbia
Road Flower Market) or the downstairs bar; the food is "well done"
too. / **Details:** www.royaloaklondon.com; 10 pm; closed Mon, Tue-Sat D only,
Sun L only.

Rules WC2 £55 Ⓐ
35 Maiden Ln   7836 5314   3–3D
"A magnet for well-heeled Americans", it may be, but few reporters
hold that against this "charming and remarkable" Covent Garden
"survivor" (London's oldest, 1798); to a surprising extent,
its "classic" and "hearty" meat and game menu "still delivers".
/ **Details:** www.rules.co.uk; 11.30 pm.

Running Horse W1 £33 Ⓐ⭐
50 Davies St   7493 1275   2–2A
"Simple food, made with quality ingredients and presented well" –
it's a good formula, but seems to inspire remarkably little feedback
on this "lovely" Mayfair pub. / **Details:** www.therunninghorselondon.co.uk;
9.30 pm; closed Sun; need 8+ to book.

Sagar £25 ⭐
157 King St, W6   8741 8563   6–2C
27 York St, TW1   8744 3868
"Spectacular-value" vegetarian cuisine – "delicately-spiced" but
"hearty" – has made a name for this "no-frills" Hammersmith
south Indian; last year's opening of a "fantastic" Twickenham spin-
off seems to have produced a slight slip in ratings. / **Details:** Sun-Thu
10.45 pm, Fri & Sat 11.30 pm.

St Alban SW1 £55
4-12 Lower Regent St, Rex Hs   7499 8558   2–3D
Fans "love the vibe", but critics just scratch their heads at the
"weird", "'70s airport lounge" interior of this Theatreland
newcomer; its Mediterranean food inspires mixed feelings too –
can the place ever hope to live up to the "über-maestro" reputation
of its backers Corbin and King (who also run the Wolseley)?
/ **Details:** www.stalban.net; midnight, Sun 11 pm.

St John EC1 £48
26 St John St   7251 0848

"Inspiring" cooking – that's "distinctively British", "confidently
straightforward" and "offaly good" – has made this "utilitarian"
Smithfield "institution" a "place of pilgrimage for chefs worldwide";
its ratings slipped a bit this year, though, and staff risk becoming
a bit "self-important". / **Details:** www.stjohnrestaurant.com; 11 pm; closed
Sat L & Sun.

St John Bread & Wine E1 £40
94-96 Commercial St   7392 0236
"The best bacon sandwich you'll ever eat" is typical of the "simple,
traditional British fare" on offer at this "noisy" canteen,
by Spitalfields Market (a worthy spin-off from the EC1
"mothership"); for some of the more "robust" dishes, though,
"you need a strong stomach". / **Details:** www.stjohnbreadandwine.com;
10.30 pm; closed Sun D.

St Johns N19 £35
91 Junction Rd   7272 1587
"A beautiful interior" adds to the "shabby-chic" charm of this large
and very popular Archway gastropub – an all-round "favourite",
it offers "rustic" scoff that's "always on the interesting side
of reliable", and "helpful" service. / **Details:** 11 pm, Sun 9.30 pm;
Mon-Thu D only, Fri-Sun open L & D; booking: max 12.

Sake No Hana SW1 £100
23 St James's St   awaiting tel   2–4C
Alan Yau (of Hakkasan and Yauatcha fame) is set to open his
most 'serious' venture yet in the autumn of 2007; this time,
it's Japanese cuisine that's getting the Yau treatment, in the striking
St James's building which formerly housed Shumi (RIP). /

Salt Yard W1 £36
54 Goodge St   7637 0657   1–1B
The "exciting" tapas – "a twist on traditional Spanish and Italian
dishes" – at this "un-flashy" Fitzrovia two-year-old are among
London's best; "despite its popularity", it remains a "friendly"
destination. / **Details:** www.saltyard.co.uk; 11 pm; closed Sat L & Sun.

San Daniele del Friuli N5 £32
72 Highbury Park   7226 1609
"Generous Italian dishes" – with game a speciality – are served
up by "friendly" staff at this "ever-reliable" Highbury "favourite".
/ **Details:** 10.30 pm; closed Mon L, Tue L, Sat L & Sun; no Amex.

Santa Maria del Buen Ayre E8 £34 🅐⭐
50 Broadway Mkt 7275 9900
"Totally packed every night", this *"proper and authentic"*
Argentinean parrilla (grill) offers an experience "like a small
restaurant in Buenos Aires", including *"steaks to die for"*.
/ **Details:** www.buenayre.co.uk; 10.30 pm; closed weekday L.

Sargasso Sea N21 £48 ⭐
10 Station Rd 8360 0990
"A top-notch restaurant in the suburbs"; this Winchmore Hill spot
may be "as expensive as a top West End joint", but it serves up fish
dishes which are often "stunning". / **Value tip:** set Sun L £29
(FP). **Details:** www.sargassosea.co.uk; 10.30 pm; closed Mon, Tue L, Wed L,
Sat L & Sun D.

Sarracino NW6 £38 ⭐
186 Broadhurst Gdns 7372 5889
The pizza – sold by the metre, with "heavenly crusts" and "tangy"
toppings – is "the real deal", at this *"cramped"* and *"genuinely*
friendly" West Hampstead Italian.
/ **Details:** www.sarracinorestaurant.co.uk; 11 pm.

La Saveur SW14 £43 ⭐
201 Upper Richmond Road West 8876 0644
"It's just what East Sheen needs!", say fans of this cramped new
bistro "from the Brula stable"; it shares its parent's restrained Gallic
styling and "sensible prices", but – given the locale – staff seem
strangely uptight around kids. / **Value tip:** set weekday L £25
(FP). **Details:** 10.30 pm.

(Savoy Grill)
Savoy Hotel WC2 £84
Strand 7592 1600 3–3D
This famously "high-powered" business "bastion" (annexed by the
Ramsay empire in recent years) seems almost certain to be closed
throughout 2008, while the hotel undergoes a much-needed total
revamp. / **Value tip:** set weekday L £51
(FP). **Details:** www.marcuswareing.com; 11 pm; jacket required.

Scarpetta TW11 £32 🅐⭐
78 High St 8977 8177
"Bringing life to central Teddington" – this *"great"* neighbourhood
Italian offers "imaginative" pasta and "delicious" pizza in a
"tasteful" setting; service is "utterly charming" too.
/ **Details:** www.scarpetta.co.uk; 11 pm; no shorts.

The Scarsdale W8 £32 🅐
23a Edwardes Sq 7937 1811 6–1D
A "beautiful" setting – "tucked-away in a leafy square", just off
Kensington High Street – sets the scene for this "lovely" boozer
(plus small garden); "it's one of the few non-trendy, non-gastro pubs
left", and serves food that's *"hearty"* and *"honest"*. / **Details:** 10 pm.

Scoffers SW11 £35 Ⓐ
6 Battersea Rise 7978 5542
*Sitting under a fig tree, it's "hard to remember you're actually in the conservatory" of this "friendly" Battersea local; the food is "nothing special", though – perhaps why the place is especially popular for brunch. / **Details:** www.scoffersrestaurant.co.uk; 11 pm.*

Scott's W1 £58 Ⓐ✪
20 Mount St 7495 7309 2–3A
*"A triumphant return"; this revived Mayfair fish veteran – the survey's most commented-on 'newcomer' – is a "smart", "stylish" and "totally professional" operation that already bears comparison with stable-mate J Sheekey; as even a sceptic admits: "the hype is justified". / **Details:** www.scotts-restaurant.com; 11 pm.*

Shampers W1 £35 Ⓐ
4 Kingly St 7437 1692 2–2D
*"An unpretentious place that never disappoints" – this "friendly" wine bar "time warp", in Soho, is usually "packed", thanks to its "simple" and "good-quality" bistro fare and its "eclectic" wine list. / **Details:** www.shampers.net; 11 pm; closed Sun (& Sat in Aug).*

Shanghai E8 £28 ✪
41 Kingsland High St 7254 2878
*A "great setting" – "the front room is exactly how it was when it was a pie and eel shop" – adds distinction to this "really nice" Dalston hang-out; dim sum which are "better than Chinatown" is a highlight of the consistently "good" Chinese food. / **Details:** www.wengwahgroup.com; 11 pm.*

Shanghai Blues WC1 £45 Ⓐ✪
193-197 High Holborn 7404 1668 3–1D
*It's "a bit pricey for what it is" (and sometimes dismissed as a "Hakkasan wannabe"), but this "smart-looking" Holborn Chinese – in an "interesting renovation" of a former civic building – scores very highly for its "superb dim sum" and its "sexy and fun" style. / **Value tip:** set weekday L £29 (FP). **Details:** www.shanghaiblues.co.uk; 11.30 pm.*

J Sheekey WC2 £59 Ⓐ✪✪
28-32 St Martin's Ct 7240 2565 3–3B
*"Oozing class", this "traditional" and "glamorous" Theatreland "classic" yet again inspired more survey reports than anywhere else in town; an "unbeatable" fish pie heads up the "brilliant" but "unfussy" fish-and-seafood menu served in its "cosy" panelled rooms. / **Details:** www.j-sheekey.co.uk; midnight.*

Shogun W1 £56 ✪
Adam's Row 7493 1255 2–3A
*Despite the odd claim that it's "over-rated", this Japanese "step-back-in-time", in a Mayfair basement, can still deliver some "excellent" dishes, including (say fans) "the best sushi in town". / **Details:** 11 pm; D only, closed Mon.*

Simpson's Tavern EC3 £26 Ⓐ
38 1/2 Ball Ct, Cornhill 7626 9985
*A "unique" Dickensian "institution", which is "a joy" for "City suits", who relish its "boarding school" staples and its "fun" and "chaotic" atmosphere. / **Details:** www.simpsonstavern.co.uk; L only, closed Sat & Sun.*

Simpsons-in-the-Strand WC2   **£57**   Ⓐ

100 Strand   7836 9112   3–3D

This "ultra-traditional" but "touristy" Edwardian temple
to roast beef can still make a "satisfying" destination for business
or breakfast (or both combined); "bad experiences" sour some
reports, though, even from long-term fans.

/ **Details:** www.fairmont.com/simpsons; 10.45 pm, Sun 9 pm; no jeans
or trainers.

Singapore Garden NW6   **£38**   Ⓐ⭐

83a Fairfax Rd   7624 8233

"Looking good" – in every respect – since its refurbishment,
this Swiss Cottage fixture is roundly praised for its "authentic"
Malaysian/Singaporean dishes, its "polite" service, and its
"very comfortable" décor. / **Details:** www.singaporegarden.co.uk; 11 pm,
Fri-Sat 11.30 pm.

Sitaaray WC2   **£30**   Ⓐ⭐

167 Drury Ln   7269 6422   3–1C

"An amusing and different place to go with a group of mates" –
there's little not to like at this Bollywood-themed Covent Garden
newcomer, which offers "great" Indian food at "reasonable" prices.

/ **Details:** www.sitaaray.com; 1 am.

606 Club SW10   **£40**   Ⓐ

90 Lots Rd   7352 5953   4–4B

"Even if the food is bad" – which it isn't, always – this hard-to-find
jazz speakeasy, in a cellar near Chelsea Harbour, is "worth a visit".

/ **Details:** www.606club.co.uk; midnight; D only; booking essential.

(Lecture Room)
Sketch W1   **£134**

9 Conduit St   0870 777 4488   2–2C

Even many fans of Parisian über-chef Pierre Gagnaire's "complex"
cuisine can't get over the "absurd" prices at this ultra-luxurious first-
floor dining room, in Mayfair; ratings improved a bit this year,
but feedback on the food is still eclipsed by that for the "bling-
tastic" loos. / **Details:** www.sketch.uk.com; 10.30 pm; closed Mon, Sat L &
Sun; booking: max 8.

(Gallery)
Sketch W1   **£57**

9 Conduit St   0870 777 4488   2–2C

"So poor, it's not even ironic...", "I felt my wallet had been
raped...", "one visit was enough..." – in the survey, critics of this
"massively overpriced" Mayfair style-scene outnumber fans by about
four to one; "the egg-loos are pretty good, though".

/ **Details:** www.sketch.uk.com; 1 am; D only, closed Sun; booking: max 12.

(Top Floor)
Smiths of Smithfield EC1   **£58**   Ⓐ

67-77 Charterhouse St   7251 7950

"Great rooftop views of St Pauls and Old Bailey" distinguish the
"more spacious and less noisy" top floor of this Smithfield landmark
– an ideal spot for "power" entertaining over some "great steak";
it's "priced for expense-accounters", though, and standards are
sometimes "underwhelming". / **Details:** www.smithsofsmithfield.co.uk;
10.45 pm; closed Sat L; booking: max 10.

Snazz Sichuan NW1 £35 ⭐
37 Chalton St   7388 0808
*"Superb" Sichuanese cuisine – "the real thing" – inspires a few
ecstatic early-days reports on this Euston newcomer.*
/ **Details:** www.newchinaclub.co.uk.

Sophie's Steakhouse SW10 £34 Ⓐ
311-313 Fulham Rd   7352 0088   4–3B
*"The no-reservation policy is a total pain" – "at weekends, it can
take up to two hours to get a table" – but most reporters feel it's
"worth the wait" for this "always fun and buzzy" Chelsea hang-out,
where the steaks and burgers are "fab".*
/ **Details:** www.sophiessteakhouse.com; 11.45 pm; no booking.

Sotheby's Café W1 £44 Ⓐ⭐
34 New Bond St   7293 5077   2–2C
*"People-watch while you eat", at this "all-round classy" café, off the
foyer of the famous Mayfair auction house; the "imaginative" food
is "excellent for a light lunch", and service is "consummately good".*
/ **Details:** www.sothebys.com; L only, closed Sat & Sun.

Souk Medina WC2 £32 Ⓐ
1A Short Gdns   7240 1796   3–2B
*"Staff may be Eastern European rather than Arabic", but this
"chaotic", "dark" and "exotic" party-Moroccan – sibling to Souk –
is still "quite a crowd-pleaser"; it's also "inexpensive".*
/ **Details:** www.soukrestaurant.co.uk; midnight.

The Square W1 £101 ⭐
6-10 Bruton St   7495 7100   2–2C
*Philip Howard's cuisine can be "astonishing", and it's complemented
by an "ultra-comprehensive" wine list and "discrete" service at this
Mayfair luminary, whose "formal" style particularly appeals
to "corporate types".* / **Details:** www.squarerestaurant.com; 10.45 pm; closed
Sat L & Sun L.

Sree Krishna SW17 £20 ⭐
192-194 Tooting High St   8672 4250
*"No matter how hard you try, it's impossible to break the bank",
at this Tooting south Indian veteran, where the "reliable" cooking
"just goes on year after year".* / **Details:** www.sreekrishna.co.uk; 10.45 pm,
Fri & Sat midnight.

Star of India SW5 £39 ⭐
154 Old Brompton Rd   7373 2901   4–2B
*After a (much-needed) "contemporary" revamp (leaving the "odd"
Italianate frescoes intact), this "upmarket" Earl's Court "stalwart"
remains a firm favourite, not least for its "interesting and delicious"
subcontinental fare.* / **Details:** 11.45 pm.

Stone Mason's Arms W6 £33 Ⓐ
54 Cambridge Grove   8748 1397   6–2C
*"A great find" on a busy Hammersmith highway, this "casual"
boozer is a "warm" and "friendly" place, offering food that's "well-
executed and occasionally adventurous".* / **Details:** 11 pm.

Story Deli
The Old Truman Brewery E1   **£23**   Ⓐ✪✪
3 Dray Walk   7247 3137
"Unbeatable" pizza and "interesting" décor win rave reviews for this shabby-chic East End hang-out; at weekends, though, it "can be too popular". / **Details:** *10 pm during summer (D only during summer); L only.*

Sugar Hut SW6   **£43**   Ⓐ
374 North End Rd   7386 8950   4–3A
"Exotic" décor lends an "illicit" and "undoubtedly romantic" ambience to this "beautiful" Fulham Thai; the food is "pleasant", but some reporters feel prices verge on the "ridiculous". / **Details:** *www.sugarhutgroup.com; midnight; D only.*

Suka
Sanderson W1   **£67**   ✖
50 Berners St   7300 1444   2–1D
Fans of this "wannabe" newcomer, in a design-hotel north of Oxford Street, say it's "miles better than Spoon+" (RIP); whether that's saying much is debatable and, to detractors, it's just a "flashy disappointment" – "you can get much better Malaysian food for a fraction of the price". / **Details:** *12.30 am Sun 10.30 pm.*

Sukho Thai Cuisine SW6   **£37**   Ⓐ✪✪
855 Fulham Rd   7371 7600
"Tucked-away in deepest Fulham", this "outstanding neighbourhood oriental" is a "classy" and "courteous" sort of place, where the "non-clichéd" Thai cooking is rated by reporters as "the best in London". / **Details:** *11 pm.*

Sumosan W1   **£75**
26b Albemarle St   7495 5999   2–3C
It's "minimalist" and "wallet-breakingly pricey", but fans claim this Mayfair Japanese is "as good as Nobu, just less hyped"; service can be poor, though, and the place sometimes has all the ambience of a "mausoleum". / **Details:** *www.sumosan.com; 11.45 pm; closed Sat L & Sun L.*

Le Suquet SW3   **£51**   ✪
104 Draycott Ave   7581 1785   4–2C
It "really does feel like Cannes", at this "comfortable" Chelsea old-timer; for "a great seafood experience", it's very hard to beat. / **Value tip:** *set weekday L £33 (FP).* **Details:** *11.30 pm.*

Sushi Hiroba WC2   **£25**   ✪
50-54 Kingsway   7430 1888   1–2D
This Korean-backed Kaiten-Zushi yearling, near Holborn tube, is praised for its "keen" service and its "inventive" and "beautifully-presented" sushi; some doubters, though, say it's "over-rated". / **Details:** *www.sushihiroba.co.uk; 11 pm; closed Sun L.*

Sushi-Hiro W5   **£37**   ✪✪
1 Station Pde   8896 3175
"I used to live in Tokyo, and I rate this place 100%"; despite "the most unlikely of locations" (and "no ambience at all"), this diner near Ealing Common tube is "much patronised by Japanese people", thanks to its "amazingly fresh" sushi. / **Details:** *9 pm; closed Mon; no credit cards.*

Sushi-Say NW2　　　　　　　　　　**£37**　　⭐⭐
33b Walm Ln　8459 7512
"Staff make you feel very welcome", at this "outstanding", family-run fixture in Willesden Green, which is known for its "beautiful, fresh sushi and traditional Japanese dishes". / **Details:** 10.30 pm; closed Mon.

The Swag & Tails SW7　　　　　**£43**　　🅐
10-11 Fairholt St　7584 6926　4–1C
"If you can find it", this "posh pub" – "just five minutes from Harrods" – has "no tourists", and serves "above-average" food in an "energetic" setting; at quiet times, it can feel a touch "cliquey". / **Details:** www.swagandtails.com; 10 pm; closed Sat & Sun.

The Swan W4　　　　　　　　　　**£33**　　🅐
119 Acton Ln　8994 8262　6–1A
A "brilliant local gastropub", "tucked-away" in "deepest Chiswick" (and with a "heaven-sent" garden for the summer); the "Mediterranean-influenced" food is "a bit less good than it was", but "still recommended". / **Details:** 10.30 pm; closed weekday L; no Amex; no booking.

Sweetings EC4　　　　　　　　　**£43**　　🅐⭐
39 Queen Victoria St　7248 3062
"They should slap a preservation order" on this "legendary City stalwart" – where "old-school fish dishes" are served in a "quaint" Dickensian setting; it's "loved by business types young and old", so "arrive early to avoid disappointment". / **Details:** L only, closed Sat & Sun; no booking.

Taiwan Village SW6　　　　　　**£28**　　⭐
85 Lillie Rd　7381 2900　4–3A
"Fulham's best-kept secret!" – this "off-the-beaten-track" Chinese delivers "spicy" cooking that's "better value than most places in Chinatown"; "the leave-it-to-us feast is the way to go".
/ **Details:** www.taiwanvillage.com; 11.30 pm; closed Mon L.

Taman Gang W1　　　　　　　　**£77**　　❌
141 Park Ln　7518 3160　1–2A
Financial difficulties have contributed to a "disappointing" year for this "cool" pan-Asian basement near Marble Arch; what the future holds… it's hard to say. / **Details:** www.tamangang.com; 11.30 pm; D only, closed Sun; booking: max 6.

Tamarind W1　　　　　　　　　　**£58**　　⭐
20 Queen St　7629 3561　2–3B
Alfred Prasad's "refined" dishes – "cooked perfectly and presented immaculately" – still win rave reviews for this "stylish" Mayfair subcontinental (London's original 'haute Indian'); "shame it's in a basement", though. / **Value tip:** set weekday L £31
(FP). **Details:** www.tamarindrestaurant.com; 11.15 pm; closed Sat L.

Tandoori Lane SW6　　　　　　**£26**　　⭐
131a Munster Rd　7371 0440
"Every dish is distinctive, and there's no grease in sight", at this long-established, high-quality curry house, in the depths of Fulham.
/ **Details:** 11.15 pm; no Amex.

Tandoori Nights SE22 £31
73 Lordship Ln 8299 4077
The "fantastic" food is "always spot-on", at this "cramped" and "homely" curry house, which is world-famous among East Dulwich folk. / Details: 11.30 pm; closed weekday L & Sat L.

Tangawizi TW1 £34
406 Richmond Rd 8891 3737
Despite an "unlikely" Twickenham location, this "crisp, contemporary" yearling wins more-than-local acclaim for its "interesting African twist on Indian cooking". / Details: www.tangawizi.co.uk; 10.30 pm; D only, closed Sun.

Tapas Brindisa SE1 £35
18-20 Southwark St 7357 8880
As you'd hope of somewhere owned by renowned Iberian food importers, this Borough Market bar serves "some of the best tapas in town"; it's pretty "cramped", though, and can get "ridiculously busy". / Details: www.brindisa.com; 11 pm; closed Sun.

Tatsuso EC2 £80
32 Broadgate Circle 7638 5863
This "very pricey" Broadgate Japanese is "one of the most prestigious City eateries", with a ground-floor teppan-yaki, and basement restaurant; sliding ratings this year coincided with a six month hiatus with no sushi chef – a new one was taken on shortly before this guide went to press. / Details: 10.15 pm; closed Sat & Sun.

Tawana W2 £33
3 Westbourne Grove 7229 3785 5–1C
Just off Queensway, a well-established spot notable for its "consistently reliable and high-quality Thai dishes". / Details: www.tawana.co.uk; 11 pm; no Amex.

Ten Ten Tei W1 £35
56 Brewer St 7287 1738 2–2D
It's "ugly" and "a bit tatty", but this Soho Japanese is "very cheap, very cheerful, and offers very authentic cooking"; set lunches, in particular, are "excellent value". / Value tip: set weekday L £18 (FP). Details: 10 pm; closed Sun; no Amex.

Tendido Cero SW5 £35
174 Old Brompton Rd 7370 3685 4–2B
"Fantastic" tapas draw a permanent crowd to this "buzzing" Earl's Court bar; there were a few quibbles this year – "can no longer BYO", "smaller portions", "new two-sittings policy" – but nothing sufficient to dent its reputation as a "classy" and "good-value" choice. / Details: www.cambiodetercio.co.uk; 11 pm.

Tentazioni SE1 £51
2 Mill St 7394 5248
Fans of this "little hidden-away spot", near Shad Thames, again tip it as "one of London's top Italians", and say "it's grown in confidence now the chef is the sole owner"; feedback was more mixed this year, though, with some reporters finding it "forgettable". / Value tip: set dinner £34 (FP). Details: www.tentazioni.co.uk; 10.45 pm; closed Mon L, Sat L & Sun.

Texture W1 £60
34 Portman Sq 7224 0028 1–2A

Two staff (including an ex-head chef) from Raymond Blanc's famous 'Manoir' are launching this newcomer on the former site of Deya (RIP), just north of Oxford Street, in late-2007; their background – and the fact that much of the seating will be given over to a champagne bar – suggests this will be a pretty upmarket affair (reflected in the price-guesstimate shown). /

Thai Elephant TW10 £33
1 Wakefield Rd 8940 5114
*"It may nestle beside an unattractive bus station", but this pleasant Thai comes mainly well-recommended by Richmond folk for its "delicious" cooking. / **Value tip:** set weekday L £20 (FP). **Details:** www.thaielephantrichmond.co.uk; 11 pm.*

Thailand SE14 £29 🅐 ⭐
15 Lewisham Way 8691 4040
*"Some of the best Thai/Laotian food in London" makes it worth seeking out this "simple café" in New Cross; service is "very good" too, but "it's a tight squeeze". / **Details:** 11.30 pm.*

Theo Randall
InterContinental Hotel W1 £65 ⭐
1 Hamilton Pl 7409 3131 2–4A
*With its "stunning" cooking – from the ex-head chef of the River Café – this Mayfair newcomer deserves to be hailed as one of London's foremost Italians; it's blighted, though, by appallingly "sterile" décor – "a bit like an airport lounge". / **Value tip:** set weekday L £41 (FP). **Details:** www.theorandall.com; 11 pm; closed Sun D.*

Thomas Cubitt SW1 £52 🅐
44 Elizabeth St 7730 6060 1–4A
*A "fun and really buzzy" vibe has helped this "lovely" boozer become Belgravia's top hang-out, and it's "always packed"; downstairs, you get "excellent burgers" and so on – upstairs, there's a more "formal" dining room. / **Details:** www.thethomascubitt.co.uk; 10 pm.*

Toff's N10 £28 ⭐
38 Muswell Hill Broadway 8883 8656
*"Lovely fish 'n' chips, old-style" – and in "big portions" too – draw "queues all year-round" to this "welcoming" Muswell Hill veteran. / **Value tip:** set always available £17 (FP). **Details:** www.toffsfish.co.uk; 10 pm; closed Sun; no booking, Sat.*

Tom Aikens SW3 £82

43 Elystan St 7584 2003 4–2C

Fans find Tom Aikens's "complex" cuisine nothing short of "sublime", and his "Zen-like" Chelsea dining room is often touted as "one of London's best"; more sceptical reporters, though, continue to complain of "fiddly" dishes and "outrageous" prices. / Value tip: set weekday L £42 (FP). Details: www.tomaikens.co.uk; 11 pm; closed Sat & Sun; jacket and/or tie; booking: max 8.

Toto's SW1 £66

Lennox Gardens Mews 7589 0075 4–2C

"It's always a pleasure", for fans to visit this "lovely" and "romantic" Knightsbridge Italian (where the "garden is a delight for lunch in good weather"); staff are "formal but friendly", and the food is "delicious", and the only gripe is that "it's a bit expensive". / Details: 11 pm.

Trader Vics
Hilton Hotel W1 £70

22 Park Ln 7208 4113 2–4A

Like the heiress Paris, the basement tiki bar of the Park Lane Hilton "trades on its reputation" – the food can taste "like mass-produced cardboard", and service is "just as drab". / Details: www.tradersvics.com; 12.30 am; closed Sat L & Sun L.

Les Trois Garçons E1 £70

1 Club Row 7613 1924

"Opulent and OTT" decor – "so madcap it's surreal" – helps set up some "very seductive" vibes at this "kitsch" East End pub-conversion; service can be "snooty", though, and the Gallic cuisine seems "unnecessarily expensive". / Details: www.lestroisgarcons.com; 9.30 pm; D only, closed Sun.

La Trompette W4 £54

5-7 Devonshire Rd 8747 1836 6–2A

"Tucked-away" in a Chiswick sidestreet, it may be, but Chez Bruce's "stylish" sibling is "one of the very best places in London"; its "knowledgeable and passionate" staff deliver "sensational" cuisine (including "legendary" cheese), plus a "really exciting" wine list. / Details: www.latrompette.co.uk; 10.30 pm; booking: max 6.

Troubadour SW5 £32

265 Old Brompton Rd 7370 1434 4–3A

This "kooky" Earl's Court coffee house has a "chilled" style all of its own; you "don't go there for the food", but – if you do – the "hangover-cure" breakfasts are the best bet. / Details: www.troubadour.co.uk; 11.30 pm; no Amex.

La Trouvaille W1 £47

12a Newburgh St 7287 8488 2–2C

"It means 'a find' and it is!"; this "lovely" bar/restaurant occupies a small Georgian townhouse – "tucked-away in an atmospheric part of Soho" – where an "energetic team of young French staff" serve up some "unfamiliar" Gallic dishes. / Value tip: set weekday L £30 (FP). Details: www.latrouvaille.co.uk; 11 pm; closed Sun.

Tsunami SW4   **£37**   Ⓐ ⭐⭐

1-7 Voltaire Rd   7978 1610

"You get Nobu without the pretence and the prices", at Ken Sam's *"truly exceptional"* but *"relaxed"* Japanese-fusion five-year-old; *"who knew somewhere in Clapham could be so good?"* / **Value tip:** set weekday L £20 (FP). **Details:** www.tsunami.co.uk; 10.30 pm, Sun 9 pm; closed weekday L.

Two Brothers N3   **£27**   ⭐

297-303 Regent's Park Rd   8346 0469

"Friendly and slightly upmarket" – the Manzi Brothers' *"old-favourite"* Finchley chippy *"runs like clockwork"*, and is *"worthy of its high local reputation"*; *"the queues can get a bit long at times"*. / **Details:** www.twobrothers.co.uk; 10.15 pm; closed Mon & Sun; no booking at D.

202

Nicole Farhi W11   **£37**   Ⓐ

202 Westbourne Grove   7727 2722   5–1B

"Brilliant for brunch", this *"very cool"* diner-cum-clothes store is one of Notting Hill's key see-and-be-seen weekend destinations – its NYC twin is apparently *"even better"*. / **Details:** www.nicolefarhi.com; 4 pm; L & afternoon tea only; no booking.

2 Veneti W1   **£47**   ⭐

10 Wigmore St   7637 0789   2–1B

A *"thoroughly enjoyable"* newcomer, where *"very knowledgeable"* staff present *"good and solid"* Venetian cooking; it seems to have mustered the *"panache"* which always eluded Eddalino (RIP) – its predecessor on this site near the Wigmore Hall. / **Details:** 10.30 pm; closed Sat L & Sun.

Ubon E14   **£91**

34 Westferry Circus   7719 7800

"Fantastic views over the Thames" jazz up the *"bland"* décor at Nobu's E14 cousin, which is probably *"Canary Wharf's top restaurant"*; bills are *"super-sized"* – for fans, *"sublime"* Japanese fusion fare justifies such expense, but sceptics say standards are getting *"a little sloppy"*. / **Details:** www.noburestaurants.com; 10.15 pm; closed Sat L & Sun.

Uli W11   **£29**   ⭐

16 All Saints Rd   7727 7511   5–1B

"Michael is still the most charming host", at this *"wonderful neighbourhood asset"* in North Kensington, which serves *"first-class"* oriental fare (and has a *"great garden in summer"*); this year, though, a few regulars found it *"below expectations"*. / **Details:** www.uli-oriental.co.uk; 11 pm; D only; no Amex.

Umu W1 £120 ⭐

14-16 Bruton Pl   7499 8881   2–2C

"Unique" and "subtle", the Kyoto-style cuisine and "mouth-watering" sushi at Marlon Abela's slickly-decorated Mayfair Japanese inspire ever-more adulatory reviews; "unbelievable" prices, though, are still a sore point. / **Details:** www.umurestaurant.com; 10.30 pm; closed Sat L & Sun; booking: max 14.

Upstairs Bar SW2 £35 🅐⭐⭐

89b Acre Ln (door on Branksome Rd)   7733 8855

"Through an unassuming door in a Brixton back street" lies this "corker" of a restaurant; it's an "unfussy", sort of place – intriguingly located on an upper floor – where Daniel Budden's food is simply "excellent". / **Details:** www.upstairslondon.com; 9.30 pm, Sat 10.30 pm; closed Mon, Tue-Sat D only, closed Sun D.

Le Vacherin W4 £41 ⭐

76-77 South Pde   8742 2121   6–1A

Malcolm John's "astonishingly authentic" bistro – "in an unlikely bit of Chiswick" – "really is like a corner of provincial France"; most reports are a hymn of praise to its "classic" cuisine and "interesting wine" – the place "can seem gloomy when empty", though, and both food and service are a bit "variable". / **Details:** www.levacherin.co.uk; 10.30 pm; closed Mon L; no Amex.

Vama SW10 £43 ⭐

438 King's Rd   7351 4118   4–3B

This "closely-packed" World's End venture has won a formidable reputation for its "memorable", "new-wave" Indian cuisine; even some fans, though, have noted "occasionally average" results of late. / **Details:** www.vama.co.uk; 11 pm.

Veeraswamy W1 £50 🅐⭐

Victory Hs, 99-101 Regent St   7734 1401   2–3D

A stone's throw from Piccadilly Circus, London's oldest Indian is still – for its fans – "the best"; that's probably overdoing it, but it does offer "interesting" cooking (in essentially "traditional" style), and its contemporary styling is "terrific". / **Details:** www.realindianfood.com; 10.30 pm; booking: max 12.

El Vergel SE1 £17 ⭐⭐

8 Lant St   7357 0057

A "little South American in a Borough back street" that's "great in so many ways" – its "entirely charming" staff serve "interesting" dishes to a "cosmopolitan" crowd at "pocket-money" prices; "shame it isn't open longer hours". / **Details:** www.elvergel.co.uk; breakfast & L only, closed Sat & Sun; no credit cards.

Viet-Anh NW1   **£19**
41 Parkway   7284 4082
"Fresh and tasty food, friendly and efficient service and great value"
*– that's the deal at this ever-popular Vietnamese café, in Camden
Town. / Details: 11 pm; no Amex.*

Vijay NW6   **£28**   ⭐
49 Willesden Ln   7328 1087
*This "always-busy" Kilburn veteran offers a "consistently high
standard" of cooking – with "superb South Indian specialities" –
at "unbeatable-value" prices; you can BYO at modest corkage.
/ Details: www.vijayindia.com; 10.45 pm, Fri-Sat 11.30 pm.*

Vijaya Krishna SW17   **£19**   ⭐
114 Mitcham Rd   9767 7688
*"Light" and "delicious" Keralan food wins fans for this "reliable" and
"extremely good-value" Tooting south Indian. / Details: 11 pm, Fri & Sat
midnight.*

Village East SE1   **£40**   Ⓐ
171-173 Bermondsey St   7357 6082
*"A stylish interpretation of the warehouse vernacular" has helped
this "bright" and "buzzy" yearling pull in a "trendy" Bermondsey
following; it generally serves "good food at reasonable prices" too.
/ Details: www.villageeast.co.uk; 10.30 pm.*

Vinoteca EC1   **£33**   Ⓐ
7 St John St   7253 8786
*"A stand-out new wine bar" – this "delightful" (if "cramped") and
"buzzy" Clerkenwell yearling offers "simple" bistro fare
to complement a "massive" and "sensibly-priced" list; staff
"ooze enthusiasm" too. / Details: www.vinoteca.co.uk; 10 pm; closed Sun;
no Amex.*

Vivat Bacchus EC4   **£43**
47 Farringdon St   7353 2648
*"An enormous glass-sided wine cellar" (where a "great South
African selection" is the highlight) dominates this "wonderful" City-
fringe basement spot, which also boasts a walk-in cheese room;
it pleases generally, but its best point is its "outstanding" service.
/ Value tip: set weekday L £26 (FP). Details: www.vivatbacchus.co.uk; 9.30 pm;
closed Sat & Sun.*

Vrisaki N22   **£29**   ⭐
73 Myddleton Rd   8889 8760
*"I still can't finish it all!"; the mezze "just keep coming", at this
"fun" Bounds Green Greek veteran, where "a humble kebab shop
leads on to a cavernous dining room". / Details: midnight; closed Sun D.*

The Wallace   Ⓐ
The Wallace Collection W1   **£45**
Hertford Hs, Manchester Sq   7563 9505   2–1A
*The "extraordinary" and "magical" atrium of this Marylebone
palazzo has taken a huge step-up from its former incarnation
(as Café Bagatelle, RIP), and it now serves some "delicious" Gallic
dishes; it is a bit "pricey", though, and service can be iffy.
/ Details: www.thewallacerestaurant.com; Fri & Sat 9 pm; Sun-Thu closed D.*

Wapping Food E1 £47 Ⓐ
Wapping Power Station, Wapping Wall 7680 2080
*"What a space!" – "a cavernous old hydraulic pumping station,
complete with old machinery, and art shows" provides the "über-
cool" setting for this "terrific" Docklands venture; the food's pretty
good too, as is the "totally Aussie" wine list.*
/ **Details:** www.thewappingproject.com; 10.30 pm; closed Sun D.

The Wells NW3 £44 Ⓐ
30 Well Walk 7794 3785
*"A wonderful location" ("especially on the terrace in summer") lends
a "lovely" ambience to this gastropub near Hampstead Heath;
the odd reporter finds the cooking "mixed", but most say it's
"consistently good".* / **Details:** www.thewellshampstead.co.uk; 10.30 pm;
no Amex; booking: max 8.

The Westbourne W2 £35 Ⓐ
101 Westbourne Park Villas 7221 1332 5–1B
*"Beautiful people" help "inject buzz" into this "bustling" Bayswater
"hotspot"; when the "aloof" staff do eventually bring the food,
it's often "unexpectedly good".* / **Details:** www.thewestbourne.com;
10.45 pm; closed Mon L; no Amex; need 4+ to book.

The Wharf TW11 £42 Ⓐ
22 Manor Rd 8977 6333
*"A fantastic setting overlooking the Thames" (with a big terrace)
is the star attraction at this modern bar/brasserie near Teddington
Lock; "if only the food was better..."* / **Details:** www.walk-on-water.co.uk;
10 pm; closed Mon.

Whits W8 £44 ★
21 Abingdon Rd 7938 1122 4–1A
*"Extremely helpful" service helps create a "cosy" atmosphere at this
Kensington bar/bistro, which serves "thoughtful" dishes at "good-
value" prices.* / **Details:** www.whits.co.uk; 10.30 pm; closed Mon, Sat L & Sun.

Wild Honey W1 £44 Ⓐ
12 St George St 7758 9160 2–2C
*The summer-2007 offshoot of Arbutus offers essentially the same
foodie-pleasing formula of well-priced cuisine, and interesting wines
by the carafe, but in the more elegant surroundings of a panelled
Mayfair dining room; on an early-days visit, the cooking was rather
inconsistent.* / **Value tip:** set weekday L £28
(FP). **Details:** www.wildhoneyrestaurant.co.uk; 10.30 pm.

Wiltons SW1 £83 Ⓐ
55 Jermyn St 7629 9955 2–3C
*Traditionalists say "it doesn't get any better" than this "plush",
"stuffy", and "very-old fashioned" St James's bastion, where the
speciality is "splendid" seafood (and game); whether it's
"reassuringly expensive", or just "hideously overpriced", remains
a matter for debate.* / **Details:** www.wiltons.co.uk; 10.30 pm; closed Sat &
Sun; jacket required.

The Windsor Castle W8 **£29** Ⓐ
114 Campden Hill Rd   7243 9551   5–2B
This Notting Hill Gate "classic" – an 18th century coaching inn – feels just "like a country pub" (and comes complete with a lovely walled garden); it serves "traditional" pub food that's on the "good" side of "average". / Details: 10 pm; no booking.

Wine Factory W11 **£33** Ⓐ
294 Westbourne Grove   7229 1877   5–1B
"Surprisingly good wine at fantastic prices" – as at all John Brinkley's joints, that's the lifeblood of this "cheap and cheerful" Notting Hill pizza joint. / Details: www.brinkleys.com; 11 pm.

(Winter Garden)
The Landmark NW1 **£60** Ⓐ
222 Marylebone Rd   7631 8000
The "stunning" setting – a "tranquil", palm-filled atrium – helps make this Marylebone hotel a popular business lunching destination; those paying their own way tend to tip it for a "classy" breakfast (or Sunday brunch), or afternoon tea.
/ Details: www.landmarklondon.co.uk; 11 pm; booking: max 12.

The Wolseley W1 **£52** Ⓐ
160 Piccadilly   7499 6996   2–3C
"The real joy is the room, and feeling part of it", at Messrs Corbin and King's "loud" and "vibrant" grand-brasserie, by the Ritz – an all-purpose favourite for many reporters (and now the survey's No. 1 tip for a business meeting); leaving aside the "perfect tea and breakfast", though, the food is often rather "ordinary".
/ Details: www.thewolseley.com; midnight.

Woodlands **£29** ★
37 Panton St, SW1   7839 7258   3–4A
77 Marylebone Ln, W1   7486 3862   1–1A
12-14 Chiswick High Rd, W4   8994 9333   6–2B
102 Heath St, NW3   7794 3080
"Light" and "tasty" south Indian food "at fair prices" still carves a solid niche for this long-established, veggie chain; despite the "superb" service, though, pizzazz is in short supply.
/ Details: www.woodlandsrestaurant.co.uk; 10.45 pm; W4 Mon-Thu D only.

Wright Brothers SE1 **£37** Ⓐ★
11 Stoney St   7403 9554
"Brilliant" oysters are the highlight of the "very good" fish-and-seafood menu at this "tremendously buzzy" Borough Market yearling – the sort of place where "everyone appears to enjoy themselves". / Details: www.wrightbros.eu.com; 10.30 pm; closed Sun.

Yauatcha W1 £50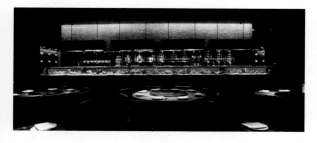
Broadwick Hs, 15-17 Broadwick St 7494 8888 2–2D

"Unbeatable dim sum" – "like little parcels of joy" – and an
"exciting" vibe have made a huge hit of Alan Yau's "groovy" Soho
oriental; pity about the "rigid" 90-minute dining-slots, though,
and the "unpredictable" service; NB as well as the "stylish"
basement, there's an "elegant" upstairs section that also does tea
and "funky cakes". / **Details:** 11.30 pm.

Yi-Ban £31
Imperial Wharf, Imperial Rd, SW6 7731 6606 4–4B
Regatta Centre, Dockside Rd, E16 7473 6699
"Planes taking off from City Airport" add interest to the "great
views" from this distant-Docklands waterside spot, and its Chinese
fare (especially dim sum) is "surprisingly good" too; the Fulham
branch attracts practically no feedback. / **Details:** www.yi-ban.co.uk;
10.45 pm; SW6 closed Sun.

Yming W1 £33
35-36 Greek St 7734 2721 3–2A
"Un-typically good service" underpins the vast popularity of Christine
Lau's "elegant" Soho Chinese, where the "interesting" cooking
is sometimes tipped as "London's finest"; this year's reports,
however, were a bit more up-and-down than usual.
/ **Details:** www.yminglondon.com; 11.45 pm; closed Sun.

Yoshino W1 £38
3 Piccadilly Pl 7287 6622 2–3D
"A best-kept secret, just off Piccadilly"; this "packed" and
"authentic" Japanese pit stop offers "superb sushi" ("some of the
best in town") to a largely expatriate clientele.
/ **Details:** www.yoshino.net; 10 pm; closed Sun.

Yum Yum N16 £29
183-187 Stoke Newington High St 7254 6751
This "Stokey institution" moved a year ago to these new "mega-
sized" premises; inevitably, some old-timers "preferred it when
it was smaller" (and less "noisy"), but the general view is that the
new look is "amazing", that service is "intelligent" and that the Thai
food is "really lovely and fresh". / **Value tip:** set weekday L £19
(FP). **Details:** www.yumyum.co.uk; 11.30 pm.

Zafferano SW1 £56
15 Lowndes St 7235 5800 4–1D

Still often hailed as "the best Italian in London", this Belgravia stalwart has become "a bit glitzier" (and less "crowded") since its enlargement a couple of years ago; it can still seem "remarkably unpretentious, given the sophistication of the food".
*/ **Details:** www.zafferanorestaurant.com; 11 pm.*

Zaffrani N1 £32
47 Cross St 7226 5522
*"A great new local Indian"; Islington reporters are very enthusiastic about the "delicious" cuisine and "friendly" service offered by this "excellent" contemporary-style spot. / **Details:** 11 pm.*

Zaika W8 £50
1 Kensington High St 7795 6533 4–1A
Thanks to Sanjay Dwivedi's "amazing" and "refined" cuisine, this is still one of London's top "innovative" Indians; the ex-banking hall setting (opposite Kensington Gardens) can sometimes seem a touch "austere", but most reporters say it's "lovely".
*/ **Details:** www.zaika-restaurant.co.uk; 10.45 pm; closed Sat L.*

Zilli Fish W1 £58
36-40 Brewer St 7734 8649 2–2D

"Excellent-quality fish" is the main point of the menu at Aldo Zilli's "happy", "buzzy" and "tightly-packed" Soho corner-site; it's also "a good spot for people-watching on a sunny day".
*/ **Details:** www.zillialdo.com; 11.30 pm; closed Sun.*

Zuma SW7 £60
5 Raphael St 7584 1010 4–1C
*"Just a damn sexy experience, every time"; this über-"happening" Knightsbridge oriental – complete with "Eurotrashy" bar – has "taken over from Nobu" as London's top fusion-Japanese; needless to say it's "mightily expensive", and the service can sometimes be "abrasive". / **Details:** www.zumarestaurant.com; 10.45 pm; booking: max 8.*

LONDON AREA
OVERVIEWS

CENTRAL

Soho, Covent Garden & Bloomsbury
(Parts of W1, all WC2 and WC1)

£80+	Savoy Grill	British, Traditional	
£70+	Lindsay House	British, Modern	Ⓐ
	L'Atelier de Joel Robuchon	French	Ⓐ★★
	Pearl	"	
£60+	L'Escargot (Picasso Room)	French	Ⓐ★
	Asia de Cuba	Fusion	Ⓐ
	Red Fort	Indian	★
	Matsuri	Japanese	★
£50+	Indigo	British, Modern	Ⓐ
	The Ivy	"	Ⓐ
	Rules	British, Traditional	Ⓐ
	Simpsons-in-the-Strand	"	Ⓐ
	J Sheekey	Fish & seafood	Ⓐ★★
	Zilli Fish	"	★
	Clos Maggiore	French	Ⓐ
	Jaan	Fusion	★
	Yauatcha	Chinese	Ⓐ★★
£40+	Joe Allen	American	Ⓐ
	L'Escargot	French	Ⓐ★
	Arbutus	"	Ⓐ
	La Trouvaille	"	Ⓐ
	Ronnie Scott's	International	Ⓐ✖
	The Forge	"	
	Barrafina	Spanish	Ⓐ★★
	Shanghai Blues	Chinese	Ⓐ★
	Malabar Junction	Indian	Ⓐ
	Patara	Thai	★
£35+	Aurora	British, Modern	Ⓐ
	Shampers	"	Ⓐ
	Konstam	"	
	Imperial China	Chinese	★
	Rasa Maricham	Indian, Southern	★★
	Edokko	Japanese	★★
	Ten Ten Tei	"	★
	Benja	Thai	★
£30+	Andrew Edmunds	British, Modern	Ⓐ
	Cork & Bottle	International	Ⓐ✖
	Balans	"	✖
	Ciao Bella	Italian	Ⓐ
	Mildred's	Vegetarian	Ⓐ★
	Souk Medina	Moroccan	Ⓐ
	Yming	Chinese	★
	Sitaaray	Indian	Ⓐ★
	Abeno Too	Japanese	★
£25+	The Easton	British, Modern	Ⓐ★
	North Sea Fish	Fish & chips	★
	Pâtisserie Valerie	Sandwiches, cakes, etc	
	Sushi Hiroba	Japanese	★
	Busaba Eathai	Thai	Ⓐ★
£20+	Gordon's Wine Bar	International	Ⓐ✖

	Le Pain Quotidien	Sandwiches, cakes, etc	(A)
£15+	Paolina Café	Italian	★
	Konditor & Cook	Sandwiches, cakes, etc	★★
	Just Falafs	"	★
	Bar Italia	"	(A)
£10+	Nordic Bakery	Scandinavian	★
	Monmouth Coffee Company	Sandwiches, cakes, etc	(A)★★
£5+	Flat White	"	★
	Maison Bertaux	"	(A)

Mayfair & St James's (Parts of W1 and SW1)

£130+	Sketch (Lecture Rm)	French	
£120+	Le Gavroche	"	(A)★
	Umu	Japanese	★
£100+	The Square	French	★
	Alain Ducasse	"	
	Sake No Hana	Japanese	
£90+	The Ritz	French	(A)
£80+	Wiltons	British, Traditional	(A)
	G Ramsay at Claridges	French	(A)
	L'Oranger	"	(A)
	The Greenhouse	"	
	Connaught	Mediterranean	
	Nobu	Japanese	★
	Nobu Berkeley	"	★
£70+	The Cuckoo Club	British, Modern	✗
	Dorchester Grill	"	
	Cipriani	Italian	✗
	Hakkasan	Chinese	(A)
	China Tang	"	✗
	Taman Gang	"	✗
	Trader Vics	Indonesian	✗
	Sumosan	Japanese	
£60+	Patterson's	British, Modern	★
	Brown's Grill	"	
	Galvin at Windows	French	(A)
	Hibiscus	"	
	Theo Randall	Italian	★
	Benares	Indian	★
	Ikeda	Japanese	★★
	Matsuri	"	★
	Miyama	"	★
£50+	Le Caprice	British, Modern	(A)★
	The Wolseley	"	(A)
	Green's	British, Traditional	(A)
	Scott's	Fish & seafood	(A)★
	Bentley's	"	
	maze	French	★
	Sketch (Gallery)	"	
	St Alban	Mediterranean	
	The Guinea Grill	Steaks & grills	★

	Kai Mayfair	*Chinese*	★
	Princess Garden	*"*	★
	Veeraswamy	*Indian*	Ⓐ ★
	Tamarind	*"*	★
	Shogun	*Japanese*	★
£40+	Sotheby's Café	*British, Modern*	Ⓐ ★
	Wild Honey	*"*	Ⓐ
	Alloro	*Italian*	★
	Levant	*Lebanese*	Ⓐ
	Chor Bizarre	*Indian*	Ⓐ ★
	Quilon	*Indian, Southern*	★
	Chisou	*Japanese*	★
	Patara	*Thai*	★
£35+	Al Sultan	*Lebanese*	★
	Rasa	*Indian*	★ ★
	Yoshino	*Japanese*	★
£30+	L'Artiste Musclé	*French*	Ⓐ
	Running Horse	*International*	Ⓐ ★
£25+	Diner	*Burgers, etc*	Ⓐ ★
	Pâtisserie Valerie	*Sandwiches, cakes, etc*	
	Woodlands	*Indian*	★
	Busaba Eathai	*Thai*	Ⓐ ★
£10+	Fuzzy's Grub	*Sandwiches, cakes, etc*	★ ★
	Crussh	*"*	★

Fitzrovia & Marylebone (Part of W1)

£80+	Pied à Terre	*French*	★
£70+	Rhodes W1 Restaurant	*French*	
£60+	Orrery	*French*	
	Texture	*"*	
	Defune	*Japanese*	★ ★
	Suka	*Malaysian*	✪
£50+	Elena's L'Etoile	*French*	Ⓐ
	The Providores	*Fusion*	★
	Locanda Locatelli	*Italian*	Ⓐ ★
	Fino	*Spanish*	★ ★
	La Porte des Indes	*Indian*	Ⓐ ★
	Roka	*Japanese*	Ⓐ ★ ★
£40+	Odin's	*British, Traditional*	Ⓐ
	Back to Basics	*Fish & seafood*	★ ★
	Galvin Bistrot de Luxe	*French*	Ⓐ ★ ★
	The Wallace	*"*	Ⓐ
	Archipelago	*Fusion*	Ⓐ
	Latium	*Italian*	Ⓐ ★ ★
	2 Veneti	*"*	★
	Koba	*Korean*	★
	Crazy Bear	*Thai*	Ⓐ ★
	Bam-Bou	*Vietnamese*	Ⓐ
£35+	Providores (Tapa Room)	*Fusion*	★
	Salt Yard	*Mediterranean*	★ ★
	Royal China	*Chinese*	★ ★

	Rasa Samudra	*Indian*	✪✪
£30+	RIBA Café	*British, Modern*	Ⓐ
	Langan's Bistro	*French*	Ⓐ
	Hellenik	*Greek*	
	Giraffe	*International*	
	Ragam	*Indian, Southern*	✪✪
	Dinings	*Japanese*	✪✪
£25+	La Fromagerie Café	*Sandwiches, cakes, etc*	Ⓐ✪✪
	Pâtisserie Valerie	*"*	
	Woodlands	*Indian*	✪
£20+	Le Pain Quotidien	*Sandwiches, cakes, etc*	Ⓐ
£15+	Golden Hind	*Fish & chips*	✪✪

**Belgravia, Pimlico, Victoria & Westminster
(SW1, except St James's)**

£80+	Rib Room	*British, Traditional*	
	Pétrus	*French*	Ⓐ✪✪
£70+	The Lanesborough	*British, Modern*	Ⓐ
	One-O-One	*Fish & seafood*	
	Foliage	*French*	Ⓐ✪✪
	La Noisette	*"*	⊗
	Tsar	*Russian*	
	Nahm	*Thai*	
£60+	The Goring Hotel	*British, Traditional*	Ⓐ
	Roussillon	*French*	✪✪
	Toto's	*Italian*	Ⓐ
£50+	Thomas Cubitt	*British, Modern*	Ⓐ
	La Poule au Pot	*French*	Ⓐ
	Pomegranates	*International*	Ⓐ
	Quirinale	*Italian*	✪
	Zafferano	*"*	✪
	Boisdale	*Scottish*	Ⓐ
	Amaya	*Indian*	Ⓐ✪✪
	The Cinnamon Club	*"*	Ⓐ✪
£40+	Olivomare	*Fish & seafood*	✪
	Le Cercle	*French*	Ⓐ✪✪
	Olivo	*Italian*	✪
	Caraffini	*"*	Ⓐ
	Il Convivio	*"*	
	Hunan	*Chinese*	✪✪
£35+	Grenadier	*British, Traditional*	Ⓐ
	Daylesford Organics	*Organic*	Ⓐ
	Ishbilia	*Lebanese*	✪
£30+	Kazan	*Turkish*	Ⓐ✪
£25+	Pâtisserie Valerie	*Sandwiches, cakes, etc*	
	Jenny Lo's	*Chinese*	✪
	Blue Jade	*Thai*	
£20+	Cyprus Mangal	*Turkish*	✪✪
	Nutmeg	*Indian*	✪

WEST

Chelsea, South Kensington, Kensington, Earl's Court & Fulham (SW3, SW5, SW6, SW7, SW10 & W8)

£100+	Gordon Ramsay	French	Ⓐ✪✪
	Blakes	International	Ⓐ
£80+	Aubergine	French	✪✪
	The Capital Restaurant	"	✪
	Tom Aikens	"	✪
£70+	The Bentley Hotel	"	
	Brunello	Italian	
	Rasoi Vineet Bhatia	Indian	✪✪
£60+	Bibendum	French	Ⓐ
	Zuma	Japanese	Ⓐ✪✪
	Nozomi	"	
£50+	Clarke's	British, Modern	✪
	Bluebird	"	Ⓐ
	Poissonnerie de l'Av.	Fish & seafood	✪
	Le Suquet	"	✪
	Belvedere	French	Ⓐ
	Papillon	"	Ⓐ
	Bombay Brasserie	Indian	Ⓐ✪
	Chutney Mary	"	Ⓐ✪
	Zaika	"	✪
	Blue Elephant	Thai	Ⓐ
£40+	Whits	British, Modern	✪
	The Abingdon	"	Ⓐ
	Ffiona's	British, Traditional	Ⓐ
	Maggie Jones's	"	Ⓐ
	Lundum's	Danish	Ⓐ✪
	La Bouchée	French	Ⓐ✪
	Racine	"	✪
	Le Colombier	"	Ⓐ
	The Enterprise	International	Ⓐ
	606 Club	"	Ⓐ
	The Swag & Tails	"	✪
	Pellicano	Italian	Ⓐ
	Frantoio	"	Ⓐ
	Il Portico	"	Ⓐ
	C Garden	"	
	Cambio de Tercio	Spanish	Ⓐ✪
	Pasha	Moroccan	Ⓐ
	Ken Lo's Memories	Chinese	✪✪
	Good Earth	"	✪
	Mr Wing	"	Ⓐ
	The Painted Heron	Indian	✪✪
	Vama	"	✪
	Awana	Malaysian	✪
	Eight Over Eight	Pan-Asian	Ⓐ✪
	Mao Tai	"	✪
	Patara	Thai	✪
	Sugar Hut	"	Ⓐ
£35+	The Farm	British, Modern	Ⓐ✪
	The Pig's Ear	French	Ⓐ
	The Cabin	International	Ⓐ

	Ottolenghi	*Italian*	ⓐⓧ
	Nuovi Sapori	*"*	ⓧ
	Polish Club	*Polish*	ⓐ
	Tendido Cero	*Spanish*	ⓧ
	Napket	*Afternoon tea*	ⓧ
	Royal China Fulham	*Chinese*	ⓐⓧ
	Made in China	*"*	ⓧ
	Haandi	*Indian*	ⓧ
	Love India	*"*	ⓧ
	Star of India	*"*	ⓧ
	Sukho Thai Cuisine	*Thai*	ⓐⓧⓧ
£30+	Joe's Brasserie	*British, Modern*	ⓐ
	The Scarsdale	*International*	ⓐ
	Balans West	*"*	ⓧ
	Balans	*"*	ⓧ
	Giraffe	*"*	
	The Atlas	*Mediterranean*	ⓐⓧ
	Sophie's Steakhouse	*Steaks & grills*	ⓐ
	Troubadour	*Sandwiches, cakes, etc*	ⓐⓧ
	Yi-Ban	*Chinese*	ⓐⓧ
	Ma Goa	*Indian*	ⓐⓧ
	Malabar	*"*	ⓐⓧ
	kare kare	*"*	ⓧ
	Noor Jahan	*"*	ⓧ
£25+	The Windsor Castle	*International*	ⓐ
	Pappa Ciccia	*Italian*	ⓐⓧ
	Pâtisserie Valerie	*Sandwiches, cakes, etc*	
	Taiwan Village	*Chinese*	ⓧ
	Tandoori Lane	*Indian*	ⓧ
	Addie's Thai Café	*Thai*	ⓧ
£20+	Costa's Fish	*Fish & chips*	ⓧ
	Le Pain Quotidien	*Sandwiches, cakes, etc*	ⓐ
	Café 209	*Thai*	ⓐ
£15+	Churchill Arms	*"*	ⓐⓧ
£10+	Crussh	*Sandwiches, cakes, etc*	ⓧ

Notting Hill, Holland Park, Bayswater, North Kensington & Maida Vale (W2, W9, W10, W11)

£60+	Beach Blanket Babylon	*British, Modern*	ⓐⓧ
	The Ledbury	*French*	ⓐⓧⓧ
£50+	Notting Hill Brasserie	*British, Modern*	ⓐⓧⓧ
	Assaggi	*Italian*	ⓧⓧ
£40+	Julie's	*British, Modern*	ⓐⓧ
	Père Michel	*French*	ⓧ
	Electric Brasserie	*International*	ⓧ
	Osteria Basilico	*Italian*	ⓐⓧ
	E&O	*Pan-Asian*	ⓐⓧ
£35+	The Ladbroke Arms	*British, Modern*	ⓐⓧ
	Paradise, Kensal Green	*"*	ⓐⓧ
	First Floor	*"*	ⓐⓧ
	The Westbourne	*"*	ⓐ
	202	*International*	ⓐ
	Ottolenghi	*Italian*	ⓧⓧ

Price	Name	Cuisine	
	The Oak	"	Ⓐ★
	Royal China	Chinese	★★
	Pearl Liang	"	★
	Bombay Palace	Indian	★★
£30+	Lucky Seven	American	Ⓐ★
	Wine Factory	International	Ⓐ
	Crazy Homies	Mexican/TexMex	Ⓐ★
	Mandarin Kitchen	Chinese	★★
	Noor Jahan	Indian	★
	Inaho	Japanese	★★
	Tawana	Thai	★
£25+	Uli	Pan-Asian	★
£15+	Fresco	Lebanese	★
£10+	Gail's Bread	Sandwiches, cakes, etc	★
£5+	Lisboa Pâtisserie	"	★★

Hammersmith, Shepherd's Bush, Olympia, Chiswick & Ealing (W4, W5, W6, W12, W14)

Price	Name	Cuisine	
£60+	The River Café	Italian	★
£50+	La Trompette	French	Ⓐ★★
£40+	High Road Brasserie	British, Modern	Ⓐ
	Pissarro's	"	Ⓐ
	Fish Hook	Fish & seafood	★
	Le Vacherin	French	★
	Cibo	Italian	★
£35+	The Anglesea Arms	British, Modern	Ⓐ★★
	Ealing Park Tavern	"	Ⓐ★
	The Havelock Tavern	"	★
	Annie's	International	Ⓐ
	Sushi-Hiro	Japanese	★★
£30+	Queen's Head	British, Modern	Ⓐ
	Stone Mason's Arms	"	Ⓐ
	Balans	International	✖
	Giraffe	"	
	The Swan	Mediterranean	Ⓐ
	Madhu's	Indian	Ⓐ★★
£25+	Patio	Polish	Ⓐ
	Ground	Burgers, etc	★
	Adams Café	Moroccan	Ⓐ
	Azou	North African	
	Chez Marcelle	Lebanese	★★
	Mohsen	Persian	★
	Agni	Indian	★
	Indian Zing	"	★
	Karma	"	★
	Woodlands	"	★
	Sagar	Indian, Southern	★
	North China	Chinese	★
	Esarn Kheaw	Thai	★★

| £20+ | Best Mangal | Turkish | ✪ |
| | Mirch Masala | Indian | ✪✪ |

| £15+ | Abu Zaad | Syrian | Ⓐ✪ |

| £10+ | Crussh | Sandwiches, cakes, etc | ✪ |

NORTH

Hampstead, West Hampstead, St John's Wood, Regent's Park, Kilburn & Camden Town (NW postcodes)

£60+	Landmark (Winter Gdn)	British, Modern	Ⓐ
	Odette's	"	
£50+	L'Aventure	French	Ⓐ✪
£40+	The Engineer	British, Modern	Ⓐ
	The Wells	"	Ⓐ
	Oslo Court	French	Ⓐ✪
	Good Earth	Chinese	✪
£35+	Holly Bush	British, Traditional	Ⓐ
	Sarracino	Italian	✪
	Royal China	Chinese	✪✪
	Snazz Sichuan	"	✪
	Eriki	Indian	✪✪
	Eriki 2	"	✪✪
	Jin Kichi	Japanese	✪✪
	Sushi-Say	"	✪✪
	Singapore Garden	Malaysian	Ⓐ✪
£30+	The Horseshoe	British, Modern	Ⓐ✪
	The Junction Tavern	"	Ⓐ
	La Cage Imaginaire	French	Ⓐ
	Lemonia	Greek	Ⓐ
	Giraffe	International	
	Don Pepe	Spanish	Ⓐ
	Atma	Indian	✪
£25+	El Parador	Spanish	✪
	Nautilus	Fish & chips	✪✪
	Alisan	Chinese	✪✪
	Vijay	Indian	✪
	Woodlands	"	✪
	Café Japan	Japanese	✪✪
£20+	Haché	Steaks & grills	Ⓐ✪
	Kenwood (Brew House)	Sandwiches, cakes, etc	Ⓐ
	Jashan	Indian	✪✪
	Five Hot Chillies	"	✪
	Kovalam	Indian, Southern	✪
£15+	Viet-Anh	Vietnamese	
£10+	Gail's Bread	Sandwiches, cakes, etc	✪

Hoxton, Islington, Highgate, Crouch End, Stoke Newington, Finsbury Park, Muswell Hill & Finchley (N postcodes)

£80+	Fifteen Restaurant	Italian	✪
£50+	Morgan M	French	✪✪
	Fifteen Trattoria	Italian	
£40+	The Lock Dining Bar	British, Modern	✪
	Frederick's	"	Ⓐ

	The Pumphouse	"	Ⓐ
	Chez Liline	Fish & seafood	Ⓐ✪
	Sargasso Sea	"	✪
£35+	Mosaica	British, Modern	✪
	The Haven	"	Ⓐ
	St Johns	British, Traditional	Ⓐ✪
	The Marquess Tavern	"	✪
	Fig	French	Ⓐ✪
	Ottolenghi	Italian	Ⓐ✪
	Rasa Travancore	Indian, Southern	Ⓐ✪
£30+	Pick More Daisies	American	Ⓐ✪
	Banners	International	Ⓐ
	Giraffe	"	
	Cantina Italia	Italian	Ⓐ✪
	San Daniele	"	Ⓐ
	Zaffrani	Indian	Ⓐ✪
	Isarn	Thai	Ⓐ✪
£25+	The Flask	British, Traditional	Ⓐ
	Vrisaki	Greek	✪
	Toff's	Fish & chips	✪
	Two Brothers	"	✪
	La Piragua	South American	Ⓐ✪
	Petek	Turkish	Ⓐ✪
	Rooburoo	Indian	✪
	Yum Yum	Thai	Ⓐ✪
£20+	Gem	Turkish	✪
	Izgara	"	✪
	Jashan	Indian	✪✪
	Rasa	"	✪✪
	Anglo Asian Tandoori	"	

SOUTH

South Bank (SE1)

£70+	Oxo Tower (Rest')	British, Modern	✪
£60+	Le Pont de la Tour	"	
£50+	Tentazioni	Italian	✪
£40+	Magdalen	French	Ⓐ✪✪
	Champor-Champor	Fusion	Ⓐ✪
	Village East	"	Ⓐ
	Hara The Circle Bar	Indian	✪✪
£35+	Garrison	British, Modern	Ⓐ
	The Anchor & Hope	British, Traditional	Ⓐ✪✪
	Wright Brothers	Fish & seafood	Ⓐ✪
	Delfina Studio Café	International	✪✪
	Tapas Brindisa	Spanish	✪
£30+	Benugo	British, Modern	Ⓐ✪
	Giraffe	International	
	La Lanterna	Italian	Ⓐ
	Bengal Clipper	Indian	Ⓐ✪
	Bincho Yakitori	Japanese	Ⓐ✪
£25+	Meson don Felipe	Spanish	Ⓐ
£20+	Le Pain Quotidien	Sandwiches, cakes, etc	Ⓐ
£15+	Konditor & Cook	"	✪✪
	El Vergel	South American	✪✪
£10+	Monmouth Coffee Company	Sandwiches, cakes, etc	Ⓐ✪✪

Greenwich, Lewisham & Blackheath
(All SE postcodes, except SE1)

£40+	Chapter Two	British, Modern	✪
	Lobster Pot	Fish & seafood	Ⓐ✪
£35+	Inside	British, Modern	✪✪
£30+	Joanna's	International	Ⓐ
	Olley's	Fish & chips	✪
	Babur Brasserie	Indian	Ⓐ✪✪
	Tandoori Nights	"	✪
£25+	Le Querce	Italian	✪✪
	Arancia	"	Ⓐ✪
	Dragon Castle	Chinese	✪
	Ganapati	Indian	✪
	Thailand	Thai	Ⓐ✪

Battersea, Brixton, Clapham, Wandsworth
Barnes, Putney & Wimbledon
(All SW postcodes south of the river)

| £50+ | Chez Bruce | British, Modern | Ⓐ✪✪ |

£40+	Lamberts	"	Ⓐ✪✪
	Four O Nine	"	Ⓐ✪
	Phoenix	"	Ⓐ✪
	La Saveur	French	✪
	Enoteca Turi	Italian	✪
	Riva	"	✪
	La Pampa	Argentinian	✪

£35+	The Mason's Arms	British, Modern	✪
	The Freemasons	"	Ⓐ
	Scoffers	"	Ⓐ
	Upstairs Bar	French	Ⓐ✪✪
	The Food Room	"	✪✪
	Annie's	International	Ⓐ
	Isola del Sole	Italian	✪
	Tsunami	Japanese	Ⓐ✪✪

£30+	The Duke's Head	British, Modern	Ⓐ✪
	Earl Spencer	"	Ⓐ✪
	Emile's	"	Ⓐ✪
	Mini Mundus	French	Ⓐ
	Giraffe	International	
	Pizza Metro	Italian	Ⓐ✪✪
	Numero Uno	"	Ⓐ
	The Fox & Hounds	Mediterranean	Ⓐ✪
	Rebato's	Spanish	Ⓐ
	Ma Goa	Indian	✪✪

£25+	Fish Club	Fish & seafood	✪✪
	Pappa Ciccia	Italian	Ⓐ✪
	Il Cantuccio di Pulcinella	"	
	El Rincón Latino	Spanish	Ⓐ
	Chutney	Indian	Ⓐ✪
	Indian Ocean	"	✪
	Nanglo	"	✪

£20+	Hot Stuff	"	✪✪
	Kastoori	"	✪✪
	Mirch Masala SW16	"	✪✪
	Sree Krishna	"	✪

| £15+ | Vijaya Krishna | Indian, Southern | ✪ |

Outer western suburbs
Kew, Richmond, Twickenham, Teddington

| £50+ | The Glasshouse | British, Modern | ✪✪ |

£40+	The Wharf	"	Ⓐ
	A Cena	Italian	Ⓐ✪
	Matsuba	Japanese	✪

£35+	Brula	French	Ⓐ✪
	Ma Cuisine	"	✪
	Origin Asia	Indian	✪

£30+	Scarpetta	Italian	Ⓐ✪
	Tangawizi	Indian	Ⓐ
	Thai Elephant	Thai	

| £25+ | Sagar | Indian | ✪ |

127

£20+	O'Zon	Chinese

EAST

Smithfield & Farringdon (EC1)

Price	Restaurant	Cuisine	
£70+	Club Gascon	French	⊙
£50+	Smiths (Top Floor)	British, Modern	Ⓐ
£40+	Malmaison Brasserie	"	Ⓐ
	St John	British, Traditional	⊙
	Bleeding Heart	French	Ⓐ⊙
	Café du Marché	"	Ⓐ⊙
	Dans le Noir	"	Ⓐ⊗
	Moro	Spanish	Ⓐ⊙⊙
£35+	Comptoir Gascon	French	Ⓐ⊙⊙
	Cicada	Pan-Asian	⊙
£30+	Vinoteca	British, Modern	Ⓐ
£25+	The Eagle	Mediterranean	Ⓐ⊙
£20+	Smiths (Ground Floor)	British, Modern	Ⓐ
	Kolossi Grill	Greek	Ⓐ
	Pham Sushie	Japanese	⊙⊙

The City (EC2, EC3, EC4)

Price	Restaurant	Cuisine	
£80+	Tatsuso	Japanese	
£70+	1 Lombard Street	British, Modern	
	Prism	"	
£60+	Rhodes 24	British, Modern	Ⓐ
£50+	Coq d'Argent	French	
£40+	The Princess	Australian	⊙
	The Don	British, Modern	Ⓐ⊙
	The Chancery	"	⊙
	Sweetings	Fish & seafood	Ⓐ⊙
	Vivat Bacchus	International	
	Leadenhall Italian	Italian	
	Bevis Marks	Kosher	
	Gt Eastern Dining Room	Pan-Asian	Ⓐ⊙
£35+	George & Vulture	British, Traditional	Ⓐ⊗
£30+	Ye Olde Cheshire Cheese	British, Traditional	Ⓐ⊗
	Kasturi	Indian	⊙
£25+	Simpson's Tavern	British, Traditional	Ⓐ
	The Diner	Burgers, etc	Ⓐ⊙
£20+	Hilliard	British, Modern	⊙⊙
	Club Mangia	"	Ⓐ⊙
£10+	Fuzzy's Grub	Sandwiches, cakes, etc	⊙⊙
	Crussh	"	⊙

East End & Docklands (All E postcodes)

Price	Restaurant	Cuisine	
£90+	Ubon	*Japanese*	
£70+	Les Trois Garçons	*French*	Ⓐ
£60+	Beach Blanket Babylon	*British, Modern*	ⒶⓍ
	Plateau	*French*	
£50+	Hawksmoor	*Steaks & grills*	★
£40+	The Gun	*British, Modern*	Ⓐ★
	The Morgan Arms	"	Ⓐ★
	Wapping Food	"	Ⓐ
	St John Bread & Wine	*British, Traditional*	★
	The Grapes	*Fish & seafood*	Ⓐ★
	Rosemary Lane	*French*	★
	Café Spice Namaste	*Indian*	★
£35+	Royal Oak	*British, Modern*	Ⓐ
	Il Bordello	*Italian*	Ⓐ★
	Green & Red Bar & Cantina	*Mexican/TexMex*	Ⓐ★★
	Royal China	*Chinese*	★★
£30+	La Figa	*Italian*	Ⓐ
	El Faro	*Spanish*	★★
	Santa Maria del Buen Ayre	*Argentinian*	Ⓐ★
	Yi-Ban	*Chinese*	Ⓐ★
£25+	LMNT	*British, Modern*	Ⓐ
	Pâtisserie Valerie	*Sandwiches, cakes, etc*	
	Shanghai	*Chinese*	★
	Memsaheb on Thames	*Indian*	★
£20+	Story Deli	*Organic*	Ⓐ★★
	Mirch Masala	*Indian*	★★
	Lahore Kebab House	*Pakistani*	★★
	New Tayyabs	"	★★
£10+	E Pellicci	*Italian*	Ⓐ
	Crussh	*Sandwiches, cakes, etc*	★

INDEXES

BREAKFAST
(with opening times)

Central
Asia de Cuba *(7)*
Balans: *all branches (8)*
Bar Italia *(8)*
Brown's Grill *(7)*
The Cinnamon Club *(Mon-Fri 7.30)*
Connaught *(7)*
Crussh: *W1 (7)*
Daylesford Organics *(8, Sun 11)*
Diner: *all branches (8, Sat & Sun 9)*
Dorchester Grill *(7, Sat & Sun 8)*
Flat White *(8, Sun 10)*
La Fromagerie Café *(Mon 10.30, Tue-Fri 8, Sat 9, Sun 10)*
Fuzzy's Grub: *all branches (7)*
Galvin at Windows *(7)*
Giraffe: *all branches (7.45, Sat & Sun 9)*
The Goring Hotel *(7)*
Indigo *(6.30)*
Jaan *(6.30, Sat 7)*
Joe Allen *(8)*
Konditor & Cook: *WC1 (9.30); W1 (9.30, Sun 10.30)*
The Lanesborough (Conservatory) *(7)*
Maison Bertaux *(8.30, Sun 9)*
Monmouth Coffee Company: *WC2 (8)*
Nordic Bakery *(Mon - Fri 10)*
Le Pain Quotidien: *Marylebone High St W1 (7, Sat & Sun 8); Great Marlborough St, Turner Building W1 (8, Sat & Sun 9)*
Pâtisserie Valerie: *all in W1: (7.30); Motcomb St SW1 (8); Hans Cr SW1 (8-8.30)*
Pearl *(6.30)*
The Providores *(9, Sat & Sun 10)*
Providores (Tapa Room) *(9, Sat & Sun 10)*
Rib Room *(7, Sun 8)*
RIBA Café *(8)*
The Ritz *(7, Sun 8)*
Simpsons-in-the-Strand *(Mon-Fri 7.30)*
Sotheby's Café *(9.30)*
The Wallace *(10)*
The Wolseley *(7, Sat & Sun 9)*

West
Adams Café *(7.30, Sat 8.30)*
Annie's: *all branches (Tue-Sun 10)*
Balans West: *all branches (8)*
Blakes *(7.30)*
Brunello *(6.45)*
Crussh: *W8 (7.30); W12 (8)*
Electric Brasserie *(8)*
Fresco *(8)*
Gail's Bread: *all branches (7, Sat & Sun 8)*
Giraffe: *all branches (7.45, Sat & Sun 9)*
High Road Brasserie *(7, Sat & Sun 8)*
Joe's Brasserie *(Sat & Sun 11)*
Julie's *(9)*
Lisboa Pâtisserie *(8)*
Lucky Seven *(10)*

Lundum's *(9)*
Napket *(8)*
Ottolenghi: *W11 (8, Sun 9)*
Le Pain Quotidien: *SW3 (7, Sat & Sun 8); W8 (7.30, Sun 8)*
Papillon *(Sat & Sun 10)*
Pâtisserie Valerie: *Brompton Rd SW3 (7); Duke of York Sq SW3, W8 (7.30)*
Pissarro's *(9)*
Sophie's Steakhouse *(Sat & Sun 11)*
Troubadour *(9)*
202 *(Mon & Sun 10 , Tue-Thu 8.30)*

North
Banners *(9, Sat & Sun 10)*
The Engineer *(9)*
Fifteen Trattoria *(7.30, Sun 9)*
Gail's Bread: *all branches (7, Sat & Sun 8)*
Giraffe: *all branches (7.45, Sat & Sun 9)*
Kenwood (Brew House) *(9)*
Landmark (Winter Garden) *(7)*
Ottolenghi: *N1 (8, Sun 9)*
Pick More Daisies *(10)*

South
Annie's: *all branches (Tue-Sun 10)*
Brula *(9)*
The Duke's Head *(10 ex sun)*
Garrison *(8, Sat & Sun 9)*
Giraffe: *all branches (7.45, Sat & Sun 9)*
Joanna's *(10)*
Monmouth Coffee Company: *SE1 (7.30)*
Le Pain Quotidien: *SE1 (8, Sun 9)*
El Rincón Latino *(Sat & Sun 11)*
Scoffers *(10)*
Tapas Brindisa *(Fri & Sat 9)*
El Vergel *(8.30)*

East
Bleeding Heart *(7)*
Club Mangia *(7)*
Comptoir Gascon *(9)*
Coq d'Argent *(Mon-Fri 7.30)*
Crussh: *One Canada Sq E14, EC3 (7); Unit 21 Jubilee Pl E14, EC4 (7.30)*
The Diner: *all branches (8, Sat & Sun 9)*
Fuzzy's Grub: *all branches (7)*
The Gun *(Sat & Sun 10.30)*
Hilliard *(8)*
Malmaison Brasserie *(7, Sat & Sun 8)*
Pâtisserie Valerie: *E1 (7.30)*
E Pellicci *(6.15)*
Prism *(8)*
St John Bread & Wine *(9, Sat & Sun 10)*
Smiths (Ground Floor) *(7)*
Story Deli *(9)*
Wapping Food *(Sat & Sun 10)*

BRUNCH MENUS

Central
Aurora
Balans: *all branches*

INDEXES

Tamarind
Theo Randall
Veeraswamy
The Wallace
Wild Honey
Wiltons
The Wolseley
Zafferano

West
Aubergine
The Bentley Hotel
Bibendum
The Capital Restaurant
Clarke's
Gordon Ramsay
The Ledbury
Poissonnerie de l'Av.
Racine
Tom Aikens
La Trompette
Zuma

North
Frederick's
Landmark (Winter Garden)

South
Delfina Studio Café
Oxo Tower (Rest')
Le Pont de la Tour

East
Bevis Marks
Bleeding Heart
Café du Marché
The Chancery
Club Gascon
Coq d'Argent
The Don
Malmaison Brasserie
Moro
1 Lombard Street
Plateau
Prism
Rhodes 24
St John
Smiths (Top Floor)
Sweetings
Tatsuso
Ubon
Vivat Bacchus

BYO

(Bring your own wine at minimal corkage. Note for £5-£15 per bottle, you can normally negotiate to take your own wine to many, if not most, places.)

Central
Golden Hind
Ragam

West
Blah! Blah! Blah!

Chelsea Bun Diner
Five Hot Chillies
Gifto's Lahore Karahi
  & Tandoori
Mohsen
Pappa Ciccia: *Munster Rd SW6*
Tendido Cero

North
Ali Baba
Geeta
Vijay

South
Amaranth
Fish Club
Hot Stuff
Mirch Masala: *SW16, SW17*

East
Mangal
New Tayyabs

CHILDREN

(h – high or special chairs
 m – children's menu
 p – children's portions
 e – weekend entertainments
 o – other facilities)

Central
Abeno Too *(h)*
Al Sultan *(h)*
Alloro *(hmp)*
Arbutus *(h)*
Asia de Cuba *(h)*
Aurora *(p)*
Back to Basics *(hp)*
Bar Italia *(hp)*
Barrafina *(p)*
Benares *(h)*
Benja *(h)*
Bentley's *(h)*
Brown's Grill *(m)*
Le Caprice *(hp)*
Le Cercle *(hp)*
Chisou *(h)*
The Cinnamon Club *(h)*
Cipriani *(hp)*
Clos Maggiore *(m)*
Connaught *(hm)*
Cyprus Mangal *(m)*
Diner: *all branches (hmp)*
Dorchester Grill *(h)*
Fino *(h)*
Foliage *(hm)*
La Fromagerie Café *(p)*
Fuzzy's Grub: *SW1 (h)*
Galvin at Windows *(h)*
Galvin Bistrot de Luxe *(h)*
Giraffe: *W1 (ehm)*
Golden Hind *(p)*
Gordon Ramsay at Claridge's *(h)*
The Goring Hotel *(hm)*
Hellenik *(p)*
Indigo *(hm)*

INDEXES

Prism *(p)*
Royal China*: E14 (h)*
Royal Oak *(h)*
St John *(h)*
St John Bread & Wine *(h)*
Santa Maria del Buen Ayre *(h)*
Smiths (Top Floor) *(h)*
Smiths (Ground Floor) *(hp)*
Story Deli *(o)*
Ubon *(hp)*
Vinoteca *(p)*
Yi-Ban*: E16 (h)*

ENTERTAINMENT
(Check times before you go)

Central
Boisdale
　(jazz, Mon-Sat)
Le Caprice
　(pianist, nightly)
Ciao Bella
　(pianist, nightly)
Connaught
　(pianist, nightly)
The Cuckoo Club
　(live music, Wed)
The Easton
　(DJ, Fri)
Hakkasan
　(DJ, nightly)
Imperial China
　(pianist, Thu-Sat)
Indigo
　(film brunches, Sun)
Ishbilia
　(live music, Thu-Sat, regular belly dancing)
Joe Allen
　(pianist, Mon-Sat; jazz, Sun)
Kai Mayfair
　(harpist, Sat)
The Lanesborough
　(Conservatory)
　(dinner dance, Fri & Sat; jazz, Sun brunch)
Levant
　(belly dancer, nightly)
Pearl
　(pianist)
La Porte des Indes
　(jazz, Sun brunch)
Red Fort
　(DJ, Thu-Sat)
Rib Room
　(pianist, Mon-Sun)
The Ritz
　(string quartet, Mon-Thu; live music, Fri & Sat)
Roka
　(DJ, Thu-Sat)
Ronnie Scott's
　(jazz, nightly)
Savoy Grill
　(pianist, nightly)
Simpsons-in-the-Strand
　(pianist, nightly)
Sketch (Gallery)
　(DJ, Thu-Sat)

Souk Medina
　(belly dancer, Thu-Sat)
Taman Gang
　(DJ, Thu-Sat)
Trader Vics
　(guitarist, nightly)

West
Azou
　(belly dancer, Fri; live music, Sun)
Beach Blanket Babylon*: W11*
　(DJ, Fri & Sat)
Belvedere
　(pianist, nightly)
The Bentley Hotel
　(pianist, nightly)
Chutney Mary
　(jazz, Sun)
The Farm
　(pianist, Sun-Mon)
Mr Wing
　(jazz, Fri & Sat)
Napket
　(ipods on tables to plug headphones in)
Notting Hill Brasserie
　(jazz, nightly)
Nozomi
　(DJ, nightly)
Pasha
　(belly dancer, nightly)
606 Club
　(live music, nightly)
Sugar Hut
　(DJ, Fri & Sat)
Troubadour
　(live music, most nights)
Vama
　(belly dancing & magician, Sat & Sun)

North
Don Pepe
　(singer, Fri & Sat)
The Haven
　(jazz, Tue-Thu)
Landmark (Winter Garden)
　(pianist & musicians, daily)
La Piragua
　(disco, weekends)
The Pumphouse
　(DJ, Fri)
Yum Yum
　(DJ, Fri-Sat)

South
Bengal Clipper
　(pianist, nightly)
The Freemasons
　(quiz night, Mon)
La Lanterna
　(live music, Fri)
Meson don Felipe
　(guitarist, nightly)
Thailand
　(karaoke, Thu-Sat)
The Wharf
　(live music, first Thu of the month)

INDEXES

East

Café du Marché
(pianist & bass, nightly)

Club Mangia
(wine tasting once a month)

Coq d'Argent
(pianist, Sat; jazz, Fri & Sun L)

Green & Red Bar & Cantina
(DJ, Thu-Sat)

LMNT
(opera, Sun)

1 Lombard Street
(jazz, Fri D)

Shanghai
(karaoke, nightly)

Smiths (Ground Floor)
(DJ, Wed-Sat)

Yi-Ban: *E16*
(live music, Fri & Sat)

LATE
(open till midnight or later as shown; may be earlier Sunday)

Central

Al Sultan
Asia de Cuba *(midnight, Thu-Sat 12.30 am)*
Balans: *Old Compton St W1 (24 hours); Old Compton St W1 (5 am, Sun 1 am)*
Bar Italia *(open 24 hours, Sun 3 am)*
Bentley's
Le Caprice
China Tang
Cyprus Mangal *(Sun-Thu midnight, Fri & Sat 1 am)*
Diner: *W1 (12.30 am, Sun midnight)*
The Forge
Hakkasan *(midnight, ex Mon & Sun)*
The Ivy
Joe Allen *(12.45 am)*
Kazan
Nobu Berkeley *(1.30 am)*
Ronnie Scott's *(3 am, Sun midnight)*
Rules
St Alban
J Sheekey
Sitaaray *(1 am)*
Sketch (Gallery) *(1 am)*
Suka *(12.30 am)*
Trader Vics *(12.30 am)*
The Wolseley

West

Balans: *W4, W8 ; SW5 (2 am)*
Best Mangal
Blue Elephant
The Cabin
Mirch Masala: *UB1*
Mohsen
Mr Wing
Papillon
Pasha *(midnight, Thu-Sat 1 am)*
606 Club
Sugar Hut

North

Banners *(Fri midnight)*
Gem
Izgara
Kovalam *(Fri & Sat midnight)*
Landmark (Winter Garden) *(1 am)*
La Piragua
Vrisaki

South

Hara The Circle Bar
Mirch Masala: *all south branches*
Sree Krishna *(Fri & Sat midnight)*
Vijaya Krishna *(Fri & Sat midnight)*

East

The Diner: *EC2*
Lahore Kebab House

OUTSIDE TABLES
(particularly recommended)*

Central

Al Sultan
Andrew Edmunds
Archipelago
L'Artiste Musclé
Aurora
Back to Basics
Balans: *Old Compton St W1*
Bam-Bou
Bar Italia
Barrafina
Boisdale
Busaba Eathai: *WC1*
Caraffini
Chisou
Ciao Bella
Daylesford Organics
Diner: *W1*
The Easton
Flat White
Giraffe: *all branches*
Gordon's Wine Bar*
The Greenhouse
Hellenik
Imperial China
Ishbilia
Jaan
Jenny Lo's
Just Falafs: *WC2*
Kazan
Konstam
Mildred's
Nutmeg
Olivomare
L'Oranger
Orrery
Pâtisserie Valerie: *Motcomb St SW1, Piccadilly W1, Marylebone High St W1*
La Poule au Pot
The Providores
RIBA Café*
The Ritz
Roka

Pizza Metro
Le Pont de la Tour*
Riva
La Saveur
Scoffers
Tapas Brindisa
Thailand
El Vergel
The Wharf*

East
Bevis Marks
Bleeding Heart
Café Spice Namaste
Cicada
Comptoir Gascon
Coq d'Argent*
The Eagle
El Faro*
La Figa
The Gun*
Hawksmoor
Kolossi Grill
LMNT
Memsaheb on Thames
The Morgan Arms
Moro
New Tayyabs
Pâtisserie Valerie: E1
Plateau
Royal China: E14
Royal Oak
Santa Maria del Buen Ayre
Smiths (Top Floor)
Smiths (Ground Floor)
Story Deli
Vinoteca
Wapping Food
Yi-Ban: all branches

ROMANTIC

Central
Andrew Edmunds
Archipelago
Asia de Cuba
Aurora
Bam-Bou
Boisdale
Le Caprice
Le Cercle
Chor Bizarre
Clos Maggiore
Crazy Bear
Elena's L'Etoile
L'Escargot
L'Escargot (Picasso Room)
Galvin at Windows
Le Gavroche
Gordon Ramsay at Claridge's
Gordon's Wine Bar
Hakkasan
The Ivy
The Lanesborough
  (Conservatory)
Langan's Bistro

Levant
Lindsay House
Locanda Locatelli
Odin's
L'Oranger
Orrery
Pétrus
Pied à Terre
Pomegranates
La Porte des Indes
La Poule au Pot
The Ritz
Roussillon
Rules
J Sheekey
Souk Medina
Taman Gang
Toto's
La Trouvaille
Tsar
The Wolseley
Zafferano

West
Assaggi
Beach Blanket Babylon: all branches
Belvedere
Bibendum
Blakes
Blue Elephant
La Bouchée
C Garden
Le Colombier
E&O
Eight Over Eight
Ffiona's
Julie's
The Ledbury
Lundum's
Maggie Jones's
Mr Wing
Notting Hill Brasserie
Osteria Basilico
Papillon
Paradise by Way of Kensal
  Green
Pasha
Patio
Pissarro's
Ognisko Polskie
Racine
The River Café
Star of India
Sugar Hut
Le Suquet
La Trompette
Le Vacherin
Zuma

North
Anglo Asian Tandoori
L'Aventure
La Cage Imaginaire
The Engineer
Fig
The Flask

LONDON MAPS

MAP 1 - WEST END OVERVIEW

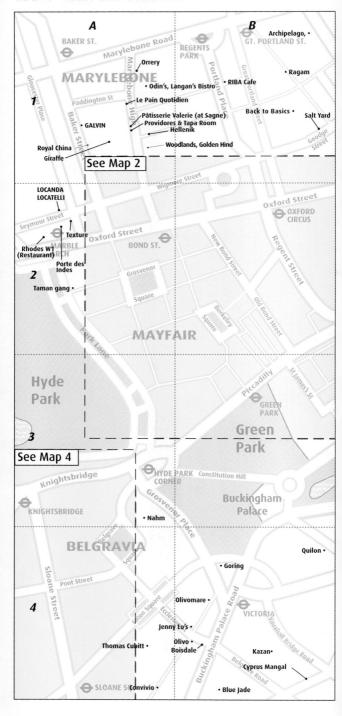

A

B

BAKER ST.

Marylebone Road

REGENTS PARK

GT. PORTLAND ST.

Archipelago •

Orrery

MARYLEBONE

• Odin's, Langan's Bistro

• Ragam

• RIBA Cafe

Paddington St

Le Pain Quotidien

Pâtisserie Valerie (at Sagne)

Back to Basics •

Salt Yard

Providores & Tapa Room

Hellenik

• GALVIN

Woodlands, Golden Hind

Royal China

Giraffe

See Map 2

LOCANDA LOCATELLI

Seymour Street

Wigmore Street

Oxford Street

OXFORD CIRCUS

Texture

Oxford Street

Rhodes W1 (Restaurant)

MARBLE ARCH

BOND ST.

New Bond Street

Regent Street

Porte des Indes

Grosvenor

Taman gang •

Square

MAYFAIR

Berkeley

Square

Old Bond Street

Park Lane

Hyde Park

Piccadilly

St James's St

GREEN PARK

Green Park

See Map 4

HYDE PARK CORNER

Constitution Hill

Knightsbridge

Grosvenor Place

Buckingham Palace

KNIGHTSBRIDGE

• Nahm

Quilon •

BELGRAVIA

Sloane Street

Pont Street

• Goring

Olivomare •

VICTORIA

Jenny Lo's •

Thomas Cubitt •

Olivo •

Boisdale

Kazan•

Cyprus Mangal

SLOANE SQ.

Convivio •

• Blue Jade

MAP 1 - WEST END OVERVIEW

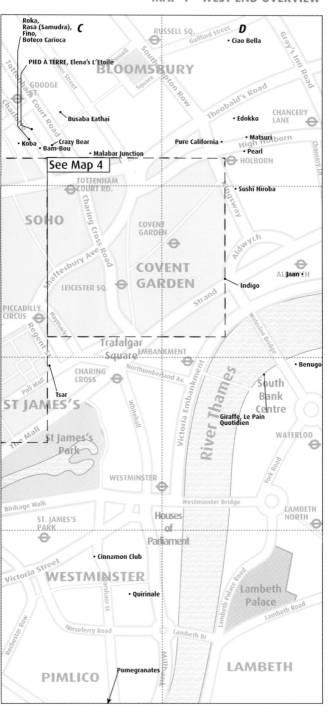

Roka,
Rasa (Samudra),
Fino,
Boteco Carioca

C

RUSSELL SQ.   Guilford Street   **D**

• Ciao Bella

PIED À TERRE, Elena's L'Etoile

BLOOMSBURY

GOODGE
ST.

Theobald's Road

CHANCERY
LANE

• Busaba Eathai

• Edokko

Pure California •   • Matsuri

• Koba   Crazy Bear

• Bam-Bou

• Malabar Junction

• Pearl

HOLBORN

See Map 4

TOTTENHAM
COURT RD.

• Sushi Hiroba

SOHO

COVENT
GARDEN

**COVENT
GARDEN**

LEICESTER SQ.

Aldwych

AL   • H

Strand   Indigo

Jaan •

PICCADILLY
CIRCUS

Trafalgar
Square   EMBANKMENT

• Benugo

CHARING
CROSS

Northumberland Av.

River Thames

South
Bank
Centre

ST JAMES'S

Tsar

Pall Mall

St James's
Park

Giraffe, Le Pain
Quotidien

WATERLOO

WESTMINSTER

Westminster Bridge

LAMBETH
NORTH

Birdcage Walk

ST. JAMES'S
PARK

Houses
of
Parliament

• Cinnamon Club

WESTMINSTER

Victoria Street

• Quirinale

Lambeth
Palace

Lambeth Road

Horseferry Road   Lambeth Br

Pomegranates

PIMLICO   **LAMBETH**

MAP 2 - MAYFAIR, ST JAMES'S & WEST SOHO

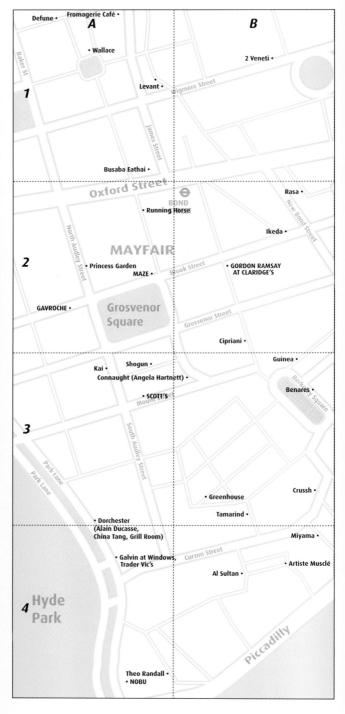

MAP 2 - MAYFAIR, ST JAMES'S & WEST SOHO

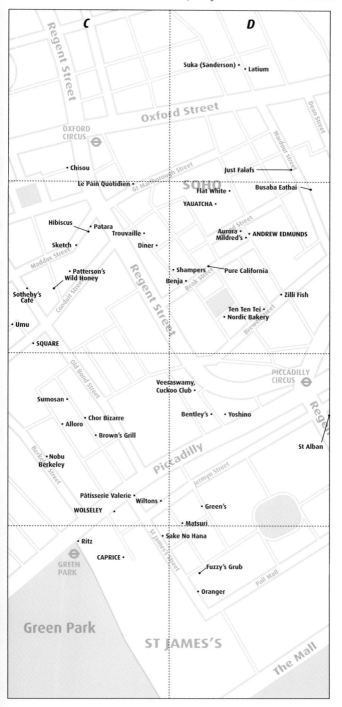

MAP 3 - EAST SOHO, CHINATOWN & COVENT GARDEN

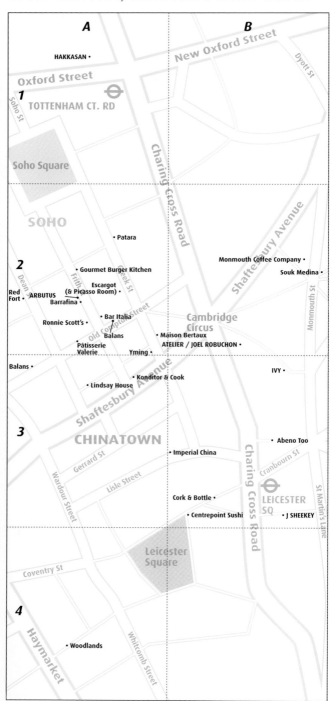

MAP 3 - EAST SOHO, CHINATOWN & COVENT GARDEN

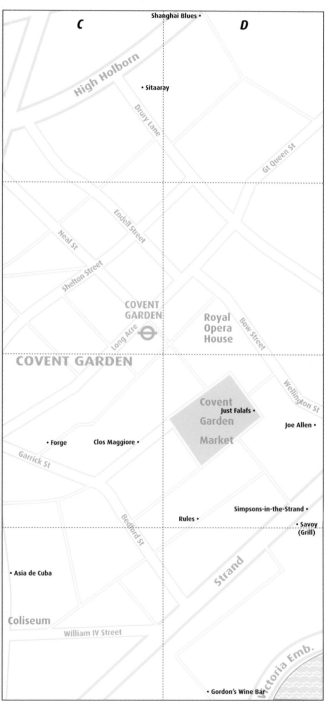

MAP 4 - KNIGHTSBRIDGE, CHELSEA & SOUTH KENSINGTON

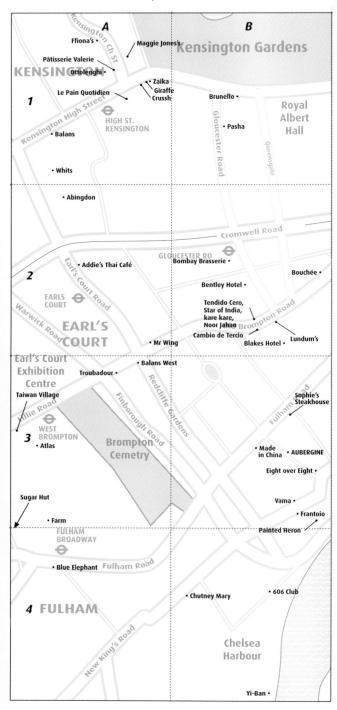

A

B

Ffiona's •

• Maggie Jones's

Kensington Gardens

Pâtisserie Valerie •

KENSINGTON

Ottolenghi •

• Zaika

Le Pain Quotidien •

Giraffe

Crussh

Brunello •

Royal Albert Hall

1

• Pasha

HIGH ST. KENSINGTON

• Balans

Gloucester Road

Queensgate

• Whits

• Abingdon

Cromwell Road

GLOUCESTER RD

• Addie's Thai Café

Bombay Brasserie •

2

Bouchée •

EARLS COURT

Bentley Hotel •

Tendido Cero,
Star of India,
kare kare,
Noor Jahan

EARL'S COURT

Cambio de Tercio •

Brompton Road

Lundum's

Warwick Road

Blakes Hotel •

• Mr Wing

Earl's Court Road

Earl's Court Exhibition Centre

• Balans West

Troubadour •

Sophie's Steakhouse

Taiwan Village

Finborough Road

Redcliffe Gardens

Fulham Road

Lillie Road

3

WEST BROMPTON

Brompton Cemetery

• Made in China

• AUBERGINE

• Atlas

Eight over Eight •

Sugar Hut

Vama •

• Frantoio

• Farm

Painted Heron •

FULHAM BROADWAY

• Blue Elephant Fulham Road

• 606 Club

4 FULHAM

• Chutney Mary

Chelsea Harbour

New King's Road

Yi-Ban •

MAP 4 - KNIGHTSBRIDGE, CHELSEA & SOUTH KENSINGTON

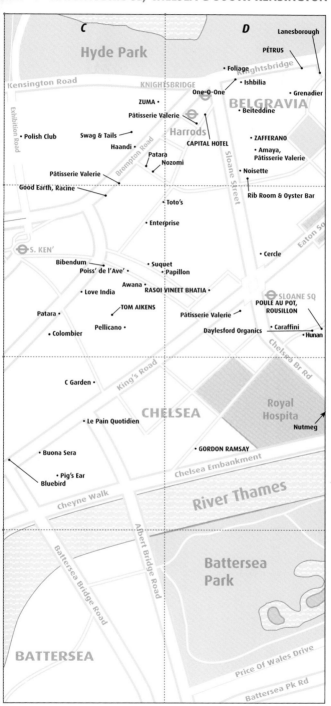

MAP 5 - NOTTING HILL & BAYSWATER

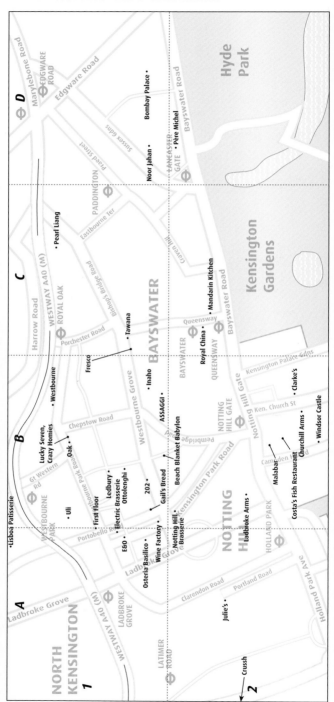

MAP 6 - HAMMERSMITH & CHISWICK

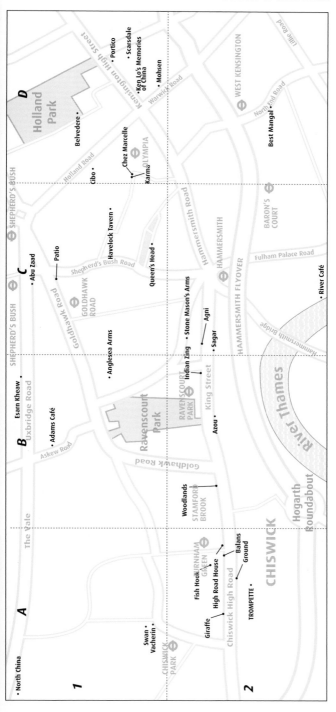

UK SURVEY RESULTS & TOP SCORERS

PLACES PEOPLE TALK ABOUT

These are the restaurants outside London that were mentioned most frequently by reporters (last year's position is shown in brackets). For the list of London's most mentioned restaurants, see page 25.

Manoir aux Quat' Saisons

1. Fat Duck (1)
   Bray, Berks
2. Manoir aux Quat' Saisons (2)
   Great Milton, Oxon
3. Waterside Inn (3)
   Bray, Berks
4. Hind's Head (–)
   Bray, Berks
5. Seafood Restaurant (4)
   Padstow, Cornwall

Yang Sing

6. Yang Sing (5)
   Manchester
7. The Witchery (11=)
   Edinburgh
8. Magpie (7)
   Whitby, N Yorks
9. Anthony's (6)
   Leeds
10. Vineyard/Stockcross (17=)
    Stockcross, Berkshire

Star Inn

11. Terre à Terre (10)
    Brighton
12. Star Inn (8)
    Harome, N Yorks
13. Chapter One (9)
    Locksbottom, Kent
14. The Olive Branch (12=)
    Clipsham, Rutland
15. Croma (12=)
    Manchester

Midsummer House

16. Rick Stein's Café (19=)
    Padstow, Cornwall
17. Hand & Flowers (–)
    Marlow, Bucks
18. Midsummer House (–)
    Cambridge, Cambs
19= Champignon Sauvage (–)
    Cheltenham, Gloucs
19= Hotel du Vin
    Bristol
20. Due South (14=)
    Brighton

TOP SCORERS

All restaurants whose food rating is ★★; plus restaurants whose price is £50+ with a food rating of ★.

£120+	Le Manoir aux Quat' Saisons *(Great Milton)*	★★ Ⓐ
	Waterside Inn *(Bray)*	★★ Ⓐ
£110+	The Fat Duck *(Bray)*	★★
£100+	Winteringham Fields *(Winteringham)*	★
£90+	Gidleigh Park *(Chagford)*	★★★ Ⓐ
	Vineyard at Stockcross *(Stockcross)*	★
£80+	Andrew Fairlie *(Auchterarder)*	★★★ Ⓐ
	Lucknam Park *(Colerne)*	★★★ Ⓐ
	Midsummer House *(Cambridge)*	★★
	Restaurant Sat Bains *(Nottingham)*	★★
	The Oak Room *(Marlow)*	★★
	Hambleton Hall *(Hambleton)*	★★ Ⓐ
	Inverlochy Castle *(Fort William)*	★★ Ⓐ
	Fischers at Baslow Hall *(Baslow)*	★
	Ynyshir Hall *(Eglwysfach)*	★
£70+	Bath Priory Hotel *(Bath)*	★★
	Bohemia *(Jersey)*	★★
	Harry's Place *(Great Gonerby)*	★★
	Champany Inn *(Linlithgow)*	★★ Ⓐ
	Kinnaird House *(Dunkeld)*	★★ Ⓐ
	L'Ortolan *(Shinfield)*	★★ Ⓐ
	Longueville Manor *(Jersey)*	★★ Ⓐ
	Paris House *(Woburn)*	★★ Ⓐ
	Summer Lodge *(Evershot)*	★★ Ⓐ
	The French Horn *(Sonning on Thames)*	★★ Ⓐ
	Fisherman's Lodge *(Newcastle upon Tyne)*	★
	Lainston House Hotel *(Winchester)*	★
	Lords of the Manor *(Upper Slaughter)*	★
	Number One *(Edinburgh)*	★
	Restaurant Martin Wishart *(Edinburgh)*	★
	Seafood Restaurant *(Padstow)*	★
	Simpsons *(Birmingham)*	★
£60+	Mr Underhill's *(Ludlow)*	★★★ Ⓐ
	Summer Isles *(Achiltibuie)*	★★★ Ⓐ
	The Harrow at Little Bedwyn *(Marlborough)*	★★★ Ⓐ
	The Three Chimneys *(Dunvegan)*	★★★ Ⓐ
	Artichoke *(Amersham)*	★★
	Champignon Sauvage *(Cheltenham)*	★★
	Le Poussin at Whitley Ridge *(Brockenhurst)*	★★
	Morston Hall *(Morston)*	★★
	Airds Hotel *(Port Appin)*	★★ Ⓐ

TOP SCORERS

	Crinan Hotel (Crinan by Lochgilphead)	✪Ⓐ
	Gilpin Lodge (Windermere)	✪Ⓐ
	Holbeck Ghyll (Windermere)	✪Ⓐ
	Mallory Court (Bishops Tachbrook)	✪Ⓐ
	Northcote Manor (Langho)	✪Ⓐ
	Read's (Faversham)	✪Ⓐ
	Seafood Restaurant (St Andrews)	✪Ⓐ
	Sharrow Bay (Ullswater)	✪Ⓐ
	Silver Darling (Aberdeen)	✪Ⓐ
	The Castle Hotel (Taunton)	✪Ⓐ
	The Crown at Whitebrook (Whitebrook)	✪Ⓐ
	White Room (Seaham)	✪Ⓐ
	Abstract (Edinburgh)	✪
	L'Enclume (Cartmel)	✪
	Tony Tobin @ The Dining Room (Reigate)	✪
	Underscar Manor (Applethwaite)	✪
£50+	Hipping Hall (Kirkby Lonsdale)	✪✪✪Ⓐ
	Monachyle Mhor (Balquhidder)	✪✪✪Ⓐ
	Plas Bodegroes (Pwllheli)	✪✪✪Ⓐ
	The Cellar (Anstruther)	✪✪✪Ⓐ
	The Peat Inn (Cupar)	✪✪✪Ⓐ
	Tyddyn Llan (Llandrillo)	✪✪✪Ⓐ
	22 Mill Street (Chagford)	✪✪
	Anthony's (Leeds)	✪✪
	Black Door (Newcastle upon Tyne)	✪✪
	Bosquet (Kenilworth)	✪✪
	Drakes (Ripley)	✪✪
	Fairyhill (Reynoldston)	✪✪
	Fraiche (Oxton)	✪✪
	Ostlers Close (Cupar)	✪✪
	The Crab at Chieveley (Newbury)	✪✪
	The Kitchin (Edinburgh)	✪✪
	The Weavers Shed (Golcar)	✪✪
	Abstract (Inverness)	✪Ⓐ
	Alma De Cuba (Liverpool)	✪Ⓐ
	Ardanaiseig Hotel (Kilchrenan by Taynuilt)	✪Ⓐ
	Cavendish (Baslow)	✪Ⓐ
	Combe House Hotel & Restaurant (Honiton)	✪Ⓐ
	Darroch Learg (Ballater)	✪Ⓐ
	Gaucho Grill (Manchester)	✪Ⓐ
	Grain Store (Edinburgh)	✪Ⓐ
	Hartwell House (Aylesbury)	✪Ⓐ
	Jesmond Dene House (Newcastle upon Tyne)	✪Ⓐ
	Langar Hall (Langar)	✪Ⓐ
	Lavender House (Brundall)	✪Ⓐ
	Leeming House Hotel (Watermillock)	✪Ⓐ
	Llangoed Hall (Llyswen)	✪Ⓐ
	Newick Park (Newick)	✪Ⓐ
	Orchid Restaurant (Torquay)	✪Ⓐ
	Percy's (Virginstow)	✪Ⓐ
	Rhubarb (Edinburgh)	✪Ⓐ

TOP SCORERS

Samuel's *(Masham)*	⭐Ⓐ
The Albannach *(Lochinver)*	⭐Ⓐ
The Galley *(Topsham)*	⭐Ⓐ
The Loft Restaurant *(Beaumaris)*	⭐Ⓐ
Allium *(Fairford)*	⭐
Castle House Restaurant *(Hereford)*	⭐
Fishes *(Burnham Market)*	⭐
Forbury's *(Reading)*	⭐
Gamba *(Glasgow)*	⭐
Goodfellows *(Wells)*	⭐
Green Inn *(Ballater)*	⭐
Hotel du Vin et Bistro *(Glasgow)*	⭐
JSW *(Petersfield)*	⭐
La Potinière *(Gullane)*	⭐
Lawtons at No 16 *(St Davids)*	⭐
Little Barwick House *(Barwick)*	⭐
Lumière *(Cheltenham)*	⭐
No 6 Café *(Padstow)*	⭐
Seafood Restaurant *(St Monans)*	⭐
Smiths Brasserie *(Ongar)*	⭐
Thackeray's *(Tunbridge Wells)*	⭐
Three Lions *(Stuckton)*	⭐
Yorke Arms *(Ramsgill-in-Nidderdale)*	⭐

£40+	Braidwoods *(Dalry)*	⭐⭐Ⓐ
	Chapter One *(Locksbottom)*	⭐⭐Ⓐ
	Ee-Usk (Seafood Restaurant) *(Oban)*	⭐⭐Ⓐ
	Great House *(Lavenham)*	⭐⭐Ⓐ
	Jeremy's at Borde Hill *(Haywards Heath)*	⭐⭐Ⓐ
	Porthminster Café *(St Ives)*	⭐⭐Ⓐ
	Drewe Arms *(Broadhembury)*	⭐⭐
	Pebble Beach *(Barton-on-Sea)*	⭐⭐
	Stagg Inn *(Titley)*	⭐⭐
	Sticky Prawn *(Falmouth)*	⭐⭐
	Storm *(Poole)*	⭐⭐
	Terre à Terre *(Brighton)*	⭐⭐
	The French Table *(Surbiton)*	⭐⭐
	The Hind's Head *(Bray)*	⭐⭐
	The Old Passage Inn *(Arlingham)*	⭐⭐
	West House *(Biddenden)*	⭐⭐

£30+	David Bann *(Edinburgh)*	⭐⭐Ⓐ
	Linen Room *(Dumfries)*	⭐⭐Ⓐ
	The Westerly *(Reigate)*	⭐⭐Ⓐ
	Wheeler's Oyster Bar *(Whitstable)*	⭐⭐Ⓐ
	Cafe Maitreya *(Bristol)*	⭐⭐
	Cotto *(Cambridge)*	⭐⭐
	Endeavour *(Staithes)*	⭐⭐
	Les Mirabelles *(Nomansland)*	⭐⭐
	Margot's *(Padstow)*	⭐⭐
	Mem Saab *(Nottingham)*	⭐⭐
	Rasa *(Newcastle upon Tyne)*	⭐⭐

TOP SCORERS

Roti *(Edinburgh)*	✪✪
Sportsman *(Whitstable)*	✪✪
The Dhabba *(Glasgow)*	✪✪
Trenchers *(Whitby)*	✪✪
Yang Sing *(Manchester)*	✪✪

£25+	El Gato Negro Tapas *(Ripponden)*	✪✪
	Golden Palace *(Harrow)*	✪✪
	Hansa's *(Leeds)*	✪✪
	Lucky Dragon *(Leeds)*	✪✪
	Magpie Café *(Whitby)*	✪✪

£20+	Akbar's Balti *(Bradford)*	✪✪Ⓐ
	Fuji Hiro *(Leeds)*	✪✪
	Mumtaz Paan House *(Bradford)*	✪✪
	Punjab Tandoori *(Manchester)*	✪✪
	Stein's Fish & Chips *(Padstow)*	✪✪

£15+	Anstruther Fish Bar *(Anstruther)*	✪✪
	Superfish *(Tolworth)*	✪✪
	The Company Shed *(West Mersea)*	✪✪

UK DIRECTORY

Harbourmaster £ 43 Ⓐ⭐

Quay Pde SA46 0BA (01545) 570755

"A fabulous location in a lovely town" helps ensure strong feedback on this *"fun"* waterside hotel, which wins consistent praise for food that's *"unfailingly good, and reasonably-priced"*. / **Sample dishes:** grilled sardines; beef fillet; chocolate fondant. **Details:** www.harbour-master.com; 9 pm; closed Mon L; no Amex. **Accommodation:** 13 rooms, from £110.

Bistro Verde £ 34 Ⓣ

Units 1-2 The Grn AB11 6NY (01224) 586180

A *"little fish restaurant with an extensive specials board, depending on the local catch"*, offering *"great food at reasonable prices"*. / **Details:** 9 pm.

Cafe 52 £ 37 ⭐

52 The Green AB11 6PE (01224) 590094

Steve Bothwell's *"tiny"* restaurant is very *"cosy"* indeed (maybe too much so); his *"very small"* menu includes some *"really inventive"* dishes. / **Sample dishes:** baked black pudding with white wine, poached pear, fresh raspberries & a raspberry sauce.; hot smoked salmon risotto with smoked bacon & red pepper.. **Details:** www.cafe52.net; 9.30 pm; closed Mon & Sun D; no Amex.

Cafe Boheme £ 38 Ⓣ

23 Windmill Brae AB11 6HU (01224) 210677

An *"authentic"* French restaurant, with a fish bias; it doesn't attract many survey reports, but such as there are say it's *"excellent"*. / **Sample dishes:** snails sauted in garlic butter served with roast butternut squash, goat cheese & rosemary risotto.; fillet steak with a blue cheese crust, sauted mushrooms & rich port sauce; orange curd crème brûlée with saffron poached pear. **Details:** www.cafebohemerestaurant.co.uk; 9 pm; closed Mon & Sun; no Amex.

Cinnamon £ 29 ⭐

476 Union St AB10 1TS (01224) 633328

"At last, an excellent Indian restaurant in Aberdeen", where the *"imaginative"* – *"with a twist"* – cuisine is praised by all who comment on it. / **Sample dishes:** ginger & cinnamon tiger prawns; fillet of chicken stuffed with pepper, soft cheese, ground spices, mixed vegetables & mincemeat sauce. **Details:** www.cinnamon-aberdeen.com; midnight.

Foyer
Trinity Church £ 38 ⭐

82a Crown Street AB11 6ET (01224) 582277

"The art exhibitions are always worth a look", if you visit this bright, *"modern"* fixture (run by a local youth homelessness charity); local reporters are full of praise for its *"lovely"* feel, *"wide range of good dishes"*, and *"uncomplicated"* style. / **Sample dishes:** char-grilled quail, sautéed jerusalem artichoke, black pudding, & crisp bacon salad; roast chump of lamb, pan-fried lamb kidneys, minted pear relish & dauphine potatoes; cinnamon spiced apple & black cherry strudel, mascarpone & red wine ice cream. **Details:** www.foyerrestaurant.com; 10 pm; closed Mon & Sun; no Amex; children: 14+ after 8 pm.

Silver Darling   **£ 62**   Ⓐ ✪
Pocra Quay, North Pier AB11 5DQ   (01224) 576229
*Didier Dejean's cooking is typically "excellent and imaginative", at this
former lighthouse – a setting which "feels like it could be miles from
anywhere", and is "worth a visit by night simply to watch the ships
going by".* / **Sample dishes:** *crab cocktail; pickled seafood sashimi & oysters
with rice noodle salad, sokura cress, & wasabi & ginger dressing; Earl Grey
mousse.* **Details:** *www.silverdarlingrestaurant.co.uk; beside harbour master's
tower; 9.30 pm; closed Sat L & Sun.*

ABERDYFI, GWYNEDD   4–3C

Penhelig Arms   **£ 36**   ✪
LL35 0LT   (01654) 767215
*"Beautifully fresh fish" and a "wonderful, realistically-priced wine list"
are the gastronomic highlights at Robert & Sally Hughes's
"very pleasant and unpretentious" inn, which has a "gorgeous"
location, overlooking Cardigan Bay.* / **Sample dishes:** *dressed crab;
roast fillet of cod, pancetta & pepper salsa; orange lemon panna cotta.*
Details: *www.penheligarms.com; 9 pm; no Amex.* **Accommodation:** *16 rooms,
from £90.*

ABERFORD, WEST YORKSHIRE   5–1C

Swan Hotel   **£ 30**   Ⓣ
Great North Rd LS25 3AA   (0113) 281 3205
*A 16th-century inn, once again tipped for its "bigger-than-average"
portions; the menu is "amazingly varied" too.* / **Sample dishes:** *chicken
liver pâté; baked monkfish; home-made sticky toffee pudding.*
Details: *www.theswanaberford.co.uk; 9.30 pm; closed Mon & Tue, Wed-Sat
closed L; book only for restaurant.*

ABERGAVENNY, MONMOUTHSHIRE   2–1A

Angel Hotel   **£ 44**   Ⓣ
15 Cross St NP7 5EN   (01873) 857121
*"A stunningly-refurbished hotel in true Jane Austen style", tipped for
its dining room (which is "always good"); however, it's "best of all
when you can sit in the courtyard in summer".* / **Sample dishes:** *seared
mackerel fillet with warm potato salad & a sweet mustard dressing; cod baked
with a horseradish crust, with green cabbage & crushed potatoes; strawberry
pavlova.* **Details:** *www.angelhotelabergavenny.com; 10 pm.*
Accommodation: *29 rooms, from ££85.*

Clytha Arms   **£ 35**
NP7 9BW   (01873) 840206
*"Tasty and satisfying meals" figure in practically all accounts of this
"busy" – and much-garlanded – family-run pub-cum-restaurant.*
/ **Sample dishes:** *baked figs & goat's cheese salad; venison in rioja; iced Tequila
soufflé.* **Details:** *www.clytha-arms.com; on Old Abergavenny to Raglan Rd;
9.30 pm; closed Mon L & Sun D.* **Accommodation:** *4 rooms, from £80.*

The Hardwick   **£ 44**
Old Raglan Rd NP7 9AA   (01873) 854220
*This "bright" gastropub two-year-old has had a mixed reception from
reporters – most say it offers "very good pub food" in a
"sympathetically modernised" setting; a minority, however, finds the
cuisine "heavy", and the overall experience "over-hyped".*
/ **Sample dishes:** *Parma ham with crunchy polenta crouton salad; chicken,
ham & leek pie with triple cooked chips; crème brûlée.*
Details: *www.thehardwick.co.uk; 10 pm; closed Mon & Sun D.*

Drakes On The Pond   **£ 61**
Dorking Rd RH5 6SA   (01306) 731174
Even fans of this roadside venture concede that – given its "extremely good" cooking – it's "a pity about the uninspiring location and décor"; even the cooking, though, doesn't impress everyone.
*/ **Sample dishes:** scallop tarte Tatin; noisette of venison with fondant potatoes; treacle & almond tart with salt caramel ice cream.*
Details: *www.drakesonthepond.com; 9 pm; closed Mon, Sat L & Sun; no Amex; booking: max 6; children: 8+.*

Summer Isles   **£ 67**   Ⓐ★★
IV26 2YG   (01854) 622282

*"Year after year we go fearing it won't be as good, but somehow they keep refreshing the experience"; this "out-of-the-way" haven wins the highest praise for its "relaxing" style, and for "perfect" cooking that's "sophisticated but not elaborate". / **Sample dishes:** smoked haddock flan; roast rib of beef; cheese trolley. **Details:** www.summerisleshotel.co.uk; 25m N of Ullapool on A835; 8 pm; no Amex; children: 8+. **Accommodation:** 13 rooms, from £119.*

Moat House   **£ 47**
Lower Penkridge Rd ST17 0RJ   (01785) 712217
*"The best bet in a poorly-served area" – this canalside hotel dining room (nothing to do with the well-known chain) offers "ambitious" food realised to a "reliable" standard. / **Sample dishes:** ravioli of lobster; pan-fried monkfish; rhum baba. **Details:** www.moathouse.co.uk; 9.30 pm; no jeans. **Accommodation:** 41 rooms, from £120.*

Fleece   **£ 32**   Ⓐ
152-4 Main St LS29 0LY   (01943) 830491
*A "popular" pub, which "specialises in local Yorkshire seasonal fare" ("superb meat and potato pie", for instance) – reports are unanimous that it's a "well-priced" destination that "scores on all fronts". / **Sample dishes:** scallops with spinach & Gruyère; roast suckling pig with roast apples; rhubarb crème brûlée with shortbread. **Details:** 9.15pm; no Amex.*

Clenaghans £ 32

48 Soldierstown Rd BT67 0ES (02892) 652952

"An old Irish pub, with an open fire and a fiddler", tipped for the quality of its cuisine; you can eat in bar or restaurant (and there are "some exceptional rooms/apartments if the drive home is too much!"). / Details: www.clenaghans.com; 9.30 pm; D only, closed Mon & Sun. Accommodation: 5 rooms, from £85.

Aldeburgh Fish And Chips £ 13

226 High St IP16 4BZ (01728) 454685

"The best fish and chips money can buy, especially when eaten on the sea wall". / Details: 8 pm; serving times vary seasonally; no credit cards.

The Lighthouse £ 35

77 High St IP15 5AU (01728) 453377

A "bright" refurb has "improved the ambience" at Sara Fox & Peter Hill's "buzzy" bistro favourite – THE place locally – which "continues to pack 'em in" (even if it's perhaps a weeny bit "over-rated"). / Sample dishes: potted shrimp; roast cod on roast red pepper; lemon tart with double cream. Details: www.thelighthouserestaurant.co.uk; 10 pm; closed for 2 weeks in Jan & 1 week in Oct.

152 £ 38

152 High St IP15 5AX (01728) 454594

Most reports praise this "bright" and "sunny" fixture for its "consistently good" and "imaginative" cooking; there are a few doubters, however, for whom the whole performance is "frankly a bit average". / Sample dishes: coarse pork & bacon terrine; sliced duck breast with confit of lamb; layered lemon curd & coconut biscuit. Details: www.152aldeburgh.co.uk; late; closed Tue (& Mon in winter).

Regatta £ 32

171-173 High St IP15 5AN (01728) 452011

"Much improved" or "steadily sliding"? – a year that's seen a major refurb on this popular café-style fish restaurant has inspired contradictory reports; the middle view is that it offers "decent food, but can get too hectic". / Sample dishes: crayfish & cucumber salad; grilled sirloin steak; pavlova with blueberry ice cream. Details: www.regattaaldeburgh.com; 9.30 pm; closed Sun D Nov-Feb.

Wentworth Hotel £ 32

Wentworth Rd IP15 5BD (01728) 452312

A "lovely old-fashioned family-run hotel", tipped for its "wholesome" food ("including lots of fresh fish"). / Sample dishes: smoked salmon; new season rump of lamb; passion fruit cheesecake. Details: www.wentworth-aldeburgh.com; 9 pm. Accommodation: 35 rooms, from £140.

The Grosvenor Arms   £ 31

Chester Rd CH3 6HJ   (01244) 620228
This "attractive" inn, has an "extensive" menu (and "a good choice
of ales and wine"), and makes full use of its impressive building near
the gates to the Eaton Estate; "other pubs try to imitate the formula,
but none has managed its all-round balance". / **Sample dishes:** black
pudding & leek tart; braised shoulder of lamb; apple tart Tatin.
Details: www.brunningandprice.co.uk; 6m S of Chester on B5130; 10 pm;
children: 14+ at D.

Dilli   £ 34

60 Stamford New Rd WA14 1EE   (0161) 929 7484
Now thoroughly outpacing its cousins in the capital (Mela and
Chowki), this "top-notch" Altrincham curry house has become
a notably "popular" haunt; "in an area awash with restaurants,
it stands out for the quality and authenticity of its food".
/ **Sample dishes:** sautéed duck meat encased in crispy Indian pastry; stir-fried
tiger prawns. **Details:** www.dilli.co.uk; 11pm, 10 sun.

Man-Zen   £ 28

169 Ashley Rd WA15 9SD   (0161) 9281222
A rather "surprising" Altrincham find, this "efficient" operation dishes
up "really well thought-through" Chinese and Thai fare.
/ **Details:** www.manzenhale.co.uk.

Baraset Barn   £ 40

Pimlico Ln CV37 7RF   (01789) 295510

It has a "lovely" setting, and fans say this "spacious and stylish" barn-
conversion makes "a great location for an informal meal";
commentary generally is a little mixed, though, especially regarding
the "very variable" service. / **Sample dishes:** grilled asparagus; fillet steak;
crème brûlée. **Details:** www.barasetbarn.co.uk; 9.30 pm; closed Sun D; no Amex.

Amberley Castle   £ 66   Ⓐ
BN18 9LT   (01798) 831992
"A genuine castle, sympathetically restored" provides one of southern England's most fairytale dining experiences (though the dining room itself is less magical than the approach), and the food is "well up to London standards"; let's hope new owners Von Essen don't wreck the place! / **Sample dishes:** *white gazpacho & white grapes; sun-blushed tomato lasagne; chocolate fondant.* **Details:** *www.amberleycastle.co.uk; N of Arundel on B2139; 9 pm; jacket or tie required; booking: max 8; children: 12+.* **Accommodation:** *19 rooms, from £155.*

Drunken Duck   £ 45   Ⓐ
Barngates LA22 0NG   (01539) 436347
Over 30 years in the same ownership, this "amazing" inn-cum-microbrewery has gathered a huge fan club who laud its "superb" food; it can also seem "over-priced and over-rated", though, and some feel the bar "has more down-to-earth Lakeland cosiness" than the restaurant. / **Sample dishes:** *aged goat cheese with tomato watermelon; loin of spring lamb with crushed apple; vanilla brûlée with armagnac prunes & ginger florentine.* **Details:** *www.drunkenduckinn.co.uk; 3m from Ambleside, towards Hawkshead; 9 pm; booking: max 6.* **Accommodation:** *16 rooms, from £120.*

The Glass House   £ 34   Ⓐ
Rydal Rd LA22 9AN   (01539) 432137
This "lovely", "romantic" former mill split opinions this year; to fans, it's a "reliable" destination with "inventive" and "well-presented" food – to critics, "the rave reviews don't square with the disappointing experience". / **Sample dishes:** *Caesar salad with warm poached egg & maple-glazed cheddar; braised lamb; Bailey's bread & butter pudding with coffee reduction.* **Details:** *www.theglasshouserestaurant.co.uk; behind Little Bridge House; 9.30 pm, Sat 10 pm; no Amex; children: 5+ at D.*

Lucy's on a Plate   £ 34
Church St LA22 0BU   (01539) 431191
"Generous portions" of "proper grub" have made quite a name for this "relaxed" and popular "stand-by"; it gets "very crowded", though, and – for a few reporters this year – "did not live up to its reputation". / **Sample dishes:** *fishcakes; lamb rump steak; fruit scones.* **Details:** *www.lucysofambleside.co.uk; centre of Ambleside; 9 pm; no Amex.*

Rothay Manor   £ 51
Rothay Bridge LA22 0EH   (01539) 433605
A "cosy" and "comfortable" country house hotel, run by the same family for over 40 years (and a favourite spot for afternoon tea); fans say its food is "delicious", but overall ratings are more middle-of-the-road. / **Sample dishes:** *smoked halibut, salmon & prawn terrine; medallions of prime beef fillets; chocolate truffle torte with white & dark chocolate sauces.* **Details:** *www.rothaymanor.co.uk; 9 pm; no jeans or trainers; no booking, Sat D; children: 7+ at D.* **Accommodation:** *19 rooms, from £140.*

Sheila's Cottage   **£ 38**
The Slack LA22 9DQ   (01539) 433079
*It has a "beautiful setting", and fans find this tea shop-cum-restaurant
a "top-quality" destination; for doubters, though, the fare can appear
"unimaginative".* / **Sample dishes:** *lamb chop; salmon; sticky toffee pudding.*
Details: *www.amblesideonline.co.uk; next to Queen's Hotel; 9 pm, Sat 9.30 pm;
closed Tue D & Wed D in winter; no Amex; children: 8+ after 6 pm.*

Zeffirelli's   **£ 28**
Compston Rd LA22 9AD   (01539) 433845
*A "reliable" destination – appealing to everyone from "families,
to walkers, to people dressed up for a night out" – that combines
cinema, jazz bar, restaurant and café; the latter two serve
"wholesome" veggie fare, and "happen to do great pizza".*
/ **Sample dishes:** *goat's cheese & chive soufflé; spinach & ricotta ravioli; tiramisu.*
Details: *www.zeffirellis.com; 10 pm; no Amex.*

AMERSHAM, BUCKINGHAMSHIRE   3–2A

Artichoke   **£ 60**
9 Market Sq HP7 0DF   (01494) 726611
*"A stylish contemporary restaurant in a 16th-century building", where
Laurie Gear's cooking displays "inventiveness and execution at a very
high level"; in spite of its high prices and its rather "small" portions,
it is certainly "well patronised", so they must be doing something
right!* / **Sample dishes:** *breast of quail & ravioli of confit of quail; chicken
steamed en papillote; ravioli of coconut tapioca with exotic fruit sabiyon.*
Details: *www.theartichokerestaurant.co.uk; 10 pm; closed Mon & Sun; no Amex.*

Famous Fish   **£ 39**
11 Market Sq HP7 0DF   (01494) 728665
*"First-class ingredients" are "not mucked about with" at this "down-
to-earth" South African spot, where "an excellent variety of fish"
is the menu highlight.* / **Sample dishes:** *salad; calamari; Malvern pudding.*
Details: *in Old Amersham; 10 pm; closed Sun; no Amex.*

Gilbey's   **£ 39**
1 Market Sq HP7 0DF   (01494) 727242
*"Cosy", "cramped" and perennially "crowded" – this long-established
local stalwart pleases most reporters with its "consistent"
performance; "interesting" and "inexpensive" wines are a particular
draw.* / **Sample dishes:** *pickled squid & crayfish; breast of wood pigeon &
Bayonne ham; lemon tart.* **Details:** *www.gilbeygroup.com; in Old Amersham;
9.30 pm.*

AN AIRD, HIGHLAND   9–3B

Crannog   **£ 41**
at the Waterfront, The Underwater Centre PH33 6DB
(01397) 705589
*"Fantastic fresh fish, nothing pretentious just excellent" – this well-
established restaurant on the pier is tipped as a "real find".*
/ **Sample dishes:** *home-smoked salmon; langoustines with scallops & butter;
sticky date, fig & cinnamon pudding.* **Details:** *www.crannog.net; 9.30 pm;
no Amex.*

ANSTRUTHER, FIFE 9–4D

Anstruther Fish Bar £19 ⭐⭐
42-44 Shore St KY10 3AQ (01333) 310518
"Fantastically fresh fish, with lovely light and crispy batter" plus
"properly hand-cut chips" win only rave reviews for this famous
"Formica-tables" chippy – eat them *"sitting on benches, overlooking
the harbour"*, and expect to queue. / **Sample dishes:** *prawn cocktail;
crayfish & hot smoked salmon salad; ice cream.*
Details: *www.anstrutherfishbar.co.uk; 10 pm; no Amex.*

The Cellar £52 Ⓐ⭐⭐
24 East Grn KY10 3AA (01333) 310378
"The menu doesn't change much, but why fix it if it ain't broke?" –
you won't find better fish than at Peter & Susan Jukes's *"superlative"*
restaurant of 25 years' standing, which is charmingly located in a
candlelit, barrel-vaulted building near the harbour.
/ **Sample dishes:** *seared diver-caught scallops; grilled halibut with smoked bacon;
terrine of layered chocolate.* **Details:** *in the harbour area; 9.30 pm; closed
Mon L & Tue L.*

APPLECROSS, WESTER ROSS 9–2B

Applecross Inn £31 Ⓐ⭐
Shore St IV54 8LT (01520) 744262
"Fish as fresh as it gets, and simply served" is the draw to this
extremely remote inn... well, if you ignore *"one of the most beautiful
settings in the world"*, that is. / **Sample dishes:** *oysters; scallops; fruit
crumble with custard.* **Details:** *www.applecross.uk.com; off A896, S of Shieldaig;
9 pm; no Amex; need 4+ to book.* **Accommodation:** *7 rooms, from £70.*

APPLETHWAITE, CUMBRIA 7–3C

Underscar Manor £60 ⭐
CA12 4PH (01768) 775000
Fans find *"exceptional"* culinary standards – *"up to the best in France
or England"* – at this *"lovely old hotel"* (which is *"great for comfort
and lake-views"*); times move on, though, and the approach can seem
"a tad dated and chintzy". / **Sample dishes:** *goat's cheese soufflé; medley
of fish; small sweet tasting.* **Details:** *www.underscarmanor.co.uk; on A66, 17m W
of M6, J40; 8.30 pm; jacket required at D; children: 12+.* **Accommodation:** *11
rooms, from £180.*

ARLINGHAM, GLOUCESTERSHIRE 2–2B

The Old Passage Inn £45 ⭐⭐
Passage Rd GL2 7JR (01452) 740547
"Great for a seafood treat!"; this *"old-favourite fish restaurant"* –
"picturesquely" located, *"on a bend of the Severn"* – is consistently
praised for its *"exceptional"* fish. / **Sample dishes:** *scallops; char-grilled
fillets of John Dory; crème brûlée & strawberries.*
Details: *www.fishattheoldpassageinn.co.uk; 9 pm; closed Mon & Sun D; no Amex.*
Accommodation: *3 rooms, from £95.*

ARMSCOTE, WARWICKSHIRE　　　2–1C

Fox & Goose　　　**£ 45**　　　🅣

CV37 8DD　(01608) 682293

*"A nice place to stay if you're going to Stratford" – a modernised country inn where the food is usually "good". / **Sample dishes:** prawn & salmon cake with herb tartar; beef sirloin; trio of mini crumbles with crème anglaise. **Details:** www.foxandgoose.co.uk; 10m S of Stratford-upon-Avon on the A4300; 9.30 pm; no Amex; booking: max 10. **Accommodation:** 4 rooms, from £85.*

ARUNDEL, WEST SUSSEX　　　3–4A

Arundel House　　　**£ 45**　　　🅐

11 High St BN18 9AD　(01903) 882136

*On most accounts, this "pleasant" restaurant-with-rooms, in the shadow of the castle, is a "relaxed" place to eat (as well as a "good place to stay"); on balance, though, reporters judge the food as "decent" rather than exciting. / **Sample dishes:** scallops with sweet chilli jam; confit belly of pork with potatoes, cream, spring onions & roasted baby carrots; elderflower crème brûlée with warm citrus muddlings.*
Details: *www.arundelhouseonline.co.uk; 9 pm; closed Mon L & Sun; children: 14+ D. **Accommodation:** 5 rooms, from £80.*

ASCOT, BERKSHIRE　　　3–3A

Ascot Oriental　　　**£ 32**　　　⭐

London Rd SL5 0PU　(01344) 621877

*"Unusual and well-cooked oriental dishes" – in a "very light Chinese/Thai" style – continue to please fans of this well-run, slightly Spartan fixture. / **Sample dishes:** prawn tempura; tenderloin of beef in teriyaki sauce; banana fritter. **Details:** www.ascotoriental.com; 2m E of Ascot on A329; 10.30 pm.*

The Thatched Tavern　　　**£ 41**　　　🅣

Cheapside Rd SL5 7QG　(01344) 620874

*It's "a good reliable gastropub" (of a fairly traditional kind), but this self-explanatory outfit attracts fewer reports than its convenient location might lead one to expect. / **Sample dishes:** open ravioli with crayfish & scallops; fillet steak; sticky toffee pudding.*
Details: *www.thethatchedtavern.co.uk; 2m from Ascot, signed to Cheapside village; 9.30 pm, Sat 10 pm.*

ASENBY, NORTH YORKSHIRE　　　8–4C

Crab & Lobster　　　**£ 48**　　　🅐⭐

Dishforth Rd YO7 3QL　(01845) 577286

*This "beautiful" and "eccentric" rural pub has won fame with a "unique" combination of "terrific" seafood, plus a "quirky" interior (which is "stuffed with an eclectic collection of miscellania"). / **Sample dishes:** goat's cheese soufflé; lobster thermidor; assiette of desserts. **Details:** www.crabandlobster.co.uk; at junction of Asenby Rd & Topcliffe Rd; 9 pm. **Accommodation:** 14 rooms, from £150.*

ASHBOURNE, DERBYSHIRE 5–3C

Dining Room £ 50

33 St. John's St DE6 1GP (01335) 300666

"Excellent attention to detail" commends this "small", ambitious and "unusual" restaurant to most reporters; it's "pricey", though, and doubters find it "too experimental", and "overpriced".
/ **Sample dishes:** home-smoked organic salmon; beef & beetroot tart; poached Wakefield rhubarb with rhubarb curd cheese ice cream.
Details: www.thediningroomashbourne.co.uk; closed Mon & Sun; no Amex; children: 12+.

ASHBURTON, DEVON 1–3D

Agaric £ 47

30 North St TQ13 7QD (01364) 654478

A "surprisingly informal", "friendly" and "unassuming" establishment (which comes complete with accommodation, and a cookery school); it's "not cheap" and can seem "pretentious", but most reporters feel that "excellent local produce" is used to good effect.
/ **Sample dishes:** hot & sour crab soup; roast tenderloin of pork with black pudding; iced honey praline with nougatine. **Details:** www.agaricrestaurant.co.uk; 9 pm; closed Mon & Tue, Sat L & Sun D; no Amex. **Accommodation:** 4 rooms, from £50.

ASKRIGG, NORTH YORKSHIRE 8–4B

Rowan Tree £ 38   Ⓣ

Market Pl DL8 3HT (01969) 650536

Under new chef/patron Patrick Crawley, this intimate restaurant is still tipped for its "great food and wine". / **Sample dishes:** Swaledale goat's cheese soufflé; rack of lamb wih minted lamb & port wine jus; tangy lemon & lime tart with crème fraîche. **Details:** 4m from Aysgarth falls; 9 pm; D only Wed-Sat, closed Mon & Tue, Sun for private parties only; no Amex; children: 12+.

AUCHTERARDER, PERTH & KINROSS 9–3C

Andrew Fairlie   Ⓐ ✪ ✪
Gleneagles Hotel £ 87

PH3 1NF (01764) 694267

"The most amazing food, in the most amazing setting"; the dark and masculine fine dining room of this famous hotel "goes from strength to strength" – thanks to Andrew Fairlie's "truly great" cooking and the "faultless" service, it's "guaranteed to impress".
/ **Sample dishes:** home-smoked lobster; roast squab with black truffle gnocchi; gingerbread soufflé & roast pear. **Details:** www.gleneagles.com; 10 pm; L only, closed Sun; booking essential; children: 12+. **Accommodation:** 273 rooms, from £320.

Hartwell House   £ 59   Ⓐ⭐

Oxford Rd HP17 8NR (01296) 747444

"Grand" and "exquisitely decorated" – this Jacobean country house has obvious advantages as a "romantic" destination, and its "well-presented" cuisine rarely diminishes the experience; "for a long summer lunch followed by a stroll in the grounds", it's particularly "hard to beat". / **Sample dishes:** *crab, langoustine & dill ravioli; noisettes of lamb; chocolate fondant with griottine cherry tart.*
Details: *www.hartwell-house.com; 2m W of Aylesbury on A418; 9.45 pm; no jeans or trainers; children: 6+.* **Accommodation:** *49 rooms, from £280.*

Mela   £ 25   Ⓣ

103 London Rd HP22 5LD (01296) 630110

An unpretentious curry house with a keen local following, thanks not least to its "lovely" staff. / **Sample dishes:** *lightly-spiced Bengal tiger fish; chicken jalfrezi; coffee & caramel dessert.* **Details:** *11 pm; D only.*

Babington House   £ 52   Ⓐ

BA11 3RW (01373) 812266

For lunching or dining, the country house outpost of the Soho House empire is open only to those staying the night (and, of course, to members); it undoubtedly has a "relaxed" and "beautiful" setting, but otherwise reports are mixed. / **Sample dishes:** *crab bruschetta with fennel, tomato, & radiccio; slow roast pork belly with greens, carrots, cider & apple sauce; apricot & almond tarte.* **Details:** *www.babingtonhouse.co.uk; 11 pm; open to residents & members only for L & D all week; booking essential.*
Accommodation: *28 rooms, from £225.*

Hassop Hall   £ 46   Ⓐ

DE45 1NS (01629) 640488

Its "a culinary time warp", but this "grand" and "delightful" old place benefits from "the personal touch" of owners, the Chapman family, and offers an overall experience that's a lot more "jolly" than some of its more ambitious peers. / **Sample dishes:** *smoked chicken & avocado salad; rack of lamb; crème brûlée with stem ginger shortbread.*
Details: *www.hassophall.co.uk; 9 pm; closed Mon L & Sun D.*
Accommodation: *13 rooms, from £95.*

The Monsal Head Hotel   £ 29   Ⓐ⭐

DE45 1NL (01629) 640250

"A delightful outside space and stunning view" are highlights at his "lovely" hotel "at the head of Monsal Dale"; the bar and restaurant share the same menu of "excellent and reliable" pub dishes, realised "with flair". / **Sample dishes:** *chicken liver pâté with port & Madeira; chicken breast with stilton, wrapped in smoked bacon; sticky toffee pudding with butterscotch sauce.* **Details:** *www.monsalhead.com; just outside the town; 9.30 pm; closed Mon-Wed in Winter; no Amex.* **Accommodation:** *7 rooms, from £70.*

BALLATER, ABERDEEN 9–3C

Darroch Learg £ 58 Ⓐ⭐
Braemar Rd AB35 5UX (01339) 755443
"Consistently superb food" and an *"unstuffy attitude"* win consistent
approval for the Franks family's *"quirky"* country house hotel,
overlooking the Dee; the patron *"knows his wines"* too.
/ **Sample dishes:** *ravioli of smoked haddock; roast beef; pear frangipane tart.*
Details: *www.darrochlearg.co.uk; 9 pm; D only, ex Sun open L &
D.* **Accommodation:** *17 rooms, from £130.*

Green Inn £ 51 ⭐
9 Victoria Rd AB35 5QQ (01339) 755701
A *"genteel"* restaurant-with-rooms which dishes up some *"creative"*
food – part of *"all-in-all, a civilised and pleasing dining experience"*.
/ **Sample dishes:** *Scottish smoked haddock soufflé; roast partridge; rhubarb &
ginger soufflé with licorice anglaise.* **Details:** *www.green-inn.com; in centre
of village, on the green; 9 pm; D only, closed Mon & Sun; no Amex; no shorts.*
Accommodation: *3 rooms, from £60.*

BALQUHIDDER, PERTHSHIRE 9–3C

Monachyle Mhor £ 50 Ⓐ⭐⭐
FK19 8PQ (01877) 384622

"A very beautiful small hotel off the beaten track", where chef/patron
Tom Lewis's *"unfailingly exciting"* food is served *"in the
most atmospheric surroundings, looking out over a beautiful loch"*.
/ **Sample dishes:** *seared foie gras, white asparagus & poached quail egg; fillet
of beef with braised oxtail; poached pear with walnut crust.*
Details: *www.monachylemhor.com; 8.45 pm; no Amex; children: 12+ at D.*
Accommodation: *14 rooms, from £95.*

BANBURY, OXFORDSHIRE 2–1D

Thai Orchid £ 29 Ⓐ⭐
56 Northbar St OX16 0TL (01295) 270833
*"In the improving Banbury restaurant scene, the Orchid sets the
pace"* – *"OTT"* décor adds to the atmosphere at this well-established
Thai restaurant, where the food is usually of *"high quality"*.
/ **Sample dishes:** *beef satay; chicken curry; chocolate crunchy bar.*
Details: *www.thaiorchidbanbury.co.uk; 10.30 pm.*

BANCHORY, ABERDEENSHIRE 9–3D

The Milton £ 39
AB31 5QH (01330) 844566
"A nice restaurant with exposed beams, in a little enclave near the opening to Crathes Castle on the road to Banchory"; "the menu is limited, but what there is is very good". | Sample dishes: salad of panfried scallops wrapped in Parma ham with saffron & wasabi hollandaise; roast venison with braised red cabbage; pear, almond & armagnac frangipane tart with basil ice cream. Details: www.themilton.co.uk; 9.30 pm, 6.30 pm Sun.

BARNET, HERTFORDSHIRE 3–2B

Dylan's Restaurant £ 35
21-22 Station Pde EN4 0DW (020) 8275 1551
For fans, you get "West End dining, albeit at West End prices" at this "good out-of-town restaurant" (run by refugees from a trendy boutique-hotel in the capital); despite continuing reports of "accomplished" cuisine, though, there were also accounts of some "very disappointing" meals this year. | Details: www.dylansrestaurant.com; 10 pm; closed Mon.

Emchai £ 24
78 High St EN5 5SN (020) 8364 9993
This "minimalist" Chinese/Malaysian is a rather "unusual" find in these parts; it wins all-round praise, though, for its "excellent food, attentive staff and modern surroundings". | Details: 11 pm.

BARNSLEY, GLOUCESTERSHIRE 2–2C

Barnsley House £ 62
GL7 5EE (01285) 740000
Reports on this "trendy" boutique-hotel remain very up-and-down; both food and setting are touted as "exceptional" by fans, but the experience can also seem "very overpriced", and service can be downright "rude". | Sample dishes: bresaola; vincisgrassi; rasberry & mascarpone brûlée. Details: www.barnsleyhouse.com; 9.30 pm, Sat 10 pm; no Amex; children: 12+ at D. Accommodation: 10 rooms, from £270.

BARTON UPON HUMBER, N LINCS 6–2A

Elio's £ 40
11 Market Pl DN18 5DA (01652) 635147
A marketplace Italian tipped for its "excellent fresh seafood". | Sample dishes: fish soup; fillet steak; panna cotta with fruit coulis. Details: A15 towards Humber Bridge, first exit into Barton upon Humber; 10 pm; D only, closed Sun. Accommodation: 5 rooms, from £85.

Pebble Beach   £ 47

Marine Drive BH25 7DZ   (01425) 627777

"Overlooking the sea and the Isle of Wight", this clifftop venture
is "a wonderful place to be on a sunny day"; it's Pierre Chevillard's
"outstanding" fishy fare, though, that makes this a "seafood jewel".
/ *Sample dishes:* buffalo Mozzarella & tomato terrine; fillet of sea bass;
raspberry bavarois. *Details:* www.pebblebeach-uk.com; 9.30 pm; booking
essential. *Accommodation:* 3 rooms, from £80.

Little Barwick House   £ 50

BA22 9TD   (01935) 423902

It's the "London restaurant-quality" food which makes this small
country house hotel – "in a village outside an not-especially-
fashionable Somerset town" – particularly worth knowing about.
/ *Sample dishes:* pan-fried scallops; medallions of beef; iced banana parfait with
rum caramel sauce. *Details:* www.littlebarwick.co.uk; 9 Tue-Fri, 9.30 Sat; closed
Mon, Tue L & Sun D; no Amex; children: 5+. *Accommodation:* 6 rooms,
from £100.

Cavendish   £ 51

Church Ln DE45 1SP   (01246) 582311

"Beautiful views of the Chatsworth estate" are just one draw to this
"well-run" establishment, which makes a great "special-occasion"
destination; for top value, seek out the no-bookings conservatory.
/ *Sample dishes:* pan-seared scallops; pan-roast duck breast; tart of Ricotta,
chocolate & orange. *Details:* www.cavendish-hotel.net; 10 pm.
Accommodation: 24 rooms, from £149.

Fischers at Baslow Hall   £ 85

Calver Rd DE45 1RR   (01246) 583259

For a "traditional" country house experience ("slightly formal" and
"quiet") plus "inventive" cooking, it's hard to beat Max & Susan
Fischer's "elegant" and "delightfully-located" hotel.
/ *Sample dishes:* quail salad; roast rabbit; chocolate fondant.
Details: www.fischers-baslowhall.co.uk; 9.30 pm; closed Mon L & Sun D; no jeans
or trainers; children: 12+ at D. *Accommodation:* 11 rooms, from £140.

Rowley's　　　　　　　　　　**£ 41** ⭐

Church Ln DE45 1RY　(01246) 583880

*Co-owned by Max Fischer (of Baslow Hall) and his head chef,
this "converted pub" offers "a high standard of cooking in an informal
atmosphere"; its popularity is such, though, that it can be "noisy".*
/ ***Sample dishes:*** *salmon & haddock fishcakes with soft poached egg,
pea purée & Hollandaise sauce; five-spiced chump of lamb, saffron crushed
potatoes, mangetout, tomato & corinader sauce; twice-roasted tomato & goats
cheese tart with rocket salad.* ***Details:*** *www.rowleysrestaurant.co.uk; 9 pm, 10 pm
Sat; closed Sun D; no Amex.*

BASSENTHWAITE LAKE, CUMBRIA　　　　7–3C

Pheasant Hotel　　　　　　　　**£ 43** Ⓐ

CA13 9YE　(01768) 776234

*Especially if you're looking for a "first-class breakfast", this ancient
coaching inn makes a notably "pleasant" destination for today's
traveller; otherwise, this year's reports on the cuisine have been
notably variable.* / ***Sample dishes:*** *chicken liver & brandy pâté; roast rack
of lamb; hot sticky toffee pudding with sticky sauce & vanilla ice cream.*
Details: *www.the-pheasant.co.uk; 8.30 pm; no Amex; no jeans or trainers;
children: 12+ at D.* ***Accommodation:*** *15 rooms, from £130.*

BATH, BATH & NE SOMERSET　　　　2–2B

It tells you rather too much about Bath that the
establishment that attracts most commentary from reporters
is part of a chain (*Fishworks*), albeit rather a superior one.
There is also one grand hotel of note (*Bath Priory*),
but otherwise the general picture of Bath dining is of
expensive mediocrity. A couple of relatively informal places
to eat – *Hudson Bar & Grill* and the *King William* – are both
of relatively recent vintage, and perhaps offer some sort
of light on the horizon.

Bath Priory Hotel　　　　　　**£ 74** ⭐⭐

Weston Rd BA1 2XT　(01225) 331922

*This "restful" luxury hotel – set in "beautiful" gardens "just a short
distance from the city-centre" – inspires nothing but rave reviews;
Chris Horridge's "interesting" food is "top-notch", as is the "formal yet
informal" service.* / ***Sample dishes:*** *foie gras; lamb; sugared almond leaves
with chocolate, peanut milk & camomile sorbet.*
Details: *www.thebathpriory.co.uk; 1m W of city centre, past Victoria Park;
9.30 pm; no jeans or trainers.* ***Accommodation:*** *26 rooms, from £245.*

Blackstones Restaurant　　　　　**£ 38**

2-3 Queen St BA1 1HE　(01225) 444403

*Fans find this family-run newcomer a "great addition to Bath's poor
selection of top-notch restaurants", and praise it for its use of "fresh,
seasonal ingredients"; critics, though, fear it "started well" but has
become "hyped" and "overpriced"; NB A relaunch with a change
of format is in progress as this guide goes to press.*
/ ***Sample dishes:*** *grilled local fennel; heavenly brownies with raspberries & vanilla
ice cream.* ***Details:*** *www.blackstonefood.co.uk; 6 pm; closed Sun.*

Demuths £ 38

2 North Parade Pas BA1 1NX (01225) 446059

It's "expensive", but "the best veggie in Bath" is a "popular" place, serving food that "is often excellent" (if sometimes a bit "fussy"); it's "more fun on the ground floor". / *Sample dishes:* asparagus & wild garlic tartlet; beetroot & blue cheese soufflé; rhubarb & ginger cheesecake. *Details:* www.demuths.co.uk; 10 pm; no Amex; booking: max 4 at D, Fri & Sat; children: 6+ at D.

The Eastern Eye £ 32

8a Quiet St BA1 2JS (01225) 422323

"Spectacular surroundings" – a Georgian room of some grandeur – make a visit to this city-centre Thai a "must-do", for some reporters; perhaps for that very reason, there is the odd fear that its performance smacks of "mass-catering". / *Sample dishes:* dhaka chicken roll; Bengali king prawn masala; kulfi. *Details:* www.easterneye.co.uk; 11.30 pm; children: after 8 pm Fri & Sat.

Firehouse Rotisserie £ 35

2 John St BA1 2JL (01225) 482070

"Unusual pizzas" and a "buzzy atmosphere" usually make this handily-located spot a "fun and simple place to eat", even if it's not inexpensive. / *Sample dishes:* Chinese chicken salad; Louisiana catfish & shrimp cakes; double chocolate brownie & coconut ice cream. *Details:* www.firehouserotisserie.co.uk; 11 pm; closed Sun.

FishWorks £ 45

6 Green St BA1 2JY (01225) 448707

"Delicous, if a little overpriced" – the original branch of the fishmonger-cum-bistro chain often offers "fantastic" fish, although reports suggest it's not 100% consistent. / *Sample dishes:* spaghetti with langoustines; sea bream baked with herbs & reisling; lemon tart. *Details:* www.fishworks.co.uk; 10.30 pm; closed Mon & Sun.

Hole in the Wall £ 36

16 George St BA1 2EN (01225) 425242

Few restaurants have the heritage of this potentially "cosy" cellar-hideaway (one of England's seminal restaurants, post WWII); it continues to attract limited and very mixed feedback – the occasional reporter says it's "superb", but too many feel it's "very disappointing at the price". / *Sample dishes:* confit of Gressingham duck leg; pan-fried fillet of beef with morel sauce; coffee & chocolate bavarois with crème anglaise. *Details:* www.theholeinthewall.co.uk; 10 pm; closed Sun L.

The Hop Pole £ 38

7 Albion Buildings, Upper Bristol Rd BA1 3AR (01225) 446327

Opposite Victoria Park, a "gorgeous old pub" tipped for its "tasty and imaginative" food. / *Sample dishes:* char-grilled Gressingham duck; herb-crusted breast of guinea fowl; bread & butter pudding. *Details:* www.bathales.co.uk; opp Victoria Park; 9 pm, 9.30 pm Fri & Sat; closed Sun D.

The Hudson Bar & Grill £ 48

14 London St BA1 5BU (01225) 332323

"A former pub, that's now a trendy bar downstairs and a very nice restaurant upstairs"; all agree that the latter – a "stylish" place, with "excellent steak, pleasant service and nice wines", offers "a satisfying evening out". / *Sample dishes:* tempura tiger prawns with spicy pozzu dip; seared yellow fin tuna with ginger, garlic, coriander, lime & soy; chocolate fondue. *Details:* www.hudsonbars.co.uk; 10.30 pm; D only, closed Sun.

King William £ 35

36 London Rd BA1 5NN (01225) 428096

"Just wonderful English cooking in a proper pub" – this revamped boozer is given a solid thumbs-up by reporters, even if the food is best when they *"keep it simple"*.

Loch Fyne £ 40

24 Milsom St BA1 1DG (01225) 750120

One of the better outlets of the national chain – a "large" space, that's a "dependable" destination for fish and seafood.
/ **Sample dishes:** herring fillets; scallops; crème brûlée.
Details: www.lochfyne.com; 9.45 pm, Fri & Sat10.45 . **Accommodation:** 9 rooms, from £85.

Mai Thai £ 29

6 Pierrepont St BA2 4AA (01225) 445557

"Among Bath's many Thai restaurants", this rather cramped establishment is a reporter favourite. / **Sample dishes:** mixed starter; green curry; lemon sorbet. **Details:** www.maithai.co.uk; 10.30 pm, Fri & Sat 10.45 pm.

Moon & Sixpence £ 40

6a Broad St BA1 5LJ (01225) 460962

This potentially "lovely", tucked-away bistro has been "variable" in recent times; for much of 2007 it's been closed for a major refurbishment – let's hope for a return to form on re-opening.
/ **Sample dishes:** seared scallops with dry vermouth & cream sauce; fillet of tuna on bed of couscous; sticky toffee pudding with Cornish clotted cream.
Details: www.themoonandsixpence.co.uk; 10.30 pm.

No 5 Bistro £ 42

5 Argyle St BA2 4BA (01225) 444499

"Well-located" by the Pulteney Bridge, this *"friendly"* Gallic bistro is, as ever, supported by a loyal fan club; a more critical view is that *"there's nothing wrong with it, but nor is it special"*.
/ **Sample dishes:** tiger prawn tempura; pan-fried sea bass with sautéed famfire, fennel & cream sauce; vanilla crème brûlée. **Details:** 10 pm, Fri 10.30 pm, Sat 11 pm.

The Olive Tree
Queensberry Hotel £ 50

Russell St BA1 2QF (01225) 447928

Fans say this "nicely-furnished" basement is a "wonderful" "reliable" and "discreet" choice; to more sceptical reporters, though, it's merely "pleasant enough". / **Sample dishes:** marinated poussin & Caesar salad; rib-eye steak; chocolate & pistachio fondue. **Details:** www.thequeensberry.co.uk; 9.45 pm; closed Mon L. **Accommodation:** 29 rooms, from £110.

Pump Rooms £ 39

The Pump Room, Stall St BA1 1LZ (01225) 444477

"The architecture and the orchestra" at this wonderful Georgian room make an *"extravagant tea"* or *"light meal"* an absolute must for any first-time visitor to Bath; *"once is enough"*, though.
/ **Sample dishes:** crab & spinach cake; chocolate éclairs, mini hazelnut meringues. **Details:** www.searcys.co.uk; by the Abbey; L only, open until 10 pm in July & Aug; no booking, Sat & Sun.

BATTLE, EAST SUSSEX 3–4C

The Pilgrims £ 35

1 High St TN33 0AE (01424) 772314

*Intriguingly housed in part of Battle Abbey – an establishment particularly tipped for its "romantic" possibilities. / **Sample dishes:** game terrine with apple chutney; pan-fried breasts of pigeon with bubble & squeak & balsamic reduction; sticky date & nut pudding with butterscotch sauce. **Details:** www.pilgrims-battle.co.uk; 9 pm; closed Sun D; no Amex.*

BAUGHURST, HAMPSHIRE 2–3D

Wellington Arms £ 44

Baughurst Rd RG26 5LP (0118) 9820110

*"A small village pub" that was "tastefully converted" a couple of years ago, and is tipped for its "delightful" and "different" cuisine. / **Sample dishes:** char-grilled king scallops wrapped in pancetta on sautéed samphire with brown butter; spring lamb & mint pot pie, braised with real ale, shallots, celery & young carrots; steamed lemon sponge topped with apples & our honey, with custard. **Details:** www.thewellingtonarms.com; 9.30 pm; closed Mon, Tue L & Sun D; no Amex.*

BAWTRY, SOUTH YORKSHIRE 5–2D

China Rose £ 32

16 South Pde DN10 6JH (01302) 710461

*"Large and somewhat anonymous" – this Chinese fixture is, nevertheless, "the best place to eat round Doncaster", and particularly good "in a group". / **Sample dishes:** crispy aromatic duck; Cantonese fillet steak; Alaska surprise. **Details:** www.chinarose-bawtry.co.uk; 10 pm; D only; no jeans or trainers.*

BEACONSFIELD, BUCKINGHAMSHIRE 3–3A

The Spice Merchant £ 43

33 London End HP9 2HW (01494) 675474

*"The best Indian in 20 miles" – this "posh" place, with a conservatory, is praised by almost all reporters for its "extensive" menu, realised to "a consistently high standard". / **Sample dishes:** leg of lamb slow roasted with royal cumin garam masala; fresh monkfish with fenugreek leaf & turmeric. **Details:** www.spicemerchantgroup.net; 11 pm.*

BEARSTED, KENT 3–3C

Soufflé £ 42

31 The Green ME14 4DN (01622) 737065

*One of the few mid-Kent destinations of any possible note; it's a "relaxed" and "charming" sort of place – especially if you get a table in the main room, overlooking the Green – but can be "variable". / **Sample dishes:** pan-fried scallops & black pudding; prime fillet of beef; pistachio soufflé. **Details:** www.soufflerestaurant.net; off M20; 9.30 pm; closed Mon, Sat L & Sun D.*

BEAUMARIS, ISLE OF ANGLESEY 4–1C

The Loft Restaurant
Ye Olde Bull's Head £ 50
Castle St LL58 8AP (01248) 810329
This ancient coaching inn has a bright, modern, brasserie extension, and a posher 'Loft' restaurant; both win high praise for their "sheer friendliness" and "London standards at local prices". / *Sample dishes: seared scallops & pickled vegetables; fillet of beef; vanilla crème brûlée & peach Melba ice cream.* **Details:** *www.bullsheadinn.co.uk; 9.30 pm; D only, closed Sun; no jeans; children: 7+ at D.* **Accommodation:** *13 rooms, from £100.*

BECKENHAM, KENT 3–3B

Mello £ 43
2 Southend Rd BR3 1SD (020) 8663 0994
A "bustling" and "good-looking" five-year-old, which can seem like an "amazing" find out in the 'burbs; while fans praise its "good standard of cooking", however, it can also seem "a bit pricey" for what it is, and service is "inconsistent". / *Sample dishes: duck with raspberry & walnut salad; wild Scottish salmon fillet; custard tart with gooseberry.* **Details:** *www.mello.uk.com; 10 pm; closed Sun D.*

BELFAST, COUNTY ANTRIM 10–1D

We hear that Belfast is on the up, but the number of places in town that reporters identify as of any particular interest remains limited. Towards the top end of the market, *Ginger, James Street South* and *Roscoff Brasserie* are the only 'stand outs'. The ethnic scene is of relatively little interest.

Aldens £ 38
229 Upper Newtownards Rd BT4 3JF (028) 9065 0079
A change of chef seems to have unsettled Jonathan Davis's well-known venture (in a former supermarket) — sometimes touted as Belfast's top place; some reporters still hail the "exceptional" cuisine — others found it "poor". / *Sample dishes: seared scallops with pak choi noodles; fillet of cod with smoked salmon sauce; baked tamarillos with raspberry coulis.* **Details:** *www.aldensrestaurant.com; 2m from Stormont Buildings; 10 PM, Sat & Sun 11PM; closed Sat L & Sun.*

Cayenne £ 47
7 Ascot Hs, Shaftesbury Sq BT2 7DB (028) 9033 1532
It attracts fewer reports than we would like, but Paul Rankin's city-centre operation is praised for its "good, bistro atmosphere", and its sometimes "outstanding" food. / *Sample dishes: salt & chilli squid; honey-glazed breast of duck; apple & blackberry crumble with blackberry ripple ice cream.* **Details:** *www.cayennerestaurant.com; near Botanic Railway Station; 10.15 pm, Fri & Sat 11pm, Sun 8.45 pm; closed Sat L & Sun L.*

Deanes £ 51
34-40 Howard St BT1 6PF (028) 9056 0000
Michael Deane is a big name in the Province, but feedback on his ventures is typically limited and a bit middle-of-the road; this applies to both this glitzy brasserie (with fine dining room above), and to his latest (and "probably best") outlet, Deane at Queens — 36-40 College Gardens, tel 9038 2111. / *Sample dishes: duck liver, foie gras & armagnac parfait; pan-fried halibut; chocolate pudding with stout ice cream.* **Details:** *www.michaeldeane.co.uk; near Grand Opera House; 10pm mon-wed, 10.30 thur-sat; closed Sun.*

Ginger £ 40

7-8 Hope St BT12 5EE (0871) 426 7885

Simon McCance's revamped bistro is tipped by some for offering "probably the best food in Belfast"; even the less enthusiastic reporters hail it as a "good all-rounder", and the set lunch in particular is "a steal". / Sample dishes: fried spiced squid with sweet chilli dip & water melon & crisp carrot salad; creamy fennel & parmesan risotto with roast spiced sweet potatoes; lime & honey crème brulée with raspberry compote. Details: www.gingerbistro.com; 9.30 pm; no Amex.

James Street South £ 48

21 James Street South BT2 7GA (028) 9043 4310

"An excellent modern restaurant in all respects" — chef/patron Niall McKenna's city-centre venture continues to get an enthusiastic thumbs-up from its small but loyal fan club. / Sample dishes: sautéed scallops with confit red pepper; lamb cutlets with apricot & fig compote; coconut parfait with confit pineapple & vanilla shortbread. Details: www.jamesstreetsouth.co.uk; 10.30 pm; closed Sun L.

Nick's Warehouse £ 42

35 Hill St BT1 2LB (028) 9043 9690

"Consistently good over many years"; this early-wave city-centre wine bar (in an area that's become "very trendy" nowadays) remains an exceedingly popular "Belfast staple". / Sample dishes: seared pepper tuna; char-grilled swordfish with salsa; pecan & raisin chocolate brownie. Details: www.nickswarehouse.co.uk; behind St Anne's Cathedral; 9.30 pm; closed Mon D, Sat L & Sun; children: 18+ at 9 pm.

Roscoff Brasserie £ 46

7-11 Linhall St BT2 8AA (028) 9031 1150

"Still offering some of Belfast's best food" — Paul Rankin's "stylish" city-centre destination remains the best-known place in town (and it's certainly the "no 1 choice for business"). / Sample dishes: foie gras with carmelised apples; confit duck leg with beetroot; crepe suzette with buttermilk ice cream. Details: www.rankingroup.co.uk; 11.15 pm; closed Sat L & Sun.

The Spaniard £ 26

3 Skipper St BT1 2DZ (028) 9023 2448

"Stephen Jeffers is one of Northern Ireland's most innovative chefs", says a fan of his bistro, which offers "great combinations of local seasonal ingredients"; it's open all day too. / Sample dishes: ciabattas; lamb stew. Details: 6 pm, 8 pm Thurs, Fri, Sat; children: 23+.

Tedfords Restaurant £ 47

5 Donegall Quay BT1 3EF (02890) 434000

A "cosy" restaurant established a couple of years ago in an old chandlery; it is tipped for its "historic" location and its "excellent" fish and steaks. / Sample dishes: grilled goat's cheese & asparagus, brioche croutons, beetroot pickle, toasted pine nuts & basil purée; sirloin of beef with triple cooked chips, slow roast tomato & crispy onions. Details: www.tedfordsrestaurant.com; 9.30 pm; closed Mon, Sat L & Sun; children: "not a family restaurant".

Zen £ 34
55-59 Adelaide St BT2 8FE   (028) 9023 2244

In a city without a huge amount of oriental competition –
a warehouse-style Japanese operation that mostly goes down well with
reporters. / *Sample dishes:* sashimi; roast duck breast fillet; roast duck with
orange slices. *Details:* www.eatbelfast.com; 11.30 pm; closed Sat L.

BEMBRIDGE, ISLE OF WIGHT 2–4D

The Crab And Lobster Inn £ 38
32 Forelands Field Rd PO35 5TR   (01983) 872244
"Try the seafood platter", if you visit this "cheerful" inn, which has
great sea-views; "great puds", too. / *Sample dishes:* seafood tagliatelli with
focaccia; half lobster & fillet steak with Madeira sauce & fries.
Details: www.crabandlobsterinn.co.uk; 9.30 pm; no Amex. *Accommodation:* 5
rooms, from £80.

BENDEROLCH, ARGYLL & BUTE 9–3B

Isle of Eriska £ 48
Ledaig PA37 1SD   (01631) 720371
This "rather isolated" hotel has a "lovely" setting, and its luxurious
style "leaves you wanting for nothing"; its restaurant won consistent
praise this year, as an "overall wonderful experience".
/ *Details:* www.eriska-hotel.co.uk; 9 pm. *Accommodation:* 25 rooms,
from £290.

BERKHAMSTED, HERTFORDSHIRE 3–2A

Eat Fish £ 40
163-165 High St HP4 3HB   (01442) 879988
"A lively, local eatery based around fresh fish" ("but there are
alternative options for meat-eaters and veggies") – a "refreshing"
destination, it's often "busy" (especially for lunch).
/ *Sample dishes:* sardine fishcakes; salmon; chocolate lime & ginger cheesecake.
Details: www.eatfish.co.uk; 10 pm.

BEVERLEY, EAST YORKSHIRE 6–2A

The Pipe & Glass Inn £ 38
West End HU17 7PN   (01430) 810246
A chef formerly at the famous Star at Harome has drawn a good
volume of reports for the fledgling régime at this "attractively-
converted boozer"; most – if not quite all – of them suggest it lives
up to its "ambitious" standards. / *Sample dishes:* ham hock & foie gras
terrine with pease pudding & walnut toast; roast lamb with braised mutton &
kidney faggot, broadbean, nettle & mint sauce; treacle tart with stewed rhubarb &
egg nog ice cream. *Details:* www.pipeandglass.co.uk; 9.30 pm; closed Mon &
Sun D; no Amex.

Three Chimneys   £ 38
Hareplain Rd TN27 8LW   (01580) 291472

A "very pretty" pub – with "lots of olde worlde charm" – that's usually judged "good in all respects"; doubters, though, can find its style "snooty" and its cooking "old-fashioned".
/ **Sample dishes:** Cheddar & spring onion potato cake; pan-roast breast of duck; pear & plum crumble with home-made rum & raisin ice cream. **Details:** A262 between Biddenden and Sissinghurst; 9.30 pm; no Amex; no booking, Sun L.

West House   £ 45 ⭐⭐
28 High St TN27 8AH   (01580) 291341
"Twice the London quality, half the London price!" – that's how fans perceive the Hewitts' "beautifully-converted Kentish building", where the cooking offers "a masterclass in unfussy but delicate flavours"; the atmosphere, though, can be a little "hushed".
/ **Sample dishes:** mackerel, cucumber pickle, horseradish crème fraîche; fillet of John Dory; rice pudding mousse. **Details:** www.thewesthouserestaurant.co.uk; 9.30 pm; closed Mon, Sat L & Sun D; no Amex.

Burgh Island Hotel   £ 73 Ⓐ
TQ7 4BG   (01548) 810514
You too can "dust down your dinner jacket" (optional, of course), and follow in the steps of "Agatha Christie, Lord Moutbatten and Jessie Matthews" to this "fabulously '30s" hotel, which is especially notable for a location "on its own island"; "the food's not bad either".
/ **Sample dishes:** seared foie gras, pear, macadamia nut & cucumber salad; salt-cured sea trout, potato purée, prawn, pimento, caper, preserved lemon salsa. **Details:** www.burghisland.com; 9.30 pm; no Amex; jacket & tie at D; children: 12+ at D. **Accommodation:** 24 rooms, from £320.

Oyster Shack   £ 35 Ⓐ⭐
Millburn Orchard Farm, Stakes Hills TQ7 4BE   (01548) 810876
"It's worth risking floods and scraped bumpers" for the "superb local fish and oysters" at this "unpretentious" fixture (reached "via a tidal road") – "one of those impossible-to-miss places that's impossible to find"; it now has a sibling in Salcombe. / **Sample dishes:** oysters Rockefeller; pan-fried scallops; lemon & raspberry posset. **Details:** www.oystershack.co.uk; 9 pm; L only, closed Mon.

BILDESTON, SUFFOLK 3–1C

The Bildeston Crown
The Crown Hotel **£ 39**
High St IP7 7EB (01449) 740510
"An old village inn that's had the 'boutique' treatment"; the service can be a touch "variable", but the food is consistently hailed for its "confident" execution. / Sample dishes: fish & chips.
Details: *www.thebildestoncrown.com; 10 pm, 9 pm Sun. Accommodation: 10 rooms, from £110.*

BILLERICAY, ESSEX 3–2C

Magic Mushroom **£ 33** 🝣
Barleyland Rd CM11 2UD (01268) 289963
A Mediterranean-inspired menu served in an age-old building; local fans say you get "first-class food", "good atmosphere" and "reasonable prices". / Sample dishes: braised ox cheek with mashed potatoes, pickled courgettes & sautéed foie gras; pan-fried curried scallops with cauliflower beignet; baked cheesecake with peanut butter ice cream & salted caramel peanuts. Details: www.magicmushroomrestaurant.co.uk; midnight; closed Mon & Sun D; no Amex; no shorts.

BILLINGE, GREATER MANCHESTER 5–2A

The Unicorn At Billinge **£ 42** 🝣
190 Upholland Rd WN5 7DJ (01695) 627692
A late-2006 opening in a former boozer; it's open all week, but is tipped in particular for its "fantastic fine dining on Friday and Saturday nights". / Sample dishes: seared foie gras with potato pancake, sauternes grapes & baby rocket; pan-fried seabass with braised puy lentils, mussels, clams, gem lettuce & jerusalem artichoke velouté; banana parfait with banana beignet, passion fruit jelly & toffee.
Details: *www.theunicornatbillinge.com; 9.30 pm; D only, closed Mon–Wed & Sun.*

BIRCHOVER, DERBYSHIRE 5–2C

Druid Inn **£ 36**
Main St DE4 2BL (01629) 650302
Not everyone likes the revamp under new owners of this "characterful country pub" (bemoaning, in particular, the "destruction of the lovely snug"); reports generally, though, suggest it's still "worth a trip". / Sample dishes: roast black pudding; rump of lamb with confit of vegetables; sticky toffee pudding with caramelised banana. Details: www.thymeforfood.co.uk; SW of Bakewell off B5056; 9.30 pm; no Amex.

BIRMINGHAM, WEST MIDLANDS 5–4C

The fact that Birmingham suddenly, in recent years, gained two restaurants which gained Michelin stars has allowed the media, rather glibly, to imply that the city is – all of a sudden – some sort of culinary wonderland. In fact, one of the two Michelin success stories has had a very brief life span. The chef of the former Jessica's has now set up on his own account in the city-centre at Purnell's (55 Cornwall St, 212 9799) . The other – and always to some extent the better of the two – is *Simpson's*. Otherwise, despite all the apparent developments in the city-centre, this great conurbation remains a remarkably poor dining out destination.

Bank £ 44

4 Brindleyplace B1 2JB (0121) 633 4466

"THE place for power-lunching", says fans – this "bright" mega-brasserie, by a canal, is an "efficient" operation, although it can seem "expensive" for what it is. / Sample dishes: butternut squash & coconut soup; confit of duck leg with Chinese greens; sticky toffee pudding.
Details: *www.bankrestaurants.co.uk; 10.30 pm, Fri & Sat 11 pm.*

Bar Estilo £ 29

110-114 Wharfside St B1 1RF (0121) 643 3443

In the Mailbox, this large and lavishly-furnished bar – part of a national chain – delivers "a great tapas spread" and a "lively" atmosphere; it's "always busy". / Sample dishes: grilled salmon fillet served with mango salsa & sweet potato mash; lamb shank slow-roasted in rosemary & white wine. Details: www.barestilo.co.uk; 11 pm.

The Bucklemaker £ 42

30 Mary Ann St, St Paul's Sq B3 1RL (0121) 200 2515

A somewhat "cave-like" fixture, that fans say is "a hidden gem in the Jewellery Quarter"; "it's been around a lot longer than pretentious new kids on the block chasing Michelin stars and focusses on providing excellent standard fare". / Sample dishes: Beef rossini fillet on a crouton with Madeira sauce; corn-fed chicken with a thyme & garlic farce on a potato rosti, whisky & tarragon cream sauce.
Details: *www.thebucklemaker.co.uk; 10.30 pm; closed Sat L & Sun.*

Café Ikon
Ikon Gallery £ 28

Oozells Sq, Brindleyplace B1 2HS (0121) 248 3226

Numerous fans of this "unassuming" white-walled arts-centre café again hail its "great" and "fresh" tapas – "worth the wait".
/ Sample dishes: grilled red peppers with anchovies; paella; lemon tart.
Details: *www.ikon-gallery.co.uk; 10 pm; closed Sun D; no Amex; children: 18+ after 9 pm.*

Chez Jules £ 29

5a Ethel St, off New St B2 4BG (0121) 633 4664

"Simple" Gallic fare that's "generally fine" has – despite the occasional "let-down" – won quite a following for this large and somewhat "shabby" bistro, new New Street station.
/ Sample dishes: foie gras; red snapper; crème brûlée.
Details: *www.chezjules.co.uk; 11 pm; closed Sun D.*

Chung Ying Garden £ 30

17 Thorp St B5 4AT (0121) 666 6622

"Probably the best Chinese in town" – this large Chinatown veteran is of note for its "extensive" and "interesting" menu (and for the fact that it's "always full of Chinese people"); it has a similarly "stalwart" twin at 16-18 Wrottesley Street (tel 622 5669).
/ Sample dishes: chicken wings; sweet & sour chicken.
Details: *www.chungying.co.uk; 11 pm.*

Cielo £ 47

6 Oozells Sq B1 2JB (0121) 6326882

A "modern"-looking, "goldfish bowl" in Brindleyplace, which "attracts Premiership footballers"; reporters note its "pleasant" service and its "good" Italian food. / Sample dishes: linguine with fresh crab meat & chilli; seared medallions of beef in a red wine & shallots sauce glazed with gorgonzola; caramelised panna cotta, white peach & tiramisu ice cream served with cantuccini biscuits. Details: www.cielobirmingham.com; 11 pm, 10 pm Sun.

Hotel du Vin et Bistro   £ 46

25 Church St B3 2NR   (0121) 200 0600

A "mind-boggling" wine list and a characterful setting (a "wonderfully restored eye hospital") help win upbeat feedback for this boutique-hotel brasserie, especially for business; the food, though, is a touch "formulaic". / **Sample dishes:** buttered white asparagus, crispy bacon & poached egg; roast chunky cod & merguez sausage; chocolate pecan brownie. **Details:** www.hotelduvin.co.uk; 9.45 pm; booking: max 10. **Accommodation:** 66 rooms, from £140.

Itihaas   £ 37

18 Fleet St B3 1JL   (0121) 212 3383

Potentially a notable central Indian (near the Science Museum); even those who say the food is "outstanding", however, can find prices "pretentious". / **Details:** www.itihaas.co.uk; 11, 10.30 Sun; closed Sat L & Sun L.

Jyoti   £ 17   ⓣ

569-571 Stratford Rd B11 4LS   (0121) 766 7199

A "consistently good", "cheap and cheerful" (BYO) Gujarati, in Sparbrook. / **Sample dishes:** assorted fritters; masala dosa; rasmalai. **Details:** 9.15 pm; closed Mon, Tue-Thu D only; no Amex.

Kinnaree Thai Restaurant   ⓣ
The Mailbox, Holiday Wharf Building   £ 28

22 Water Front Walk B1 1SN   (0121) 6656568

Canalside oriental, winning praise for its "lovely" food, and "nice view", even if the service can be "slow". / **Sample dishes:** fishcakes; curry. **Details:** www.kinnaree.co.uk; 11 pm, 10.30 pm Sun.

Lasan   £ 40   ★

3-4 Dakota Buildings, James St B3 1SD   (0121) 2123664

"A lovely contemporary Indian restaurant in Birmingham's hip jewellery quarter"; it wins all-round praise for its "interesting" dishes. / **Sample dishes:** yoghurt & mint-marinated fillet of lemon sole; cardamom & clove-smoked lamb chops in spicy curry; shredded carrots with cream & nuts in puff pastry. **Details:** www.lasan.co.uk; 11 pm; closed Sat L.

Malmaison   £ 44

Royal Mail St B1 1RD   (0121) 246 5000

A "busy, busy place full of the Birmingham glitterati"; foodwise, this design-hotel brasserie has its detractors, but also its fans – a London-based reporter of long standing, for example, found his meal "fresh, and beautifully presented". / **Sample dishes:** caramelised onion & goat's cheese tart; poached lemon sole; strawberries & cream with shortbread. **Details:** www.malmaison.com; 10.30 pm. **Accommodation:** 189 rooms, from £150.

MUST   £ 29

11-13 Newhall St B3 3NY   (0121) 212 2266

A new dim sum bar and restaurant in the Business Quarter which opened in mid-2007, too late for the survey; reports please. / **Details:** www.mustgroup.co.uk/.

Opus Restaurant   £ 36

54 Cornwall St B3 2DE   (0121) 200 2323

This relative newcomer is rated by a good number of reporters as a "great addition" to the city; it is especially popular as the location for a business lunch. / **Sample dishes:** caramelised onion & Ricotta tart; pan-fried scallops & belly pork; cheese platter. **Details:** www.opusrestaurant.co.uk; 10.30 pm, Sat 11.30 pm; closed Sun.

Pascal's £ 55

1 Montague Rd B16 9HN (0121) 455 0999
*The Edgbaston establishment formerly known as Jessica's closed
in mid-2007, and the site was taken over by Pascal Cluny, formerly
maître d' there; the look of the place is unchanged – the cuisine
is perhaps a fraction less ambitious.*

San Carlo £ 38

4 Temple St B2 5BN (0121) 633 0251
*This "energetic and noisy upmarket Italian" in the city centre has
reached something approaching 'veteran' status, in spite of its "basic"
cuisine, and its sometimes rather "pushy" service.*
/ **Sample dishes:** *Parma ham & melon; fillet steak; tiramisu.*
Details: *www.sancarlo.co.uk; near St Philips Cathedral; 11 pm.*

Simpsons £ 70 ⭐

20 Highfield Rd B15 3DU (0121) 454 3434
*"The best food in Birmingham" – "always inventive, delicious and
beautifully presented" – makes Andreas Antona's "superb all-rounder"
very popular with reporters; it occupies a stylishly-modernised
Georgian mansion, in Edgbaston.* / **Sample dishes:** *loin of tuna; fillet
of beef; pineapple & raspberry ravioli.* **Details:** *www.simpsonsrestaurant.co.uk;
9.30 pm; closed Sun D.* **Accommodation:** *4 rooms, from £160.*

BISHOP'S STORTFORD, HERTFORDSHIRE   3–2B

The Lemon Tree £ 36 ⭐

14-16 Water Ln CM23 2LB (01279) 757788
*"Very good food" is reported in all feedback on the Fishpools' town-
centre bistro, which occupies a "pleasant" setting that's rather like
a "rabbit warren".* / **Sample dishes:** *black pudding, new potatoes, poached
egg & pancetta; fillets of Dover sole with prawns, button mushrooms, & chive
cream; bread & butter pudding.* **Details:** *www.lemontree.co.uk; 9.30 pm; closed
Mon & Sun D; no Amex.*

BISHOPS TACHBROOK, WARWICKSHIRE   5–4C

Mallory Court £ 67 Ⓐ⭐

Harbury Ln CV33 9QB (01926) 330214

*This "fine" Lutyens-designed country house hotel is widely
recommended as an "impressive" venue with "gorgeous" and "subtle"
cuisine; this year, however, some reporters thought it had "gone off
the boil".* / **Sample dishes:** *bisque of shellfish; pan-fried escalope of bream
fillet & roast langoustines; passion fruit soufflé with passion fruit sorbet & exotic
fruit salad.* **Details:** *www.mallory.co.uk; 2m S of Leamington Spa, off B4087;
9 pm.* **Accommodation:** *29 rooms, from £135.*

BISPHAM GREEN, LANCASHIRE   5–1A

Eagle & Child   £ 33
Maltkiln Ln L40 3SG   (01257) 462297
*This "great village pub" is very well-known and can get "so crowded
it's hard to move"; its "traditional British food" is "good" to "OK".*
/ **Sample dishes:** grilled Bury black pudding; pan-fried breast of duck with
orange & port sauce; sticky toffee pudding. **Details:** M6, J27; 8.30 pm; no Amex.

BLACKPOOL, LANCASHIRE   5–1A

Kwizeen   £ 33   ★
47-49 King St FY1 3EJ   (01253) 290045
"The chef makes virtually everything himself", at Marco Calle-
Calatayud's "laudable" oasis, "in a gastronomic desert"; the set lunch
offers "stupendous value". / **Sample dishes:** Lancashire cheese & crispy
pancakes; local suckling pig; banana sticky toffee crumble & butterscotch ice
cream. **Details:** www.kwizeen.co.uk; 9 pm; closed Sat L & Sun; no Amex;
no shorts.

BLAIRGOWRIE, PERTH & KINROSS   9–3C

Kinloch House   £ 62   ⊤
PH10 6SG   (01250) 884237
*It's only the paucity of commentary that makes this a 'tip'; feedback
continues to suggest that the Allen family's country house hotel serves
"extremely good" food, and it has a "beautiful location" too.*
/ **Sample dishes:** breast of pigeon; loin of lamb; poached pear shortcake with
a caramel & lime sauce. **Details:** www.kinlochhouse.com; past the Cottage
Hospital, turn L, procede 3m along A923, (signposted Dunkeld Road); 8.30 pm;
jacket required; children: 7+ at D. **Accommodation:** 18 rooms, from £210.

BLAKENEY, NORFOLK   6–3C

The White Horse Hotel   £ 36
4 High St NR25 7AL   (01263) 740574
"The standard never drops" at this seaside inn; reporters judge
it somewhere between "an excellent all-rounder", and "nothing
amazing, but good all the same". / **Sample dishes:** chicken liver parfait
with saffron-pickled courgettes & toast; deep-fried cod; chocolate cheesecake.
Details: www.blakeneywhitehorse.co.uk; 9 pm; D only; no Amex.
Accommodation: 9 rooms, from £70.

BOLLINGTON, CHESHIRE   5–2B

Briscola   £ 34   ⊤
88 Palmerston St SK10 5PW   (01625) 573898
"Under new ownership, standards are still very high", says a fan
of this "cheap and cheerful" village Italian, where the menu is strong
on pizza and pasta. / **Sample dishes:** king prawns & scallops cooked with
garlic & chilli, served on bruschetta; whole barbecue seabass with mint dressing.
Details: www.briscolarestaurant.co.uk; 10 pm. 10.30 pm Fri & Sat; closed
Mon & Sun.

BOLNHURST, BEDFORDSHIRE   3–1A

The Plough At Bolnhurst   £ 45   **A** **★**
MK44 2EX   (01234) 376274
*"There is simply nothing negative to be said about this exquisite
pub/restaurant"* – typical of the enthusiastic commentary inspired
by this *"delightful"* establishment; *"'gastropub' doesn't do justice
to it"*. / **Sample dishes:** *foie gras with home-made black pudding; grilled turbot;
lemon tarte with crème fraîche.* **Details:** *www.bolnhurst.com; 9.30 pm; closed
Mon & Sun D; no Amex.*

BOLTON ABBEY, NORTH YORKSHIRE   8–4B

Devonshire Arms   £ 76
BD23 6AJ   (01756) 710441
"The emperor's new clothes" are – many feel – much in evidence,
so to speak, in the *"very formal"* restaurant of this ducally-owned inn,
where the prices *"make even a Londoner gasp"*; the answer seems
to be to drink a lot, as the wine list is *"biblical"* in proportions,
and (relatively) reasonably priced. / **Sample dishes:** *red mullet on poached
oysters; poached pigeon with its own ballantine; lavender honey with wild
strawberry parfait.* **Details:** *www.devonshirehotels.co.uk; on A59, 5m NE
of Skipton; 9.30 pm; closed Mon, Tue-Sat D only, Sun open L & D; no jeans
or trainers.* **Accommodation:** *40 rooms, from £230.*

BONCHURCH, ISLE OF WIGHT   2–4D

Pond Café   £ 38   **★**
Pond Church Village Rd PO38 1RG   (01983) 855666
*This "cute" establishment (with a terrace overlooking the eponymous
water feature) is a "professional set-up", and chef Luke Borley
is consistently praised for the "top-notch" cooking.*
/ **Sample dishes:** *ham hock & foie gras terrine & home-made piccalilli; sweet
potato & smoked haddock fish cake, guacamole & chilli oil.*
Details: *www.thepondcafe.com; 9.30 pm; closed Mon; no Amex.*

BOSHAM, WEST SUSSEX   3–4A

Millstream Hotel   £ 48
PO18 8HL   (01243) 573234
*"A beautiful location by the stream in this unspoilt Sussex seaside
village"* adds charm to this *"comfortable"* location (where you
"can eat on the lawn in summer"); its food is praised by practically all
reporters. / **Sample dishes:** *crab mousse with herb oil & sun-dried tomatoes;
fillet of lamb; chocolate sponge pudding & chocolate sauce.*
Details: *www.millstream-hotel.co.uk; A259 from Chichister; 9.15 pm; no jeans
or trainers.* **Accommodation:** *35 rooms, from £142.*

BOUGHTON LEES, KENT   3–3C

A

The Manor Restaurant
Eastwell Manor   £ 59
Eastwell Pk TN25 4HR   (01233) 213000
*This "gracious" country house undoubtedly makes a good destination
if you wish to dine in "baronial splendour"; on the food front, reports
are less clear, but fans insist it's "great".* / **Sample dishes:** *Mediterranean
vegetable risotto; pan-roast sea bream; panna cotta with fruit.*
Details: *www.eastwellmanor.co.uk; 3m N of Ashford on A251; 9.30 pm; no jeans
or shorts; booking: max 8.* **Accommodation:** *23 rooms, from £140.*

Bistro on the Beach　　　　£ 31　　Ⓐ
Solent Promenade, Southbourne Coast Rd BH6 4BE
(01202) 431473
"Tucked-away at the bottom of a cliff", at Southbourne, this self-
explanatory set-up has the "lovely setting" its name suggests;
the cooking, however, "could do with a little renewal and
experimentation". / **Sample dishes:** scallops & tiger prawns; monkfish
wrapped in Parma ham & sage; walnut & caramel tart with clotted cream.
Details: www.bistroonthebeach.com; 2m E of town centre in Southbourne;
9.30 pm; D only, closed Sun-Tue (open Tue in Summer); no Amex.

Chez Fred　　　　£ 17　　★
10 Seamoor Rd BH4 9AN　(01202) 761023
In accordance with tradition, most reporters this year rate this
Westbourne institution as an "unbeatable" chippy – one or two,
though, found the product too "mass-produced".
/ **Sample dishes:** cod & chips; treacle sponge & custard.
Details: www.chezfred.co.uk; 1m W of town centre; 9.45 pm; closed Sun L;
no Amex; no booking.

Mandarin　　　　£ 30　　Ⓣ
194-198 Old Christchurch Rd BH1 1PD　(01202) 290681
Service can be "hit-and-miss", but this Chinese veteran is said by its
supporters to serve "fantastic" food. / **Sample dishes:** garlic salt & chili
roasted spare ribs; stir-fried scallops with ginger & spring onion.
Details: www.themandarin.net; 11 pm.

Ocean Palace　　　　£ 32
8 Priory Rd BH2 5DG　(01202) 559127
"Really good, especially if you go on a quieter night" – this typically
"bustling" and "echo-y" Chinese fixture continues to deliver some
"lovely" food. / **Sample dishes:** smoked chicken; crispy Mongolian lamb;
banana fritter. **Details:** www.oceanpalace.co.uk; 11 pm.

West Beach　　　　£ 43
Pier Approach BH2 5AA　(01202) 587785
"Still the best bet in Bournemouth" – this big and "fun" fish
restaurant "yards from the beach" offers food that's "simply cooked
and full of fresh flavours", plus a "beautiful" outlook; service, though,
can be "slow". / **Sample dishes:** grilled mackerel; fillet of sea bass; limoncello
brûlée. **Details:** www.west-beach.co.uk; 10 pm.

BOWNESS, CUMBRIA　　　　7–3D

Linthwaite House　　　　£ 63　　Ⓐ
Crook Rd LA23 3JA　(01539) 488600
With its "dramatic" lake-views, this "lesser-known gem" of a country
house hotel is a "perfect place for romance", with cooking (from chef
Simon Bolsover) that consistently "hits the mark".
/ **Sample dishes:** risotto with parsley & nutmeg; duck breast with parsnip purée;
strawberry fool & compote. **Details:** www.linthwaite.com; 9 pm; no jeans
or trainers; children: 7+ at D. **Accommodation:** 27 rooms, from £180.

Miller Howe   **£ 56**   Ⓐ

Rayrigg Rd LA23 1EY   (01539) 442536

"The best view in the Lakes" is the draw to this once-famous country house hotel; opinion divides between those who say the food is "very good, with a lighter touch under new owners" and those who say it's "trying too hard, and not properly executed".

/ **Sample dishes:** *roast squab pigeon & ballotine of sweetbreads; roast duck breast & sautéed girolles; plum Tatin & honey ice cream.*

Details: *www.millerhowe.com; on A592 between Windermere & Bowness; 8.45 pm; no jeans or trainers; children: 8+.* **Accommodation:** *15 rooms, from £105.*

BRADFORD, WEST YORKSHIRE   5–1C

Akbar's Balti   **£ 23**   Ⓐ ⭐ ⭐

1276 Leeds Rd BD3 3LF   (01274) 773311

"The one in Leeds is good, but Bradford seems to have the edge…" – Shabir Hussain's "vibrant" and ever-expanding curry house continues to delight reporters with its "enthusiastic" staff and "excellent-value" food. / **Sample dishes:** *masala fish; chicken tikka & garlic balti; chocolate fudge cake.* **Details:** *www.akbars.co.uk; midnight; D only.*

Karachi   **£ 9**   ⭐

15-17 Neal St BD5 0BX   (01274) 732015

"Don't expect cutlery – just great value and authentic food", at this very cheap subcontinental of long standing, still vaunted as "the best in the area", by some reporters. / **Sample dishes:** *chicken tikka masala; chicken masala; kulfi.* **Details:** *1 am, 2 am Fri & Sat; no credit cards.*

Kashmir   **£ 11**   ⭐

27 Morley St BD7 1AG   (01274) 726513

An "awesome bargain-basement curry house" that's now firmly established as "a Bradford tradition". / **Sample dishes:** *fish pakora; chicken krai with chapati; caramel fantastic.* **Details:** *3 am.*

Love Apple Cafe   **£ 26**   Ⓣ

34 Great Horton Rd BD7 1AL   (01274) 744075

This all-day café is, apparently, "the regular haunt of the Bradford litterati"; it's also a "very friendly" place, with "good-value" food. / **Sample dishes:** *burritos; chicken burritos; sticky toffee pudding.* **Details:** *www.loveapplecafe.co.uk; 9 pm.*

Mumtaz Paan House   **£ 24**   ⭐ ⭐

Great Horton Rd BD7 3HS   (01274) 571861

"Bradford's finest" inspires fans from far and wide ("I've travelled from Manchester monthly for about 20 years!"); Kashmiri food "of unique quality" is delivered in a "vibrant, large and bustling" space; no alcohol. / **Sample dishes:** *sikh kebab; chicken tikka masala; rasmalai.* **Details:** *www.mumtaz.com; midnight.*

BRAMPTON, CUMBRIA 7–2D

Farlam Hall £ 52
CA8 2NG (01697) 746234
"The ambience is slightly formal perhaps, but lovely" – this isolated
country house hotel, which attracts impressively consistent reports
across the board (especially when the weather is good enough to dine
in the garden). / **Sample dishes:** spiced shrimp in a pastry case;
beef medallions with horseradish mashed potato; hazelnut meringue with
raspberries. **Details:** www.farlamhall.co.uk; 2.5m S.E of Brampton on A689,
not in Farlam Village; 8.30 pm; D only; no shorts; children: 5+.
Accommodation: 12 rooms, from £280.

BRANCASTER STAITHE, NORFOLK 6–3B

White Horse £ 36
Main Rd PE31 8BY (01485) 210262
A stunningly-located pub, with *"wonderful views"* over *"wild salt
marshes"*; *"wonderful"* food makes it a *"winner"* for most reporters,
but gripers say *"standards have slipped"*. / **Sample dishes:** oysters with
a julienne of vegetables & chilli sauce; grilled fillet of lemon sole with tagliatelli
of leek & saffron butter sauce; home-made ice cream.
Details: www.whitehorsebrancaster.co.uk; 9 pm; no Amex.
Accommodation: 15 rooms, from £120.

BRAY, WINDSOR & MAIDENHEAD 3–3A

The Fat Duck £112
1 High St SL6 2AQ (01628) 580333

"More an extravaganza than a meal!"; few reporters would disagree
that the *"weird and wonderful"* tasting menu at Heston Blumenthal's
"world-famous" restaurant is a *"once-in-a-lifetime experience"*; there
are refuseniks who find prices (and, indeed, the whole experience)
"excessive", but for the vast majority it's *"worth every penny"*.
/ **Sample dishes:** ballotine of foie gras; saddle of venison; chocolate fondant with
harissa ice cream. **Details:** www.fatduck.co.uk; 9 pm; closed Mon & Sun D;
closed 2 weeks at New Year.

The Hind's Head £ 42
High St SL6 2AB (01628) 626151
With the prospect of a smidgeon of *"the magic of the Fat Duck"*,
it's no surprising that Heston's *"perfect"* English pub, just over the
road, generates a huge volume of reports, most (if not quite all)
of them to the effect that its *"obsessively-prepared British pub grub"*
is *"awesome"*. / **Sample dishes:** potted shrimp; oxtail & kidney pudding;
"quaking" pudding. **Details:** www.hindsheadhotel.co.uk; 9.30 pm; closed Sun D.

Riverside Brasserie £ 46
Monkey Island Ln, Bray Marina SL6 2EB (01628) 780553
"A riverside delight" – this Bray Marina operation is "hard to find"
but can be "excellent"; the odd reporter says it's "not worth
a detour", though, or more particularly that it's "only great
in summer". / **Sample dishes:** foie gras & chicken liver parfait with red onion
marmalade; crispy pork salad with lemon & fennel; coconut panna cotta.
Details: www.riversidebrasserie.co.uk; follow signs for Bray Marina off A308;
10 pm.

Waterside Inn £127
Ferry Rd SL6 2AT (01628) 620691

"If you're looking for old-fashioned romance", this "magnificent"
Thames-side veteran is a "stunning" choice thanks to its "idyllic
location", "wonderful professionalism", and "Alain Roux's brilliant
continuation" of its "classic" Gallic cuisine; if there is a gripe
("outrageous prices" aside), it's that the staff can seem "dated".
/ **Sample dishes:** potato gnocchi; pan-fried medallions of veal; milk chocolate
mousse. **Details:** www.waterside-inn.co.uk; off A308 between Windsor &
Maidenhead; 10 pm; closed Mon & Tue (open Tue D Jun-Aug); no jeans
or trainers; booking: max 10. **Accommodation:** 11 rooms, from £200.

BREARTON, NORTH YORKSHIRE 8–4B

The Malt Shovel £ 37
HG3 3BX (01423) 862929
The new owners of this "tucked-away country pub" have given
it "a real shot in the arm"; not only are they opera-singers (who may
"end the evening with a recital"), but they also offer consistently
"good" food. / **Sample dishes:** garlic creamed mushrooms on brioche; steak &
ale pie; sticky toffee pudding. **Details:** off A61, 6m N of Harrogate; 9 pm; closed
Sun D; no Amex; need 8+ to book.

BRECON, POWYS 2–1A

Felin Fach Griffin £ 40
Felin Fach LD3 0UB (01874) 620111
Imagine "Hotel du Vin goes rustic", and you have some idea of the
feel of this "busy, busy gastro-inn", which is located in "fantastic
countryside" in the Brecon Beacons; service can be "patchy", but the
food is "usually very good". / **Sample dishes:** smoked salmon; slow-roasted
pork belly; bitter chocolate tart with blood orange sorbet.
Details: www.eatdrinksleep.ltd.uk; 20 mins NW of Abergavenny on A470; 11 pm;
closed Mon L; no Amex. **Accommodation:** 7 rooms, from £97.50.

BRIDGE OF ALLAN, STIRLINGSHIRE   9–4C

⭐

Clive Ramsay   **£ 32**
Henderson St FK9 4HR (01786) 831616
*A contemporary café/bistro "in a busy small town"; "haggis, neeps
and tatties to die for" is typical of its "freshly-cooked fare, with a
Scottish twist". / Details: www.cliveramsay.com; 8.45 pm; no Amex.*

BRIDPORT, DORSET   2–4B

Ⓣ

The Bull Hotel   **£ 37**
34 East St DT6 3LF (01308) 422878
*"A new boutique hotel in a small market town"; making "the best use
of local ingredients to create tasty dishes", it's tipped as "a great
addition to the local dining scene". / Sample dishes: potato rösti,
goat cheese, roasted onions, tomatoes & rocket. Details: www.thebullhotel.co.uk.*

Ⓐ⭐

Hive Beach Cafe   **£ 40**
Beach Rd DT6 4RF (01308) 897070
*Every day of the year (except 25 December), this "unfussy" café
offers "a taste of foodie heaven of a type that's hard to find in this
part of the world" (as well as some "breathtaking views"); in summer
there's an evening seafood restaurant which "is often booked out".
/ Sample dishes: whole plaice with crayfish tails; seabass with balsamic glaze.
Details: www.hivebeachcafe.co.uk; L only, varies seasonally; no Amex.*

⭐

Riverside   **£ 42**
West Bay DT6 4EZ (01308) 422011
*"Nothing changes, thank goodness", at this "joy" of a seaside café,
"on stilts over the water"; "wooden floors and tables emphasise the
simplicity" of a formula focussed on "fresh fish, straight off the boat,
unfussily cooked and served"; Marx Hix (ex-Caprice) will take over
here some time in 2008. / Sample dishes: lobster & crab linguini; fillet
of brill with crispy spinach & sorrell sauce; rice pudding & cardamom plums.
Details: www.thefishrestaurant-westbay.co.uk; 9 pm; closed Mon & Sun D (closed
end of Nov until mid February); no Amex.*

BRIGHOUSE, WEST YORKSHIRE   5–1C

Ⓐ⭐

Brook's   **£ 38**
6 Bradford Rd HD6 1RW (01484) 715284
*One reporter discerned a "small-French-town-bistro feel", at this
"busy", candlelit pub-conversion, where the cuisine of ex-Savoy chef
Darrell Brook "continues to improve". / Sample dishes: fried goat's
cheese & breadcrumbs; rack of mustard-crusted lamb; chocolate cake & brandy
snap ice cream. Details: www.brooks-restaurant.co.uk; 11 pm; D only, closed Sun;
booking essential.*

BRIGHTON, EAST SUSSEX   3–4B

The dining scene of 'London by the Sea' continues to mimic
that of the capital, albeit on a much reduced scale. Many
of the better restaurants, for example, are ethnic, with the
city offering pretty good-quality establishments offering
most of the more obvious cuisines. There are a number
of pleasant mid-price restaurants, among which *Due South* and
Gingerman are pre-eminent.

There are two areas – brunching and vegetarian dining – where Brighton arguably trumps the metropolis, *Bills* and *Terre à Terre* being the two respective big names. The city is, however, still looking for a champion at the top end of the market – the evidence is now unassailable that *One Paston Place*, currently the only contender, is not it.

Aumthong Thai £ 25 Ⓐ ★
60 Western Rd BN3 1JD (01273) 773922
This well-established Thai restaurant doesn't attract much feedback, but it's all to the effect that it's "a lovely place with a great variety of consistently good food". / **Sample dishes:** *spring rolls; marinated sirloin steak, grilled over charcoal & flamed with rice wine; ice cream.* **Details:** *www.aumthong.com; 11 pm, 10 pm Sun; closed Mon L.*

Bill's £ 27 ★
100 North Rd, The Depot BN1 1YE (01273) 692894
"Like a slice of Greenwich Village, served up in Brighton" – this "vaguely chaotic but fun" deli/café has made itself enormously popular, thanks not least to its "fabulous fresh food". / **Sample dishes:** *home-made muesli with yoghurt, fruits, nuts & honey; eggs Benedict with smoked salmon; buttermilk pancakes with maple syrup.* **Details:** *www.billsproducestore.co.uk; 8 pm; closed Sun D; no Amex.*

Blanch House £ 45
17 Atlingworth St BN2 1PL (01273) 603504
Fans speak of the "beautifully presented" dishes – and with "outstanding flavour" too – at this boutique-hotel; there are quite a few critics, though, who find the whole performance "posy and pretentious". / **Sample dishes:** *tagliatelle with crab; beef Wellington; chocolate tart with espresso ice cream.* **Details:** *www.blanchhouse.co.uk; 10 pm; closed Mon & Sun D.* **Accommodation:** *12 rooms, from £100.*

Casa Don Carlos £ 20 Ⓐ ★
5 Union St BN1 1HA (01273) 327177
Local fans of this "heaving" and "cosy" Lanes spot claim it's "the best and friendliest tapas bar this side of Barcelona"; that may be over-doing it a bit, but it's certainly the best Spanish place in town. / **Sample dishes:** *tapas; home-made crème brûlée.* **Details:** *11 pm.*

China Garden £ 35 ★
88-91 Preston St BN1 2HG (01273) 325124
"Still Brighton's best Chinese"; this well-established oriental near the seafront puts in a "consistently good" performance, and the dim sum – in particular – is "excellent". / **Sample dishes:** *salt & pepper prawns; kung po chicken; toffee bananas.* **Details:** *www.chinagarden.name; opp West Pier; 11.30 pm.*

Donatello £ 30
1-3 Brighton Pl BN1 1HJ (01273) 775477
"It's always busy, so they must be doing something right", at this "fun", "no-surprises" Lanes Italian, which owes its consistent popularity to "cheap and solid pizzas and pastas". / **Sample dishes:** *deep-fried whitebait with paprika; grilled king prawns in a white wine, garlic & parsley sauce; cherries in liqueur syrup with vanilla, strawberry & pistachio ice cream & whipped cream.* **Details:** *www.donatello.co.uk; 11.30 pm.*

Due South £ 43
139 King's Arches BN1 2FN (01273) 821218

For most reporters, this "chilled" hang out at the heart of the beach-front action deserves its huge popularity; it uses "great local produce" to produce some "excellent" dishes, and lucky diners get views "second to none" – "get there early for a window seat!"
/ **Sample dishes:** fish soup; lamb; chocolate brownie with warm chocolate sauce.
Details: www.duesouth.co.uk; Brighton Beach, below the Odeon cinema; 10 pm.

English's £ 50
29-31 East St BN1 1HL (01273) 327980
Fans of this age-old parlour in the Lanes say it's a "lovely, lovely place to eat" – "expensive, but still one of the best old-fashioned fish restaurants around"; doubters, though, find the food "not particularly good" (... or worse). / **Sample dishes:** lobster bisque; pan-fried scallops with sesame seed & chilli oil; chocolate & raspberry terrine.
Details: www.englishs.co.uk; 10 pm.

Food for Friends £ 37
17-18 Prince Albert St BN1 1HF (01273) 202310
"Stylishly revamped" by new owners, this long-established veggie in the Lanes inspires somewhat mixed reviews – "an inventive menu which sometimes fails to deliver on the taste front" is fairly typical.
/ **Sample dishes:** Dolcelatte & red onion tartlet; Middle Eastern platter; chocolate pudding. **Details:** www.foodforfriends.com; 10 pm.

La Fourchette £ 41
105 Western Rd BN1 2AA (01273) 722556
Reports on this well-established Gallic fixture are unusually mixed – to fans, its "classic French bistro fare" is "the best value for money around", while foes just find it "underwhelming in every respect"; it must be doing something right, though as they've just expanded into new premises. / **Sample dishes:** ravioli of scallops & prawns; duck breast; red fruit sabayon & champagne ice cream. **Details:** www.lafourchette.co.uk; 10.30 pm; closed Sun D.

The Ginger Pig £ 33
Hove St BN3 2TR (01273) 736123
This new Hove gastropub offers a meaty menu that's "simpler and cheaper than at the same owners' Gingerman"; it's already "busy", but reports emphasise its consistent "high quality".
/ **Sample dishes:** sesame crusted tuna; roast partridge with cauliflower purée & red wine; dark chocolate & pecan brownie with honeycomb ice cream.
Details: www.gingermanrestaurant.com; 10 pm. **Accommodation:** 0 rooms, from £-.

Gingerman £ 39

21a Norfolk Sq BN1 2PD (01273) 326688

Ben McKellar's "bustling", small venture may look like
"an unassuming bolt hole" in The Lanes, but it remains one of the
most acclaimed places in town, thanks to its "absolutely splendid food
and service". / **Sample dishes:** millefeuille of English asparagus with poached
duck egg & chive butter; crispy pork belly, Savoy cabbage, bacon & thyme
potatoes; lemon & pine nut biscotti soufflé with limoncello ice cream.
Details: www.gingermanrestaurants.com; off Norfolk Square; 9.15 pm;
closed Mon.

The Gingerman
Drakes Hotel £ 45

44 Marine Pde BN2 1PE (01273) 696934

Food that's now "as good as at the original" (well, almost) helps make
Gingerman's offshoot – in a Kemp Town design-hotel – very popular
with all who report on it; with its "low lighting and candles", it strikes
some as "romantic" too. / **Sample dishes:** duck & lentil salad; peppered fillet
of beef; soft-spiced apple turnover. **Details:** www.gingermanrestaurants.com;
10 pm. **Accommodation:** 20 rooms, from £95.

Graze £ 41

42 Western Rd BN3 1JD (01273) 823707

An "informal" but "glamorous" Hove newcomer, where the "small
portions of interesting food" live up happily to the establishment's
name. / **Sample dishes:** crab salad with avocado & harissa dressing; roasted
wood pigeon, morel risotto & mushroom essence.
Details: www.graze-restaurant.co.uk; 10 pm; closed Mon L & Sun D.

Havana £ 51

32 Duke St BN1 1AG (01273) 773388

This Lanes venue is often applauded for its "amazing", if "hectic",
ambience and for food – from a "limited" menu – that's "not cheap"
but "surprisingly good"; for some tastes, though, the place
is "pretentious" and "glitzy". / **Sample dishes:** roast baby artichoke hearts;
cod fillet, roast squid ink & sauté of calamari; brioche pain perdu.
Details: www.havana.uk.com; 10.30 pm, Fri & Sat 11 pm, Sun 10 pm; no jeans
or trainers; booking essential; children: 6+ at D.

Hotel du Vin et Bistro £ 45

Ship St BN1 1AD (01273) 718588

The food can seem "a bit predictable" at this extremely popular,
"buzzy" boutique hotel dining room; even less enthusiastic reporters,
though, generally "have an enjoyable time, down to its good
atmosphere", "brilliant" wine list and "excellent" sommelier.
/ **Sample dishes:** paupiette of salmon, avocado salsa & gazpacho sauce; chicken
breast with seared foie gras & truffles; gooseberry fool with lime sherbet.
Details: www.hotelduvin.com; 9.45 pm; booking: max 10. **Accommodation:** 37
rooms, from £160.

Indian Summer £ 26

69 East St BN1 1HQ (01273) 711001

"Infinitely more interesting than standard subcontinental, and not
expensive" – this "small" venture near The Lanes pleases all
reporters with its "modern European take on Indian cuisine";
some claim the Hove branch (5 Victoria Terrace, tel 773090) is even
better. / **Sample dishes:** khasta kachori; prawns rogani; mango brûlée with
cinnamon shortbread. **Details:** www.indian-summer.org.uk; 10 pm Mon & Sun,
10.30 pm; closed Mon L.

Murasaki £ 35

115 Dyke Rd BN1 3JE (01273) 326231

"A great selection of sushi, sashimi and Japanese tapas" are offered
at this "friendly" and "atmospheric" café, in the "up and coming
Seven Dials area". / **Sample dishes:** sushi; aubergine miso yuki.
Details: 11 pm; closed Mon; no Amex.

One Paston Place £ 56

1 Paston Pl BN2 1HA (01273) 606933

This grand Kemp Town townhouse polarizes reporters ever more
starkly – fans say it's a "Michelin-contender", with "acccomplished"
presentation and "attentive" service, but there are as many critics
who dismiss it as a "below-average" place with "zero ambience".
/ **Sample dishes:** beef carpaccio with French bean salad & warm goat's cheese;
pan-fried veal fillet & veal sweetbreads; orange & grand marnier soufflé with blood
orange sorbet. **Details:** www.onepastonplace.co.uk; between the pier & marina;
10 pm; closed Mon & Sun; children: 7+.

Pintxo People £ 36

95-99 Western Rd BN1 2LB (01273) 732323

This "traditional Spanish restaurant" – and "really lively" ground floor
tapas bar – is a "sexy" destination that made a big splash when
it launched a year or so ago; its "interesting" food can still
be "fantastic", but performance has seemed more "erratic" of late.
/ **Sample dishes:** lightly-fried octopus with paprika & sweet aioli; mango ravioli;
Spanish cheese board. **Details:** www.pintxopeople.co.uk; 11.30 pm.

Real Eating Company £ 42

86-87 Western Rd BN3 1JB (01273) 221444

An organic deli/restaurant often tipped for "Brighton's best brunch",
not least "the best eggs Benedict" – "and that's allowing for lots
of local competition". / **Sample dishes:** baked figs with honey, thyme & goat's
cheese; lobster, crab, tomato & rocket risotto with spiced crab butter & pea shoots;
toasted marshmallows, coconut parfait & hot chocolate.
Details: www.real-eating.co.uk; 9.30 pm; closed Sun D.

Regency £ 23

131 Kings Rd BN1 2HH (01273) 325014

It has a "great location on the seafront", and this "old-favourite"
chippy maintains quite a name for "fish 'n' chips at their best"; those
who insist its standards are "nothing special", though, are getting
quite voluble. / **Sample dishes:** prawn cocktail; salmon in dill sauce; tiramisu.
Details: www.theregencyrestaurant.co.uk; opp West Pier; 11 pm.
Accommodation: 30 rooms, from £65.

Riddle & Finns £ 45
12b, Meeting House Ln BN1 1HB (01273) 323008
"Colossal" and "really fresh" seafood platters – the stock-in-trade
of this "informal" and "tightly-packed" newcomer, which has quickly
made itself hugely popular. / *Sample dishes:* smoked eel with herbed potato
cake & tomato chutney; roast halibut with mushy pea purée.
Details: www.riddleandfinns.co.uk; 10 pm.

Seven Dials £ 44
1-3 Buckingham Pl BN1 3TD (01273) 885555
"Good-humoured and friendly" waiting staff set an upbeat tone
at this "delightful local", where the cooking may be quite simple,
but is often "delicious"; even fans, though, can find prices "on the
high side". / *Sample dishes:* roast Mascarpone-filled fig; highland beef
Wellington; strawberry & vanilla cream tart.
Details: www.sevendialsrestaurant.co.uk; 10.30 pm; closed Sun D.

Strand £ 40
6 Little East St BN1 1HT (01273) 747096
"Ideal for the Theatre Royal" – this "intimate" spot again wins praise
for its "comforting" and "romantic" style and its "delicious", "rustic"
cuisine; the odd reporter, though, found it "didn't quite deliver".
/ *Sample dishes:* caramelised goat's cheese chalet tart; duck breast & truffle
potato gratin; caramelised orange & Cointreau panna cotta.
Details: www.thestrandbrighton.co.uk; closed Mon L & Tue L; booking: max 8,
Fri & Sat.

Tallula's Tea Rooms £ 23
9 Hampton Pl BN1 3DA (01273) 710529
"Perfect cooked breakfasts" – "the Scottish one, complete with
haggis" is one of the more eye-catching options – win a more-than-
local following for this "very welcoming" café. / *Sample dishes:* fishcakes;
caramelised red onion, beetroot & goat's cheese tart. *Details:* 6 pm; L only.

Terre à Terre £ 43
71 East St BN1 1HQ (01273) 729051
"Mind-blowing flavour combinations without a hint of meat" again
make this celebrated Lanes fixture "the UK's best veggie bar none".
/ *Sample dishes:* rock salt bruschetta with warm garlic sauce; horchata &
Manchego soufflé; rhubarb & rosehip trifle. *Details:* www.terreaterre.co.uk;
10.30 pm; closed Mon; booking: max 8 at weekends.

BRINKWORTH, WILTSHIRE 2–2C

The Three Crowns £ 36
The Street SN15 5AF (01666) 510366
"There's little competition around Swindon", yet this extended pub –
"in England's longest village" (apparently) – "shows no sign
of complacency", offering a large and "interesting" selection
of "enjoyable" dishes. / *Sample dishes:* venison & pork pie; slices
of kangaroo, venison & ostrich; sticky toffee pudding.
Details: www.threecrowns.co.uk; 9.30 pm.

Perhaps it's partly accounted for by the large number
of student customers, but Bristol is emerging as a city with
an impressive ethnic (and particularly Indian) restaurant
scene. There are also a good number of upmarket and
attractively-located café/brasseries. When it comes to more
serious, non-ethnic restaurants, however, the city lacks a real
figurehead, and the pickings remain relatively thin – *Bell's
Diner* and *Culinaria* are the only destinations of any real note.

The Albion   £ 43
Boyces Ave BS8 4AA   (0117) 9733522
*"Classic" British dishes help win popularity for this "big and noisy"
trendified pub – if you are seeking a quieter environment, head for
the restaurant upstairs.* / **Sample dishes:** *rib of beef with roast bone
marrow & horseradish sauce; roast cod with chanterelles, wet garlic, wood sorrel &
mash.* **Details:** *www.thealbionclifton.co.uk; 10 pm; closed Mon & Sun.*

Bell's Diner   £ 42   Ⓐ ⭐
1 York Rd BS6 5QB   (0117) 924 0357
*"Adventurous, risky, clever, amusing and – unusually for slightly avant-
garde food – easy to enjoy"; Chris Wicks's Montpelier old favourite
may be "casual" in style, but is winning ever-greater local acclaim for
its "innovative" culinary combinations.* / **Sample dishes:** *braised pork;
banana soufflé with toffee ice cream.* **Details:** *www.bellsdiner.co.uk; 10 pm;
closed Mon L, Sat L & Sun.*

Bocacina   £ 24   ⭐
184c, Wells Rd, Lower Knowle BS4 2AL   (0117) 9713377
*"Extremely tasty pizzas" with a "Brazillian influence" wins acclaim for
this café/deli – a sibling to Bocanova – in Lower Knowle.*
/ **Sample dishes:** *carnival seafood pizza with marinated seafood, Mozzarella,
basil & olive oil.* **Details:** *www.bocacina.co.uk; 10:30pm Mon to Sat, 10pm Sun;
no Amex.*

Bocanova   £ 43
90 Colston St BS1 5BB   (0117) 929 1538
*"Consistently good cooking, a warm welcome and a good wine list" –
the attractions of this "zingy" Brazilian; brace yourself, though,
for "long periods between courses".* / **Sample dishes:** *crab shells stuffed
with crab meat; moqueca of salmon; Tia Maria tiramisú.*
Details: *www.bocanova.co.uk; 10.30 pm, Fri & Sat 11 pm; closed Sun; no Amex.*

Bordeaux Quay   £ 43
Canons Rd BS1 5UH   (0117) 943 1200
*A "beautiful waterfront setting" and "an innovative reliance on all
things green" set the scene at this "bright" and "cavernous"
warehouse-conversion, which serves "bistro fare"; to fans it's "a very
enjoyable and relaxing experience" – to critics "chaotic" and "lacking
ambience".* / **Sample dishes:** *salad with herbs & flowers; rump of spring lamb
with borlotti beans, beetroot, chard & salsa verde; chocolate nemesis with
cherries & kirsch cream.* **Details:** *www.bordeaux-quay.co.uk; 10 pm; closed Sun;
no Amex.*

Boston Tea Party £ 18 Ⓐ ⭐

75 Park St BS1 5PF   (0117) 929 8601

"A shabby-chic tea house with principles"; this "quirky" café thrives on "organic and locally-sourced food", "great breakfasts" and "the best coffee in town"; it even has "a small garden for the summer". / **Sample dishes:** *falafel; falafel wraps; carrot cake.* **Details:** *www.bostonteaparty.co.uk; 7.30 pm, Thu-Sat 10 pm; no Amex; no booking.*

Budokan £ 24 ⭐

31 Colston St BS1 5AP   (0117) 914 1488

"Better than Wagamama, which it rather resembles" – a "quick" and "inexpensive" pan-Asian canteen of particular note for its early-evening deal; there's a branch at 31 Colston Street (tel 914 1488). / **Sample dishes:** *crispy spring rolls with plum sauce; thick rice noodles with beef, vegetables & black bean sauce; chocolate fondant with green tea ice cream.* **Details:** *www.budokan.co.uk; 11 pm; closed Sun.*

Cafe Maitreya £ 32 ⭐⭐

89 St Marks Rd, Easton BS5 6HY   (0117) 951 0100

It may be in a "surprising" area (near Stapleton Road Station), but this backstreet operation attracts rave write-ups for "outstanding gourmet vegetarian fare", that's "well worth seeking out". / **Sample dishes:** *roast red pepper & goat's cheese bavarois; wild mushroom, walnut & Gruyère tortellini with sage cream & caramelised apple; white chocolate & almond pudding with damson sauce & damson ice cream.* **Details:** *www.cafemaitreya.co.uk; 9.45; D only, closed Mon & Sun; no Amex.*

A Cozinha £ 36

40 Alfred Pl BS2 8HD   (0117) 944 3060

"The chef insists on cooking everything" – "and I mean everything, with no apparent delegation" – at this "small and welcoming" Portuguese "one-off", in Kingsdown. / **Sample dishes:** *pan-fried chorizo, cherry tomatoes, spinach & red onions; porco na cataplana; orange & almond roulade.* **Details:** *9 pm, Fri & Sat 9.30 pm; D only Tue-Sat, L only Sun; no Amex; booking essential, Sun; children: 14+ at D.*

Culinaria £ 37 ⭐

1 Chandos Rd BS6 6PG   (0117) 973 7999

"The menu may be small, but each dish is imaginative" and "beautifully cooked", at Stephen Markwick's "informal" and "understated" Redland bistro; it "sets the Bristol standard" nowadays, so it's a welcome bonus that you can also take away. / **Sample dishes:** *crab & langoustine risotto; pot roast pheasant; St Emillion au chocolate.* **Details:** *www.culinariabristol.co.uk; 9.30 pm; closed Sun-Tue, Wed L & Thu L; no Amex.*

Dynasty £ 36 ⭐

16a St.Thomas St BS1 6JJ   (0117) 925 0888

"It may be a barn of a place, but the food is fantastic", say fans of this "fast" and "efficient" Chinese operation, which is often praised for its "authentic" fare (not least some "fresh, inspiring and delicious dim sum"). / **Sample dishes:** *steamed sea bass with ginger & spring onions; Emperor's chicken; braised beef brisket.* **Details:** *www.dynasty-bristol.co.uK; 11.30 pm.*

FishWorks £ 45
128 Whiteladies Rd BS8 2RS (0117) 974 4433
*Now eclipsing the Bath original in the consistency of the reports
it inspires – this outpost of the fishmonger-cum-café chain similarly
offers "fresh fish cooked simply but effectively"; (also similarly,
however, it can seem "bloody expensive"). / **Sample dishes:** spaghetti
with langoustines; sea bream baked with herbs & reisling; lemon tart.*
Details: *www.fishworks.co.uk; 10.30 pm; closed Mon & Sun.*

Glasnost £ 30
1 William St BS3 4TU (0117) 972 0938
*A small and "welcoming" Tottertown spot, where "unusual" dishes
of eclectic inspiration are served in a "friendly" and "relaxed"
manner. / **Sample dishes:** black pudding crostini with cherry tomatoes; salmon
en paupiette; Bailey's & Malteser cheesecake.*
Details: *www.glasnostrestaurant.com; 9.45 pm; D only, closed Mon & Sun;
no Amex.*

The Glass Boat £ 43
Welsh Back BS1 4SB (0117) 929 0704

*"For a romantic dinner at sunset", this permanently-moored barge
is a popular local destination; it was re-fitted in mid-2007.
/ **Sample dishes:** braised shank of lamb with couscous salad & apricot & mint
relish; roast duck breast with creamed polenta; crema Catalana with roast black
figs & maple syrup. **Details:** www.glassboat.co.uk; below Bristol Bridge; 9.30 pm;
closed Sat L & Sun D.*

Goldbrick House £ 46
69 Park St BS1 5PB (0117) 945 1950
*"A great newcomer", on most accounts, comprising "an upper-level
restaurant, with a champagne bar, and a street-level cafe"; it's a
"fun" and "funky" place, where the cuisine offers "top-quality
ingredients, simply presented". / **Sample dishes:** beef wellington with
celeriac mash & wild mushrooms; salt baked sea bass with aioli, Swiss chard &
peas. **Details:** www.goldbrickhouse.co.uk; 11 pm, Sun 6 pm; closed Sun D.*

Hotel du Vin et Bistro £ 46
Sugar Hs, Narrow Lewins Mead BS1 2NU (0117) 925 5577
*That it's "entirely reliable for a fun evening" is the draw to this
"wonderfully atmospheric" warehouse-conversion – still the
most popular destination in town, thanks not least to the chain's
"outstanding" wine list; standards, generally, however, seem a bit
more "complacent" of late. / **Sample dishes:** goujon of plaice with tomato
salad; roast rump of lamb; crème brûlée. **Details:** www.hotelduvin.com; 9.45 pm;
booking: max 10. **Accommodation:** 40 rooms, from £135.*

Kathmandu **£ 25**

Colston Tower, Colston St BS1 5AQ   (0117) 9294455
*"Bristol's best-kept secret"; this "Nepalese/Indian" establishment
is tipped for its "subtle" and "interesting" cuisine, and its
"very friendly" service.* / ***Sample dishes:*** *spiced chicken, lamb & lentils patty;
chicken tikka cooked with mushrooms & spring onions; oriental ice cream with
almonds & pistachio nuts.* ***Details:*** *www.kathmandu-curry.com; 11 pm,
Sat 11.30 pm.*

Krishna Inn **£ 17**

4 Byron Pl, Triangle South BS8 1JT   (01179) 276864
*"The wait is over… first class, cheap, south Indian food has arrived
in Bristol"; despite occasionally "erratic" service, this "modern"
operation wins acclaim from locals for its "delicious fare".*
/ ***Sample dishes:*** *onion bhaji; green mutton masala.*

**Mud Dock Café
CycleWorks** **£ 39**

40 The Grove BS1 4RB   (0117) 934 9734
*"A fun place for coffee of lunch" – this "chilled" first-floor waterside
café has a "great location", and attracts a "laid-back" crowd;
the service is unimpressive, but the food generally delivers.*
/ ***Sample dishes:*** *grilled sardines; char-grilled lamb cutlets; chocolate brownie &
white chocolate sauce.* ***Details:*** *www.mud-dock.com; close to the Industrial
Museum & Arnolfini Gallery; 10 pm; no Amex.*

**Old India
Stock Exchange Buildings** **£ 28**

34 St Nicholas St BS1 1TL   (0117) 9221136
*"Delicious, unusual, and authentic dishes" ("the crab dish
is amazing… and I don't like crab!") in "a beautiful listed building" –
that's the deal at this truly impressive all-rounder, where a curry
dinner has a "true sense of occasion".* / ***Sample dishes:*** *battered king
prawns; salmon cooked with mustard seeds & coconut; pistachio kulfi.*
Details: *www.oldindia.co.uk.*

Olive Shed **£ 36**

Floating Harbour, Princes Whf BS1 4RN   (0117) 929 1960
*It's not just the "great waterfront setting" that wins fans for this
"pleasingly out-of-the-way" spot – its "unpretentious" food is "worth
the visit".* / ***Sample dishes:*** *crab ravioli with apple tarragon sauce; blue cheese
gnocchi with beetroot remoulade & walnut salsa; rhubarb & elderflower Eton
mess.* ***Details:*** *www.therealolivecompany.co.uk; 10 pm; closed Mon & Sun D;
no Amex*

One Stop Thali Café £ 21

12 York Rd BS6 5QE (0117) 942 6687

The style may be "entertainingly '60s", but there's nothing flaky about the cooking at this "satisfying veggie thali house" in Montpelier, where the "cheap" and "simple" fare is "always delicious".
/ **Sample dishes:** spinach pakora; saag paneer; kulfi.
Details: www.onestopthali.co.uk; 10 pm; D only, closed Mon; no Amex.

Primrose Café £ 33

1 Boyces Ave BS8 4AA (0117) 946 6577
This "crammed little place" in a Clifton backstreet is one of the most popular haunts in town; by day you "queue and jostle for seating" to enjoy "excellent breakfasts" or "handsomely large sandwiches" – by night it's a "happy bistro", with "above-average" food. / **Sample dishes:** mutton & caper faggot with sautéed kidney; herb-crusted rack of lamb with red wine sauce; chocolate brownie with cheesecake filling.
Details: 9.30 pm; Sun D; no Amex; no booking at L.

Quartier Vert £ 38

85 Whiteladies Rd BS8 2NT (0117) 973 4482
*This veteran Clifton tapas bar bizarrely divides opinion; supporters say it serves "beautiful food", and "always delivers", but there are almost as many critics who – "despite the wonderful organic credentials" – just find the cooking "bland". / **Sample dishes:** shellfish soup; loin of lamb with grilled polenta & salsa verde; pear & ginger pudding.
Details: www.quartiervert.co.uk; 10 pm; Sun D only in summer; no Amex.

Rajpoot £ 37

52 Upper Belgrave Rd BS8 2XP (0117) 973 3515
*A "sophisticated" Indian, with "elegant" décor and "some out-of-the-ordinary" menu offerings; the food is "always good", and "well about the Bristol average for the subcontinent". / **Sample dishes:** calamari; chicken tikka masala; hot jalebies. **Details:** www.rajpootrestaurant.co.uk; 11 pm; D only, closed Sun.

riverstation £ 43

The Grove BS1 4RB (0117) 914 4434
*"Downstairs, with the terrace and the water-views, is the place to be", if you visit this striking-looking former (river) police station; on both levels – upstairs is more formal – the food is, for the most part, "interesting" and "well-presented". / **Sample dishes:** hare & juniper ravioli; red snapper fillet with fennel & potato gnocchi; pear & ginger crumble with bay leaf crème anglaise. **Details:** www.riverstation.co.uk; 10.30 pm; no Amex.

Sands **£ 32** Ⓐ

95 Queens Rd BS8 1LW (0117) 973 9734

This "romantically-lit" joint is a "a great subterranean Lebanese",
with "very friendly" service and "a large selection" of "good-value"
dishes; opinions differ as to whether or not you should "avoid the belly
*dancer". / **Sample dishes:** falafel; baked fillet of snapper with garlic & tomato*
*sauce; baklava. **Details:** www.sandsrestaurant.co.uk; 11 pm.*

Severnshed **£ 38**

The Grove, Harbourside BS1 4RB (0117) 925 1212

"Great site, disappointing food" – that is the gist of many of the
numerous reports on this "stylish" and "bustling" riversider;
*the lunchtime menu, though, is "a steal". / **Sample dishes:** risotto*
of lobster & asparagus; fillet of lamb; Severnshed mess & crushed meringue.
***Details:** www.severnshed.co.uk; 10.30 pm.*

The Star & Dove **£ 35** Ⓣ

75-78 Saint Luke's Rd BS3 4RY (0117) 300 3712

A new boozer that's attracted early praise for food fans say
*is "superb". / **Sample dishes:** slow cooked shin of beef; rump of beef*
*w/ dressed beetroots, horseradish & rocket. **Details:** www.thestaranddove.co.uk;*
11.30 pm, 10.30 pm Tues; closed Mon, Tue-Fri D only, Sat & Sun open L & D.

Teohs **£ 25** ⭐

26-34 Lower Ashley Rd BS2 9NP (0117) 907 1191

It's "a bit like a refectory, with its wooden benches", but this Pan-
Asian canteen remains a "winner", thanks to its "quick, tasty and very
*inexpensive" food. / **Sample dishes:** pad Thai; green curry with prawns;*
*coconut pancake filled with mango. **Details:** 100 yds from M32, J3; 10.30 pm;*
closed Sun; no Amex.

BRITWELL SALOME, OXFORDSHIRE 2–2D

The Goose **£ 49** ⭐

OX49 5LG (01491) 612304

This "quiet", "stylishly refurbished" pub was catapulted to fame
by the attentions of the men from the French tyre company; reports
suggest it lives up, with a "small menu" of "haute" dishes realised
*to a very consistent standard. / **Sample dishes:** fillet of pork; honey roasted*
*barbary duck. **Details:** www.thegooserestaurant.co.uk; M40, J6 near Watlington;*
9.30 pm; closed Mon & Sun D.

BROAD HAVEN, PEMBROKESHIRE 4–4B

Druidstone Hotel **£ 36** Ⓐ⭐

SA62 3NE (01437) 781221

"A gem... in the rough perhaps, but a gem nonetheless";
this "stunningly-located" clifftop spot – with its "'60s-commune values
and aesthetics" – doesn't just offer "fantastic" views, but also "locally-
sourced food of a surprisingly high standard"; "the bar offers better
*value than the restaurant". / **Sample dishes:** salmon potato cake; best end*
of lamb with butter bean & mushroom cassoulet; plum compote with almond cake.
***Details:** www.druidstone.co.uk; from B4341 at Broad Haven turn right, then left*
*after 1.5m; 9.30 pm. **Accommodation:** 11 & 7 holiday cottages rooms,*
from £65.

Drewe Arms £ 43

EX14 3NF (01404) 841267

"A lovely, thatched pub in a typical Devon village"; the speciality is "simply-served" fish and seafood, which on practically all accounts is "fantastic". / *Sample dishes:* mixed seafood; sole & lemon posset; bread & butter pudding. *Details:* 5m from M5, J28, on A373 to Honiton; 9 pm; closed Sun D.

Buckland Manor £ 72

WR12 7LY (01386) 852626

A romantic country house hotel (part of the Von Essen group); as a dinner-destination, it can seem "expensive" for what it is, but lunch is "good value". / *Sample dishes:* pan-fried scallops; warm poppy seed tartlet filled with a ragout of spring vegetables & wild mushrooms; black cherry & kirsch bombe with mixed berry compote. *Details:* www.bucklandmanor.co.uk; 2m SW of Broadway on B4632; 9 pm; jacket & tie at D; booking: max 8; children: 12+. *Accommodation:* 14 rooms, from £250.

Lygon Arms £ 59

High St WR12 7DU (01386) 852255

This famous coaching inn changed hands yet again shortly before this guide went to press; it has really been through the mill in recent years – let's hope its new owners and new chef can finally re-build its reputation. / *Sample dishes:* salad of wood pigeon; roast breast of duckling; chocolate plate. *Details:* www.paramount-thelygonarms.co.uk; just off A44; 9 pm; no jeans. *Accommodation:* 76 rooms, from £179.

Russell's £ 51

20 High St WR12 7DT (01386) 853555

"A huge break from the traditional gloom-ridden provincial restaurant" – this "busy" village brasserie offers "well cooked and presented" food in a "smart", contemporary setting; in the context of the undoubtedly high prices, though, some reporters find standards only "OK". / *Sample dishes:* baked goat's cheese in filo pastry; grilled fillet of sea bream; fresh raspberry & lemon curd crème brûlée with raspberry sorbet. *Details:* www.russellsofbroadway.co.uk; 9.30 pm; closed Sun D. *Accommodation:* 7 rooms, from £115.

Le Poussin at Whitley Ridge   **£ 63**   ●●
Beaulieu Rd SO42 7QL   (0238) 028 2944
"The best local ingredients, expertly prepared" continue to win rave
reviews for the Aitkten family's *"very professional and consistently
good"* small country house hotel; the wines are *"outstanding"* too.
/ **Sample dishes:** *poached breast of quail & crispy quail leg; venison with glazed
pear & walnuts; passion fruit soufflé.* **Details:** *www.lepoussin.co.uk; 9.30 pm;
no Amex; children: 8+ at D.* **Accommodation:** *18 rooms, from £190.*

Rhinefield House   Ⓐ
Hand Picked Hotels   **£ 54**
Rhinefield Rd SO42 7QB   (01590) 622922
*This luxurious Victorian country house hotel, in the New Forest,
generated only limited feedback this year, but again to the effect that
its cooking is "thoughtful and creative".* / **Sample dishes:** *marinated foie
gras; rack of lamb with seared kidney, artichoke purée, tomato lyonnaise, &
rosemary oi supplement; raspberry millefeuille.* **Details:** *www.handpicked.co.uk;
9.30 pm.* **Accommodation:** *50 rooms, from £230.*

Simply Poussin   **£ 32**
The Courtyard, Brookley Rd SO42 7RB   (01590) 623063
*The 'original' Poussin is a simple (and "hard-to-find") affair that
sometimes seems a little "tired" nowadays; on a good day, though,
it still offers "delicous" food from an "interesting" menu.*
/ **Sample dishes:** *ham hock & foie gras terrine with port jelly; cheese soufflé;
passion fruit soufflé.* **Details:** *www.simplypoussin.co.uk; behind Bestsellers
Bookshop; 9 pm; closed Mon & Sun; no Amex; children: 8+ at D.*

Creelers Seafood Restaurant   **£ 39**   ●
Home Farm KA27 8DD   (01770) 302810
"Wonderful seafood, personal service and a good wine list" – that's
the draw to this bistro-style operation (which has
an outpost in Edinburgh). / **Sample dishes:** *home-smoked & cured salmon;
fish stew with langoustine, saffron, & fennel; chocolate chip bread & butter
pudding with vanilla crème anglaise.* **Details:** *www.creelers.co.uk; 9.30 pm; closed
Mon; no Amex.*

Tamasha   **£ 41**   Ⓐ●
131 Widmore Rd BR1 3AX   (020) 8460 3240
*Its "the best Indian on the fringes of south London", say fans of this
"old colonial"-style venture, whose menu offers "a vast array
of unexpected delights for the adventurous diner", and "always to a
very high standard".* / **Sample dishes:** *mixed kebab Karara; king prawns
marinated with almonds & cream.* **Details:** *www.tamasha.co.uk; 10.30 pm;
no shorts.* **Accommodation:** *7 rooms, from £65.*

BRUNDALL, NORFOLK　　　　　　　6–4D

Lavender House　　　　　　　**£ 50**　　Ⓐ⭐
39 The St NR13 5AA　(01603) 712215
*"There is always something special on the menu" – and Richard
Hughes's cooking can be "sublime" – at this "friendly" restaurant,
which is housed in a "beautiful" old cottage. / **Sample dishes:** crispy
grilled fillet of mackerel, warm potato tartare, wilted spinach; lobster with bisque &
potato salad; banana tarte tatin. **Details:** www.thelavenderhouse.co.uk;
12.30 am; D only, closed Sun & Mon; no Amex.*

BUCKDEN, CAMBRIDGESHIRE　　　　3–1A

The George Hotel　　　　　　**£ 45**
High St PE19 5XA　(01480) 812300
*"An elegant and stylish restaurant-with-rooms", located in a "great
little village" (just off the A1); it's praised by almost all reporters for its
"good" food and wines. / **Sample dishes:** pan-fried seabass, lobster mash,
leeks & chives with spring cabbage; best end of lamb, broad beans, spinach,
new potatoes & mustard sauce. **Details:** www.thegeorgebuckden.co.uk; 9.30 pm,
9 pm Sun. **Accommodation:** 12 rooms, from £100.*

BUCKHORN WESTON, DORSET　　　　2–3B

　　　　　　　　　　　　　　　　　⭐
The Stapleton Arms　　　　　**£ 34**
Church Hill SP8 5HS　(01963) 370396
*"Since the renovation, the food from the new owners has been much
better" – this "more-sophisticated-than-usual" country pub is praised
for its "good, honest and well-cooked dishes" (not least "excellent
Sunday roasts"). / **Sample dishes:** char-grilled asparagus spears with
a poached egg & parmesan; seared seabass fillets on a chorizo croquette with
spinach & prawn broth; vanilla panac otta with champagne-poached
blackberries & basil. **Details:** www.thestapletonarms.com; 10 pm, 9.30 pm Sun.
Accommodation: 4 rooms, from £110.*

BUNBURY, CHESHIRE　　　　　　5–3B

The Dysart Arms　　　　　　**£ 36**
Bowes Gate Rd CW6 9PH　(01829) 260183
*A "lovely country pub", with a strong local fan club; it serves
"good food and a good range of well-kept beers too".
/ **Sample dishes:** peppered mackerel croquette, with tomato & cucumber salsa;
bangers with mash & onion gravy; raspberry fool with shortbread biscuits.
Details: www.dysartarms-bunbury.co.uk; 9.30 pm, 9 pm Sun; no Amex; children:
10 + after 6 pm.*

BURFORD, OXFORDSHIRE　　　　　2–2C

　　　　　　　　　　　　　　　　　Ⓐ
The Lamb　　　　　　　　**£ 47**
Sheep St OX18 4LR　(01993) 823155
*This "lovely old-fashioned pub" – which changed hands a few years
ago – has yet to re-establish its culinary credibility with reporters;
fans do praise its "excellent", if "pricey", fare, but there's too much
feedback to the effect that it's "pretentious" or a "rip-off".
/ **Sample dishes:** crab tian with saffron potatoes & a smoked salmon dressing;
sirloin steak; steamed chocolate pudding with orange curd & chocolate orange
sorbet. **Details:** www.lambinn-burford.co.uk; A40 from Oxford toward
Cheltenham; 9.30 pm, 9 pm Sat & Sun; no jeans or trainers.
Accommodation: 17 rooms, from £145.*

Fishes £ 54 ⭐

Market Pl PE31 8HE (01328) 738588

"A gem in the wilds of Norfolk" – the Owsley-Brown's celebrated fish restaurant offers cooking where the *"quality and imagination shines through"*; malcontents, though, complain it's *"sold out to the Chelsea-on-Sea crowd"*. / **Sample dishes:** *fish soup with rouille & Parmesan; roast halibut & caramelised fennel; blueberry & almond tart with hand-churned blueberry ice cream.* **Details:** *www.fishesrestaurant.co.uk; 9.30 pm; closed Mon & Sun L; no Amex; children: 8+ after 8.30 pm.* **Accommodation:** *2 rooms, from £160.*

Hoste Arms £ 39

The Green PE31 8HD (01328) 738777

Fans claim Paul Whittome's fashionable rural rendezvous *"has got better"*, and hail its *"warm"* service and *"lovely"* ambience; if you didn't know better, though, you might just think it was *"a good coaching inn, with solid but uninspired food and a good wine list"*. / **Sample dishes:** *leek & Gruyère tart; fillet steak; banana cake with almond toffee ice cream.* **Details:** *www.hostearms.co.uk; 6m W of Wells; 8.45 pm; no Amex.* **Accommodation:** *36 rooms, from £122.*

Maison Bleue £ 38 🅰⭐

30-31 Churchgate St IP33 1RG (01284) 760623

"Always reliable for a bit of seaside France in East Anglia!" – the Crépy family's *"charming"* bistro wins impressively consistent acclaim for its *"excellent fresh fish"*, its *"friendly"* and *"professional"* service, and its *"wonderful"*, *"buzzy"* atmosphere. / **Sample dishes:** *smoked prawns, smoked haddock, smoked trout; lobster; crème brûlée.* **Details:** *www.maisonbleue.co.uk; near the Cathedral; 9.30 pm; closed Mon & Sun; no Amex; booking essential.*

St James £ 41

30 High St WD23 3HL (020) 8950 2480

"Recent expansions" confirm they're doing something right at this *"friendly"* family-run restaurant, which some reporters tip as *"the best in the area by far"*; *"thanks to business popularity, it's best to book ahead, even at lunchtime"*. / **Sample dishes:** *tiger prawns & scallops; fillet of sea bass & noodles; fruit platter.* **Details:** *www.stjamesrestaurant.co.uk; opp St James Church; 9 pm; closed Sun; booking essential.*

The Place £ 40

New Lydd Rd TN31 7RB (01797) 225057

The *"unpretentious"* dining room of this motel-like building is a *"friendly"* place, offering *"better-than-average"* cooking. / **Sample dishes:** *steamed Scottish scallops; grilled mackerel fillets glazed with chilli jam; home-made truffle tart with crème anglaise.* **Details:** *www.theplacecambersands.co.uk; 9 pm, Fri & Sat 9.30 pm.* **Accommodation:** *18 rooms, from £80.*

The perception still swirls around Cambridge dining that it doesn't have much to offer. In the city-centre that largely remains true, but the city is home to one of the UK's top foodie Meccas (*Midsummer House*), a very solid mid-ranger (*22 Chesterton Road*) and an excellent informal restaurant (*Cotto*). Its attractions are certainly now notably greater than Oxford's.

Backstreet Bistro £ 38
2 Sturton St CB1 2QA (01223) 306306
"Decent food, cooked with care" has made this "off-the-beaten-track" bistro very popular, even if it's a "useful" destination, rather a hugely gastronomic one; there used to be a well-rated 'Brasserie' too, but they're selling it – apparently to concentrate on standards here. / **Sample dishes:** aubergine, red pepper & goat's cheese terrine; pan-fried fillet of beef with sautéed lambs kidneys in a red wine sauce; sticky toffee pudding. **Details:** www.back-street.co.uk; 9.30 pm; children: 4+.

The Black Cat Cafe £ 14
2 The Broadway CB1 3AH (01223) 248972
A "'50s-style café" tipped for its "wonderful sandwiches" and its "inventive and delicious cakes". / **Details:** www.blackcatcafeonline.com; 7 pm, Sun 6 pm; no booking.

Browns £ 30
23 Trumpington St CB2 1QA (01223) 461655
"Always OK" (and "very handy for the Fitzwilliam Museum" too), say fans of this well-known outpost of the famous brasserie chain; critics, though, disagree 100% – they say it's "really not what it once was", and that the food is "always poor". / **Sample dishes:** soup; battered haddock & chips; sticky toffee pudding. **Details:** www.browns-restaurants.com; opp Fitzwilliam Museum; 11; need 5+ to book.

Bruno's Brasserie & Gallery £ 39
52 Mill Rd CB1 2AS (01223) 312702
"Good, innovative food" commends this "pleasant" spot to many reporters; it can seem "overpriced", though, and service can be "haphazard". / **Sample dishes:** chicken liver parfait with plum chutney; fillet of beef with wild mushrooms; chocolate devil's food cake with home-made cardamom ice cream. **Details:** www.brunosbrasserie.com; 9.30 pm; closed Mon L & Sun.

Charlie Chan £ 24
14 Regent St CB2 1DB (01223) 359336
"The best oriental restaurant in Cambridge", say fans of this "stalwart Chinese" praised for its "consistently high standards"; you even "get dancing too!" / **Sample dishes:** sweet & sour pork; crispy duck. **Details:** 11 pm.

Cotto £ 38
183 East Rd CB1 1BG (01223) 302010
"There are no pretentions – just excellent, simple cooking" – at this "sensational", if "small". dining room above a deli ("on an otherwise unattractive street"); a "short but distinctive" menu is realised from "first-class" produce. / **Sample dishes:** tartlet of wild mushroom, Berkswell & spring onion; seared diver-caught Scottish scallops with tagliatelle; wood-roast figs stuffed with local honey & bio-live yoghurt. **Details:** www.cottocambridge.co.uk; 9.30 pm; opening times based on seasons; no Amex.

Curry Queen £ 22

106 Mill Rd CB1 2BD (01223) 351027

The menu is "fairly standard", but this long-established curry house near the Botanical Gardens remains "the best Indian in town". / **Sample dishes:** *onion bhaji; chicken korma; ice cream.* **Details:** *midnight; no Amex.*

Dojo £ 21

1-2 Millers Yd, Mill Ln CB2 1RQ (01223) 363471

A "quick and fast" noodle bar, near the river; it's a "buzzy" place, nicely pitched for a "student budget". / **Sample dishes:** *wok-fried pork dumplings; Pad Thai.* **Details:** *www.dojonoodlebar.co.uk; off Trumpington St; 11 pm; no Amex; no booking.*

Fitzbillies £ 39

52 Trumpington St CB2 1RG (01223) 352500

An offshoot of the famous bakery; its location – "close to the hub of Cambridge social life" – particularly commends it as a lunch spot. / **Sample dishes:** *pumpkin ravioli with sage butter; seared lamb noisette; chocolate, orange & Grand Marnier pot de crème.* **Details:** *www.fitzbillies.com; 9.30 pm; closed Sun D.*

Graffiti
Hotel Felix £ 51

Whitehouse Ln CB3 0LX (01223) 277977

The décor may be a bit "weird", but this design-hotel dining room is usually a "pleasant discovery" ("Thank God, somewhere nice in Cambridge, with interesting food"); service and ambience, though, can be "hit-and-miss". / **Sample dishes:** *frothy green pea soup; beef cooked two ways; pomegranate & ginger brûlée.* **Details:** *www.hotelfelix.co.uk; 10 pm, Fri & Sat 10.30 pm.* **Accommodation:** *52 rooms, from £168.*

Loch Fyne £ 37

37 Trumpington St CB2 1QY (01223) 362433

Despite improvements of recent years, it remains an indictment on Cambridge eating, that this branch – the original, in fact – of the mid-market national fish & seafood chain remains one of the most popular places in town; it's "not inspiring" but "not bad" either. / **Sample dishes:** *deep-fried squid; pan-fried salmon; sticky toffee pudding.* **Details:** *www.lochfyne.com; opp Fitzwilliam Museum; 10 pm.*

Midsummer House £ 84

Midsummer Common CB4 1HA (01223) 369299

Daniel Clifford brings "real flair and ingenuity" – "the ingredients can't possibly work together, but somehow they do" – at this "sensational" dining room, in a "lovely" setting "next to the Cam"; prices, though, are "astronomical". / **Sample dishes:** *ravioli of pork belly & ham hock; braised turbot with peanuts & pistachios; coffee & chocolate fondant & walnut ice cream.* **Details:** *www.midsummerhouse.co.uk; 9.30 pm; closed Mon, Tue L & Sun.*

Peking Restaurant   £ 33

21 Burleigh St CB1 1DG   (01223) 354755

*Some reporters feel the surroundings are "tired and dated",
but almost all agree that the food at this "very friendly", family-run
Chinese stalwart is "impressive". / **Sample dishes:** deep-fried squid & chilli;
Hunan prawns; toffee oranges. **Details:** 10.30 pm; no Amex.*

Rainbow Café   £ 32

9a King's Pde CB2 1SJ   (01223) 321551

*A "vegetarian delight" – this "worthy" caff offers "wholesome" and
"tasty" food (and "actually serves a lot of meat-eaters").
/ **Sample dishes:** Latvian potato bake; spinach lasagne.
Details: www.rainbowcafe.co.uk; 9 pm; no Amex.*

Savino's   £ 14

3 Emmanuel St CB1 1NE   (01223) 566186

*A popular deli tipped for "the best coffee in Cambridge",
plus "very Italian paninis, salads and good home-made soups".
/ **Sample dishes:** paninis; soups. **Details:** 8 pm, 6 pm Sun; no Amex.*

22 Chesterton Road   £ 36

22 Chesterton Rd CB4 3AX   (01223) 351880

*David Carter's "warm and friendly" stalwart in an Edwardian house
maintains quite a following, and a name for "fantastic" value; in fact,
the "very ambitious" style of the cuisine can sometimes seem
"at odds" with the "snug" and "very conservative" setting.
/ **Sample dishes:** figs & parma ham with celeriac & walnut remoulade; pan-fried
sea bass with samphire, steamed spring onions & shrimp Bearnaise; peanut butter
parfait with hazelnuts & chocolate sauce. **Details:** www.restaurant22.co.uk;
9.45 pm; D only, closed Mon & Sun; children: 12+.*

Yim Wah House   £ 30

Ermine St CB3 8PE   (01954) 718330

*A Chinese reporter rates this "tasteful" oriental as "the best Chinese
around Cambridge"; other feedback about this "high-quality" spot
is also very enthusiastic. / **Details:** www.yimwahhouse.co.uk; 11 pm;
no Amex.*

CANTERBURY, KENT   3–3D

Augustines   £ 45

1-2 Longport CT1 1PE   (01227) 453063

*The food at this Georgian townhouse is consistently well-rated
by reporters; its newish régime, though, doesn't seem to have 'gelled'
and a number of reporters feel "it's lacking something" (especially
service). / **Sample dishes:** pan-fried scallops; chump, shoulder & sweetbreads
of lamb; vanilla poached rhubarb with apple struddle & mascarpone sorbet.
Details: near the Cathedral; 9 pm; closed Mon & Sun D; booking: max 7.*

Café des Amis   £ 29

95 St Dunstan's St CT2 8AD   (01227) 464390

*"A fun venue, with reliable food" – in this under-served city, this "laid-
back" Mexican, by Westgate Towers, remains remarkably popular.
/ **Sample dishes:** nachos; fajitas; chocolate fundido. **Details:** www.cafedez.com;
by Westgate Towers; 10 pm; booking: max 6 at D, Fri & Sat.*

Cafe Mauresque £ 30

8 Butchery Ln CT1 2JR (01227) 464300

"One of the better places in this city lacking in good restaurants" – this "stylish" little establishment "takes its inspiration from Moorish Spain and North Africa", and serves "tasty tagines", cous cous and so on; "in summer you can eat out on the pedestrianised street". / **Sample dishes:** *steamed buttered couscous & moroccan vegetable stew; lamb shank tagine with baby aubergines & dates.* **Details:** *www.cafemauresque.com; 10 pm.*

Goods Shed £ 39

Station Road West CT2 8AN (01227) 459153

"Interesting" is a word reporters apply both to the food ("sourced from the farmer's market below") and the setting (a former railway shed near Canterbury West station) at this popular haunt; there seemed to be a few more off-days this year, though. / **Sample dishes:** *breast of pigeon; roast chicken with wild garlic; apple & rhubarb crumble.* **Details:** *9.30 pm; closed Mon & Sun D.*

CARDIFF, CARDIFF 2–2A

Our account of this depressingly under-developed dining-out city remains materially unchanged from last year's. The only place of any real standing is *Le Gallois Y Cymro* in the smart suburb of Canton. In the city-centre, the vast and long-established complex based on a pleasant but dated steak 'n' fish formula incorporating *Champers* and *Le Monde* continue to dominate. Trendy Cardiff Bay still continues to show more style than substance: with an hotel like *Tides* as its landmark, this is perhaps hardly surprising.

Ana Bela Bistro £ 39 Ⓣ

5 Pontcanna St CF11 9HQ (029) 2023 9393

"Always a pleasure to eat here", says a fan of this "lovely little bistro", which is tipped for its "great food and wine". / **Sample dishes:** *breast of duck with raspberries & cassis; fresh grilled pacific oysters with watercress & fennel pesto; chocolate mocha tart.* **Details:** *www.ana-bela.co.uk; 9.30 pm, 10 pm Sat & Sun; closed Mon & Sun.*

Champers £ 35

61 St Mary St CF10 1FE (029) 2037 3363

A long-established steak 'n' fish specialist (offering a very similar formula to the neighbouring La Brasserie), where you choose at the counter, and your main dish is then cooked (simply) for you. / **Sample dishes:** *prawns & garlic; sirloin steak; pâtisserie.* **Details:** *www.le-monde.co.uk; near Castle; 10.30 pm; closed Sun L.*

The Cinnamon Tree £ 29 Ⓣ

173 Kings Rd CF11 9DE (029) 2037 4433

An "upmarket" Indian, tipped for its consistently good use of "fresh ingredients" and "good service". / **Sample dishes:** *fresh water fish; venison.* **Details:** *www.thecinnamontree.co.uk; 10.45 pm; closed Fri L.*

Le Gallois Y Cymro £ 43

6-10 Romilly Cr CF11 9NR (029) 2034 1264

"Still the best in Cardiff" – this brasserie-style "oasis" in Canton eclipses all local competition with its "serious" and "well-presented" food; there's an argument, though, that it's just "the best of a bad bunch", and some reporters feel it's "lost its way a bit in recent times". / **Sample dishes:** *escabeche of mackerel; honey-glazed duck breast; prune & armagnac soufflé.* **Details:** *www.legallois-ycymro.com; 1.5m W of Cardiff Castle; 9 pm, Fri & Sat 10 pm; closed Mon & Sun D; no Amex.*

Gilbys £ 45

Old Port Rd CF5 6ND (029) 2067 0800

*Since the arrival of a new chef, the food "has improved" at this out-of-town venue, tipped for its "good Anglo-French cuisine" (and especially for the value offered by "lunch and early-dinner menus"). / **Sample dishes:** medallions of monkfish & salmon salad; rump steaks. **Details:** www.gilbysrestaurant.co.uk; 5 miles from coverhill cross; 10 pm; closed Sun D; children: 7+.*

Happy Gathering £ 28

233 Cowbridge Road East CF11 9AL (029) 2039 7531

*"Authentic" and "reasonably-priced" – this unchanging Canton Cantonese continues to be "worth travelling from the city-centre for". / **Sample dishes:** crispy duck; toffee bananas with ice cream. **Details:** 10.30 pm.*

Kemi's Cafe
Makers Guild In Wales £ 18

The Flourish, Lloyd George Ave CF10 4QH (029) 20453335

*A "menu that's constantly updated" is part of the formula that earns a tip for this simple café, next door to a craft gallery. / **Sample dishes:** salads; jacket potatoes. **Details:** www.makersguildinwales.org.uk; L only; no credit cards.*

Le Monde £ 37

62 St Mary St CF10 1FE (029) 2038 7376

*Some feel the food is "unspectacular", but this upmarket upstairs sibling to La Brasserie (where "you pick and weigh your own fish") remains a popular city-centre destination. / **Sample dishes:** deep-fried squid; Dover sole; chocolate mousse. **Details:** www.le-monde.co.uk; midnight; closed Sun; need 10+ to book.*

Thai House £ 32

3-5 Guiford Cr CF10 2HJ (029) 2038 7404

*"One of Cardiff's very best restaurants" – this "authentic" spot wins strong majority support from reporters for its "fresh and well-presented" fare. / **Sample dishes:** spiced cod & broccoli steamed in banana leaves; Welsh lamb in a southern Thai curry with peanuts & potatoes. **Details:** www.thaihouse.biz; 11.15 pm; closed Sun.*

Tides Bar And Grill
St David's Hotel & Spa £ 54

Havannah St CF10 5SD (029) 2045 4045

*The view of Cardiff Bay is "nice", but many reporters just "don't understand why people go" to the "poorly-run" dining room of the Welsh capital's top hotel. / **Sample dishes:** smoked salmon; beef medallions & tiger prawn tails; chocolate assiette. **Details:** www.principle-hotels.com; in Cardiff Bay; 10.15 pm. **Accommodation:** 120 rooms, from £120.*

Woods Brasserie £ 44

Pilotage Building, Stuart St CF10 5BW (029) 2049 2400

*"Solid" seems to be the key word in reports on this Bay-side restaurant, which "rarely falls below an acceptable standard"; it can seem too safe, though – "you always feel that could be a very good restaurant if they got out of the 'comfort zone' a bit". / **Sample dishes:** ravioli of wild mushrooms; char-grilled swordfish medallions; raspberry, chocolate & cherry crème brûlée. **Details:** www.woods-brasserie.com; in the Inner Harbour; 10 pm.*

Ty Mawr £ 39

Brechfa SA32 7RA   (01267) 202332
A small hotel, praised for "stunning food, professionally served".
*/ **Sample dishes:** warm oak smoked duck breast & quails egg salad; half lobster with dill mayonnaise, salad leaves & new potatoes; Belgian chocolate & hazelnut cake. **Details:** www.wales-country-hotel.co.uk; 8.30 pm; D only; children: 12+.*
***Accommodation:** 5 rooms, from £98.*

The Fox and Hounds Inn £ 35

DL8 2LG   (01845) 567433
A freehouse, run by the same family since 1983, tipped for its "extremely good food and service at very reasonable prices".
*/ **Details:** www.foxandhoundscarthorpe.co.uk.*

Aynsome Manor £ 38

LA11 6HH   (015395) 36653
Near the genteel resort of Grange-over-Sands, a country house hotel whose style is – unsurprisingly – "not adventurous"; it's tipped, however, as a "cosy" and "reliable" destination.
*/ **Sample dishes:** pheasant & guinea fowl terrine; pan-fried tenderloin of British beef rested on sweet potato ragout finished with Bordelaise sauce; sticky toffee pudding. **Details:** www.aynsomemanorhotel.co.uk; off A590, 0.5m N of village; 8.30 pm; D only, ex Sun open L only; children: 5+ in restaurant at D.*
***Accommodation:** 12 rooms, from £168.*

L'Enclume £ 66

Cavendish St LA11 6PZ   (01539) 536362

*Many tip the "elaborate", "very chefy" tasting menu as the way to go, if you visit this foodie temple – a former forge which enjoys a "perfect" Lakeland location; it can seem like "a load of pretentious foam and air", though, and it remains to be seen how it will fare when Simon Rogan opens a secondary establishment in distant Henley-on-Thames (scheduled for spring 2008). / **Sample dishes:** sea scallops; 24-hour roast lamb shoulder & Feta flageolet; parmesan cake with white chocolate & celery. **Details:** www.lenclume.co.uk; just off the ; 9.15 pm; closed Mon, Tue L & Wed L; no Amex; no jeans or trainers; children: 10+ at D.*
***Accommodation:** 10 rooms, from £98.*

Uplands £ 46 Ⓐ⭐

Haggs Ln LA11 6HD (01539) 536248

"Standards never slip", say fans of this slightly old-fashioned establishment, overlooking Morecambe Bay; game and meat dishes (in particular) are "beautifully cooked and presented".
/ **Sample dishes:** *marinated breast of wood pigeon cooked pink served on pineapple salad with Cumberland sauce; honey-roast duckling; banana, walnut & ginger pie with warm butterscotch sauce.* **Details:** *www.uplands.uk.com; 8 pm; D only, ex Fri & Sun open L & D, closed Mon; no booking, Sat; children: 8+ at D.* **Accommodation:** *5 rooms, from £89.*

CATTERLINE, ABERDEEN 9–3D

Creel Inn £ 34 Ⓐ⭐

AB39 2UL (01569) 750254

"A clifftop location in a little fishing village" adds authenticity to this "friendly" and "relaxed" operation, which offers an "extensive" menu of "seafood cooked in innovative ways". / **Sample dishes:** *crab soup; Cajun sea bass; sticky apple & carrot pudding.* **Details:** *www.thecreelinn.co.uk; 4m S of Stonehaven on A92; 9.30 pm, 9 pm Sun.*

CAUNTON, NOTTINGHAMSHIRE 5–3D

Caunton Beck £ 36

Main St NG23 6AB (01636) 636793

"Good food at any time of day" has made this country restaurant particularly popular as a "stopping-off" point, near the A1; a few disenchanted recent reports, however, raise the fear of "slipping standards". / **Sample dishes:** *garlic & rosmary-infused sardines; anchovy-infused rump of lamb; raspberry cranachan.*
Details: *www.wigandmitre.com; 6m NW of Newark past British Sugar factory on A616; 10 pm.*

CHADDESLEY CORBETT, WORCESTERSHIRE 5–4B

Brockencote Hall £ 46 Ⓐ⭐

DY10 4PY (01562) 777876

"Superb", mainly Gallic service adds to the surprising, "it-could-be-France" feeling some diners have at this very English-looking country house hotel; its cuisine is "lovely" too. / **Sample dishes:** *ballotine of chicken & Parma ham; roast rump of beef; banana crème brûlée & banana cake.* **Details:** *www.brockencotehall.com; on A448, just outside village; 9.30 pm; closed Sat L.* **Accommodation:** *17 rooms, from £120.*

CHAGFORD, DEVON 1–3D

Gidleigh Park £ 94 Ⓐ⭐⭐

TQ13 8HH (01647) 432367

"An absolute delight"; this famous Tudorbethan "retreat" has emerged from a recent relaunch (following a change of ownership) to rapturous acclaim; Michael Caines's food is still "superb", service has "lots of charm" and the setting, on the edge of Dartmoor, is as "magical" as ever. / **Details:** *www.gidleigh.com; from village, right at Lloyds TSB, take right fork to end of lane; 9 pm; children: 7+ at D.* **Accommodation:** *14 rooms, from £440.*

22 Mill Street   £ 54   ★★

22 Mill St TQ13 8AW (01647) 432244

You get "stunning food at half the price of Gidleigh Park", at Duncan Walker's "serious but fun" little gaff, in the village near the gates of his former employer; "personal service from the chef" and a wine list with "ungrabby mark-ups" complete the experience.
/ *Sample dishes:* crab lasagne; roast loin of rabbit; blackcurrant soufflé.
Details: www.22millstreetrestaurant.co.uk; 9 pm; closed Mon, Tue L & Sun; no Amex; children: 14+. *Accommodation:* 2 rooms, from £75.

CHALFONT ST GILES, BUCKINGHAMSHIRE   3–2A

Ivy House   £ 35   ★

London Rd HP8 4RS (01494) 872184

"Excellent" is a word applied frequently to the cuisine at this old freehouse in the Chilterns; it offers an "extensive" menu too, and is "always busy". / *Details:* 10 pm.

CHANDLER'S CROSS, HERTFORDSHIRE   3–2A

Colette's
The Grove   £ 73

WD3 4TG (01923) 296015

"Memorable" meals are sometimes to be had in the fine-dining room of this contemporary-style luxury hotel, and it's certainly "hard to beat in the area"; there's a feeling, however, that the food may be "lovely stuff", but it's "way too expensive". / *Sample dishes:* crab & sevruga caviar; sea bass with langoustine Parmesan gnocchi; coconut parfait with pineapple fritters, black cherries & pina colada sauce. *Details:* www.thegrove.co.uk; J19 or 20 on M25; 10 pm; D only, closed Mon & Sun; no jeans or trainers. *Accommodation:* 227 rooms, from £295.

The Glasshouse
The Grove   £ 55

WD3 4TG (01923) 296015

A "wide" and "novel" selection of dishes makes this groovy-grand hotel buffet "better than many carvery-restaurants"; reporters feel it's "gone down" of late, though, and is no longer "what you'd really expect for the price". / *Sample dishes:* confit of baby octopus & artichokes; roast prime rib of beef; lemon panna cotta with mandarin compote.
Details: www.thegrove.co.uk; 9.30 pm, Sat 10 pm. *Accommodation:* 227 rooms, from £295.

CHELMSFORD, ESSEX   3–2C

The Punch Bowl   £ 55   ⊤

The Street CM1 4QW (01245) 231222

It's "almost impossible to get a booking", notes a fan of this restaurant in a Tudor inn, where a particular attraction is "the most fantastic cellar". / *Sample dishes:* supreme of chicken, filled with cream cheese & baked with a Dijon mustard, Parmesan & wine sauce; Châteaubriand with Bearnaise sauce; raspberry & champagne sorbet.
Details: www.thepunchbowl.co.uk; 9.30 pm; closed Mon, Tue, Wed, Thu, Fri L, Sat L & Sun D.

Café Paradiso
Hotel Kandinsky £ 39
Bayshill Rd GL50 3AS (01242) 527788
This "very buzzy" design-hotel brasserie doesn't please all reporters,
but most find the cooking "interesting" (with "great" pizzas
a highlight), and they say the wine list is "superb" too.
/ **Sample dishes:** beef carpaccio; pan-fried cod fillet; toffee & melted honeycomb
cheesecake. **Details:** www.aliashotels.com; 10 pm. **Accommodation:** 48 rooms,
from £120.

Champignon Sauvage £ 64
24-28 Suffolk Rd GL50 2AQ (01242) 573449

David Everitt-Matthias is an "unsung hero of British cuisine", and his
"bold and exciting" cooking draws foodies from far and wide to his
(and wife Helen's) pleasant and "brightly-lit" 20-year-old, near the
town-centre; "self-assured" but "not pompous", it even manages
to offer a "top-rate" wine list at very "reasonable" prices!
/ **Sample dishes:** roast duck foie gras; lamb; fig tart with brown butter ice cream.
Details: www.lechampignonsauvage.co.uk; near Cheltenham Boys College; 9 pm;
closed Mon & Sun.

Daffodil £ 40
18-20 Suffolk Pde GL50 2AE (01242) 700055
Forget the "average" food – it's the "absolutely wonderful" Art Deco
setting which makes this former cinema of particular interest;
the "basic" prix-fixe menu is "good value" too.
/ **Sample dishes:** asparagus & carrot brisée tart; oven-roast duck breast; pear &
brown sugar cheesecake. **Details:** www.thedaffodil.co.uk; just off Suffolk Square;
9.45 pm; closed Sun.

Lumière £ 51
Clarence Pde GL50 3PA (01242) 222200
Though it "lives in the shadow of the 'Wild Fungus'", the occasional
reporter actually prefers Lin & Geoff Chapmans' town-centre bistro
to the local eminence, and praises its "carefully-prepared" dishes that
"never disappoint". / **Sample dishes:** foie gras wrapped in Parma ham
on sautéed potatoes with caramelised apple & balsamic; char-grilled spring bok
fillets, with truffle-scented mushrooms; pecan torte. **Details:** www.lumiere.cc;
off the promenade on the inner ring; 8.30 pm; D only, closed Mon & Sun;
no Amex; booking: max 10; children: 6+.

Mayflower £ 36
32-34 Clarence St GL50 3NX (01242) 522426
"A good old-fashioned Chinese", in business for over a quarter of a
century. / **Sample dishes:** chicken pastry; king prawns with spicy red pepper
sauce; toffee bananas with sesame seeds.
Details: www.themayflowerrestaurant.co.uk; 10.30 pm.

Ruby   **£ 25**

52 Suffolk Rd GL50 2AQ   (01242) 250909

*"It's best to book", if you want to check out this popular spot, which offers some "agreeably different" Chinese fare. / **Details:** near Cheltenham Boys College; 11.15 pm.*

Storyteller   **£ 34**   Ⓐ

11 North Pl GL50 4DW   (01242) 250343

*It's the "interesting", "pick-your-own" wine room which makes ten-year-old venture of note – the food is "fine", but not what it's all about. / **Sample dishes:** dipping bread with sauces; kebab of pork fillet marinated with cider & mustard; home-made vanilla cheesecake. **Details:** www.storyteller.co.uk; near the cinema; 10 pm; no Amex.*

CHESTER, CHESHIRE   5–2A

Albion Inn   **£ 21**   Ⓐ

Park St CH1 1RN   (01244) 340345

*"Home-cooked food like your granny used to make" is the stock-in-trade of this stoutly "traditional" boozer, near the Newgate; for some reporters, the fact that "no children are allowed" is a "bonus" too. / **Sample dishes:** boiled gammon; Cumberland sausage; rhubarb crumble & custard. **Details:** www.albioninnchester.co.uk; 8 pm; closed Sun D; no credit cards; need 6+ to book; children: 18+. **Accommodation:** 2 rooms, from £75.*

Aqua-Vitus   **£ 28**   ★

58 Watergate St CH1 2LA   (01244) 313721

*Probably the city's top choice for lunch – this "welcoming" bistro is a "good find", thanks to its "fresh and original" (Swedish/French) cuisine, and its "hospitable but not intrusive" service. / **Sample dishes:** crab carbonara; pheasant with chestnut & smoked bacon ragout; orange & milk chocolate bread & butter pudding with grand marnier anglaise. **Details:** www.aquavitus.co.uk; 10.30 pm; closed Sun.*

Arkle

The Chester Grosvenor   **£ 85**

Eastgate CH1 1LT   (01244) 324024

*If you can "ignore the prices", there's no doubt that this city-centre dining room offers a "superb" dining experience, commensurate with the grandeur of the Duke of Westminster's hotel – if you can't, however, you might simply find it "over-rated". / **Sample dishes:** frogs' legs, langoustines & truffles; grilled fillet of veal; banana soufflé. **Details:** www.chestergrosvenor.com; 9.30 pm; D only, closed Mon & Sun; no jeans or trainers; booking essential; children: 12+. **Accommodation:** 80 rooms, from £185.*

Francs   **£ 32**   Ⓣ

14 Cuppin St CH1 2BN   (01244) 317952

*An "atmospheric" bistro of long standing; critics find it "mediocre", but its "good-value" lunch in particular has a following. / **Details:** www.francs.co.uk; 10 pm, Sun 7 pm.*

Moules A Go Go   **£ 37**   Ⓣ

39 Watergate Row CH1 2LE   (01244) 348818

*"Still a reliable destination", this nicely-located bistro – whose menu has a wider range than its name implies – is tipped as an excellent place for a "tasty" bite. / **Sample dishes:** moules; scallops; Swiss Toblerone fondue. **Details:** www.moulesagogo.co.uk; 10 pm, Sun 9 pm.*

CHETTLE, DORSET 2–4C

Castleman Hotel £ 35 Ⓐ ⭐
DT11 8DB (01258) 830096
"What a traditional, small country hotel should be" – a "very good-value destination", with an "entertaining" owner and "good" food.
/ **Sample dishes:** halibut gratin; roast duck; frangipane tart.
Details: www.castlemanhotel.co.uk; 9 pm; D only, ex Wed & Sun open L & D; no Amex. **Accommodation:** 8 rooms, from £80.

CHICHESTER, WEST SUSSEX 3–4A

Comme Ça £ 47
67 Broyle Rd PO19 6BD (01243) 788724
A "wonderful pre-theatre menu" and "lovely" al fresco dining area add lustre to this "charming" Gallic stalwart; to fans, it's "the friendliest place" with "excellent food", but there are others for whom it's "no more than average" but which seems to think it's "the bees' knees". / **Sample dishes:** pan-fried tiger prawns & cucumber spaghetti; confit of wild rabbit; ice cream. **Details:** www.commeca.co.uk; 0.5m N of city-centre; 10.30 pm; closed Mon, Tue L & Sun D; no Amex.

Dining Room £ 48 Ⓣ
31 North St PO19 1LY (01243) 537352
"A civilised setting, with good food and wine" – that's the deal at this restaurant (and now adjoining tapas bar), elegantly housed in the Georgian premises of a wine merchant. / **Sample dishes:** crab au gratin with ginger, leeks & Gruyère; breast of wood pigeon with cabbage purée & a gratin of beetroot; passion fruit & orange tart. **Details:** www.thediningroom.biz; 8.45 pm; closed Sun; children: 14+.

CHIGWELL, ESSEX 3–2B

The Bluebell £ 50
117 High Rd IG7 6QQ (020) 8500 6282
This popular gaff in an "under-served" area is "perfect for lunch"; at night, however, it can get "noisy", and not all reporters are convinced that the food ("uninspiring") is up to the prices ("enormous" portions notwithstanding). / **Sample dishes:** finely-sliced sugar-cured salmon pickled; roast fillet of pork; Belgian Valrhona chocolate tart.
Details: www.thebluebellrestaurant.co.uk; 10 pm, Sat 12.30 am; closed Mon, Sat L & Sun D.

CHILGROVE, WEST SUSSEX 3–4A

White Horse £ 46
High St PO18 9HX (01243) 535219
"You go for the wine" – the list is "to die for" – to this "pleasant" South Downs inn; good al fresco dining possibilities too.
/ **Sample dishes:** crab & lobster; loin of venison; raspberry soufflé with ice cream.
Details: www.whitehorsechilgrove.co.uk; 8m NW of Chichester on B2141; 9.30 pm; closed Mon & Sun D; no Amex. **Accommodation:** 9 rooms, from £95.

CHILLESFORD, WOODBRIDGE, SUFFOLK 3–1D

The Froize Inn £ 36 ⭐
The St IP12 3PU (01394) 450282
"A superb choice of beautifully-cooked dishes" – from a "hot buffet" – rewards visitors to this country inn; its atmosphere is boosted by a "charming" host, and "very pleasant" staff. / **Sample dishes:** salad of smoked duck breast with plum sauce; fresh sea trout with spinach & local cheese; home-made sticky toffee pudding. **Details:** www.froize.co.uk; 8.30 pm but varies seasonally; closed Mon, Tue D, Wed D & Sun D.

CHINNOR, OXFORDSHIRE 2–2D

Sir Charles Napier **£ 47** **Ⓐ**
Spriggs Alley OX39 4BX (01494) 483011
*A feeling that it's "much-sought-after by those in-the-know" helps
create a "lovely" ambience at this "tucked-away" Chilterns "stalwart",
which has "log fires in winter" and a "magnificent garden"
in summer; service can "let them down", though, and – as ever –
some reporters "can't see what the fuss is about".*
/ **Sample dishes:** *scallops with celeriac purée, tortollino & velouté; rib-eye steak;
banana cheesecake & maple syrup ice cream.*
Details: *www.sircharlesnapier.co.uk; M40, J6 into Chinnor, turn right
at roundabout, carry on straight up hill for 2 miles; 10 pm; closed Mon & Sun D;
children: 6+ at D.*

CHIPPENHAM, WILTSHIRE 2–2C

Bybrook Restaurant
Manor House Hotel **£ 70** **Ⓣ**
Castle Combe SN14 7HR (01249) 782206
*An impressive old manor house, tipped as an all-round "totally
wonderful experience", with "top-notch food" ("and a bill to match").*
/ **Sample dishes:** *poach roasted saddle of rabbit with braised leg & kidney
faggot, with swede, green kale, & braised shallot, green peppercorn jus;
warm caramelised pear tart, caramel ice cream & pear foam.*
Details: *www.exclusivehotels.co.uk; 9.30 pm, Fri & Sat 10 pm; no trainers.*
Accommodation: *48 rooms, from £235.*

CHIPPING CAMPDEN, GLOUCESTERSHIRE 2–1C

Juliana's
Cotswold House Hotel **£ 62** **Ⓣ**
GL55 6AN (01386) 840330
*A "pleasant-all-round", modern Cotswold village hotel that boasts both
a restaurant (Juliana's) and a brasserie (Hicks); reports suggest both
are decent, with the former the better of the two.* / **Sample dishes:** *tian
of crab; loin of lamb; citrus soufflé, gin & tonic sorbet.*
Details: *www.cotswoldhouse.com; 9.45 pm; D only, ex Sun open L &
D.* **Accommodation:** *29 rooms, from £150.*

CHOLMONDELEY, CHESHIRE 5–3A

Cholmondeley Arms **£ 31** **Ⓣ**
SY14 8HN (01829) 720300
*A "good dining pub" in one of the prettiest parts of Cheshire;
it's located in a former schoolhouse, "opposite the entrance to the
Cholmondeley Estate".* / **Sample dishes:** *remoulade of celeriac with sliced
avocado; roast guinea fowl with apple, cream & calvados sauce; hot fudged
bananas.*

CHRISTCHURCH, DORSET 2–4C

FishWorks **£ 45** **★**
10 Church St BH23 1BW (01202) 487000
*Near the Priory, one of the best-received branches of the pricey fish
and seafood chain, accorded "firm favourite" status by some
reporters.* / **Sample dishes:** *spaghetti with langoustines; sea bream baked with
herbs & reisling; lemon tart.* **Details:** *www.fishworks.co.uk; 10 pm; closed
Mon & Sun.*

Seven Tuns   £ 32
Queen St GL54 4AE   (01285) 720242
"Staff who could not be more friendly or helpful" add to the appeal
of an inn offering *"very good gastropub fare"*. / *Sample dishes:* fish &
chips; steak & chips; lamb shank. *Details:* 9.30 pm, 9 pm Sun; no Amex.

Tatyan's   £ 30
27 Castle St GL7 1QD   (01285) 653529
A Chinese stalwart – 20 years old this year – tipped for its *"lovely
food for both vegetarians and meat-eaters"*. / *Sample dishes:* beet-fried
courgette; stir-fried chicken; ice cream. *Details:* www.tatyans.com; near junction
of A417 & A345; 10.30 pm; closed Sun L.

Loch Fyne Oyster Bar   £ 37
PA26 8BL   (01499) 600236
"Brilliantly located" by the water – the original LFOB (owned
separately from the chain) is still hailed as a *"great place"* with
"spankingly fresh" fish; pricing can seem high though, and some
reporters say the food is *"OK"*, but that *"there's better elsewhere"*.
/ *Sample dishes:* sea-baked oysters; bradan rost; chocolate & brandy truffle cake.
Details: www.loch-fyne.com; 10m E of Inveraray on A83; 8.30 pm, after Oct
7.30 pm.

The Cricketers   £ 39
Wicken Rd CB11 4QT   (01799) 550442
Brace yourself for *"a surfeit of Jamie Oliver memorabilia"*, but this
"welcoming" 16th-century inn (run by his folks) can delivery some
"outstanding" food; the place can sometimes get *"packed"*, though,
and a few reports this year were *"a little disappointing"*.
/ *Sample dishes:* marinated prawns & scallops; roast rack of lamb; sticky toffee
pudding. *Details:* www.thecricketers.co.uk; on B1038 between Newport &
Buntingford; 9.45 pm. *Accommodation:* 14 rooms, from £110.

The Bell And Cross   £ 36
Holy Cross DY9 9QL   (01562) 730319
"A really lovely country pub", said to offer *"very good value"* on the
food front. / *Details:* www.bellandcrossclent.co.uk; 9 pm, 9.30 pm Fri & Sat;
no Amex.

Four Stones   £ 36
Adams Hill DY9 9PS   (01562) 883260
A *"very friendly Italian that serves large helpings of good food"* –
useful to know about if you find yourself in this under-provided part
of the world. / *Sample dishes:* fish; wild sea bass; raspberry delight.
Details: www.thefourstones.co.uk; 10 pm; closed Mon & Sun D.

CLIPSHAM, RUTLAND

6–4A

The Olive Branch £ 39
Main St LE15 7SH (01780) 410355

Sean Hope & Ben Jones's "terrific" venture enjoys a gigantic following, despite its "rural Rutland" setting; proximity to the A1 helps, but the main draw is "perfect execution" of its gastropub formula, with "consistently excellent" food served in an "informal" and "wonderfully buzzy" setting; (now offering rooms, too).
/ **Sample dishes:** *tempura-battered tiger prawns; pan-fried liver; egg custard tart.* **Details:** *www.theolivebranchpub.com; 2m E from A1 on B664; 9.30 pm; no Amex.* **Accommodation:** *6 rooms, from £90.*

CLITHEROE, LANCASHIRE

5–1B

Inn at Whitewell £ 39
Forest of Bowland BD7 3AT (01200) 448222
"The best location" – in the "wonderful" Trough of Bowland – adds to the lustre of this "quaint" country hotel; it's "improving again" having "gone downhill following the extension" last year, and though not yet up to its best past form, is highly-rated for its "lovely pub cooking".
/ **Sample dishes:** *seared king scallops; roast breast of wood pigeon; sticky toffee pudding.* **Details:** *www.innatwhitewell.com; 9.30 pm; D only (bar meals only at L); no Amex.* **Accommodation:** *23 rooms, from £93.*

COBHAM, SURREY

3–3A

La Capanna £ 42
48 High St KT11 3EF (01932) 862121
A "pretty" restaurant with "good" Italian food and a "delightful" garden, or an "overpriced dinosaur"? – the debate about this "stockbroker-belt-beautiful-people hang-out" continues…
/ **Sample dishes:** *crab; fillet of monkfish with anchovy, rosemary, nut butter; hazelnut meringue with fresh raspberries & vanilla cream.* **Details:** *www.lacapanna.co.uk; 10.30 pm.*

COCKERMOUTH, CUMBRIA

7–3C

Kirkstile Inn £ 30
Loweswater CA13 0RU (0190) 085219
In a "superb setting", an ancient inn with quite a name for its "straightforward" food; it's "well worth a visit, even though it's always too busy for comfort". / **Sample dishes:** *black pudding pan-fried in beer batter with rich red wine sauce; baked lamb shoulder with rosemary & red wine sauce; sticky toffee pudding.* **Details:** *www.kirkstile.com; 9 pm; no Amex.* **Accommodation:** *9 rooms, from £41.50.*

Quince & Medlar   £ 36

13 Castlegate   CA13 9EU   (01900) 823579

This "just charming" townhouse venture retains a small but loyal fan club, who praise "veggie food that's so lovely you don't miss meat"; they like its "romantic" ambience too. / **Sample dishes:** *pastry case filled with smoked Cumberland cheese soufflé & button mushrooms; Wensleydale cheese & Sicilian globe artichoke hearts; dark chocolate & orange pistachio cake.* **Details:** *www.quinceandmedlar.co.uk; next to Cockermouth Castle; 9.30 pm; D only, closed Mon & Sun; no Amex; children: 5+.*

COLERNE, WILTSHIRE   2–2B

Lucknam Park   £ 83

SN14 8AZ   (01225) 742777

Hywel Jones's "simply superb" cuisine — not to mention "flawless" service and an "idyllic" location — make this "very grand" Georgian country house hotel (set in 500 acres) a "perfect retreat for unwinding and pampering". / **Sample dishes:** *duck three ways; fillet of turbot; iced honeycomb parfait, banana tart, bitter chocolate sorbet.* **Details:** *www.lucknampark.co.uk; 6m NE of Bath; 9.45 pm; D only, ex Sun open L & D; no jeans or trainers; children: 5+ at D.* **Accommodation:** *41 rooms, from £255.*

COLNBROOK, BERKSHIRE   3–3A

The Ostrich Inn   £ 36

High St   SL3 0JZ   (01753) 682628

This 900-year-old inn was refurbished just last year; fans say it now "a pleasure to eat at" what's now an "excellent all-round" gastropub. / **Sample dishes:** *ostrich Wellington; fillet of beef Stroganoff; peanut brittle cheesecake with raspberry coulis.* **Details:** *www.theostrichcolnbrook.co.uk; 9.15 pm, 5.30 pm Sun.*

COMPTON, SURREY   3–3A

The Withies Inn   £ 42

Withies Ln   GU3 1JA   (01483) 421158

A very popular pub in the Surrey Hills that's "particularly nice on a sunny day"; many reporters feel it's "lost its way rather", though, with food that's "not what you'd expect for the price". / **Sample dishes:** *crab; suckling pig; treacle tart.* **Details:** *off A3 near Guildford, signposted on B3000; 10 pm, Sun 4 pm; closed Sun D.*

CONGLETON, CHESHIRE 5–2B

Pecks £ 43 ⭐
Newcastle Rd CW12 4SB (01260) 275161
"The format remains unique" (a seasonally-changing, no-choice five
or seven-course menu, served at a single sitting) and *"adds a special
touch"* to the Peck family's well-established venture; all reports this
year attested to its *"very consistent"* standards. / **Sample dishes:** *baked
baby halibut with carrot & orange vinaigrette; roasted porchetta with apple confit,
parisienne potatoes & Madeira gravy.* **Details:** *www.pecksrest.co.uk; off A34;
8 pm; closed Mon & Sun D; booking essential.*

CONSTANTINE, CORNWALL 1–4B

Trengilly Wartha Inn £ 34 🅐
Nancenoy TR11 5RP (01326) 340332
"Finding it is half the challenge", but when you have winkled out this
"popular, rural inn" you may find the *"lovely"* setting a safer attraction
than the food; *"a large range of quality wines and beers"* also offers
much consolation. / **Sample dishes:** *Thai crab soup; John Dory
fillet; amaretto & pistachio parfait.* **Details:** *www.trengilly.co.uk; 1m outside
village; 9.30; no Amex.* **Accommodation:** *8 rooms, from £80.*

COOKHAM, BERKSHIRE 3–3A

Bel & The Dragon £ 39 🅐
High St SL6 9SQ (01628) 521263
*Huge but "cosy", this "fun" gastropub "looks great", and attracts
pretty consistent commentary praising its "good pub food".*
/ **Sample dishes:** *salmon & smoked haddock fishcakes; pan-fried salmon fillet
on a tomato fondue & fennel purée; sticky toffee pudding.*
Details: *www.belandthedragon-cookham.co.uk; opp Stanley Spencer Gallery;
10 pm.*

Inn on the Green £ 58
The Old Cricket Common SL6 9NZ (01628) 482638
*It has a "gorgeous" Thames Valley location, but this much-marketed
inn (where Garry Hollihead is consultant chef) again inspired mixed
reports this year; fans were "blown away" by its "beautiful" food –
critics, though, just say that standards are "getting progressively
worse".* / **Sample dishes:** *roast sea scallops with bacon & black pudding;
smoked rump of lamb; chocolate fondant with peanut butter ice cream.*
Details: *www.theinnonthegreen.com; 10 pm; closed Mon & Sun D; booking:
max 6 on Sat.* **Accommodation:** *9 rooms, from £120.*

Maliks £ 40 ⭐
High St SL6 9SF (01628) 520085
*"Superb Indian cooking, all freshly cooked and with wonderful spices
and aromas"* has created a sizeable fan club for this superior curry
house. / **Sample dishes:** *spiced chicken on a skewer; tender lamb; rice pudding.*
Details: *www.maliks.co.uk; 11.30 pm.*

CORBRIDGE, NORTHUMBERLAND 8–2B

The Angel of Corbridge £ 38
Main St NE45 5LA (01434) 632119
*In a cute village, a former coaching inn which was given a make-over
a couple of years ago; "reliable but not spectacular" is the
gist of most reports.* / **Sample dishes:** *crab salad; duck breast with baby
spinach; apple strudel.* **Details:** *8.45 pm; closed Sun D.* **Accommodation:** *5
rooms, from £85.*

The Valley £ 29 ⭐

Old Station Hs NE45 5AY (01434) 633434

*For easy access, "take the 'curry train'" (from Newcastle – you order en route), when you visit this rural Indian; it well known locally for its "great" food and its "very good" service. / **Sample dishes:** bhuna prawn on purée; shatkora delight with special lemon; gulab jamun.*
Details: *www.valleyrestaurants.co.uk; 11 pm; D only, closed Sun.*

CORSCOMBE, DORSET 2–4B

Fox Inn £ 37 🅐

DT2 0NS (01935) 891330

*A "picture-perfect" pub that some find "an absolute culinary delight"; one former fan was "disappointed in the extreme" this year, though, adding to a rather mixed pattern of feedback. / **Sample dishes:** chicken breast stuffed with Mozzarella & basil, wrapped in smoked bacon; 5-spiced breast of duck with red wine & cranberry sauce; bread & butter pudding.*
Details: *www.thefoxinn.co.uk; 5m off A37; 9 pm; no Amex; children: 5+.*
Accommodation: *4 rooms, from £80.*

CORSE LAWN, GLOUCESTERSHIRE 2–1B

Corse Lawn Hotel £ 44

GL19 4LZ (01452) 780771

*Many traditionalists say it's "always a treat" to visit the Hine family's elegant (Queen Anne) village house hotel; it can "lack atmosphere", though, and provoked a couple of downbeat reports this year. / **Sample dishes:** smoked chicken breast salad; roast saddle of venison; chocolate brownie with orange caramel sauce. **Details:** www.corselawn.com; 5m SW of Tewkesbury on B4211; 9.30 pm; no jeans or trainers. **Accommodation:** 19 rooms, from £145.*

COVENTRY, WEST MIDLANDS 5–4C

Thai Dusit £ 30

39 London Rd CV1 2JP (024) 7622 7788

*"Consistently-good cooking" continues to draw an enthusiastic local following to this reliable Thai; well, it isn't the location – near the ring road. / **Sample dishes:** green curry; fish; banana fritter. **Details:** 11 pm.*

COWBRIDGE, VALE OF GLAMORGAN 2–2A

Farthings £ 36

54 High St CF71 7AH (01446) 772990

*"A market-town restaurant, frequented by locals and visitors" alike, serving "reliable" bistro fare; bookings, though, are only taken for the relatively "austere" upstairs, so "arrive early" for a table in the "jovial" room below. / **Sample dishes:** French onion soup; pan-fried pork fillet with a rosemary & ciderjus; hazelnut & raspberry meringue.*
Details: *www.farthingsofcowbridge.co.uk; 9.30 pm, 10 pm Fri & Sat; closed Mon D & Sun D; no Amex.*

COWLEY, GLOUCESTERSHIRE 2–1C

Cowley Manor £ 51 ❌

GL53 9NL (01242) 870900

*"One visits this contemporary country house hotel for the spa treatments and the modern room designs and the location" – the food can be "somewhat boring". / **Sample dishes:** seared scallops; beef Wellington; squidgy chocolate pudding with pistachio ice cream.*
Details: *www.cowleymanor.com; 10 pm, Fri & Sat 11 pm. **Accommodation:** 30 rooms, from £245.*

CRACKINGTON, CORNWALL   1–2C

Trevigue Restaurant   £ 35   Ⓣ
EX23 0LQ   (01840) 230418
*"A fine old farm on the Cornish cliffs, offering a small menu of top-notch local fare"; "much of the food is produced on the family's own farm and many of the ingredients are organic". / **Sample dishes:** pork loin with prune stuffing wrapped in dry-cured bacon; steak Stroganoff.*
Details: *www.trevigue.co.uk; 8.30 pm; D only, closed Mon–Wed & Sun; no Amex.*

CRAGG VALE, WEST YORKSHIRE   5–1B

The Hinchliffe   £ 33   Ⓣ
Mytholm Rd HX7 5TA   (01422) 883256
*This "hidden gem" of a pub "at the head of a picturesque valley" is especially tipped as "a nice place for Sunday lunch" ("either in the restaurant or bar area")… so long as you don't have kids that is ("it's adults only"). / **Sample dishes:** deep fried brie with apricot & red onion chutney; roast lamb with Yorkshire pudding & vegetables; plum crumble with vanilla ice cream. **Details:** www.thehinchliffe.com; 9 pm; closed Mon; no Amex; children: 18+.*

CRANBROOK, KENT   3–4C

Apicius   £ 42   ★
23 Stone St TN17 3HF   (01580) 714666
*"Outstandingly good" food is served in the "small and simple modern dining room" of Tim Johnson's town-centre operation – all reporters agree is "well worth a visit"; "pre-booking essential".
/ **Sample dishes:** deep-fried veal sweetbreads; roast loin of lamb; cinnamon-poached apple with crème fraîche sorbet.
Details: www.restaurantapicius.co.uk; 9 pm; closed Mon, Tue L, Sat L & Sun D; no Amex; children: 8+.*

CRASTER, NORTHUMBERLAND   8–1B

Jolly Fisherman   £ 17   Ⓣ
NE66 3TR   (01665) 576461
*"Jolly might be pushing it", says one reporter, but this coastal boozer's crab soup still has quite a name; the location is "beautiful" too.
/ **Sample dishes:** kipper pâté with Melba toast; crab & whisky soup; apple crumble. **Details:** www.thejollyfisherman.org.uk; near Dunstanburgh Castle; 8 pm; L only; no credit cards; no booking.*

CREIGIAU, CARDIFF   2–2A

Caesars Arms   £ 38   ★
Cardiff Rd CF15 9NN   (029) 2089 0486
*You choose your food from the chillers and they cook it for you, at this rural counterpart to Cardiff city-centre's La Brasserie; it's "nothing sophisticated" – just "good honest food" – but fish, in particular, is "fantastic". / **Sample dishes:** asparagus & shaved Parmesan; lamb with leek; raspberry & hazelnut Pavlova. **Details:** beyond Creigiau, past golf club; 10 pm; closed Sun D.*

CRICKHOWELL, POWYS   2–1A

The Bear   £ 36
High St NP8 1BW (01873) 810408
A "cosy" and ancient coaching inn; the food can seem a touch
"basic", but it's generally "well prepared". / *Sample dishes: grilled
asparagus & mushroom puff pastry; duo of roast lamb shoulder; dark chocolate &
orange mousse.* **Details:** *www.bearhotel.co.uk; 9.30 pm; D only, ex Sun open
L only, closed Mon; children: 7+.* **Accommodation:** *34 rooms, from £84.*

Nantyffin Cider Mill   £ 41
Brecon Rd NP8 1SG (01873) 810775
This former drovers' inn has, since the early '90s, had a style that's
called a 'gastropub' nowadays; most reporters still say it's a "perennial
favourite" with "surprisingly good" food, but not everyone is convinced
that standards are being maintained. / *Sample dishes: crispy
cider-battered wild mushrooms; Caesar salad; Belgian dark chocolate & brandy
tart.* **Details:** *www.cidermill.co.uk; on A40 between Brecon & Crickhowell;
9.30 pm; closed Mon (& Sun D in winter).*

CRINAN BY LOCHGILPHEAD, ARGYLL   9–4B

Crinan Hotel   £ 61   Ⓐ ⭐
PA31 8SR (01546) 830261
"Stunning sea food" and "one of the best views in the country...
when it's not raining" win praise for this elegant hotel, which offers
a number of dining options; "the rooms are comfortable too".
/ *Sample dishes: jumbo prawns; fillet steaks.* **Details:** *www.crinanhotel.com;
8.30 pm; no Amex.* **Accommodation:** *20 rooms, from £95/person.*

CROCKERTON, WILTSHIRE   2–3B

The Bath Arms   £ 35   Ⓣ
Clay St BA12 8AJ (01985) 212262
This revamped inn on the Longleat estate has gathered only
a modest number of reports, but all to the effect that it's a "really
excellent gastropub". / *Sample dishes: fishcake with crab; sticky beef with
braised red cabbage.* **Details:** *www.batharmscrockerton.co.uk; 9.30 pm; no Amex.*
Accommodation: *2 rooms, from £75.*

CROSTHWAITE, CUMBRIA   7–4D

The Punch Bowl   £ 45
LA8 8HR (01539) 568237
"A stylish pub in the middle of nowhere"; post-revamp and with a new
chef, it seems to have "lost something", though ("the Drunken Duck
at Ambleside – same owners – is very much better"); let's hope it's
just a phase. / *Sample dishes: air-dried beef; fillet of beef; dark chocolate
fondant with white chocolate mousse.* **Details:** *www.the-punchbowl.co.uk;
off A5074 towards Bowness, turn right after Lyth Hotel; 11 pm.*
Accommodation: *9 rooms, from £110.*

CROYDON, SURREY   3–3B

Banana Leaf   £ 27   ⭐
7 Lower Addiscombe Rd CR0 6PQ (020) 8688 0297
In a "suburban wasteland" – and it's a local we're quoting! –
this "friendly" curry house has made a big name for its "quality and
value"; as you'd expect for a south Indian, the veggie selection
is "better than average" too. / *Sample dishes: chicken chettinad; carrot
halwa.* **Details:** *www.a222.co.uk/bananaleaf; near East Croydon station; 11 pm.*

CUCKFIELD, WEST SUSSEX 3–4B

Ockenden Manor £ 64

Ockenden Ln RH17 5LD   (01444) 416111

"Tasteful, intimate, and old-fashioned in a good way" – this *"superb"* country house hotel is hailed by its many fans for its *"unvarying"* standard of excellence; as a regular, however, notes: *"standards have improved over the years, but below-par meals are still far from unknown"*. / **Sample dishes:** crayfish salad; assiette of rabbit; fruit with vanilla ice cream. **Details:** www.hshotels.co.uk; 9 pm; no jeans. **Accommodation:** 22 rooms, from £160.

CUPAR, FIFE 9–3D

Ostlers Close £ 50

25 Bonnygate KY15 4BU   (01334) 655574

"Jimmy and Amanda deliver every time", say fans of their long-established, town-centre venture, known for its expert handling of *"fresh fish, meat and game"*. / **Sample dishes:** scallops & garden herb risotto; roast breast of duck with Bombay potatoes on a plum sauce; individual pear Tatin served with toasted almond ice cream & a blackcurrant sauce. **Details:** www.ostlersclose.co.uk; centrally situated in the Howe of Fife; 9.30 pm; closed Sun & Mon, Tue-Fri D only, Sat L & D; children: 6+ at D.

The Peat Inn £ 50

KY15 5LH   (01334) 840206

"My guests thought it was the best food they had ever eaten…!"; under new chef/patron Geoffrey Sneddle, this famous restaurant-with-rooms near St Andrews is going from strength to strength; reporters rave about its *"stunning"* cooking and *"friendly attitude"* (not to mention its *"renowned"* cellar). / **Sample dishes:** seared scallops, crushed fresh peas & pancetta; fillet of sea trout, lobster & herb risotto; chocolate marquise, caramelised banana & espresso ice cream. **Details:** www.thepeatinn.co.uk; at junction of B940 & B941, SW of St Andrews; 9.30 pm; closed Mon & Sun. **Accommodation:** 8 rooms, from £165.

DALRY, AYRSHIRE 9–4B

Braidwoods £ 42

Drumastle Mill Cottage KA24 4LN   (01294) 833544

"A level of culinary precision matched only by the grandest of three-star chefs" makes Keith and Nicola Braidwoods' *"nicely informal"* restaurant (converted from a pair of cottages) a hit with all who report on it; *"people come all the way from Edinburgh and Glasgow for it!"* / **Sample dishes:** quail stuffed with black pudding; roast fillet of turbot on clam risotto; caramelised rice pudding. **Details:** www.braidwoods.co.uk; 9 pm; closed Mon, Tue L & Sun D; closed 2 weeks in Jan & Sep; children: 12+ at D.

DANEHILL, EAST SUSSEX 3–4B

Coach And Horses £ 35

School Ln RH17 7JF   (01825) 740369

"A hard-to-find gastropub, where the cooking is more refined than you would expect"; all reporters agree that – with its *"pleasant garden, and good real ale"* – it's *"well worth that special trip"*.
/ **Details:** www.coachandhorses.danehill.biz.

DARTMOUTH, DEVON

1–4D

New Angel £ 58

2 South Embankment TQ6 9BH (01803) 839425

For its many fans, John Burton-Races's harbourside restaurant (once the Carved Angel) is a "superb" all-rounder, which makes "fantastic" use of "fresh local produce" (and has a "beautiful" view too, from some tables); the many others who find it "overpriced" and "officious", though, are mystified by its Michelin star.

/ **Sample dishes:** beef & scallops; chump of lamb; chocolate fondant with pistachio ice cream. **Details:** www.thenewangel.co.uk; opp passenger ferry pontoon; 10 pm; closed Mon & Sun D. **Accommodation:** 6 rooms, from £120.

DATCHWORTH, HERTFORDSHIRE

3–2B

Ⓐ

Coltsfoot Country Retreat £ 46

Coltsfoot Ln, Bulls Grn SG3 6SB (01438) 212800

It's the "really peaceful, get-away-from-it-all setting" which is of most note at this converted barn; on most feedback, the "simple" food is "reliable", but the odd sceptic finds it "bland".

/ **Sample dishes:** marinated duck breast; lamb cutlets & grilled goat's cheese; strawberry vacherin. **Details:** www.coltsfoot.com; midnight; D only, closed Sun; children: 12+. **Accommodation:** 15 rooms, from £135.

DAVENTRY, NORTHANTS

2–1D

Ⓐ

Fawsley Hall £ 56

NN11 3BA (01327) 892000

It's as a venue for a "long, lazy and very enjoyable lunch" (and "good value" too) that this grand but "relaxed" country house hotel is of most note; as a serious dinner destination it can seem "expensive" for what it is. / **Sample dishes:** pork terrine; pigeon with smoked bacon polenta; exotic fruit trifle. **Details:** www.fawsleyhall.com; on A361 between Daventry & Banbury; 9.30 pm. **Accommodation:** 43 rooms, from £185.

DEAL, KENT

3–3D

Dunkerley's £ 44

19 Beach St CT14 7AH (01304) 375016

"Local seafood, well-presented in a friendly and relaxed atmosphere" – the deal that's sustained Ian Dunkerley's establishment for three decades; its performance can sometimes seem "amateurish" though.

/ **Sample dishes:** scallops with light velouté & bacon; Dover sole; chocolate soufflé. **Details:** www.dunkerleys.co.uk; 9.30 pm; closed Mon L. **Accommodation:** 16 rooms, from £100.

DEDHAM, ESSEX

3–2C

Ⓐ★

Boathouse £ 36

Mill Ln CO7 6DH (01206) 323153

"A good alternative to the Milsom empire" – "in Constable country, and overlooking the river", this former boathouse offers "a very pleasing experience on all fronts"; perhaps unsurprisingly, "service in summer can be slow". / **Sample dishes:** plate of Italian meats & cheeses; grilled lemon hake with fennel-slaw & new potatoes; chocolate brownie & hot chocolate sauce. **Details:** www.dedhamboathouse.com; 9.30 pm; closed Mon & Sun D; no Amex.

Milsoms £ 41

Stratford Rd CO7 6HW (01206) 322795

*"Busy" but "dependable" – this "atmospheric" bistro impresses most reporters rather more favourably than the Milsom family's more celebrated Talbooth restaurant; "no booking, so arrive early for weekend lunch". / **Sample dishes:** shredded duck tacos; roast rump of lamb; chocolate brownie. **Details:** www.milsomhotels.com; 9.30 pm; no booking. **Accommodation:** 15 rooms, from £100.*

The Sun Inn £ 36 ⭐

High St CO7 6DF (01206) 323351

*"A true gastropub, in the heart of Constable country", where the "ever-changing seasonal menu" is praised for its "excellent value for money". / **Sample dishes:** grilled & marinated sardines; duck breast, baby beet root, spinach & blackberries; almond & amaretto cake. **Details:** www.thesuninndedham.com; 11 pm, Sun 9.30 pm; no Amex. **Accommodation:** 5 rooms, from £85.*

Le Talbooth £ 56 ✖

Gun Hill CO7 6HP (01206) 323150

*This "age-old haunt" undoubtedly has "beautiful surroundings", but it has "seen better days"; even fans may find it "overpriced", and too many critics find it "pretentious", "dated", and "disappointing". / **Sample dishes:** ravioli of tiger prawns; sea bass; peach melba. **Details:** www.milsomhotels.com; 5m N of Colchester on A12, take B1029; 9.30 pm; closed Sun D; no jeans or trainers. **Accommodation:** 10 rooms, from £170.*

DENHAM, BUCKINGHAMSHIRE 3–3A

Swan Inn £ 36 🅰⭐

Village Rd UB9 5BH (01895) 832085

*"Obliging" staff and a "relaxing" and "unpretentious" atmosphere help win huge popularity for this "great" gastropub, tucked away in a picturebook village, near the M40 (J1); the menu of "staples" is "always good". / **Sample dishes:** rustic breads with roast garlic; grilled sea bass fillet; bread & butter pudding. **Details:** www.swaninndenham.co.uk; 11 pm.*

DERBY, DERBYSHIRE 5–3C

Anoki £ 38 🅣

First Floor, 129 London Rd DE1 2QN (01332) 292888

*"A great place for any kind of celebration or just some good Indian food"; this former cinema is lauded for its "great food, service and atmosphere". / **Sample dishes:** chicken makhami; methi lamb. **Details:** www.anoki.co.uk; 11.30 pm; D only.*

Darleys £ 50

Darley Abbey Mill DE22 1DZ (01332) 364987

*The "delightful setting" (with water-view terrace) is the star feature of this former mill; some reporters say the food is "excellent" too – others, though, decry it as "style over substance". / **Sample dishes:** risotto of crab; breast of duck; banana soufflé with home-made vanilla fudge ice cream. **Details:** www.darleys.com; 2m N of city centre by River Derwent; 9.30 pm; closed Sun D; no Amex.*

Restaurant Zest £ 41

16d, George St, Friar Gate DE1 1EH (01332) 381101

"Given that Derby isn't exactly over-run with good eating places, we can't understand why this hasn't yet made it into your pages", complains one reporter – we are pleased to remedy the omission of this "good and reasonably-priced" bistro, which offers "very enjoyable" food. / *Sample dishes:* balsamic roasted tomato crostini, goats cheese & red onion; slow-cooked veal, olives, preserves lemon & tomatoes; raspberry crumble tart, panna cotta ice cream. *Details:* www.restaurantzest.co.uk; 10 pm.

Soul Restaurant £ 32

28 Green Ln DE1 1RP (01332) 346989

"Worth knowing about" in the city-centre – a "very popular" cafe/deli, with a "great pre-theatre offer". / *Sample dishes:* home-smoked venison loin with spiced cherries, spiced pickled beetroot & radish salad; baked fillet of brill served with gratin potatoes & moules à la basque; orange brioche pudding served with almond & honey ice cream. *Details:* www.souldeli.com; 9.30 pm; no Amex.

DIDCOT, OXFORDSHIRE 2–2D

Sweet Olive £ 42

Baker St OX11 9DD (01235) 851272

This "favourite local" – a Gallic bistro in a village pub – wins nothing but praise for its very good cuisine. / *Sample dishes:* tiger prawn tempura with spicy soy dressing; escalope of venison, port wine sauce, creamed cabbage & chips; treacle sponge. *Details:* www.sweet-olive.com; 9 pm; closed Feb.

DINTON, BUCKINGHAMSHIRE 2–3C

La Chouette £ 43

Westlington Grn HP17 8UW (01296) 747422

You get "fine food and insults in equal measure!", at this "unique" and "extraordinary" experience, where chef/patron Freddie the Belgian is "as uncompromising as ever" – "he can be both charming and rude, but his cooking is wonderful and you get a 'cabaret' too". / *Sample dishes:* fillet of brill with duxelles sauce; pheasant à la brabançonne; chocolate soufflé. *Details:* off A418 between Aylesbury & Thame; 9 pm; closed Sat L & Sun; no Amex.

DODDISCOMBSLEIGH, DEVON 1–3D

Nobody Inn £ 30

EX6 7PS (01647) 252394

A "remarkable wine list" ("like the Manhattan phone book"), "an amazing selection of whiskies" and "a veritable array of cheeses" – there are the reasons to visit this "quirky" rural "hideaway", which is otherwise rather "standard". / *Sample dishes:* duck liver pâté; fillet of beef with creamy tarragon sauce; crème brûlée. *Details:* www.nobodyinn.co.uk; off A38 at Haldon Hill (signed Dunchidrock); 9 pm; D only, closed Mon & Sun; children: 14+. *Accommodation:* 7 rooms, from £40.

DORCHESTER, DORSET

Sienna ☆ **£ 45**
36 High West St DT1 1UP (01305) 250022
*"A lovely little restaurant, serving delicate 'Michelin-style' food";
it's "too small to be very atmospheric" – even more likely to please
the tyre-men, then! – but "otherwise excellent". / **Sample dishes:** duck
rillettes with toasted onion bread & moscatel raisin jelly; roast fillet of pollack with
a warm chorizo & potato salad & lemon foam; lemon curd mousse millefeuille
with sweet lemon confit. **Details:** www.siennarestaurant.co.uk; 9.30 pm; closed
Mon & Sun; no Amex; children: 10+.*

DORE, SHEFFIELD
5–2C

Moran's ⓣ **£ 41**
289 Abbeydale Road South S17 3LB (01142) 350101
*This "small and intimate" wine bar, of recent vintage, is tipped for its
"fresh and clean-tasting" dishes using "top-quality ingredients".
/ **Sample dishes:** pan-fried scallops with sweet chili dressing & rocket; pan-fried
calves liver with caramelised onions & sage; plum pudding parfait with orange
shortbreads & rhubarb & ginger compote. **Details:** www.moranssheffield.co.uk;
9.30 pm; closed Mon, Tue L & Sun D.*

DORKING, SURREY
3–3A

Stephan Langton **£ 40**
Friday St, Abinger Common RH5 6JR (01306) 730775
*"The magical location of this country pub makes it a firm favourite";
the former chef left around the time of our survey – let's hope the
place remains "very much worth seeking out". / **Sample dishes:** crab,
tomato & saffron tart; lambs liver baked with onion & mashed potatoes;
buttermilk pudding. **Details:** www.stephan-langton.co.uk; off A25 at Wotton;
9.30 pm; closed Mon & Sun D.*

DUMFRIES, DUMFRIES AND GALLOWAY
7–2C

Linen Room Ⓐ☆☆ **£ 38**
53 St Michaels St DG1 2QB (01387) 255689
*"Relaxed, friendly, exciting, innovative, fresh, chic…" – all of the
(relatively few) reports on Russell Robertson's ambitious, black-walled
three-year-old are nothing short of a hymn of praise.
/ **Sample dishes:** coconut mousse & grilled lobster; seabass sandwich with Thai
basil polenta; iced honey with raspberry & white truffle infusion.
Details: www.linenroom.com; 9.30 pm; closed Mon & Tue L.*

DUNDRUM, COUNTY DOWN
10–1D

Mourne Seafood Bar Ⓐ☆ **£ 31**
10 Main St BT33 0LU (028) 4375 1377
*"It's noisy, it's basic, it's busy", but this "delightfully casual" rural
venture wins acclaim from all reporters, thanks to its "terrific"
seafood (much of it from their own farm); it now has a Belfast sibling
(at 34-36 Bank St, Tel 028 9024 8544), which is approved by most,
if not quite all, who report on it. / **Details:** www.mourneseafood.com;
no Amex.*

Kinnaird House £ 74 Ⓐ⭐

Kinnaird Estate PH8 0LB (01796) 482440

*If you go in for "flunkies everywhere", you'll love this grand Edwardian country house hotel (Relais & Châteaux), which sits in 9,000 acres, and serves "very good" food. / **Sample dishes:** pan-fried scallops; roast duck breast; white chocolate & tonka bean truffle pavé. **Details:** www.kinnairdestate.com; 8m NW of Dunkeld, off A9 onto B898; 9.30 pm; closed Mon-Wed in Jan & Feb; jacket; children: 12+. **Accommodation:** 9 rooms, from £295.*

The Three Chimneys £ 64 Ⓐ⭐⭐

Colbost IV55 8ZT (01470) 511258

*"Memorable" scenery, a "special" atmosphere, and "the freshest fish you are likely to encounter" make a visit to Eddie and Shirley Spear's isolated crofters' cottage an experience "beyond compare" for many reporters; it's admittedly no bargain, but most reporters say it's "worth every penny". / **Sample dishes:** dressed crab; salad of seared king scallops & sea bass; marmalade pudding with Drambuie custard. **Details:** www.threechimneys.co.uk; 5m from Dunvegan Castle on B884 to Glendale; 9.30 pm; closed Sun L; children: 8+. **Accommodation:** 6 rooms, from £255.*

Bistro 21 £ 42

Aykley Heads Hs DH1 5TS (0191) 384 4354

*This riverside warehouse-conversion is "the best of the bunch in a woefully underserved city"; but while fans praise its "all-round excellence", others feel its "basic" food can seem "very pricey for what it is". / **Sample dishes:** cheddar & spinach soufflé; fishcakes with parsley cream & chips; crème brûlée. **Details:** near Durham Trinity School; 10.30 pm; closed Sun; booking: max 10.*

Pump House £ 49

Farm Rd DH1 3PJ (0191) 386 9189

*"Footballers' wives might love it, but I don't"; fans say this former Victorian pumping station has a "beautiful interior", an "attractive" summer courtyard and "interesting" food, but there's also a school of thought which says "Durham deserves a good restaurant", and that this "gloomy" place "isn't it". / **Sample dishes:** crab & lobster fishcake with chilli tartare; breast of chicken stuffed with king prawns; sticky toffee pudding. **Details:** www.thepumphouserestaurant.co.uk; 9.30 pm.*

Jolly Sportsman £ 40 ⭐

Chapel Ln BN7 3BA (01273) 890400

*"A good rural restaurant", in a "hard-to-find" former pub, amidst the "fabulous walking country" of the South Downs; "interesting" food of "high quality" ensures "it's always popular", but it's "especially delightful when you can eat on the terrace in summer". / **Sample dishes:** chicken liver terrine with beetroot chutney; crispy duck confit; apricot, walnut & ginger toffee pudding. **Details:** www.thejollysportsman.com; NW of Lewes; 9 pm; closed Mon & Sun D; no Amex.*

EAST GRINSTEAD, WEST SUSSEX 3–4B

Gravetye Manor £ 75 Ⓐ
Vowels Ln RH19 4LJ (01342) 810567
*The allure of this "beautiful" Elizabethan manor hotel – with its
remote and "delightful" rural setting – still seduces most reporters
(especially those of mature years); prices can seem "outrageous",
though, inducing a feeling in some quarters that the food is no better
than it ought to be.* / **Sample dishes:** *tian of crab; roast pigeon with foie gras;
mango soufflé.* **Details:** *www.gravetyemanor.co.uk; 2m outside Turner's Hill;
9.30 pm; jacket & tie; children: 7+.* **Accommodation:** *18 rooms, from £155.*

EAST LOOE, CORNWALL 1–4C

Trawlers £ 40 ★
On The Quay PL13 1AH (01503) 263593
*"The harbourside location is engaging at any time of year" and,
on most accounts, the cooking at this "small and well-run" restaurant
is "excellent" too.* / **Sample dishes:** *Louisiana-style gumbo; roast monkfish;
lemon posset, crème brûlée & strawberry Pimm's jelly.*
Details: *www.trawlersrestaurant.co.uk; 9.30 pm; D only, closed Mon & Sun.*

EAST WITTON, NORTH YORKSHIRE 8–4B

Blue Lion £ 40 Ⓐ
DL8 4SN (01969) 624273
*For most reporters, this famous Dales inn remains a "really special"
place, notable for maintaining "high standards" of "traditional
Yorkshire hospitality"; for cynics, "the location is special, but the food
isn't".* / **Sample dishes:** *baked goat's cheese in hazlenut brioche; char-grilled
fillet of beef; apple Tatin with vanilla ice cream.* **Details:** *www.thebluelion.co.uk;
between Masham & Leyburn on A6108; 9.15 pm; D only, ex Sun open L &
D; no Amex.* **Accommodation:** *15 rooms, from £79.*

EASTBOURNE, EAST SUSSEX 3–4B

The Mirabelle
The Grand Hotel £ 55
King Edwards Pde BN21 4EQ (01323) 412345
*For an ambience that's "very 'grand hotel'" (unfortunately including
sometimes "condescending" service), it's hard to better this five-star
"Edwardian time warp"; the food is "sometimes excellent, sometimes
not so good", but the wine list always impresses.* / **Sample dishes:** *foie
gras parfait; roast best end of lamb with rösti potato & tarragon jus; dark Valrhona
chocolate & pear sorbet.* **Details:** *www.grandeastbourne.com; 10 pm; closed
Mon & Sun; jacket or tie required at D; children: 12+ at D.*
Accommodation: *152 rooms, from £180.*

EDENBRIDGE, KENT 3–3B

Haxted Mill £ 45 Ⓐ★
Haxted Rd TN8 6PU (01732) 862914
*A former mill which makes a "lovely place for summer's day lunch";
it doesn't attract a huge amount of feedback, but almost all reporters
find the food "consistently good".* / **Sample dishes:** *grilled oysters
on spinach & Parmesan; pan-fried escalope of veal; dark chocolate nemesis.*
Details: *www.haxtedmill.co.uk; between Edenbridge & Lingfield; 9 pm; closed
Mon & Sun D; no Amex.*

Until a few years ago, Edinburgh had few restaurants which might be said to be causing culinary excitement. Now it has two. The city's unchallenged standard-bearer is the ever more ambitious *Restaurant Martin Wishart*, but there is a growing fear that it is striving too hard for further blessings from the Michelin men. The pretender, *The Kitchin*, has not yet fallen into that groove – let's hope it never does.

There are also some mid-range restaurants of real culinary interest – *David Bann* (a veggie good enough for carnivores) and *Roti* (an unusually good Indian restaurant). There are also a couple of places which stand out for the remarkable charm of their setting – the *Witchery by the Castle* (the best-known place in town) and the *Vintners' Rooms* (currently the top all-rounder).

There is also an impressive supporting cast of mid-range restaurants worthy of one of our 'star" awards. For casual dining, Leith, and its waterside, remains the best place to go for a range of fun and relatively inexpensive options.

Abstract £ 64 ⭐
33-35 Castle St EH1 2EL (0131) 229 1222

"A slightly odd and very 'London'-style transfer… from Inverness"; its "complicated" food is its best feature, with all reporters finding it "well-judged" – otherwise reports tend to find the place "a bit of a mixed bag". / **Sample dishes:** crispy langoustines, guacamole, sweet mango & mustard ice cream; pig assiette with home-made gnocchi & butternut squash; dark chocolate & raspberry dome, coconut nougatine & amaretto emulsion. **Details:** www.abstractedinburgh.com; 10 pm; closed Sun.

The Atrium £ 50
10 Cambridge St EH1 2ED (0131) 228 8882
It still has its fans, but Auld Reekie's original trendy restaurant – "off a theatre lobby" – has a pretty limited following among reporters nowadays, rather tending to support those who find it: "average, average, average". / **Sample dishes:** pan-fried mackerel; wild sea bass; apple tarte Tatin & grape ice cream. **Details:** www.atriumrestaurant.co.uk; by the Usher Hall; 10 pm; closed Sat L & Sun (except during Festival).

Bell's Diner £ 25 ⭐
7 St Stephen St EH3 5EN (0131) 225 8116
"No-nonsense burgers in a no-nonsense environment" – that's the deal at this long-established Stockbridge diner, where the star menu item is "beautifully presented, bountiful and tasty". / **Details:** closed Mon L, Tue L, Wed L, Thu L, Fri L & Sun L; no Amex.

Black Bo's £ 34

57-61 Blackfriar's St EH1 1NB (0131) 557 6136
*"Huge portions" of "scrumptious veggie food" win praise for this "laid-back" and candlelit bar/café. / **Sample dishes:** peanut butter & blue cheese stroodle with port honey & plum sauce; pitas.*
Details: www.blackbos.co.uk; 10.30 pm; D only, except Fri & Sat open L & D; no Amex.

blue bar café £ 43

10 Cambridge St EH1 2ED (0131) 221 1222
*For a "light-bite", the Atrium's less expensive upstairs sibling is staging a come-back with reporters, almost all of whom judge it a "good-value" destination. / **Sample dishes:** pigeon breast; braised oxtail; vanilla cheesecake with whisky parfait.* **Details:** www.bluebarcafe.com; by the Usher Hall; 10.30 pm, Fri & Sat 11 pm; closed Sun (except during Festival).

Café Royal Oyster Bar £ 45

17a West Register St EH2 2AA (0131) 556 4124
*Standards seem to have "slipped" of late at this Victorian gem, in "both the bar and the restaurant" – shame, as the "exceptional" period setting (complete with "tiled murals" and "stained glass windows") is simply "stunning". / **Sample dishes:** oysters; Dover sole; raspberry brûlée.* **Details:** www.thespiritgroup.com; opp Balmoral Hotel; 10 pm.

Le Café St-Honoré £ 45

34 NW Thistle Street Ln EH2 1EA (0131) 226 2211
*"Hidden-away, but still in the heart of things", this "cosy" and "very French" New Town brasserie offers "classic" dishes done to a dependable standard. / **Sample dishes:** braised squid & mussels; duck breast with sweet potato pancetta; chocolate fondant with kirsch blackcherry syrup.* **Details:** 10 pm.

Calistoga £ 33

93 St Leonards St EH8 9QY (0131) 668 4207
*The "flat-rate mark up of £5" on "a big list of US wines" is a big selling-feature in this thrifty town; this "small, busy and cramped" venture, however, also offers "eclectic" California-inspired food that's "inventive and beautifully-presented". / **Sample dishes:** poached pear, orange & beet salad; rum-soaked swordfish; blueberry & maple syrup pancake cheesecake.* **Details:** www.calistoga.co.uk; 10 pm; closed Tue L & Wed L.

Centotre £ 38

103 George St EH2 3ES (0131) 225 1550
*"Big" and very "buzzy", this "absolutely central" New Town linchpin is a handy all-day rendezvous, from breakfast onwards; it inspires many, mainly positive, reports, but – as even one fan observes – "quality of both food and service can fluctuate a lot".
/ **Sample dishes:** Mozzarella, Parma ham & char-grilled vegetables; deep-fried calamari, tiger prawns, monkfish & courgette; 70-percent chocolate cake.*
Details: www.centotre.com; Mon - Fri 10 pm, Fri & Sat 11 pm, Sun 8 pm(winter 5 pm); closed Sun D.

Creelers £ 44

3 Hunter Sq EH1 1QW (0131) 220 4447
*"Somewhere that still sells good fresh fish, in a decent sized portion, plainly-cooked" – "what more could you want?", say fans of this unpretentious spot, just off the Royal Mile. / **Sample dishes:** seafood platter; halibut with herb & Parmesan crust; vanilla & lemon curd cheesecake.*
Details: www.creelers.co.uk; 10.30 pm.

Daniel's   £ 34

88 Commercial St EH6 6LX   (0131) 553 5933

"Quality at a reasonable price" – that's the deal at Daniel Vencker's "pleasant" Leith bistro, which specialises in the hearty cuisine of Alsace. / **Sample dishes:** *salade Lyonnaise; confit of duck; tarte Tatin.* **Details:** *www.daniels-bistro.co.uk; 10 pm.*

David Bann   £ 31

56-58 St Marys St EH1 1SX   (0131) 556 5888

"You'd never think this very stylish place, with a fantastic location in the Old Town, was vegetarian" – but it is, and "even the most hardened carnivore" is usually pleased to eat here. / **Sample dishes:** *mushroom medley with tarragon; artichoke & thyme curd open lasagne; dark chocolate soufflé.* **Details:** *www.davidbann.com; 10 pm.*

Duck's at Le Marché Noir   £ 46

14 Eyre Pl EH3 5EP   (0131) 558 1608

Malcolm Duck's "quite formal" New Town restaurant delivers some "good" cuisine; the "amazing wine list", though, is arguably a greater attraction – "there's a real sense of joy in the selection". / **Sample dishes:** *smoked salmon; beef; cappuccino parfait.* **Details:** *www.ducks.co.uk; 9.30 pm; closed Mon L, Sat L & Sun L.*

Dusit   £ 39

49a Thistle St EH2 1DY   (0131) 220 6846

"Sublime" Thai cuisine won warmer-than-ever praise this year for this New Town spot; "even on a really busy night", service is "excellent" too. / **Sample dishes:** *sea bass salad; massaman curry; banana fritter.* **Details:** *www.dusit.co.uk; 11 pm.*

First Coast   £ 31

99-101 Dalry Rd EH11 2AB   (0131) 3134404

"Very good value" is the drift of all reports on the "nicely varied" dishes served at this "brilliant local restaurant", near Haymarket Station. / **Sample dishes:** *roast aubergine with apricot chutney; lythe fillet, fennel, mustard, ginger & chickery salad; coconut & mango rice pudding.* **Details:** *www.first-coast.co.uk; 10.30 pm; closed Sun.*

Fishers Bistro   £ 38

1 The Shore EH6 6QW   (0131) 554 5666

This well-known bistro has built a name for its "excellent fish" – it has a "lovely" Leith location too, as well as a "cosy and atmospheric" interior. / **Sample dishes:** *grilled queen scallops; fillet of sea bass; caramelised date pudding.* **Details:** *www.fishersbistros.co.uk; 10.30 pm.*

Fishers in the City £ 36

58 Thistle St EH2 1EN (0131) 225 5109

This "busy" and "bustling" New Town warehouse-conversion is now arguably even better-known than its Leith sibling; it's "still pipped by the original", but is nevertheless a "consistently good experience", offering often "excellent" fish and seafood. / **Sample dishes:** salmon & smoked haddock fishcakes; fillet of char with tomato confit; crème brûlée. **Details:** www.fishersbistros.co.uk; 10.30 pm.

Forth Floor
Harvey Nichols £ 58

30-34 St Andrew Sq EH2 2AD (0131) 524 8350

"Great views" are the highpoint at this department store restaurant, which, given its not inconsiderable prices, can otherwise seem "bog-standard" – remarkably, though, reporters still award it the highest ratings in the Harvey Nics empire. / **Sample dishes:** seared scallops with duck foie gras; basil crèpe with feta, red peppers, beetroot & orange; caramel panna cotta with cured pineapple. **Details:** www.harveynichols.com; 10 pm; closed Mon D & Sun D; booking: max 8.

Le Garrigue £ 39

31 Jeffrey St EH1 1DH (0131) 557 3032

Jean-Michelle Gauffre and his wife's outfit in the Old Town may only be "smallish" (and "slightly cramped"), but it's won a huge following among reporters with its "authentic" and "rustic" (Languedoc) cuisine. / **Sample dishes:** pigeon with celeriac black pudding; bouillabaisse; crème brûlée. **Details:** www.lagarrigue.co.uk; 9.30 pm; closed Sun.

Glass & Thompson £ 25

2 Dundas St EH3 6HZ (0131) 557 0909

"For a lingering weekend brunch mulling over the papers", "yummy cakes", "wonderful sarnies", and "great coffee", this trendy New Town café/deli makes an "excellent" choice. / **Sample dishes:** pâté platter; lemon tart. **Details:** L only.

Grain Store £ 50

30 Victoria St EH1 2JW (0131) 225 7635

"A definite Edinburgh favourite"; this "very romantic" Old Town yearling (in a "beautiful building") continues to impress with its "deft" cuisine (from "excellent ingredients") and "lovely" service. / **Sample dishes:** buttered lobster tail with truffle lobster sauce; roe deer & beetroot saddle with parsley; date sponge with caramel-spiced Earl Grey ice cream. **Details:** www.grainstore-restaurant.co.uk; 10pm.

Henderson's £ 29

94 Hanover St EH2 1DR (0131) 225 2131

A characterfully grungy but "good-value" Auld Reekie institution of over 40 years' standing – this New Town veggie basement comprises a 'Salad Bar' (a cafeteria, for which there are frequently queues) and bistro. / **Sample dishes:** chunky vegetable soup; nut loaf with turnip mash; trifle. **Details:** www.hendersonsofedinburgh.co.uk; 10 pm; closed Sun; no Amex.

Iglu £ 37

2b, Jamaica St EH3 6HH (0131) 476 5333

"An ethical eatery with style" – a tiny place, in the New Town tipped for "good preparation of the freshest organic and wild ingredients". / **Sample dishes:** white crab meat omelette; baked halibut; gooseberry & lime parfait with home-made raspberry ice cream. **Details:** www.theiglu.com; 10 pm.

Indian Cavalry Club £ 40

3 Atholl Pl EH3 8HP (0131) 228 3282

*"Let's hope high standards continue", says a fan – this popular
West End subcontinental decamped to new premises in mid-2007,
too late to gather any survey commentary in its new home.*
/ **Sample dishes:** *crispy pakora with mixed vegetables; chicken tikka masala;
kulfi.* **Details:** www.indiancavalryclub.co.uk; between Caledonian Hotel &
Haymarket Station; 10.45 pm.

Kalpna £ 25

2-3 St Patrick Sq EH8 9EZ (0131) 667 9890

*"Still the best Indian food in Edinburgh", say fans of this long-
established Gujarati, near the University, where "great" veggie fare
comes at "good-value" prices.* / **Sample dishes:** *hara kebab; dam aloo
kashmiri; mango kulfi.* **Details:** www.kalpnarestaurant.com; 10.30 pm; closed
Sun; no Amex or Switch; no booking at L.

The Kitchin £ 55

78 Commercial Quay EH6 6LX (0131) 555 1755

*"The best new arrival in Edinburgh since the early days of Martin
Wishart" – an "awesome" spot where Tom Kitchin serves up a "short
sharp menu" of "beautifully-cooked, seasonal food"; not all reporters
are "sure about the interior design", but most acclaim the "laid-back"
warehouse setting.* / **Sample dishes:** *pan-fried foie gras with haggis, neeps, &
tatties; rolled pig's head with roasted langoustine tails & crispy ear salad; crème
brûlée of coffee with orange topping, with white chocolate sorbet.*
Details: www.thekitchin.com; 10 pm; closed Mon & Sun.

Maison Bleue £ 41

36-38 Victoria St EH1 2GW (0131) 226 1900

*This "romantic and rustic" Old Town spot is, say fans, "as great as its
neighbour, the Grain Store"; reports are much more limited, though,
and the food here can sometimes seem rather "prosaic".*
/ **Sample dishes:** *confit of duck; seafood gumbo; fondue.*
Details: www.maison-bleue.co.uk; 11 pm.

Mussel Inn £ 32

61-65 Rose St EH2 2NH (0131) 225 5979

*This New Town bistro is still touted by some reporters for its
"well presented and very tasty fish dishes" – others, though, strongly
feel it's "not as good as it used to be".* / **Sample dishes:** *smoked salmon
Caesar salad; mussels, white wine, garlic & cream; crème brûlée.*
Details: www.mussel-inn.com; 10 pm.

Number One
Balmoral Hotel £ 77

1 Princes St EH2 2EQ (0131) 557 6727

*"Why isn't it more popular with the critics?"; despite a low profile
in recent years the basement fine-dining room of Edinburgh's
"premier" hotel put in a particularly strong showing this year,
with much acclaim for Jeff Bland's "exquisite" cuisine (in particular his
"tasting menu with matching wines").* / **Sample dishes:** *millefeuille
of crab & soft-boiled quail egg; loin of lamb; lemon soufflé with strawberry
shortbread & strawberry sorbet.* **Details:** www.roccofortehotels.com; 10 pm;
D only; no jeans or trainers. **Accommodation:** 188 rooms, from £290.

Oloroso £ 51

A

33 Castle St EH2 3DN (0131) 226 7614

"It's the view that does it" – especially "from the balcony in summer"
– at this "stylish rooftop restaurant"; "having been a fashionable
hotspot, it's going through a mid-life crisis" at present – the food
is "variable", and can seem "grossly overpriced".
/ **Sample dishes:** asparagus; chump of lamb with confit shoulder; triple chocolate
millefeuille. **Details:** www.oloroso.co.uk; 10.15 pm.

Original Khushi's £ 23

A ★

26-30 Potterow EH1 2HE (0131) 220 0057
Newly re-located (for the second time in living memory) – with a
"splendid new building, and rather more elaborate delivery" –
this age-old BYO Indian veteran is "back on form", serving "good-
value" grub, including "the best chapatis in the known world".
/ **Sample dishes:** grilled khushi lamb; butter chicken; home-made sweets - ras
malai, kulfi. **Details:** www.khushis.com; 11 pm.

Outsider £ 31

A ★

15-16 George IV Bridge EH1 1EE (0131) 226 3131
An "unexpected" (and "spectacular") view of the Castle is not the
only surprise at this "cool and buzzy" ("noisy") hang-out, which
is under the same ownership as the The Apartment; it features
an "unconventional" menu, including "sharing" plates, realised to a
"very good" standard. / **Sample dishes:** marinated salmon, scallops, & king
prawns; duck confit; panna cotta with poached red wine fig & coconut biscotti.
Details: 11 pm; no Amex; booking: max 10.

Le Petit Paris £ 34

38-40 Grassmarket EH1 2JU (0131) 226 2442
The name says it all about this Grassmarket bistro, which – according
to its large following among reporters – offers "authentic French food
at reasonable prices"; there is a West End branch at 17 Queensbury
Street (tel 226 1890). / **Sample dishes:** steamed mussels in creamy cheese
sauce; marinated chicken in red wine; crème brûlée.
Details: www.petitparis-restaurant.co.uk; near the Castle; 10.30; no Amex.

Restaurant Martin Wishart £ 71

★

54 The Shore EH6 6RA (0131) 553 3557
Are the Wisharts striving too hard for a second Michelin star?; their
ambitious Leith dining room still inspires rave reviews for its "sublime"
food and "first-class" service, but complaints are beginning to creep
in about "fussy" food, "alarming" prices and an "over-formal"
attitude. / **Sample dishes:** lobster & smoked haddock soufflé; poached pigeon;
dark chocolate soup with cherries & almonds. **Details:** www.martin-wishart.co.uk;
near Royal Yacht Britannia; 9 pm; closed Mon & Sun; booking: max 10.

Rhubarb

Prestonfield Hotel   **£ 59**

Priestfield Rd EH16 5UT   (0131) 225 1333

*"You always feel like a princess!" (well, if you're female anyway),
at this "opulent" country house outpost of The Witchery – where
"delicious" food and a "sexy" ambience combine to create "a perfect
retreat for a treat". / **Sample dishes:** salad of Bresse pigeon; roast fillet
of beef Rossini; dark chocolate fondant with basil anglaise & Greek yoghurt ice
cream. **Details:** rhubarb-restaurant.com; 10pm, 11pm fri&sat; children: 12+
at D, none after 7pm. **Accommodation:** 22 rooms, from £225.*

Roti   **£ 36**

70 Rose St North Ln EH3 8BU   (0131) 221 9998

*It's hidden "down an alley" – and not everyone likes the interior –
but this New Town modern Indian (on the site that was once Martin's,
RIP), dazzles reporters with "unusual" cooking that's simply "out of
this world". / **Sample dishes:** Kashmiri style lamb shank with masala lentil,
deep-fried lotus stem & green tea rice; spicy Goanese-style fish curry, lemon
rice, & stirfry okra. **Details:** www.roti.uk.com; 11pm; closed Mon, Sat L & Sun.*

Skippers   **£ 41**

1a Dock Pl EH6 6LU   (0131) 554 1018

*"A wonderful find, tucked-away in Leith"; this "intimate" and
"bustling" waterfront bistro is a "friendly" sort of place, serving
a "short and imaginative" menu of "super-fresh" fish.
/ **Sample dishes:** king scallops with smoked haddock risotto; Dover sole with
langoustine butter; nectarines poached in rose wine. **Details:** www.skippers.co.uk;
10 pm.*

Stac Polly   **£ 49**

29-33 Dublin St EH3 6NL   (0131) 556 2231

*While "not exceptional", the food at this "homely" and "old-
fashioned" Scottish "cellar" is sometimes said to be "surprisingly
good"; there are also branches at 8-10 Grindlay St and 38 St Mary's
St. / **Sample dishes:** baked filo parcels of haggis with a red wine & sweet plum
sauce; crispy fillet of sea bream served with crushed baby new potatoes, fine beans
served with lime & chive clotted cream. **Details:** www.stacpolly.co.uk; 9.15 pm,
9.30 pm Sat & Sun; closed Sat L & Sun L.*

The Stockbridge   **£ 45**

54 St Stephen's St EH3 5AL   (0131) 2266766

*"The best restaurant we have found that is not yet listed in Harden's",
says one reporter – a "quiet" and "pleasant" basement operation,
says another, offering "an interesting short menu, good cooking and
service". / **Sample dishes:** smoked salmon terrine with aruga caviar, melba
toast, cucumber carpaccio & lemon caper dressing; grilled halibut with a crab
crust, sautéed potatoes, cherry tomatoes courgette ribbons & a lemon butter
sauce. **Details:** www.thestockbridgerestaurant.com; 9.30 pm; closed Mon, Tue L,
Sat L & Sun L.*

Sweet Melindas   **£ 37**

11 Roseneath St EH9 1JH   (0131) 229 7953

*"The most perfect neighbourhood restaurant" – this "sweet, small
and cosy" (and "crammed-full") outfit, in Marchmont, is praised
by hordes of locals for its "interesting", "top-notch" fish dishes.
/ **Sample dishes:** squid salad with chilli, garlic & coriander; pan fried scallops
with sweet chilli sauce & crème fraîche; mango & gin ice cream.
Details: www.sweetmelindas.co.uk; 10 pm; closed Mon L & Sun.*

The Tower
Museum of Scotland   £ 49

Chambers St EH1 1JF   (0131) 225 3003

"A truly jaw-dropping view of the castle" is the one undisputed draw to this top-floor-dining room; to fans, it's a "slick" all-rounder where everything's "top notch" – to its (many) critics though it's just a typical room-with-a-view, offering food that's "a let down... especially at the price". / **Sample dishes:** char-grilled asparagus & Serrano ham; grilled seabass, warmed king prawn & wakame seaweed; baked pecan pie with maple syrup & peanut butter ice cream. **Details:** www.tower-restaurant.com; 11 pm.

Valvona & Crolla   £ 39

19 Elm Row EH7 4AA   (0131) 556 6066

A reputation for "the best lunch in town" still excites rave reviews for the "cramped" café of this famous Italian deli, on the way to Leith (and queues are still the norm); however, the raspberries from those who complain of "careless cooking", "very slow" service and "rip-off" prices are becoming very loud indeed. / **Sample dishes:** aubergines stuffed with Mozzarella, olives, & anchovies; ravioli with Ricotta; lemon torte. **Details:** www.valvonacrolla.com; at top of Leith Walk, near Playhouse Theatre; L only.

VinCaffe   £ 42

11 Multrees Walk EH1 3DQ   (0131) 557 0088

Associated with Valvona & Crolla, a busy Italian operation near Harvey Nics; there is a widespread feeling that "its reputation runs ahead of its performance". / **Sample dishes:** pork & beef minced meatballs; egg pasta with cream; lemon tart with crème fraîche. **Details:** www.valvonacrolla.com; 9.30 pm, Fri & Sat 10.30 pm; closed Sun D.

Vintners Rooms   £ 49

87a Giles St EH6 6BZ   (0131) 554 6767

If you're looking for "a wonderfully atmospheric old venue", you won't do much better than this candlelit former whisky-shippers' warehouse, on the way to Leith; its "top-grade Franco-Scottish food" is a far from incidental attraction, but portions, if anything, are "too large". / **Sample dishes:** seared scallops; pavé of venison; raspberry crème brûlée. **Details:** www.thevintnersrooms.com; 10 pm; closed Mon & Sun.

The Waterfront   £ 36

1c Dock Pl EH6 6LU   (0131) 554 7427

"Consistently good standards" – "fine seafood" in particular – are attested to by all commentary on this long-established restaurant/wine bar, in Leith. / **Sample dishes:** baked crab thermidor with a cheddar gratin; char-grilled game fish marinated in rosemary & garlic on warm spiced aubergine caviar; sticky toffee pudding. **Details:** www.waterfrontwinebar.co.uk; near Royal Yacht Britannia; 10 pm.

The Witchery by the Castle   £ 60

Castlehill, The Royal Mile EH1 2NF   (0131) 225 5613

"Sexy" decor – from the "sumptuous" Secret Garden to the "Gothic", "candle-lit dungeon" – inspires the usual rave reviews for this Old Town veteran; at the "complacent" prices, the food can seem "mundane", but the "encyclopaedic wine list" is "stunning". / **Sample dishes:** butter-poached Scottish lobster; duo of lamb; dark chocolate torte. **Details:** www.thewitchery.com; 11.30 pm. **Accommodation:** 7 rooms, from £295.

EGLWYSFACH, POWYS
4–3D

Ynyshir Hall
£ 84

SY20 8TA (01654) 781209

A country house hotel in a "lovely" location (part of an estate once owned by Queen Victoria), where many reporters rate Shane Hughes's cooking nothing short of "outstanding". / **Sample dishes:** *loin of rabbit with scallop & ratatouille; pork ballantine; local lobster with new potatoes, mayonnaise, & vegetables.* **Details:** *www.ynyshir-hall.co.uk; signposted from A487; 8.45 pm; no jeans or trainers; children: 9+.* **Accommodation:** *9 rooms, from £180.*

ELLAND, WEST YORKSHIRE
5–1C

La Cachette
£ 27

31 Huddersfield Rd HX5 9AW (01422) 378833

It doesn't inspire reports of great eloquence, but nearly all feedback on this popular brasserie suggests it's good value. / **Sample dishes:** *dill-cured salmon; roast duck; saffron-poached pears & blackcurrant parfait.* **Details:** *www.lacachette-elland.com; 9.30 pm, Fri & Sat 10pm; closed Sun; no Amex.*

ELLESMERE PORT, CHESHIRE
5–2A

Jabula Restaurant
£ 32

1 South Pier Rd CH65 4FW (0151) 3551163

"Live African music" adds to the Saturday-evening vibe at this South African spot, "overlooking the Ship Canal"; the food is "well-cooked and presented" and "the house wines are good too". / **Details:** *www.jabula-restaurant.co.uk; 9.30 pm; closed Mon L.*

ELSTEAD, SURREY
3–3A

The Golden Fleece
£ 25

Farnham Rd GU8 6DB (01252) 702349

A Thai-in-a-pub, tipped for its "genuine" cuisine and its "fantastic, personal service". / **Details:** *11 pm; no Amex; children: 14+ after 6 pm.*

ELSTOW, BEDFORDSHIRE
3–1A

St Helena's
£ 47

High St MK42 9XP (01234) 344848

"Bedford's most sought-after eatery"; that's not the double-edged compliment it might sound – all reporters praise the "superb food, delivered without pretension", at this "fun", "friendly" and "discreet" operation, "in the Tudor portion of Elstow". / **Sample dishes:** *foie gras; fillet of beef St. Helena stuffed with stilton wrapped with bacon & served in a madeira sauce; raspberry soufflé.* **Details:** *off A6, S of Bedford; 9 pm; closed Mon, Sat L & Sun; children: 12+.*

ELY, CAMBRIDGESHIRE
3–1B

Old Fire Engine House
£ 39

25 St Mary's St CB7 4ER (01353) 662582

"An Ely institution"; the Jarmans' 40-year-old veteran, near the Cathedral, is still largely seen as a "treat", with "excellent plain cooking" (and "they even offer second helpings!"); the occasional reporter, though, finds the formula "wholesome but unexciting". / **Sample dishes:** *beef braised in Guinness & port; apricot & almond crumble.* **Details:** *www.theoldfireenginehouse.co.uk; 9 pm; closed Sun D; no Amex.*

EMSWORTH, HAMPSHIRE

2–4D

Fat Olives

£ 41

⭐

30 South St PO10 7EH (01243) 377914

*"What you might hope for in a personally-run establishment" –
this "small" venture (in an old cottage, on the way to the harbour)
wins praise for "lovely" food that's "served with care".*
/ **Sample dishes:** *seared scallops & leek risotto; sea bass, tiger prawn & mussel
pot au feu; chocolate mousse & orange sorbet.* **Details:** *www.fatolives.co.uk;
10 pm; closed Mon & Sun; no Amex; children: 8+.*

36 on the Quay

£ 63

47 South St PO10 7EG (01243) 375592

*"A beautiful seaside location, sumptuous decor and high-class nosh"
commend Ramon Farthing's long-established restaurant
to most reporters; it can seem "expensive for what it is", though,
and – by the standards that might therefore be expected – service
is sometimes "poor".* / **Sample dishes:** *pan-fried scallops; fallow deer
on sliced rösti potatoes; banana & caramel in five miniature desserts.*
Details: *www.36onthequay.co.uk; off A27 between Portsmouth & Chichester;
9.45 pm; closed Mon & Sun.* **Accommodation:** *4 (plus cottage) rooms,
from £95.*

ENGLEFIELD GREEN, SURREY

3–3A

Edwinns

£ 36

Wick Rd TW20 0HN (01784) 477877

*Tucked-away on the fringe of Windsor Great Park, this buzzy member
of a small and unpretentious chain offers "good and honest" food,
and "friendly" service.* / **Sample dishes:** *pan-fried calamari & prawn salad;
roast rack of lamb; sticky toffee pudding.* **Details:** *www.edwinns.co.uk; 10 pm,
Sun 8.30.*

EPSOM, SURREY

3–3B

Le Raj

£ 24

211 Fir Tree Rd KT17 3LB (01737) 371371

*This "high-class Indian" puts "a twist on the usual experience",
and has become well-known down Surrey way; even fans concede it's
"relatively pricey", though.* / **Sample dishes:** *Bangladeshi fish, cooked with
garlic, ginger & parsley; chicken tikka masala; mango, pistachio & gingerbread ice
cream.* **Details:** *www.lerajrestaurant.co.uk; next to Derby race course; 11 pm;
no jeans or trainers.*

ESCRICK, NORTH YORKSHIRE

5–1D

Sangthai

£ 30

⭐

Church Cottage YO19 6EX (01904) 728462

*"A very nice Thai restaurant, not far from York"; it was again well-
rated for its "authentic" and "delicious" food.* / **Sample dishes:** *chicken
satay; stir-fried beef; Thai custard.* **Details:** *www.sangthai.co.uk; flexible; closed
Mon, Tue-Thu & Sat D only.*

ESHER, SURREY

3–3A

Good Earth

£ 43

⭐

14-18 High St KT10 9RT (01372) 462489

*"Smoothly professional", if "somewhat pricey" – this long-established
Chinese operation (part of a small group) maintains a wide following
with its "refined" dishes and civilised approach.* / **Sample dishes:** *spicy
spare ribs; Mongolian lamb; toffee apples & ice cream.* **Details:** *11.15 pm;
booking: max 12, Fri & Sat.*

Sherpa £ 31
132 High St KT10 9QJ (01372) 470777
"At the far end of the high street", this "airy" and "calming" fixture has a strong following, thanks to its "friendly" style and its "honest" Nepalese dishes (which are "based on flavour rather than a spice kick"). / **Sample dishes:** *steam-cooked pork dumplings; spiced boneless lamb with coriander; ice cream.* **Details:** *www.sherpakitchen.co.uk; 11 pm.*

Siam Food Gallery £ 38
95-97 High St KT10 9QE (01372) 477139
A popular, upmarket suburban oriental, consistently hailed for its "well-executed" cuisine. / **Sample dishes:** *spring rolls; green curry with chicken; coconut ice cream.* **Details:** *11 pm.*

ESKMILLS, EAST LOTHIAN 9–4D

The Glasshouse At Eskmills £ 35
Station Hs, Station Rd EH21 7PQ (0131) 2735240
"The walls are windows" – and overlook a large and attractive courtyard – at this "brave" and strikingly-designed newcomer; it has won immediate praise for its "assured cooking", at prices "well below what you'd expect for the quality". / **Sample dishes:** *tiger prawn & crab salad, citrus mayonnaise, pickled lemon; pan-fried seabream, carrots, leek, spring onions & chive beurre blanc.* **Details:** *www.theglasshouseateskmills.com; 10 pm.*

ETON, WINDSOR & MAIDENHEAD 3–3A

Gilbey's £ 38
82-83 High St SL4 6AF (01753) 854921
A "civilised" and "friendly" place, where the food is "generally reliable", and with an above-par wine list. / **Sample dishes:** *seared scallops & smoked salmon; pan-fried pavé steak, shallot purée & wild mushrooms; baked white chocolate & hazelnut cheesecake.* **Details:** *www.gilbeygroup.com; 10 min walk from Windsor Castle; 9.30 pm.*

EVERSHOT, DORSET 2–4B

The Acorn Inn £ 41
28 Fore St DT2 0JW (01935) 83228
"A good pub/restaurant owned by the Summer Lodge people", located in "lovely countryside"; a "friendly" place, it is universally hailed by reporters for offering "good dishes from local produce". / **Sample dishes:** *battered cod with chips; lamb with braised leeks & baked mushroom.* **Details:** *www.acorn-inn.co.uk; One mile off A37 Yeovil - Dorchester Road; 9 pm.* **Accommodation:** *9, 1 suite rooms, from £135.*

Summer Lodge
Country House Hotel & Restaurant £ 70
Summer Lodge DT2 0JR (01935) 482000
With its "OTT but fun" style, the "formal dining room/conservatory" of this "beautifully-renovated" hotel wins nothing but rave reviews from reporters for its "first-rate" cuisine and its "amazing wine list". / **Sample dishes:** *seared scallops; fillet of sole; chocolate & orange fondant.* **Details:** *www.summerlodgehotel.co.uk; 12m NW of Dorchester on A37; 9.30 pm; no shorts.* **Accommodation:** *24 rooms, from £185.*

Evesham Hotel £ 42 Ⓐ
Coopers Ln WR11 1DA (01386) 765566
"Super-eccentric... super-relaxing... super-great with families" –
these are all virtues of *"humorous eccentric"* John Jenkinson's long-
established hotel; it is, however, the *"super-odd"* and wildly *"eclectic"*
wine list (*"from every wine producing country... except France"*)
which has really made its name. / **Sample dishes:** green Thai chicken;
lemon sole; treacle tart. **Details:** www.eveshamhotel.com; 9.30 pm; booking:
max 12. **Accommodation:** 40 rooms, from £124.

Effings £ 33 ★
50 Fore St TQ9 5RP (01803) 863435
This *"dining place above a deli"*, in the city-centre, is *"an epicurean
delight"*, say fans, thanks to its *"friendly staff and delicious home-
made food"*; it can, however, also seem a bit *"pretentious"*.
/ **Sample dishes:** artichoke & saffron risotto; smoked haddock.
Details: www.effings.co.uk; 5 pm; closed Sun; no Amex.

Café Paradiso Ⓐ
Hotel Barcelona £ 42
Magdalen St EX2 4HY (01392) 281000
In a funky design-hotel, a *"buzzy, modern dining room serving good
food"*; thanks not least to its *"lovely outdoor seating area"*, it makes
a *"refreshingly different find in the heart of a traditional city"*.
/ **Sample dishes:** seared scallops with Jerusalem artichoke purée; ling cod & pork
belly, chickpea salsa, & mash samphire; lemon tart with limoncello syrup.
Details: www.aliasbarcelona.com; 10 pm; booking: max 8.
Accommodation: 46 rooms, from £119.

Michael Caines
Royal Clarence Hotel £ 55
Cathedral Yd EX1 1HD (01392) 223 638
Reporters are warming to this *"calm"* contemporary dining room,
which has a *"great location, near the Cathedral"*, and is of particular
note for an *"exceptional-value lunch"*; critics who find it *"regularly
disappointing"*, however, have not quite gone away.
/ **Sample dishes:** scallops with lemon purée; poached halibut with smoked
bacon & peas fricassee & langoustine; coconut panna cotta with pineapple sorbet.
Details: www.abodehotels.co.uk; 9.30 pm; closed Sun. **Accommodation:** 53
rooms, from £125.

Allium £ 50 ★
1 London St GL7 4AH (01285) 712200
*"A delightful small restaurant with a large bay window overlooking the
marketplace"*, where James Graham's cuisine is *"sometimes amazing"*
(*"if sometimes a bit fussy"*), and service from wife Erica
is *"charming"*; it re-opens, post-flood, in late-2007.
/ **Details:** www.allium.uk.net; 9 pm; closed Mon & Tue; no Amex; booking:
max 10.

Bistro de la Mer   **£ 39**

28 Arwenack St TR11 3JB   (01326) 316509

*Tony and Alison Ward's small bistro near the National Maritime Museum is enthusiastically tipped for "exciting" cuisine that's "as good as it gets" in these parts. / **Sample dishes:** beef fillet with foie gras, black truffle, madeira sauce & truffle oil; linguine arrabiata with lobster, prawns & crab; trio of fish, roast tomatoes, wild rocket & basil pesto.* **Details:** www.bistrodelamer.com; 9:30pm, 10pm weekend; no Amex.

**The Flying Fish Restaurant
St Michael's Hotel & Spa**   **£ 36**

Gyllyngvase Beach TR11 4NB   (01326) 312707

*"Excellent food at good prices in stylish surroundings" win praise for this contemporary hotel; for a livelier atmosphere, prefer the 'Flying Fish bistro' to the restaurant proper. / **Sample dishes:** pan-seared mackerel; crab cakes.* **Details:** www.stmichaelshotel.co.uk; 9 pm, 9.30 pm Sat & Sun. **Accommodation:** 62 rooms, from £82.

Sticky Prawn   **£ 46**

Flushing Quay TR11 5TY   (01326) 373734

*You get "a fantastic view of Falmouth harbour" at this outfit "right on the quayside" (and "you almost feel like you were in a boat"); it serves "super-fresh seafood, plucked from the water around you". / **Sample dishes:** open crab sandwich with chive mayo, salad & French fries; baked fillets of tandoori halibut served with a potato, pea & prawn deep-fried samosa & a red lentil dhal; roast peach & raspberry clafoutis.* **Details:** www.thestickyprawn.co.uk; midnight; closed Sun D.

Museum Inn   **£ 42**

DT11 8DE   (01725) 516261

*The style may be a bit "London comes to the country" ("don't forget the 4x4"), but this "very relaxed" gastropub has an impressive fan club among reporters, thanks to its "varied" menu of food that's "a clear cut above". / **Sample dishes:** mini fishcakes; fillet of lemon sole; crème brûlée & raspberry sorbet.* **Details:** www.museuminn.co.uk; 9.30pm, 9pm Sun; no Amex. **Accommodation:** 8 rooms, from £95.

Read's   £ 65

Macknade Manor, Canterbury Rd ME13 8XE   (01795) 535344

*For 30 years, "fine food, unpretentious service and a great wine list"
have made Rona & David Pitchford's restaurant – now located in a
Georgian country house – a much-appreciated destination.
/ **Sample dishes:** soufflé of mature Montgomery Cheddar; duckling cooked three
ways; caramel & orange panna cotta with Cointreau sorbet.*
Details: *www.reads.com; 9.30 pm; closed Mon & Sun.* **Accommodation:** *6
rooms, from £250.*

General Tarleton   £ 41   ★

Boroughbridge Rd HG5 0PZ   (01423) 340284
*No longer associated with the Angel at Hetton, this "good-all-round"
roadside gastropub (with "lovely" rooms) continues to impress
most reporters with its "high-quality" cuisine. / **Sample dishes:** seafood
in filo pastry with lobster sauce; roast halibut with soft herb crust; trio of rhubarb
desserts.* **Details:** *www.generaltarleton.co.uk; 2m from A1, J48 towards
Knaresborough; 9.15 pm; closed Sun D.* **Accommodation:** *14 rooms, from £97.*

The Bricklayers Arms   £ 41   ★

Hogpits Bottom HP3 0PH   (01442) 833322
*For "outstanding food and service in a pleasant rural location",
many reporters recommend this "historic country pub"; "it has won
countless awards for its cuisine, and rightly so".
/ **Sample dishes:** home-smoked fish plate with a coriander butter & tomato
chutney; brochette of pan-fried tiger prawns with stir-fry & light curry cream sauce;
best end of lamb served with pea flan in a rosemary jus.*
Details: *www.bricklayersarms.com; 9.30 pm, Sun 8.30 pm.*

The Griffin Inn   £ 41

TN22 3SS   (01825) 722890
*Is this "attractive" pub-cum-restaurant just "too popular" for its own
good?; that's not to say that the food (including a BBQ in summer)
isn't often "great", just that there's a feeling in some quarters that
"it isn't as good as they seem to think it is". / **Sample dishes:** pan-seared
scallops & chorizo; papparadelle, girolles mushrooms, thyme & truffle oil; double
chocolate mousse with Cointreau & Benedictine.* **Details:** *www.thegriffininn.co.uk;
off A272; 9.30 pm; closed Sun D (in winter).* **Accommodation:** *13 rooms,
from £85.*

FONTHILL GIFFORD, WILTSHIRE 2–3C

Beckford Arms **£ 36**
SP3 6PX (08702) 314116
*This "country house-style pub" – with its "wide and varied menu",
its "several sitting areas" and its "very attractive" garden – makes
"a nice surprise in a culinary desert".* / **Sample dishes:** seared duck
breast, pea risotto, parsnip purée, poached fig & asparagus; grilled smoked
haddock fillet served with creamy leek mash, glazed carrots & parsley sauce.
Details: www.thebeckfordarms.co.uk; 9.30 pm, Sun 9 pm; no Amex.
Accommodation: 8 rooms, from £80.

FORT WILLIAM, HIGHLAND 9–3B

Inverlochy Castle **£ 85** Ⓐ⭐
Torlundy PH33 6SN (01397) 702177
*With its "superb wine and food", its "outstanding" service and its
wonderful highland setting (at the foot of Ben Nevis), this baronial pile
offers a picturebook Caledonian experience (though not, of course,
a particularly inexpensive one).* / **Sample dishes:** crab with green apple
salad, sorbet & crisps; gin-poached loin of venison; bitter chocolate & hazelnut
pavé. **Details:** www.inverlochycastlehotel.com; off A82, 4 m N of Ft. William;
10 pm; jacket & tie required at D; children: 8+ at D. **Accommodation:** 17 &
gate lodge rooms, from £300.

FOWEY, CORNWALL 1–4B

Restaurant Nathan Outlaw Ⓣ
Marina Villa Hotel **£ 57**
Esplanade PL23 1HY (01726) 833315
*The new perch of a chef who's left a trail of Michelin stars in his
wake; an early reporter notes "an unhealthy obsession with foams",
but still says the cooking could be of "two-star standard"; NB arrival
is via "a near-vertical hike down from the main car park on the edge
of the village".* / **Details:** www.themarinahotel.co.uk; 9 pm; D only, closed Mon;
no jeans or trainers; children: 12+.

The Other Place **£ 36** ⭐
41 Fore St PL23 1AH (01726) 833636
*It can get "crowded and hectic", but this small "Cornish gem"
is "as outstanding as ever", thanks to its "relaxed and convivial" style,
its "friendly" staff and its "tremendous" local fish; try and nab
a window seat for a river-view.* / **Sample dishes:** Thai fishcakes; John Dory
with foie gras; triple chocolate torte. **Details:** www.samsfowey.co.uk; 9.30 pm;
no Amex.

Zutshis At The Toll Bar **£ 32** Ⓐ⭐
1 Lostwithiel St PL23 1BD (01726) 833001
*A "beautiful sun-drenched terrace overlooking the river" is the star
'feature' at this popular (and "child-friendly") local hang-out; this is
an all-day place, where standards are much higher than you might
expect – also surprisingly, "fantastic" curries are a highlight
of the diverse evening menu.* / **Sample dishes:** salmon & tiger prawns in a
coriander sauce with saffron rice; salt & pepper calamari with sweet chilli.
Details: 9pm; closed Thu D.

FOWLMERE, CAMBRIDGESHIRE 3–1B

Chequers £ 42
SG8 7SR (01763) 208369
*Under the newish owners, views on the popular foodie pub have
become divided; most still say it's a "cosy" place (with a "lovely"
garden), offering "hearty comfort-fare" – critics, though, feel it has
"lost its edge".* / **Sample dishes:** *char-grilled venison liver; pan-fried figs laced
in amaretto with crème fraîche.* **Details:** *www.thechequersfowlmere.co.uk;
on B1368 between Royston & Cambridge; 9.30 pm; children: 14+.*

FRESSINGFIELD, SUFFOLK 3–1D

The Fox & Goose £ 38
IP21 5PB (01379) 586247
*"A wonderful place – historic, atmospheric, warm and cosy – where
the food is local, well-sourced, varied and always great".*
/ **Sample dishes:** *crab salad with fennel & chervil remoulade, apple crisps &
mint; monkfish fillet with samphire linguini, pickled artichokes & crayfish tempura;
caramel mousse with strawberries, almond shortbread, & balsamic vinegar.*
Details: *www.foxandgoose.net; off A140; 8.45 pm, 9 pm Sat, 8.15 Sun; closed
Mon; no Amex; children: 9+ for D.*

FRITHSDEN, HERTFORDSHIRE 3–2A

Alford Arms £ 37 ★
HP1 3DD (01442) 864480
*"You will need to book well in advance, and use SatNav" to secure
and locate a table at this "hard-to-find" and "picturesque" inn (which
is a favourite weekend destination, especially for Sunday lunch); given
its excessive popularity, the many reports it attracts are impressively
consistent.* / **Sample dishes:** *bubble & squeak; grilled pancetta-wrapped cod;
treacle tart with lemon grass crème fraîche.*
Details: *www.alfordarmsfrithsden.co.uk; near Ashridge College and vineyard;
10 pm; booking: max 12.*

GAINFORD, DURHAM 8–3B

Headlam Hall £ 41 Ⓐ
DL2 3HA (01325) 730238
*Modestly-priced by the standards of country house hotel dining rooms
– with its "superb" cuisine, this "very friendly" destination "never
disappoints".* / **Sample dishes:** *smoked chicken & mango salad; roast fillet
of salmon & lobster ravioli; banana Tatin & banana ice cream.*
Details: *www.headlamhall.co.uk; 9.15 pm; no shorts.* **Accommodation:** *40
rooms, from £110.*

GAIRLOCH, ROSS-SHIRE 9–2B

Ⓣ

The Creel Restaurant
Charleston House £ 50
IV21 2AH (01445) 712497
*"A small, friendly and welcoming family-run restaurant near the
Harbour"; it's tipped for "the freshest seafood", and "quality that
never varies from excellent".* / **Sample dishes:** *seared scallops with sweet
chilli sauce; langoustines with garlic butter.* **Details:** *www.charlestonhouse.co.uk;
9.30 pm; D only; no Amex.* **Accommodation:** *4 rooms, from £80.*

Elephant Royale   £ 46
579-581 Cranbrook Rd IG2 6JZ   (020) 8551 7015
*"The right sort of atmosphere for a night out" – plus "good Thai
food" too – wins praise for this lavishly-decorated suburban oriental
(which has a relation at the tip of the Isle of Dogs).*
/ ***Sample dishes:*** *Thai dim sum; chilli tiger prawns; dessert platter.*
Details: *www.elephantroyale.com; 11.30 pm.*

GATESHEAD, TYNE & WEAR   8–2B

Eslington Villa Hotel   £ 35
8 Station Rd NE9 6DR   (0191) 487 6017
*"An old-fashioned country house hotel", which attracts particular
praise for its "good-value midweek set menus" (and "the occasional
theme-nights are also good"). /* ***Sample dishes:*** *cherry tomato salad with
feta cheese, olives, red onion & shaved fennel; marinated loin of venison with
shallot tarte Tatin; chocolate truffle with black cherries & vanilla mascarpone.*
Details: *www.eslingtonvilla.co.uk; A1 exit for Team Valley Retail World, then left
off Eastern Avenue; 9.30 pm; closed Sat L & Sun D.* ***Accommodation:*** *18
rooms, from £89.50.*

GLASGOW, CITY OF GLASGOW   9–4C

Perhaps it's the inspiration of *Rogano* – the famously Art
Deco seafood restaurant – which has led to a certain fish-
and-seafood bias among Glasgow's leading restaurants. Such
dishes are the speciality at *Gamba* (foodwise, probably the
best place in town) as well as at the popular *Two Fat Ladies*.
There are also a couple of good non-fishy names, both of
which, as it happens, are new or in new ownership – the new
Hotel du Vin has above-average standards for the group,
and *étain* seems to be flourishing outside the Conran empire
(as it did within it). There are two other notable aspects
of dining out in this populous city. One is a tendency
to sustain and cherish 'institutions', such as *Rogano*,
the *Ubiquitous Chip* and *Sarti's*. The other is the existence of a
good number of quality Indian restaurants, among which
Mother India and *Dhabba* stand out.

Babbity Bowster   £ 33
16-18 Blackfriar's St G1 1PE   (0141) 552 5055
*"A Glasgow institution that's the best place to spend a Sunday
morning"; it's the bar, though, that's the place to be – the upstairs
restaurant "lacks the vibrancy of down below". /* ***Sample dishes:*** *goat's
cheese tart; monkfish; cheese board.* ***Details:*** *www.babbity.com; 10.30 pm;
D only, closed Mon & Sun.* ***Accommodation:*** *6 rooms, from £60.*

Brian Maule at Chardon D'Or   £ 56
176 West Regent St G2 4RL   (0141) 248 3801
*"If you want to impress", it's worth considering this "sombre" venture
near Blythswood Square, where Gavroche-trained chef Brian Maule
serves up "classy" and "enjoyable" (if pricey and perhaps
"unexciting") fare. /* ***Sample dishes:*** *fried scallops with Serrano ham;
roast-dried sirloin; chocolate tart.* ***Details:*** *www.brianmaule.com; 9.30 pm; closed
Sat L & Sun.*

(Two Fat Ladies at) The Buttery £ 57
652 Argyle St G3 8UF (0141) 221 8188
This "old Glasgow eating house" changed hands in mid-2007, and is
to re-open around the publication date of this guide; it seems likely
to continue the "clubby" style of the previous régimes on the site,
and to offer a somewhat broader and less fishy menu than the other
*TFL establishments. / **Sample dishes:** open lasagne of duck confit;*
chestnut-crusted loin & shank of lamb; soft-centred chocolate & pistachio pudding.
***Details:** www.eatbuttery.com; 10 pm; closed Mon, Sat L & Sun.*

Café Gandolfi £ 39 Ⓐ
64 Albion St G1 1NY (0141) 552 6813
This "charming" café/restaurant is an "eternal" Merchant City stand-
by – "not a bad destination for a midweek meal, even if the food isn't
*honestly that great". / **Sample dishes:** cullen skink; haggis; cappuccino pot.*
***Details:** www.cafegandolfi.com; near Tron Theatre; 11.30 pm; no booking, Sat.*

Café India £ 35
171 North St G1 1LH (0141) 248 4074
Having burnt down in late-2006, this popular Glaswegian fixture has
now found this new home in the Merchant City – too late, sadly,
*for any assessment by the survey. / **Sample dishes:** chicken pakora;*
*chicken tikka masala; gulab jamun. **Details:** www.cafeindiaglasgow.com; midnight.*

The Dhabba £ 34 ⭐⭐
44 Candleriggs G1 1LE (0141) 5531249
A "non-clichéd" menu, "excellent" value and "consistently high"
standards commend this "outstanding" Merchant City Indian to all
*who report on it. / **Sample dishes:** chicken tikka; dal palak gohst; kulfi.*
***Details:** www.thedhabba.com; 11 pm.*

étain £ 49 Ⓐ⭐
The Glass Hs, Springfield Ct G1 3JX (0141) 225 5630
At the top of the Princes Square Shopping Centre, this elegant former
Conran establishment – now part of the Individual Restaurant Co –
is "still excellent" in all departments; the "superb" lunch menu,
*in particular, is "a real bargain". / **Sample dishes:** smoked salmon; grilled*
lamb chump with roast sweetbreads; banana soufflé with dark chocolate sorbet.
***Details:** 9.30; closed Sat L & Sun D; booking essential.*

La Fiorentina £ 41 Ⓣ
2 Paisley Rd, West G51 1LE (0141) 4201585
"A great Italian in a less-than-promising location", tipped for offering
*"the best cooking of its type in south Glasgow". / **Sample dishes:** fillet*
steak medallions au poivre; pasta tossed in seafood sauce; tiramisu.
***Details:** www.la-fiorentina.com; 10.30 pm; closed Sun.*

Gamba £ 52 ⭐
225a West George St G2 2ND (0141) 572 0899
"Cracking" seafood complemented by an "unexpectedly good" and
"reasonably-priced" wine list makes this city-centre basement a great
"find" for those who haven't discovered it already; service is generally
*"flawless" too. / **Sample dishes:** tartare of organic salmon; pan-fried halibut*
with crayfish tails; chocolate & hazelnut pudding with Mascarpone sorbet.
***Details:** www.gamba.co.uk; 10.30 pm; closed Sun L; children: 14+.*

Hotel du Vin et Bistro   **£ 55** ⭐

1 Devonshire Gdns G12 0UX   (0141) 339 2001

Early-days reports (relatively few) on the new régime at the restaurant formerly called Room are excellent, lauding its "spacious" setting and food that's easily "the best in the Hotel du Vin chain".
/ ***Sample dishes:*** *terrine of sardine with piquillo peppers, sesame seed caramel & balsamic ice cream; cannelloni of beef blade & morrels wrapped in turnip with confit beetroot; tonka bean crème brûlée with eucalyptus ice cream, warm orange & vanilla madeleine.* ***Details:*** *www.onedevonshiregardens.com; 9.45 pm; closed Sat L.* ***Accommodation:*** *49 rooms, from £140.*

Ichiban   **£ 23** ⓣ

50 Queen St G1 3DS   (0141) 204 4200

"Still reliable and good value" – a city-centre noodle parlour, in the style of Wagamama, but arguably rather better; there's another branch at 184 Dumbarton Road (tel 334 9222).
/ ***Details:*** *www.ichiban.co.uk; 10 pm, 11.30 Thurs Fri Sat; need 10+ to book.*

The Italian Kitchen   **£ 33** ⓣ

64 Ingram St G1 1EX   (0141) 5721472

A "buzzy modern interpretation of the Italian trattoria" that "goes down well with the Merchant City trendies"; "great pizzas" are particularly tipped. / ***Sample dishes:*** *crostino ai gamberoni; spaghetti con filetto with strips of beef fillet with chillies, tomato sugo & red wine; crème brûlée.* ***Details:*** *www.italian-kitchen.co.uk; 10 pm, 10.30 pm Fri & Sat.*

Kember & Jones   **£ 26** ⓣ

134 Byres Rd G12 8TD   (0141) 337 3851

A tip for "ladies who lunch in the West End" – a "friendly" deli/café offering "wholesome rustic food" in "ample portions"; the queues, though, "can be daunting". / ***Sample dishes:*** *houmous & toast; feta, butternut squash & calamata olive salad; apple & rhubarb crumble.* ***Details:*** *www.kemberandjones.co.uk; 10 pm, Sun 5 pm; no Amex.*

Mother India   **£ 30** ⭐

28 Westminster Ter G3 7RU   (0141) 221 1663

For "the best curry and service in Glasgow", many reporters would recommend this "authentic" and "interesting" Indian café, south of Kelvingrove Park. / ***Sample dishes:*** *spiced haddock; chilli garlic chicken; home-made mango kulfi.* ***Details:*** *www.motherindia.co.uk; beside Kelvingrove Hotel; 10.30 pm; closed Mon L.*

Number 16   **£ 32** ⭐

16 Byres Rd G11 5JY   (0141) 339 2544

"Good food is served with good humour", at this tiny bistro, near Dumbarton Road – some of the (few) reports on dining here have been of a truly "memorable" experience. / ***Sample dishes:*** *crispy confit duck leg with orange & lambs leaf salad; pan-roast chump of lamb with boulangère potatoes; chocolate cassata & rum syrup.* ***Details:*** *www.number16.co.uk; 10 pm, 9 pm Sun.*

Paperinos   **£ 31** ⓣ

283 Sauchiehall St G2 3HQ   (0141) 332 3800

"The best pizza house in Glasgow", rated a "10/10" experience by a handful of reporters; since 2005, it's also had a West End branch (at 227 Bryres Road, tel 0141 334 3811). / ***Sample dishes:*** *ricotta & spinach ravioli; black tagliatelle with seafood & white wine sauce; pizzas.* ***Details:*** *www.paperinos.com; 10.50 pm, 11.45 Fri & Sat.*

Rogano £ 59 Ⓐ

11 Exchange Pl G1 3AN (0141) 248 4055

*Reports from this "glorious" Art Deco fish and seafood legend –
now under new ownership – are very mixed; the interior is still
"stunning", of course, but the food too often seems "average and
overpriced". / **Sample dishes:** grilled langoustine & garlic butter; grilled lemon
sole; crème brûlée. **Details:** www.roganoglasgow.com; 10.30 pm.*

Sarti's £ 28 Ⓐ

121 Bath St G2 2SZ (0141) 204 0440

*This "characterful" "deli/trattoria" has long been the sort of place
"where Italians eat", serving "the best pizza" and other "interesting"
dishes; the feeling is growing, though, that it's drifting towards
becoming "bog-standard". / **Sample dishes:** minestrone; spaghetti allo
scoglio; home-made tiramisu. **Details:** www.sarti.co.uk; 10.30 pm; no booking
at L.*

78 St Vincent £ 42

78 St Vincent's St G2 5UB (0141) 248 7878

*An "impressive" former banking hall provides the setting for this
modern city-centre brasserie, which, on the whole, continues to put
in a decent all-round performance. / **Sample dishes:** haggis; lamb; sticky
toffee pudding. **Details:** www.78stvincent.com; 2 mins from George Sq; 10 pm,
Fri & Sat 10.30.*

Stravaigin £ 41

28 Gibson St G12 8NX (0141) 334 2665

*Colin Clydesdale's innovative ground floor bar (and "ever so slightly
more formal downstairs restaurant") is closed as we to go press;
the website promises 'a new look Stravaigin', around the publication
date of this guide. / **Sample dishes:** Thai-dressed squid salad; smoked salmon;
banana cake & home-churned vanilla ice cream. **Details:** www.stravaigin.com;
11 pm; closed Mon.*

Two Fat Ladies £ 37 ★

88 Dumbarton Rd G11 6NX (0141) 339 1944

*"The tiny little original" has long been known as a quirky, "intimate"
spot for some "great" fish and seafood; its newer city-centre spin-off –
at 118a Blythswood Street, tel 847 0088 – similarly "hits the spot".
/ **Sample dishes:** smoked haddock & potato scone; salmon & sole roulade; sticky
toffee pudding. **Details:** www.twofatladies.org; 10.30 pm; closed Sun L.*

Ubiquitous Chip £ 58 Ⓐ

12 Ashton Ln G12 8SJ (0141) 334 5007

*A "Glasgow institution" since 1971, whose characterful interior and
huge wine list make it "a favourite for special occasions"; its cuisine
"with a Scottish twist" has had its ups-and-downs in recent years –
fans vaunt "seriously top nosh", but others leave "disappointed".
/ **Sample dishes:** salmon brandade; salmon; chocolate brioche.
Details: www.ubiquitouschip.co.uk; behind Hillhead station; 11 pm.*

GODALMING, SURREY 3–3A

Bel & The Dragon £ 42 Ⓐ
Bridge St GU7 3DU (01483) 527333
*Although the "tastefully-converted" former church setting is even
more "fun", this "friendly" gastropub inspires more variable feedback
than its Cookham sibling – fans say the food is "great", but critics find
it too "samey". / Sample dishes: smoked haddock & spring onion cakes;
lamb shoulder; sticky toffee pudding.*
Details: *www.belandthedragon-godalming.co.uk; 10 pm, Sat 10.30, Sun 9 pm.*

La Luna £ 47 Ⓐ★
10-14 Wharf St GU7 1NN (01483) 414155
*"A great modern Italian, with an interesting wine list and personal
service"; a "stylish" sort of place, in the town-centre, it generates
almost invariably positive reports. / Details: www.lalunarestaurant.co.uk;
10 pm; closed Mon & Sun D.*

GODSTONE, SURREY 3–3B

The Bell £ 33 Ⓣ
128 High St RH9 8DX (01883) 741877
*A "wide selection" of "good, honest gastropub fare" wins a tip for this
"friendly" inn. / Sample dishes: smoked trout pâté with horseradish
remoulade; steak bavette & frites. Details: www.thebellgodstone.co.uk.*

GOLCAR, WEST YORKSHIRE 5–1C

The Weavers Shed £ 50 ★★
Knowl Rd HD7 4AN (01484) 654284
*The Jackson family's converted mill of two decades' standing remains
"a wonderful oasis", where much of the "tremendous" food is grown
in their own back-garden; the style is "relaxed", but the room can
seem a tad "hushed". / Sample dishes: scallops; venison; soup soufflé
of chocolate. Details: www.weaversshed.co.uk; 9 pm; closed Mon, Sat L & Sun.
Accommodation: 5 rooms, from £90.*

GOLDSBOROUGH, NORTH YORKSHIRE 8–3D

The Fox And Hounds Inn £ 37 Ⓐ★
YO21 3RX (01947) 893372
*"Perched on a cliff above the bay around Whitby, and with astounding
views", this "tiny and quirky" three-year-old is a real "find"; ex-Ivy
chef, Jason Davies offers a "short but interesting" blackboard menu
of "accomplished" dishes from "seasonal ingredients".
/ Sample dishes: linguine with fresh crab meat & chilli; char-grilled lamb leg
steak. Details: 8.30 pm; closed Mon, Tue & Sun D; no Amex.*

GORING, BERKSHIRE 2–2D

Leatherne Bottel £ 56 Ⓐ
Bridleway RG8 0HS (01491) 872667
*"A dreamy riverside setting that's perfect for romance" is the
undoubted special attraction of this long-established Thames-side
spot; Julia Storey's menu is "pricey" – results vary from "OK to
inspired". / Sample dishes: crab; roast tenderloin of veal; brandy snap basket.
Details: www.leathernebottel.co.uk; 0.5m outside Goring on B4009; 9 pm; closed
Sun D; children: 10+.*

Kaye Arms   £ 37
29 Wakefield Rd WF4 4BG   (01924) 848385
*Most reports still rate the cooking at this long-established "rural"
pub/bistro as "imaginative and of good quality"; occasionally, though,
it is judged "good, but a bit over-priced". / **Sample dishes:** crab &
Gruyère cheese tart; hake en cocotte; raspberry soufflé.*
Details: *www.thekayearms.co.uk; 9.30 pm; closed Mon; no Amex; no booking
on Sat; children: 14+ at D.*

Hazelmere   £ 31
1-2 Yewbarrow Ter LA11 6ED   (01539) 532972
*The Tea Guild's "Best Tearoom in England, 2006" is tipped not only
for its "fantastic cakes" and an appropriately "extensive range
of teas", but also for "superbly-presented local dishes" from
"very good ingredients". / **Sample dishes:** tea-smoked duck breast.*
Details: *www.hazelmerecafe.co.uk; L only.*

The Jumble Room   £ 37
Langdale Rd LA22 9SU   (01539) 435188
*"A really special little restaurant in a gorgeous village"; reports are not
copious, but all sing the praises of its "good home cooking" and
"value for money"; downstairs seating is best.
/ **Sample dishes:** home-cured bresaola & cherries; hake fish stew with chorizo &
saffron potatoes; hand-made game pie topped with a crisp double crusted pastry
served with roasted root vegetables & a sweet damson jelly.*
Details: *www.thejumbleroom.co.uk; midnight; closed Mon & Tue; no Amex.*

Lancrigg Country House Hotel   £ 37
Easedale Rd LA22 9QN   (01539) 435317
*A country house hotel with "great views", and where the cooking
is often of a "very high standard"; overall, however, this year's reports
were not quite the usual hymn of praise.
/ **Sample dishes:** roast artichoke, olive, cherry tomato & pine kernel tart;
chestnut & wild mushroom en croûte; chocolate & walnut truffle pudding.*
Details: *www.lancrigg.co.uk; 8 pm; no Amex.* **Accommodation:** *13 rooms,
from £120.*

The Foxcote   £ 35
Station Ln CH3 7JN   (01244) 301343
*"A pleasantly-situated ex-pub"; it can be "a bit variable", but, "on a
good day" its (speciality) fish dishes are "very good".
/ **Sample dishes:** crab & brown shrimp; sea bass fillet with crab & banana
crumble; sticky toffee pudding.* ***Details:*** *www.thefoxcote.com; 9.30; closed Sun D.*

GREAT DUNMOW, ESSEX   3–2C

Starr   £ 61
Market Pl CM6 1AX   (01371) 874321
"An interesting menu using local produce" heads up the all-round
attractions (which also include a conservatory) of this eminent
restaurant in the market square. / **Sample dishes:** *rare-roasted yellow fin
tuna with crisp-fried quail egg & anchovy mayonnaise; aged fillet of beef with
horseradish crust, roasted ceps, celeriac purée, & foie gras jus; lemon chiboust,
lemon curd meringue & lemon & Earl Grey tea sorbet.*
Details: *www.the-starr.co.uk; 8m E of M11, J8 on A120; 9.30 pm; closed Sun D;
no jeans or trainers.* **Accommodation:** *8 rooms, from £120.*

GREAT GONERBY, LINCOLNSHIRE   5–3D

Harry's Place   £ 75   ⭐⭐
17 High St NG31 8JS   (01476) 561780
"A unique experience"; Harry Hallam's *"tiny"* and *"intimate"* (10-
cover) operation yet again inspires adulation, both for his wife's
"very special hospitality", and for his own *"exceptional"* and
sometimes *"intricate"* food; perhaps inevitably for such a personal
venture, there is the odd reporter for whom the whole approach hits
the wrong note. / **Sample dishes:** *sautéed foie gras in spicy sherry aspic; fillet
of beef; rhubarb soufflé.* **Details:** *on B1174 1m N of Grantham; 9.30 pm; closed
Mon & Sun; no Amex; booking essential; children: 5+.*

GREAT MALVERN, WORCESTERSHIRE   2–1B

Anupam Restaurant   £ 30   Ⓣ
85 Church St WR14 2AE   (01684) 573814
*Mr Khayser's colourfully-decorated Indian, near the theatre,
is consistently highly rated by a more-than-local fan club; it turns
20 this year, so they must be doing something right.*
*/ **Sample dishes:** *jalfrezi chicken; kashmiri lamb.* **Details:** *www.anupam.co.uk;
midnight.*

GREAT MILTON, OXFORDSHIRE   2–2D

Le Manoir aux Quat' Saisons   £126   Ⓐ⭐
Church Rd OX44 7PD   (01844) 278881

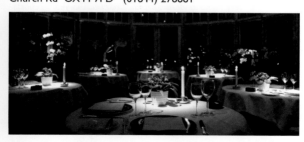

*Raymond Blanc's "perfect and romantic" manor house hotel, praised
by most reporters for "simply the very best food"; it's "horrendously
expensive" of course (and the style can seem a little bit "corporate").
/ **Sample dishes:** *cannelloni of langoustines; slow-cooked breast of chicken;
iced orgeat parfait & lemon confit in biscuit leaves.* **Details:** *www.manoir.com;
from M40, J7 take A329; 10 pm.* **Accommodation:** *32 rooms, from £380.*

GREAT TEW, OXFORDSHIRE

Falkland Arms £ 34 Ⓐ

The Green OX7 4DB (01608) 683653

*"Historic and fascinating" – this Cotswold inn is certainly strong
on atmosphere, but it also offers food of "consistent good quality",
plus "service with a smile". / **Sample dishes:** soup with crusty bread;
roast pork fillet wrapped in pancetta; sticky toffee pudding.
Details: www.falklandarms.org.uk; A361 between Banbury & Chipping Norton;
8 pm; closed Sun D; children: 16+. **Accommodation:** 5 rooms, from £80.*

GREAT TEY, ESSEX
3–2C

The Barn Brasserie £ 35

Brook Rd CO6 1JE (01206) 212345

*A "vast" and spectacular barn "in the middle of nowhere", which
attracts limited feedback; fans say the food's "very good" – sceptics
feel "it's trying to be a destination, but is more a neighbourhood
option". / **Sample dishes:** Parma ham & goats cheese, sunblush tomatoes &
basil; char-grilled rib eye steak, celeriac, potato cake, roast courgette & herb
butter; baked vanilla cheesecake. **Details:** www.barnbrasserie.co.uk; 10 pm;
no Amex.*

GRINSHILL, SHROPSHIRE
5–3A

The Inn At Grinshill £ 44 Ⓣ

The High St SY4 3BL (01939) 220410

*Can this be the destination Shrewsbury has been waiting for? –
a couple of reporters tip this inn "just outside the town", as simply
"exceptional"; more reports, please. / **Sample dishes:** seared king scallops,
citrus & spinach risotto; roasted pork fillet, choucroute, creamed potato & apple
sauce; coconut pyramid with a chilli lime vodka jelly.
Details: www.theinnatgrinshill.co.uk; 9.30 pm; no Amex. **Accommodation:** 6
rooms, from £120.*

GUERNSEY, CHANNEL ISLANDS

Auberge £ 44 Ⓐ

Jerbourg Rd, St Martin's GY4 6BH (01481) 238485 *A "truly
lovely setting, on a hill overlooking St. Peter Port", contributes to the
popularity for this contemporary bistro; on some feedback, the food
is "exquisite" too, but reports remain limited. / **Sample dishes:** pan-fried
scallops; cottage pie; chilled peach & Malibu soup. **Details:** www.theauberge.gg;
9 pm.*

Christophe £ 48 ⒶⓍ

Fermain Ln GY1 1ZZ (01481) 230725

*"A top-class restaurant, in a newly-renovated hotel on a hill
overlooking the sea"; this "very friendly" newcomer has been instantly
hailed as offering "some of the best food on the island".
/ **Sample dishes:** ballotine of foie gras, ginger melba toast, sauternes jelly; rib of
beef, roasted cherry tomatoes & chips; lavender mousse with honey gel.
Details: www.christophe-restaurant.co.uk; 10 pm; closed Mon & Sun D.*

Da Nello £ 34

46 Lower Pollet St, St Peter Port GY1 1WF (01481) 721552

*"A nice find", in the heart of St Peter Port; this long-established Italian
remains "highly recommended" on most accounts – even the odd
negative report concedes the place is "so popular".
/ **Sample dishes:** balsamic onions with Mozzarella & tomato salad; beef barolo;
Mascarpone & ginger cheesecake. **Details:** 10 pm.*

Le Petit Bistro £ 41

56 Le Pollet (01481) 725055

"Very friendly and authentically French" – a *"cramped"* and
sometimes *"crowded"* establishment, in St Peter Port.
/ **Sample dishes:** coq au vin with braised chicory & dauphinoise potatoes;
steamed monkfish. **Details:** www.lepetitbistro.co.uk; 10 pm, 10.30 pm Fri & Sat.

GUILDFORD, SURREY 3–3A

Café de Paris £ 40

35 Castle St GU1 3UQ (01483) 534896

*On most accounts, this "typically French" town-centre veteran
is "always a reliable destination"; as even though, it doesn't do it for
everyone.* / **Sample dishes:** sautéed diver scallops; roast of Parma-rolled
venison; terrine of white-spiced pear. **Details:** www.cafedeparisguildford.co.uk;
9.30 mon-thu, 10.30 fri&sat; closed Sun.

Cambio £ 50

2-4 South Hill GU1 3SY (01483) 577702

*Local fans insist this long-established (but recently revamped) Italian
is "the best place in the area", with "authentic" cuisine and
"interesting" wine; even a long-term fan, however, scents "decline",
and the feeling that the place "isn't all it's cracked up to be"
permeates a number of reports.* / **Sample dishes:** roast asparagus with
porcini mushrooms; slow-cooked pork fillet; wild cherries semifreddo.
Details: www.cambiorestaurant.com; by Guildford Castle; 10pm Mon-Thu, 10.30
Fri & Sat; closed Sat L & Sun D.

Dolce Vita £ 43

Trinity Gate, 14 Epsom Rd GU1 3JQ (01483) 511544

*"The best tapas bar in Guildford" is a "popular" destination;
the "posh" restaurant upstairs inspires less interest.*
/ **Sample dishes:** crab salad; tuna steak; sticky toffee pudding.
Details: www.dolcevitarestaurant.co.uk; 10.30pm; closed Sun D.

Rumwong £ 33

16-18 London Rd GU1 2AF (01483) 536092

*"After a very successful refurbishment", this "long-established, family-
run" Thai "continues to provide lovely, traditional food", but nowadays
"in a very smart modern setting".* / **Details:** www.rumwong.com; 10.30 pm;
closed Mon; no Amex or Switch.

The Thai Terrace £ 33

Castle Car Pk, Sydenham Rd GU1 3RT (01483) 503350

*"A beautiful ambience and a wonderful view from the terrace" make
this "tasteful" oriental Guildford's "ultimate dining experience"
("even if it is over a car park!"); what's more, "it's five-star in every
respect", with "very attentive" service and "excellent", "spicy"
cooking.* / **Sample dishes:** chicken in pandanus leaves; soft-shelled crab; green
tea cheesecake. **Details:** opposite Guildford Castle in town centre; 11 pm;
closed Sun.

GULLANE, EAST LOTHIAN　　　　　　　　9–4D

Greywalls Hotel　　　　　　　　£ 61　　　🅣
EH31 2EG　(01620) 842144

Lutyens-designed country house hotel, run by the same family since the war, and enjoying fine views; the kitchen "does wonderful things with local ingredients". / **Sample dishes:** *honey-roast quail with summer truffle risotto; braised brisket with raisins; crannachan parfait, chilled raspberry soup, raspberry sorbet & caramelised pecans.* **Details:** *www.greywalls.co.uk; 9.30 pm; Mon-Thu D only, Fri-Sun open L & D, Closed Jan & Feb; jacket at D.* **Accommodation:** *23 rooms, from £140.*

La Potinière　　　　　　　　£ 50　　　⭐
Main St　EH31 2AA　(01620) 843214

"Very impressive food" from a "thoughtful" menu shows this "destination restaurant" to be very much "back on form" under owners of five years standing, Keith Marley and Mary Runciman; its "low-key" ambience seems to suits its mature following well. / **Sample dishes:** *Thai coconut soup with poached scallops; seared monkfish on smoked salmon & cucumber mash; passion fruit mousse & coconut tart.* **Details:** *www.la-potiniere.co.uk; 20m E of Edinburgh, off A198; 8.30 pm; closed Mon & Tue; Oct-Apr closed Sun D; no Amex; booking essential.*

GULWORTHY, DEVON　　　　　　　　1–3C

Horn of Plenty　　　　　　　　£ 62
PL19 8JD　(01822) 832528

A long-established restaurant-with-rooms, with a "spectacular setting" overlooking the Tamar Valley; most feedback is to the effect that it's a "wonderful" place with food that lives up to its "superb" reputation, but it again provoked one or two "really very bad" reports this year. / **Sample dishes:** *pan-fried sea bass, sweet potato blinis & fried mussels; roast pork tenderloin; hot raspberry & lemon meringue cake with a raspberry sauce.* **Details:** *www.thehornofplenty.co.uk; 3m W of Tavistock on A390; 9 pm; no jeans or trainers; children: 7+ at D.* **Accommodation:** *10 rooms, from £160.*

GUNTHORPE, NOTTINGHAMSHIRE　　　　5–3D

Tom Browns Brasserie　　　　　　£ 39　　　🅣
The Old School Hs　NG14 7FB　(0115) 9663642

"The perfect place for a romantic dinner or weekend lunch by the river" – it has a "beautiful" setting, and is a "friendly and relaxed" sort of place offering a "very varied" menu. / **Sample dishes:** *seared king scallops, curried risotto & mango vinaigrette; baked pork fillet stuffed with black pudding served with champ, baby leeks, cider sauce & baby toffee apples; apple & blackberry crumble with star anise ice cream.* **Details:** *www.tombrowns.co.uk; 10 pm.*

HALE, CHESHIRE　　　　　　　　5–2B

Amba　　　　　　　　£ 35
106-108 Ashley Rd　WA14 2UN　(0161) 928 2343

This "reliable mid-market contemporary restaurant", in Hale, has quite a name for its "ever-changing menu"; it can be "noisy", though – ask for a table upstairs. / **Sample dishes:** *grilled fillet of sea bass on stir-fried veggies & noodles; cranberry & sourbread sirloin steak with chips, mushrooms & tomatoes.* **Details:** *www.amba.uk.com; 0.5m SE of Altrincham; 10.30 pm; no Maestro.*

HALIFAX, WEST YORKSHIRE

Design House £ 40

Dean Clough HX3 5AX   (01422) 383242
A converted mill also housing an arts and media centre; it offers "consistently good standards of food in a stylish setting".
*/ **Sample dishes:** crab & sweet corn ravioli; lemon-marinated ostrich fillet; pineapple Tatin with praline ice cream. **Details:** www.designhouserestaurant.co.uk; from Halifax follow signs to Dean Clough Mills; 9.30 pm; closed Sat L & Sun.*

Shibden Mill Inn £ 39

Shibden Mill Fold HX3 7UL   (01422) 365840
"A nice old inn, serving honest, unpretentious food".
*/ **Sample dishes:** Aberdeen-smoked haddock; sea bass, curried couscous, pumpkin & tarragon dressing; vanilla cream & pot-roast plums.*
***Details:** www.shibdenmillinn.com; off the A58, Leeds/Bradford road; 9.15 pm, Sun 7.30 pm. **Accommodation:** 11 rooms, from £85.*

HAMBLETON, RUTLAND

Finch's Arms £ 32

Oakham Rd LE15 8TL   (01572) 756575
*"Overlooking Rutland Water", "a little pub with a fine old interior", and a restaurant with a panoramic terrace at the back; it serves "gastropub-type food of perfectly good quality". / **Sample dishes:** fish & chips; calves' liver & bacon. **Details:** www.finchsarms.co.uk; 9.30 pm, Sun 8 pm. **Accommodation:** 6 rooms, from £75.*

Hambleton Hall £ 85

LE15 8TH   (01572) 756991
*"OTT" prices crop up time and again in feedback on Tim Hart's "luxurious" mansion overlooking Rutland Water; even so, reporters rate it a "superb country house experience", thanks to its "special" atmosphere and "slick" service, and to Aaron Patterson's "stunning" traditional cuisine. / **Sample dishes:** mosaic of chicken, veal sweetbreads & foie gras; roast loin & fallow venison; passion fruit soufflé.*
***Details:** www.hambletonhall.com; near Rutland Water; 9.30 pm.*
***Accommodation:** 17 rooms, from £200.*

HAMPTON COURT, SURREY

Caffe La Fiamma £ 35

Hampton Court Rd KT8 9BY   (020) 8943 2050
*Reports on this "friendly" (if sometimes "slow") Italian restaurant tend to focus on its "superb views of Bushey Park"; the "good" to "variable" cuisine seems rather incidental. / **Sample dishes:** baked mushroom pasta; pan-fried chicken liver in a balsamic vinegar sauce; blackcurrant sorbet. **Details:** www.clfuk.co.uk; 11 pm.*

HARLECH, GWYNEDD

Castle Cottage £ 46

Pen Llech LL46 2YL   (01766) 780479
A restaurant-with-rooms overlooking Harlech Castle, where the cooking "is all home-made"; "good use of local produce".
*/ **Sample dishes:** boned & rolled suckling pig served with red cabbage, black pudding, apple sauce & a calvados jus; baked fillet of cod served on buttered linguine with a basil, vermouth & cream sauce; tarragon crème brulée with a brandy snap basket of berries. **Details:** www.castlecottageharlech.co.uk; nr the castle, just off the high street; 9 pm; D only; no Amex; booking essential.*
***Accommodation:** 7 rooms, from £100.*

Maes y Neuadd £ 47

Talsarnau LL47 6YA (01766) 780200

*"A hidden gem" – on most accounts, this pleasant country house
hotel, with views of Snowdon, continues to "exceed expectations".
/ **Sample dishes:** roast loin of pork with local shitake mushrooms & a redcurrant
sauce; confit of duck; bara brith pudding with ginger custard.*
Details: www.neuadd.com; 3m N of Harlech off B4573; 8.45 pm; no Amex;
no jeans or trainers; children: 8+. **Accommodation:** 15 rooms, from £150.

HAROME, NORTH YORKSHIRE 8–4C

Star Inn £ 49

YO62 5JE (01439) 770397

"What's not to love?"; Andrew & Jacquie Pern's *"eternally popular"
gastropub legend, out in "truly magnificent Yorkshire countryside",
offers a "seasonally-changing" menu which delivers "robust but not
heavy cooking, with intense flavours"; and it is served by "professional
but unfussy" staff too. / **Sample dishes:** grilled black pudding with pan-fried
foie gras; breast of local wood pigeon; baked Bramley apple & Hawes Wensleydale
cheesecake.* **Details:** www.thestaratharome.co.uk; 3m SE of Helmsley off A170;
9.30 pm; closed Mon & Sun D; no Amex. **Accommodation:** 14 rooms,
from £130.

HARPENDEN, HERTFORDSHIRE 3–2A

Bean Tree £ 44

20a Leyton Rd AL5 2HU (01582) 460901

"You pay London prices, but it's genuinely worth it", says a fan of this
"French-influenced" hidden "gem", often hailed as the *"best place
in the area for a special meal"*; there are also quite a few doubters,
though, who say it charges *"London prices, without the London gloss"*.
/ **Sample dishes:** seared foie gras; venison loin steak; mango soufflé with coconut.
Details: www.thebeantree.com; 9.30 pm; closed Mon, Sat L & Sun D.

Chef Peking £ 32

5-6 Church Grn AL5 2TP (01582) 769358

*If you leave out of account the "terrible piped music",
the "high standards" of this Chinese stalwart mostly continue
to impress. / **Sample dishes:** special mixed hors d'oeuvres; sizzling filet mignon
in fruity sauce; toffee apples & bananas with Italian vanilla ice cream.*
Details: just off the High Rd; 10.45 pm.

The Fox £ 39

469 Luton Rd AL5 3QE (01582) 713817

"Always an enjoyable evening"; this popular boozer – *"more a
restaurant" nowadays* – offers *"better value than the local
competition"*, and cuisine that's *"generally reliable"*.
/ **Sample dishes:** scallops; spit chicken; sticky ginger toffee pudding.
Details: www.thefoxharpenden.co.uk; 10 pm; closed Sun D.

White Horse £ 49 ⊗
Hatching Grn AL5 2JP (01582) 713428
*"The sort of place that gets gastropubs a bad name"; this heavily celeb-chef-branded boozer strikes roughly half of reporters as "very overrated" — "if this is a 'Touch of Novelli', it certainly isn't magic". / **Sample dishes:** dressed crab with gazpacho; roast Anjou pigeon; baked Granny Smith tart. **Details:** www.atouchofnovelli.com; 9.30 pm; closed Sun D.*

HARROGATE, NORTH YORKSHIRE 5–1C

Bettys £ 32 🅐 ⭐
1 Parliament St HG1 2QU (01423) 877300
*"Step back in time to an era of elegant living", say fans of this famously time-warped tea shop, who insist its overall "attention to detail" is "worth the queue"; perhaps inevitably, though, it can also seem "overpriced". / **Sample dishes:** smoked salmon fishcakes; Florentine rosti; rhubarb crumble tartlet. **Details:** www.bettysandtaylors.co.uk; 9 pm; no Amex; no booking.*

The Boar's Head £ 45 🅐
Ripley Castle Estate HG3 3AY (01423) 771888
*A grand village inn with a "beautiful" setting, and quite a name for the "interesting" food on offer in its "smart country restaurant" (and bistro); one or two reporters sensed "standards had slipped a bit" this year — let's hope it's just a blip. / **Sample dishes:** tartlet of Nidderdale lamb shank; baked halibut fillet with a pinenut crust; gratin of sautéed strawberries & orange segments. **Details:** www.boarsheadripley.co.uk; off A61 between Ripon & Harrogate; 9 pm. **Accommodation:** 25 rooms, from £125.*

Brio £ 33 🆃
Hornbeam Pk, The Lenz HG2 8RE (01423) 870005
*Two "cheap, cheerful Italians" — this town-centre branch, and also one at Hornbeam Park (tel 870005) — which are spin-offs from the Leeds operation of the same name. / **Sample dishes:** ravioloni agli asparagi; grilled peppers aubergines courgettes & feta cheese focaccine. **Details:** www.brios.co.uk.*

Drum & Monkey £ 36 ⭐
5 Montpellier Gdns HG1 2TF (01423) 502650
*"Wonderful for seafood, but it gets very, very busy" — the "reliable" standards at this "atmospheric" inn mean it is still a treasured local "favourite"; quite a few reporters, though, still regret the passing of the old régime, a few years back. / **Sample dishes:** scallops in cheese & garlic; sea bass with herb butter; home-made treacle tart. **Details:** www.drumandmonkey.co.uk; 10 pm, 6.45 pm; no Amex; booking: max 10.*

Hotel du Vin et Bistro £ 45
Prospect Pl HG1 1LB (01423) 856800
*Though "one of the better H du V restaurants", this "pleasant" boutique-hotel dining room has sadly acquired the "formulaic" feel which is now the group norm — the "great choice of wines" is now its only real stand-out attraction. / **Sample dishes:** deep-fried goat's cheese in macadamia crust; confit fillet of salmon; dark chocolate galette with roast hazelnuts. **Details:** www.hotelduvin.com; 9.45 pm. **Accommodation:** 43 rooms, from £95.*

Loch Fyne £ 39
Cheltenham Pde HG1 1DD   (01423) 533070
"It may be part of a chain, but standards are good" – this very popular branch is praised by reporters for its *"good choice of well-presented fish"* (and seafood). / **Sample dishes:** oysters; mussels. **Details:** www.loch-fyne.com; 10 pm, Fri & Sat 10.30 pm.

Orchid £ 42 ⭐
28 Swan Rd HG1 2SE (01423) 560425
Thanks to the *"excellent quality of its Asian-fusion cuisine"*, this *"pleasant, contemporary-style establishment"* can be notably *"hard to book"*. / **Sample dishes:** crispy fried prawns served with an oriental mayonnaise topped with sesame seeds & chopped shallots; crispy fried seabass with pineapple, peppers & onions with a Thai sweet & sour sauce. **Details:** www.orchidrestaurant.co.uk; 10 pm; closed Sat L. **Accommodation:** 36 rooms, from £99.

Quantro £ 35
3 Royal Pde HG1 2SZ   (01423) 503034
A *"relaxed"*, *"friendly"* and *"popular"* city-centre spot that's almost invariably hailed as *"good and sensibly-priced"*; its *"excellent-value lunch"* is particularly worth seeking out. / **Sample dishes:** goat's cheese tart with glazed beetroot; corn-fed duck breast; sticky toffee pudding. **Details:** www.quantro.co.uk; 10 pm, Sat 10.30 pm; closed Sun; children: 8+.

Rajput £ 33 ⭐
11 Cheltenham Pde HG1 1DD   (01423) 562113
"Marvellous" cooking with *"a fair number of fusion dishes"* makes this *"recently-expanded"* restaurant a smash hit locally; *"you don't go for the ambience"*, though. / **Sample dishes:** cheese pakora; Goan chicken masala; mango kulfi. **Details:** www.rajput.co.uk; midnight; D only; no Amex.

HARROW, MIDDLESEX 3–3A

Golden Palace £ 28 ⭐⭐
146-150 Station Rd HA1 2RH   (020) 8863 2333
"Is there a better Chinese in the South East?"; *"terrific authentic food with a great range, especially dim sum"* wins a huge following for this *"very busy"* Cantonese spot, which was recently *"expanded and refurbished"*. / **Sample dishes:** sesame prawn toast; chilli beef; coconut pudding. **Details:** 11.30 pm; no booking, Sat & Sun.

Incanto £ 43
41 High St, Harrow On The Hill HA1 3HT   (0208) 426 6767
"Brilliant" service won particular praise this year at this *"lovely"* suburban Italian, often hailed as an overall *"enjoyable experience"* that's *"good value"* too. / **Sample dishes:** platter of cured meats; oven-baked halibut wrapped in a potato crust with pea purée; poached peaches in white wine sauce & Mascarpone ice cream. **Details:** www.incanto.co.uk; 10.30 pm; closed Mon & Sun D.

Old Etonian £ 30
38 High St, Harrow On The Hill HA1 3LL   (020) 8422 8482
"A friendly French local"; its approach can seem *"outdated"*, but it still pleases most reporters most of the time. / **Sample dishes:** king prawns; fillet Dijon; lime cheesecake. **Details:** www.oldetonian.com ; 10.30 pm; closed Sat L & Sun D. **Accommodation:** 13 rooms, from £70.

Skipjacks £ 15
268-276 Streatfield Rd HA3 9BY   (020) 82047554
*A locally renowned chippie; "if we are just talking about just, cooking
and eating of really fresh, lovingly prepared fish at yesterday's prices
then Skipjacks is it".*

HARWICH, ESSEX 3–2D

The Pier at Harwich £ 44
The Quay CO12 3HH   (01255) 241212
*Part of the Milsom (of Tollbooth fame) empire, this waterside spot
offers "enjoyably old-fashioned" dishes, with "superb" seafood
a highlight; the restaurant, though, "is no better than the ground-floor
bistro".* / **Sample dishes:** *ham hock terrine with pistachio nuts & home-made
piccalilli; roast monkfish with crayfish sauce; raspberry mousse.*
Details: *www.the-pier-hotel.co.uk; 9.30 pm.* **Accommodation:** *14 rooms,
from £97.50.*

HASLEMERE, SURREY 3–4A

The Inn On The Hill £ 41
Lower St GU27 2PD   (01428) 642006
*A trendified pub near the station, where the top tip is the "excellent-
value lunches".* / **Sample dishes:** *crab & sweetcorn cakes; steak with
mushroom sauce, cheese, bacon & fried egg, surrounded with onion rings; plaice.*
Details: *www.tailormadepub.co.uk; 10 pm, Sun 9 pm; booking essential.*
Accommodation: *8 rooms, from £80.*

HASTINGS, EAST SUSSEX 3–4C

The Mermaid Café £ 24
2 Rock-a-Nore Rd TN34 3DW   (01424) 438100
*This famous chippy changed hands towards the end of our survey
year; initial reports are largely positive, but – in the circumstances –
we think a proper appraisal of the new régime should wait until the
next edition.* / **Sample dishes:** *prawns & bread; shepherd's pie; treacle
pudding.* **Details:** *7.30 pm; closed Mon D, Tue D, Wed D & Thu D; no credit
cards; no booking.*

HATCH END, GREATER LONDON 3–3A

Rotisserie £ 40
316 Uxbridge Rd HA5 4HR   (020) 8421 2878
*"Simple food is done well", at this "friendly" grill-restaurant (part of
a reviving north London chain), and its "brasserie-style menu" has
"something for everyone".* / **Sample dishes:** *crab & avocado salad;
club sirloin; brownies with hot chocolate sauce & ice cream.*
Details: *www.therotisserie.co.uk; 10.30 pm; closed weekday L.*

Sea Pebbles £ 24
348-352 Uxbridge Rd HA5 4HR   (020) 8428 0203
*"Great fish, whether you have it grilled or fried" – this "favourite
North London chippy" certainly has an impressive following, and the
main complaint it inspires is that there is "too little space for too
many people".* / **Sample dishes:** *fishcakes; grilled cod & chips; home-made
bread & butter pudding.* **Details:** *10 pm; closed Sun; debit cards only; need 10+
to book.*

HATFIELD PEVEREL, ESSEX   3–2C

Blue Strawberry   £ 37
The Street CM3 2DW   (01245) 381333
*This "good-value" modern bistro remains consistently praised
as "a haven for good food and service", and "in a friendly
atmosphere" too.* / **Sample dishes:** crispy duck salad; braised shank of lamb;
crème brûlée. **Details:** www.bluestrawberrybistro.co.uk; 3m E of Chelmsford;
10 pm; closed Sat L & Sun D.

HATFIELD, HERTFORDSHIRE   3–2B

Nolita   £ 47   Ⓐ
Great North Rd AL9 6NA   (01707) 644858
*With a formula "similar to its sister restaurant, Little Italy in Soho",
this "pleasant" Italian turns out to be "much better than its odd and
isolated location would suggest"; as in W1, "dancing follows dining,
if you have the stamina!"* / **Sample dishes:** marinated seabass with fennel
shavings & watercress leaves; deep-fried baby squid & samphire served with
home-made tartare sauce. **Details:** www.nolitarestaurant.co.uk; midnight, 2 am
Thurs, Fri, Sat; no shorts.

HATHERSAGE, DERBYSHIRE   5–2C

The Walnut Club   £ 46
Unit 6, The Sq, Main Rd S32 1BB   (01433) 651155
*"A fully-organic restaurant offering relaxed dining in cool
surroundings" (sometimes with "live jazz" too); unfortunately,
however, even those who rate the food as outstanding can find
it notably "overpriced".* / **Sample dishes:** mosaic of sweet breads & chicken
with exotic mushrooms served with a sauce gribiche; pan-roasted halibut with
cauliflower purée & apple & vanilla syrup; raspberry crème brulée with white
chocolate sorbet. **Details:** www.thewalnutclub.com; 10 pm. 6 pm Sun; closed
Mon & Sun D; no Amex.

HAWORTH, WEST YORKSHIRE   5–1C

Weaver's   £ 33   ★
15 West Ln BD22 8DU   (01535) 643822
*"Still a must-visit", say fans of this "cosy" Bronteland restaurant-with-
rooms, which is progressively being taken over by the younger
generation of the Rushworth family.* / **Sample dishes:** Bury black
pudding & corned beef hash; meat & potato pie with beef, rich gravy & short
crust pastry; sticky toffee pudding. **Details:** www.weaversmallhotel.co.uk; 1.5m W
on B6142 from A629, near Parsonage; 9 pm; closed Mon, Tue L, Sat L & Sun D;
children: 5+ on Sat. **Accommodation:** 3 rooms, from £85.

HAYWARDS HEATH, WEST SUSSEX   3–4B

The Half Moon   £ 29   Ⓐ★
The St RH17 5TR   (01444) 461227
*"Young management with plenty of zest and new ideas" are making
a name for this "superbly-revamped" pub in a "sleepy hamlet";
the only real downside is that you "can't book".*
/ **Sample dishes:** seabass fillet with a shrimp bisque, potato rosti & mange tout
stir fry; calves liver with streaky bacon lightly smoked, with onion gravy, mash &
cabbage. **Details:** www.thehalfmoonwarninglid.co.uk; 9.30 pm; closed Sun D;
no Amex; no booking; children: 14+.

Jeremy's at Borde Hill £ 45 Ⓐ ⭐ ⭐

Balcombe Rd RH16 1XP (01444) 441102

*"Very classy indeed"; Jeremy Ashpool's country restaurant "goes from strength to strength", with its "imaginative" cuisine, and "beautiful" setting too (especially when you can lunch on the terrace) – and all at "value-for-money" prices! / **Sample dishes:** tarragon egg mouse & tomato jelly; pan-fried scallops; sticky toffee pudding.*
Details: *www.jeremysrestaurant.com; 9.30 pm; closed Mon & Sun D.*

HEATON, TYNE & WEAR 8–2B

Sky Apple Cafe £ 21 Ⓣ

182 Heaton Rd NE6 5HP (01912) 092571

*"I'm not a veggie, but I can happily eat here and not notice the absence of meat" – such is the "fine" cuisine at this evenings-only café (which observes a different régime during the day); you can BYO too. / **Sample dishes:** polenta & gazpacho shot; green risotto cakes; branded cherry & chocolate steamed pudding. **Details:** www.skyapple.co.uk; 9 pm; closed Mon, Tue D, Wed D & Sun D; no credit cards.*

HELMSLEY, NORTH YORKSHIRE 8–4C

Feversham Arms Hotel £ 54

YO62 5AG (01439) 770766

*Fans find "fine cuisine" and a "comfortable and relaxing atmosphere" at this chic country inn; reports, however, remain uneven. / **Sample dishes:** lobster ravioli; corn-fed duck breast, endive & gooseberry tian, with violet potatoes; raspberry soufflé. **Details:** www.fevershamarmshotel.com; 9.30 pm; no jeans or trainers; children: 12+ after 7 pm. **Accommodation:** 23 rooms, from £140.*

HELSTON, CORNWALL 1–4A

Halzephron Inn £ 33 ⭐

TR12 7QB (01326) 240406

*"Yummy seafood", "a superb range of puddings", "pleasant" sea views and a proprietor who "takes a personal interest in each customer's dining experience" – all are virtues of this unsurprisingly "popular" pub. / **Sample dishes:** pork & wild mushroom fricasse; scampi. **Details:** www.halzephron-inn.co.uk; 9 pm. **Accommodation:** 2 rooms, from £84.*

HEMEL HEMPSTEAD, HERTFORDSHIRE 3–2A

Cochin £ 25 ⭐

61 High St HP1 3AF (01442) 233777

*Thanks to its "good-value" Keralan menu ("primarily based around vegetarian and fish dishes"), this "very popular" and "different" south Indian offers "a nice change from your local curry house". / **Sample dishes:** julienne of chicken marinated with black pepper, green chillies, curry leaves & batter-fried.; lamb & spinach; banana bosa. **Details:** www.thecochincuisine.com; 10.45 pm, Sat & Sun 11.30 pm.*

Cherry Tree Inn £ 36

RG9 5QA (01491) 680430

Fans insist that this trendified "lovely old pub" offers "top-quality" modern bistro fare – others say that, though "everyone raves", the food is "unexciting". / **Sample dishes:** buffalo Mozzarella & plum tomato tart; grilled sea bass with roast vegetables; sticky toffee pudding with a caramel sauce & crème fraîche. **Details:** www.thecherrytreeinn.com; 10; closed Sun D; no Amex. **Accommodation:** 4 rooms, from £95.

Hotel du Vin et Bistro £ 48

New St RG9 2BP (01491) 848400

It's usually "heaving", but "sparkle is missing" from this recent addition to the popular boutique-hotel chain (which has a "lovely setting in an old brewery near the river"); for "wannabe country folk and local bigshots", however, this is the place. / **Sample dishes:** seared squid, pancetta, feves & aioli; braised shank of venison, truffle mash & braised red cabbage. **Details:** www.hotelduvin.com; 9.30 pm. **Accommodation:** 43 rooms, from £135.

Spice Merchant £ 48 ⭐

Thameside RG9 2LJ (01491) 636118

A "trendy" Indian restaurant, where "atmosphere can seem a little lacking" but where the food is often "superb" (if, perhaps, a mite "overpriced"); they can even lay on "a boat down the Thames for drinks and nibbles before dinner". / **Sample dishes:** leg of lamb slow roasted with royal cumin garam masala; fresh monkfish with fenugreek leaf & turmeric. **Details:** www.spicemerchantgroup.net; 11 pm.

Café at All Saints £ 22 ⓣ

All Saints Church, High St HR4 9AA (01432) 370415

"An inspiring location" – a church – helps create a "friendly buzz" at this popular veggie, praised for its "wonderful home cooking". / **Sample dishes:** casserole of roast peppers & chick peas in roast paprika sauce; pan-fried mackerel fillet with melted onions & black olives, flat bread & dressed leaves; chocolate & stout cake in chocolate sauce. **Details:** near Cathedral; L only; closed Sun; no Amex; no booking; children: 6+ upstairs.

Castle House Restaurant
Castle House Hotel £ 52 ⭐

Castle St HR1 2NW (01432) 356321

The dining room of this Georgian townhouse (fka La Rive) has a "wonderful riverside setting", and the cooking is often "really imaginative" too; fans say it gets "overlooked", despite being "easily the best hotel restaurant in town". / **Sample dishes:** carpaccio of cured venison with horseradish & walnut cream & red wine caviar; fillet of beef; char-grilled pineapple & Malibu rice pudding. **Details:** www.castlehse.co.uk; 10 pm, Sun 9 pm. **Accommodation:** 15 rooms, from £175.

The Dining Room   **£ 40**
10 Queens Rd KT12 5LS   (01932) 231686
*"A good take on British classics" ("you must leave room for
puddings") wins high praise for this "lovely little restaurant" –
a "cottage with a series of interlinked rooms".*
/ **Sample dishes:** *cheese & ale pot; prime Scottish beef & chunky chips with slow
roasted plum tomato, raspberry glazed earthy mushrooms & velvety bearnaise
sauce.; spotted dick & custard.* **Details:** *www.thediningroom.co.uk; 10.30 pm;
closed Sat L & Sun D.*

Luciano's   **£ 37**
2 Ferriby Rd HU13 0PG   (01482) 641109
*"A good little place for coffee, or for ladies-who-lunch" – a "buzzy"
Italian establishment, which can sometimes seem a bit "pricey",
but where standards are "reliable".* / **Details:** *9 pm; no Amex.*

The Angel   **£ 42**
BD23 6LT   (01756) 730263

*Nearly a quarter of a century in the same ownership, Juliet Watkins's
famous Dales dining pub is still "well worth the effort of getting
there", thanks to its "consistently reliable" cooking (in particular,
its "very imaginative" fish dishes), and its "well-priced" wines.*
/ **Sample dishes:** *cheese soufflé; braised shoulder of mutton; rhubarb brûlée.*
Details: *www.angelhetton.co.uk; 5m N of Skipton off B6265 at Rylstone; 9 pm;
D only, ex Sun open L only.* **Accommodation:** *5 rooms, from £130.*

Barnacles   **£ 39**
Watling St LE10 3JA   (01455) 633220
*One fan "can't believe" that this "challenging and exciting seafood
restaurant" has not formerly been listed in this guide – more reports
please.* / **Sample dishes:** *shellfish platter; lobster thermidor flamed in brandy.*
Details: *www.barnaclesrestaurant.co.uk; 9.30 pm; closed Sat L & Sun.*

The Lamb Inn £ 32

High St SP3 6DP (01747) 820573
"Still what it always was... a good local pub with very nice food";
this "quaint" operation, off the A303 – a country sibling to London's
Boisdale – wins fans with its "good mix of pub classics and 'gastro'-
type dishes". / **Sample dishes:** Crayfish tails with fennel, cherry vine
tomatoes & rocket salad; Gorgonzola & walnut tortellini served with walnut
dressing & rocket salad; Poached pear in spiced red wine with creamy rice
pudding. **Details:** www.lambathindon.co.uk; 9.30 pm. 9 pm Sun.
Accommodation: 14 rooms, from £99.

HINTLESHAM, SUFFOLK 3–1C

Hintlesham Hall £ 60 Ⓐ

Dodge St IP8 3NS (01473) 652334
A "great setting and spacious dining conditions" have of late been the
most reliable attractions of this "wonderful" 16th-century, country
house hotel; reports suggest its cuisine has "improved" of late,
however – "it's well into its stride after some lacklustre showings
in recent years". / **Sample dishes:** smoked chicken & mixed herb rillette;
grilled fillet of lemon sole; mocha délice with espresso syrup.
Details: www.hintleshamhall.com; 4m W of Ipswich on A1071; 9.30 pm; closed
Sat L; jacket at D; children: not welcome at dinner. **Accommodation:** 33 rooms,
from £150.

HINTON ST GEORGE, SOMERSET 2–3A

Lord Poulett Arms £ 32 Ⓣ

TA17 8SE (01460) 73149
A "lovely cosy, pub" – "beautifully done up" in recent times, into a
gastropub-with-rooms – that's praised for its "fantastic" food.
/ **Sample dishes:** mozzarella, peach & beetroot salad; chowder of gurnard, conga
eel, & smoked bacon; dark chocolate brownie with cherries.
Details: www.lordpoulettarms.com; 11 pm.

HOLBETON, DEVON 1–4D

The Dartmoor Union Inn £ 32 Ⓣ

Fore St PL8 1NE (01752) 830288
A "surprisingly modern and stylish pub/restaurant in a pretty village";
home-brewed beers add further interest to its "reasonably priced"
food. / **Sample dishes:** Proscuitto ham salad with red pepper dressing;
breast of chicken, sautéed wild mushrooms, smoked bacon & potato hash; banana
tatin with Devon clotted cream. **Details:** www.dartmoorunion.co.uk.

HOLKHAM, NORFOLK 6–3C

Victoria Hotel £ 42

Park Rd NR23 1RG (01328) 711008
This "stylish" beach-facing pub – often "rammed with the Chelsea
set" – is praised by most reporters for its "good and tasty food"
("especially game"); those who find it a "rip-off", though, have yet
to be entirely silenced. / **Sample dishes:** mussels with cider; venison burger;
chocolate fondant with brownie ice cream. **Details:** www.victoriaatholkham.co.uk;
9 pm; no Amex. **Accommodation:** 10 rooms, from £120.

HOLT, NORFOLK　　　　　　　　6–3C

Cookies Crab Shop　　　　　　**£ 16**
The Grn, Coast Rd　NR25 7AJ　(01263) 740352
*"If you don't mind slumming it", this establishment – which
is "basically a shed" – offers "sea-fresh fish dishes" and "shellfish
galore" (including "the best crab around"); "get there early if you
haven't booked".* / **Sample dishes:** *lobster royal; smoked salmon.*
Details: *www.cookies.shopkeepers.co.uk; 7.30 pm; Nov-Feb bookings only;
no credit cards.*

HONITON, DEVON　　　　　　　2–4A

Combe House Hotel & Restaurant　**£ 55**
EX14 3AD　(01404) 540400

*"Everything is set up for romance" at this "magical" destination –
a "sumptuous", family-run Elizabethan country house hotel,
"beautifully set" in 3,000 acres; the restaurant doesn't let the side
down, offering "lovely" food and a "first-class" wine list.*
/ **Sample dishes:** *foie gras with duck rillette; bream pomme purée, asparagus,
baby leeks with beurre noisette; caramelised banana rum & raisin parfait.*
Details: *www.thishotel.com; 9.30 pm; no Amex.* **Accommodation:** *16 rooms,
from £168.*

HOOK, HAMPSHIRE　　　　　　2–3D

Oak Room Restaurant
Tylney Hall　　　　　　　　**£ 61**
Rotherwick RG27 9AZ　(01256) 764881
*An impressive but "hard-to-find" country house hotel, tipped as a
"superb, if expensive", dining destination; the terrace makes
a "perfect setting for a snack" too.* / **Sample dishes:** *roulade of salmon
with crème fraîche & cucumber dressing; rump of lamb served with aubergine
caponata.* **Details:** *www.tylneyhall.com; 10 pm, 9.30 pm; jacket and/or tie.*
Accommodation: *112 rooms, from £195.*

HORNDON ON THE HILL, ESSEX　　3–3C

The Bell Inn　　　　　　　　**£ 37**
High Rd　SS17 8LD　(01375) 642463
*"Hidden-away from the hustle 'n bustle of modern life, you can enjoy
a fine glass of wine and some fantastic cooking" – and for
"good prices" – at this "friendly" and "historic" pub, in a sleepy
village.* / **Sample dishes:** *sautéed scallops; pepper duck breast with red
wine-poached fig; maple crème brûlée.* **Details:** *www.bell-inn.co.uk; signposted off
B1007, off A13; 9.45 pm; booking: max 12.* **Accommodation:** *15 rooms,
from £50.*

Lino's £ 38 ⭐

122 Market St CH47 3BH (0151) 632 1408

After a quarter century in business, the Galantini family's "consistently excellent" service continues to win fans for "the Wirral's best-kept secret" – a "very friendly" and "traditional" Italian.
/ Sample dishes: lambs kidneys purr pastry parcel with bacon & button mushrooms; half roast duck; crème brûlée. **Details:** *www.linosrestaurant.co.uk; 3m from M53, J2; 10 pm; closed Mon & Sun; closed Aug; no Amex.*

HUDDERSFIELD, WEST YORKSHIRE 5–1C

Bradley's £ 34 ⭐

84 Fitzwilliam St HD1 5BB (01484) 516773

"For the prices charged, this is a real find!" – Andrew Bradley's town-centre spot is unanimously hailed by reporters for its "good value"; "it can get very busy, especially at weekends". / Sample dishes: seared scallops; cappuccino mousse. **Details:** *www.bradleys-restaurant.co.uk; 10 pm; closed Sat L & Sun; no Amex.*

Huddersfield Jumbo Buffet £ 18 ⓣ

70-76 John William St HD1 1EH (01484) 549201

An unpretentious oriental spot that's "worth a visit", thanks to its "terrific-value buffet". / Sample dishes: spicy curry chicken. **Details:** *10.30 pm.*

Nawaab £ 26 ⓣ

35 Westgate HD1 1NY (01484) 422775

A town-centre subcontinental, strongly tipped for its "tasty" food; look out for "great offers". / Sample dishes: Balti chicken; chicken tikka makhani; kulfi. **Details:** *www.nawaab.net; between bus & railway stations; 11 pm; D only.*

HULL, KINGSTON UPON HULL 6–2A

Cerutti's £ 45 ⓣ

10 Nelson St HU1 1XE (01482) 328501

A locally-renowned restaurant, in a Georgian house, where the fish and seafood "can be excellent". / Sample dishes: pan-fried scallops; salmon & halibut; mini house selection. **Details:** *www.ceruttis.co.uk; follow signs to fruit market; 9.30 pm; closed Sat L & Sun.*

HUNSDON, HERTFORDSHIRE 3–2B

The Fox And Hounds £ 38 ⭐

2 High St SG12 8NH (01279) 843999

"The most fantastic bread, great cider and a super, seasonal menu!" – virtues typical of this "unexpectedly good" gastropub.
/ Sample dishes: beer battered squid & aioli; rack of lamb & gratin dauphinoise; chocolate pot & expresso ice cream. **Details:** *www.foxandhounds-hunsdon.co.uk; 10 pm; closed Mon & Sun D; no Amex.*

Old Bridge Hotel   £ 42   **A** ⭐

I High St PE29 3TQ   (01480) 424300

This "stalwart" establishment, near the river, put in a strong showing this year, with high praise for its "delicious" food; the star of the show, however, is still its "exceptional" wine list chosen by owner John Hoskins (who split up the Huntsbridge Group this year to focus on this property). / **Sample dishes:** marinated buffalo Mozzarella with courgette; sautéed corn-fed chicken breast; lemon tart with crème fraîche. **Details:** www.huntsbridge.com; off A1, off A14; 10 pm. **Accommodation:** 24 rooms, from £125.

The Pheasant   £ 43   ⭐

Loop Rd PE28 0RE   (01832) 710241

"A village pub with an excellent restaurant"; managers Jay & Taffeta Scrimshaw bought it back from the Huntsbridge Group this year, but it maintains its hallmark "good-value wine list".

/ **Sample dishes:** fillet steak; braised shoulder of lamb; citrus tart with crème fraîche. **Details:** www.huntsbridge.com; 1m S of A14 between Huntingdon & Kettering, J15; 9.30 pm.

Black Boys Inn   £ 42

Henley Rd SL6 5NQ   (01628) 824212

Most reporters are "never disappointed" by this "newish" gastropub, in a 17th-century inn, praising its "real value for money"; an apparent striving "to get as many ingredients on the plate as possible", however, is a turn-off for some reporters. / **Sample dishes:** crab; caramelised veal sweetbread "petit choucroute" with mustard sauce; apple tart for two. **Details:** www.blackboysinn.co.uk; 9 pm; closed Mon & Sun; no Amex; children: 12+. **Accommodation:** 8 rooms, from £75.

11 The Quay   £ 49

11 The Quay EX34 9EQ   (01271) 868090

"If Ilfracombe was a trendier town, this place would be packed", says a fan of Damien Hirst's harbour-side venture (adorned with his art), where the "delightful" window tables are particularly prized; the food is usually fair value, but can sometimes "over-reach its technical skills". / **Sample dishes:** avocado & prosciutto salad; belly of pork; sticky toffee pudding. **Details:** www.11thequay.co.uk ; 9.30 pm.

Bettys   £ 36   **A** ⭐

32-34 The Grove LS29 9EE   (01943) 608029

"A fun time warp"; this "wonderful" traditional tea room is "just as good as ever"; "there's always a queue, despite the high prices".

/ **Sample dishes:** prawns & smoked salmon open sandwich; buffalo Mozzarella, slices of plum tomato, & pesto in a Parmesan & herb roll; organic brown bread ice cream with almond macaroon, chopped pecan nuts, & Betty's Toffee sauce, topped with whipped cream. **Details:** www.bettysandtaylors.com; 5.30 pm; no Amex; no booking.

The Box Tree £ 60

35-37 Church St LS29 9DR (01943) 608484

"The food's improved recently", admits one critic of this veteran fine dining destination, but it still divides reporters; fans say it's a "quiet" and "intimate" place, which, with Simon Gueller's "excellent" cooking, has been "returned to glory" – for doubters, though, it's still most notable for being "stuffy" and "overpriced".
/ **Sample dishes:** *roast sea scallops with celeriac purée & truffle vinagrette; fillet of grass-fed beef; hot raspberry soufflé.* **Details:** *www.theboxtree.co.uk; on A65 near town centre; 9.30 pm; closed Mon & Sun D; no Amex; children: 10+ at D.*

Far Syde £ 34

1-3 New Brook St LS29 8DQ (01943) 602030

This surprisingly metropolitan-looking restaurant (for a small town) is a strong local "favourite", with an "early-bird offer" that's particularly popular. / **Sample dishes:** *crab cake soufflé served on a sweetcorn & avocado salad; breast of chicken filled with asparagus, wrapped in Prosciutto; lemon & honey rum baba.* **Details:** *www.thefarsyde.co.uk; 10 pm; closed Mon & Sun; no Amex.*

Ilkley Moor Vaults £ 34

Stockeld Rd LS29 9HD (01943) 607012

"A gastropub that really lives up to the name" – Joe McDermott's "relaxed" operation offers "home-produced" fare to tasty recipes. / **Sample dishes:** *lamb with vegetables & puy lentils; potted crab & toast.* **Details:** *www.ilkleymoorvaults.co.uk; 9 pm, 9.30 pm Fri & Sat; closed Sun D.*

ILMINGTON, WARWICKSHIRE 2–1C

The Howard Arms £ 35

Lower Grn CV36 4LT (01608) 682226

"Don't expect to just roll up and get a table", if you visit this "cracking Cotswold gastropub" – it has become "justifiably well-established", thanks to its "lovely" atmosphere and "consistently good" cooking from "carefully-sourced" ingredients. / **Sample dishes:** *oak-smoked salmon with warm potato cake; char-grilled pork medallions; cappuccino coffee crème brûlée.* **Details:** *www.howardarms.com; 8m SW of Stratford-upon-Avon off A4300; 9 pm; no Amex; children: 8+ at D.* **Accommodation:** *3 rooms, from £105.*

INVERNESS, HIGHLAND 9–2C

Abstract
Glenmoriston Townhouse Hotel £ 59

Ness Bank IV2 4SF (01463) 223777

Perhaps "simpler would be better" at this hotel dining room, on the banks of the River Ness, but that's not to detract from its "excellent" cooking (using "ingredients of superb quality") and "great wine list" too; for economy, seek out the "cheaper brasserie".
/ **Details:** *www.abstractrestaurant.com; 10 pm; D only, closed Sun.* **Accommodation:** *30 rooms, from £130.*

Mustard Seed £ 38

16 Fraser St IV1 1DW (01463) 220220

"Great place... great value... great food!", say fans of this attractive, two-tier space (overlooking the river), who praise its "buzzy" and "cheerful" style, and its "quality food with a modern European twist".
/ **Sample dishes:** *crispy fillet of salmon with Parmesan mash & sauce vierge; grilled fillets of scrabster red fish with saffron-infused market vegetable consommme; confit of duck leg salad with grilled black pudding & green grapes.* **Details:** *www.themustardseedrestaurant.co.uk; 10 pm.*

Rocpool £ 40
1 Ness Walk IV3 5NE (01463) 717274
An ambitious "Italian/fusion" joint – "well-positioned" by a river – that makes a surprising find in this part of the world; it generally satisfies reporters, if occasionally seeming "expensive for what it is".
*/ **Sample dishes:** crab salad with avocado & crème fraîche; roast loin of venison with black pudding & Parma ham; white chocolate cheesecake with glazed banana. **Details:** www.rocpool.com; 10 pm; closed Sun L; no Amex.*

Russell's At Smiddy House £ 40
Spean Bridge PH34 4EU (01397) 712335
*"Excellent value and polite, friendly and helpful service" win praise for the restaurant at this luxury B&B. / **Sample dishes:** medley of sea fish; rack of lamb. **Details:** www.smiddyhouse.co.uk; 9 pm; D only, Closed Mon & Tues during Winter; no Amex. **Accommodation:** 4 rooms, from £75.*

IPSWICH, SUFFOLK 3–1D

Baipo £ 31
63 Upper Orwell St IP4 1HP (01473) 218402
A "shining star", implausibly located in a "dodgy" street, where the "top-class" Thai cooking is "more authentic than most".
*/ **Sample dishes:** spicy chicken wrapped in spinach leaves; sirloin steak grilled over charcoal; steamed banana in coconut milk. **Details:** www.baipo.co.uk; 10.45 pm; closed Mon L & Sun; no Amex.*

Il Punto £ 36
Neptune Quay IP4 1AX (01473) 289748
*"Another Crépy family success" – this "boat moored at Ipswich marina" is, for its fans, "first port of call when looking for a meal in Ipswich", thanks to its "romantic" setting and its "good-value" Gallic cuisine. / **Sample dishes:** gratinée of scallops, prawns & mushrooms; fillet of beef; passion fruit on chocolate cake with crème anglaise. **Details:** www.ilpunto.co.uk; 9.30 pm; closed Mon & Sun; no Amex.*

The Ship Inn £ 33
Church Ln IP10 0LQ (01473) 659573
*Conditions may be "cramped", but this "olde worlde pub" is tipped for the "consistent" quality of its "surprisingly imaginative" menu. / **Details:** 9.30 pm, 9 pm Sun; no Amex; children: 14+.*

Trongs £ 29
23 St Nicholas St IP1 1TW (01473) 256833
*Thanks to its "wonderful" food and "welcoming" service, this "top-quality Cantonese" is "always busy" – "book weeks ahead!" / **Sample dishes:** spare ribs & spring rolls; chicken with ginger; toffee apples. **Details:** 10.30 pm; closed Mon; booking essential.*

IRELAND, BEDFORDSHIRE 3–1A

Black Horse £ 42
SG17 5QL (01462) 811398
*This "idyllic" gastropub is "worth a diversion from the A1 or M1", and is "very popular" with the locals too, thanks to its generally "very good" food – "book well in advance if you want a table in the conservatory". / **Sample dishes:** smoked mackerel, avocado & bacon salad; medallions of lamb shoulder; cherry brandy crème brûlée.*
*Details: www.blackhorseireland.com; 10 pm; closed Sun D. **Accommodation:** 2 rooms, from £55.*

ISLE OF MAN, ISLE OF MAN 7–4A

Ciappelli's £ 63 Ⓣ
Admiral Hs, 12 Loch Promenade IM1 2LX (01624) 677442
A small hotel dining room, tipped for its "very good" cuisine.
/ *Sample dishes: terrine of foie gras, brioche & salad; grilled Dover sole;
hot strawberry soufflé & strawberry ice cream. Details: www.ciappellis.com.*

ISLE OF SEIL, ARGYLL 9–3B

Willowburn Hotel £ 46 Ⓣ
PA34 4TJ (01852) 300276
*On the edge of Clachan Sound, this small hotel is tipped for its
"wonderful host, cooking and location". / Sample dishes: medallions
of venison saddle on potato scones with hazelnut stuffing, & orange & juniper
sauce; rack of lamb; honey wafers with pecan butter ice cream & poached pears.
Details: www.willowburn.co.uk; 7 pm; D only; no Amex; children: 8+ at
D. Accommodation: 7 rooms, from £164.*

ITTERINGHAM, NORFOLK 6–4C

Walpole Arms £ 36 Ⓐ
The Common, Itteringham NR11 7AR (01263) 587258
*It's "hard to find", but – once you have – this "traditional" pub
is "just what you'd hope for in a country hostelry"; "the bar is more
atmospheric than the restaurant, but the food is the same
throughout". / Sample dishes: bruschetta with baby octopus, borlotti beans &
roast peppers; lamb shank; Jewish semolina & yoghurt cake.
Details: www.thewalpolearms.co.uk; 9 pm; closed Sun D; no Amex.*

JERSEY, CHANNEL ISLANDS

Bohemia ✪✪
The Club Hotel & Spa £ 70
Green St, St Helier JE2 4UH (01534) 880588
*For some fans, Shaun Rankin's "excellent" cuisine at this
"contemporary"-style dining room is simply "the best ever"
("and that's after three visits!"); it can be a "noisy" place,
but "top people-watching" is a compensation. / Sample dishes: crab;
confit of belly pork with glazed pig cheek, apple pavé, roast foie gras & langoustine
brochette; lemon soufflé. Details: www.bohemiajersey.com; 10 pm; closed Sun.
Accommodation: 46 rooms, from £195.*

Green Island Restaurant £ 42 Ⓣ
St Clement JE2 6LS (01534) 857787
*We wish we got more reports on Jersey; this seafood-
specialist is tipped as a top-quality all-rounder; book ahead for a table
on the seaside terrace. / Details: www.greenislandrestaurant.com; 9.30 pm;
closed Mon & Sun D; no Amex.*

Longueville Manor £ 75 Ⓐ✪
Longueville Rd, St Saviour JE2 7WF (01534) 725501
*For "perfect old-fashioned high-class dining", this grand and ancient
country house hotel inspires pretty consistent reports, even if –
perhaps inevitably – prices can seem "OTT". / Sample dishes: lobster;
partridge; vanilla crème brûlée. Details: www.longuevillemanor.com; 10 pm.
Accommodation: 31 rooms, from £300.*

JEVINGTON, EAST SUSSEX   3–4B

Hungry Monk   £ 45
Long Jevington Rd BN26 5QF   (01323) 482178
*Generally much more upbeat reports this year on this cutely-housed
village-restaurant (which claims to be the birthplace of Banoffi pie);
there was still the odd misfire, but most reports speak in terms
of "comfort eating at its best".* / **Sample dishes:** *salmon & prawn
mousseline with Melba toast; halibut roasted in Prosciutto with asparagus; white
chocolate crème brulée with blueberry compote.* **Details:** *www.hungrymonk.co.uk;
5m W of Eastbourne; 9.30 pm; D only, ex Sun open L & D; children: 4+.*

KEMPSTON, BEDFORDSHIRE   3–1A

Ⓣ

Kohinoor
The Jasbar   £ 29
281-285 Bedford Rd MK42 8QB   (01234) 857766
*Particularly tipped for its "amazing specials" – this "bright" new
Pujabi restaurant (over a jazz bar) won a couple of very enthusiastic
recommendations, even if "the location – unlike the food –
is uninspiring".* / **Details:** *www.thejasbar.com; 11.30 pm.*

KENILWORTH, WARWICKSHIRE   5–4C

⭐⭐

Bosquet   £ 50
97a Warwick Rd CV8 1HP   (01926) 852463
*"Gourmet food, in generous portions at extremely good-value prices,
plus knowledgeable service" have made Bernard and Jane Lignier's
"friendly" venture a notable success-story, for over a quarter of a
century.* / **Sample dishes:** *scallop of foie gras; fillet of veal with veal
sweetbreads; blueberry & almond tart.* **Details:** *www.restaurantbosquet.co.uk;
9.30 pm; closed Mon, Sat L & Sun; closed Aug.*

Simply Simpsons   £ 44
101-103 Warwick Rd CV8 1HL   (01926) 864567
*The cradle of the Simpson's empire (the main establishment now
having decamped to Birmingham); it's still a pretty "reliable"
destination, but not quite as sparkling as once it was.*
/ **Sample dishes:** *goat's cheese on wilted rocket; fillet steak with chunky chips;
peach with amaretti crumble.* **Details:** *www.simplysimpsons.com; 10 pm; closed
Mon & Sun.*

KESWICK, CUMBRIA   7–3D

Ⓣ

Cottage In The Wood   £ 35
Whinlatter Forest CA12 5TW   (01768) 778409
*A small hotel in "a lovely Lakeland location", run by a husband-and-
wife team; the evening set meal offers "no choice", but is
recommended as a "delightful, good-value dining experience".*
/ **Details:** *www.thecottageinthewood.co.uk; 10.30 pm; D only, closed Mon;
no Amex; children: 10+.* **Accommodation:** *9 rooms, from £39.50/person.*

Ⓣ

Lakeland Pedlar Wholefood Café   £ 27
Hendersons Yard, Bell Close CA12 5JD   (01768) 774492
*A self-explanatory establishment, tipped for its "fresh and varied
menu" and its "lovely relaxed ambience".* / **Sample dishes:** *soups.*
Details: *www.lakelandpedlar.co.uk; 5 pm, 9 pm Fri.*

Firenze £ 42 ⭐
9 Station St LE8 0LN (0116) 279 6260

"A little bit of Italy in the middle of Leicestershire"; the Poli family's well-reputed restaurant wins praise for "warm" service, "first-class" food and "well-chosen" wine; as this guide went to press, they opened a nearby pizza/pasta spin off, Boboli (88 Main Street, Kibworth Harcourt, tel 0116 2793 303). / *Sample dishes:* artichoke risotto & seared scallops; griddled tuna steak with salsa verde; panna cotta with chocolate sauce & biscotti. *Details:* www.firenze.co.uk; 10 pm; closed Sun; no Amex.

Ardanaiseig Hotel £ 55 🅰⭐
PA35 1HE (01866) 833333
"The most sensational views across Loch Awe" are not the only attraction of this baronial-style hotel, which is said to offer "wonderful food, especially seafood". / *Sample dishes:* smoked haddock ravioli; velouté of pumpkin with shaved parmesan & truffle; vanilla pana cotta with pear jam & rice pudding croquettes. *Details:* www.ardanaiseig.com; sits on a peninsula jutting out into Loch Awe; 9 pm; D only; children: 10+ . *Accommodation:* 18 rooms, from £90.

Ardeonaig Hotel & Restaurant £ 48 🅰⭐
South Loch Tay Side FK21 8SU (01567) 820400
"A place for total relaxation, whatever the weather"; with its "wonderful food and wine", and its "breathtaking" views, this "remote" Saffa-run hotel, by Loch Tay, is simply "one of the best places to eat in Scotland". / *Sample dishes:* crab; loin of hare; banana & plum crumble with clotted cream. *Details:* www.ardeonaighotel.co.uk; 9 pm; no Amex; children: 12+. *Accommodation:* 20 rooms, from £85.

Ballathie House £ 57 🅰
PH1 4QN (01250) 883268
"A lovely setting by the River Tay" sets the scene at this country house hotel; most reporters laud "food that matches the ambience" and "eager, young staff" – the odd critic, though, rails at "average" food and "disgraceful" service. / *Sample dishes:* beetroot-cured salmon; fillet of Scottish beef; vanilla crème brûlée with plum & cinnamon compote. *Details:* www.ballathiehousehotel.com; off B9099, take right from 1m N of Stanley; 8.45 pm; jacket at D; children: 10+ at D. *Accommodation:* 42 rooms, from £150.

Bradley's   **£ 39**   Ⓣ

10 South Quay PE30 5DT   (01553) 819888

"A wine bar and restaurant on the quayside", tipped for its
"good food" and "wide and well-chosen" wine selection (including
*"many choices by the glass"). / **Sample dishes:** fillet of sea bass on braised*
fennel & celeriac with dry vermouth sauce; honey glazed duck breast with mead &
*kumquat sauce.. **Details:** www.bradleysbytheriver.co.uk; 9.30 pm; closed Sun.*

Ayudhya   **£ 34**

14 Kingston Hill KT2 7NH   (020) 8549 5984

Still "popular" after over a decade in business, this "authentic" Thai
restaurant remains a "dependable" option for many locals, if perhaps
*a slightly complacent one. / **Sample dishes:** chicken lemon grass; chicken*
*lemon grass; banana in coconut milk. **Details:** www.ayudhya.co.uk; 11 pm,*
Mon & Sun 10.30 pm; closed Mon L; no Amex.

Canbury Arms   **£ 38**   ★

49 Canbury Park Rd KT2 6LQ   (020) 8255 9129

The "emphasis is very much on the food", at this "family-orientated"
gastropub of two years' standing; it has proved a "much-needed
*addition to eating out in the area". / **Sample dishes:** roast pumpkin &*
butternut squash with balsamic dressing; burger with smoked bacon & cheddar;
*chocolate fondant with vanilla ice cream. **Details:** www.thecanburyarms.com;*
10 pm, Sun 9 pm.

fish!kitchen   **£ 14**

58 Coombe Rd KT2 7AF   (020) 8546 2886

"A quality fish 'n' chip shop – with other dishes also available –
next door to a fishmongers"; if you're looking for "great food, quickly
*served", this is the place. / **Details:** www.fishkitchen.com; 10 pm;*
closed Mon.

Frère Jacques   **£ 40**   Ⓐ

10-12 Riverside Walk KT1 1QN   (020) 8546 1332

Near Kingston Bridge, a "wonderful" riverside location that's "great
in summer" contributes to the popularity of this "friendly" bistro;
*its "authentic" Gallic fare pleases too. / **Sample dishes:** pâté de foie gras;*
*rib-eye steak with Bearnaise sauce; tarte Tatin. **Details:** www.frerejacques.co.uk;*
next to Kingston Bridge and market place; 11 pm.

Riverside Vegetaria   **£ 31**   ★

64 High St KT1 1HN   (020) 8546 7992

"Adored by veggies and carnivores alike", this "fun" fixture, near the
Thames, delivers an "eclectic" menu of "spicy veggie fare"
in "substantial portions", and at "very reasonable prices".
*/ **Sample dishes:** falafel with houmous; masala dosa; mixed fruit crumble.*
***Details:** www.rsveg.plus.com; 10 mins walk from Kingston BR; 11 pm; no Amex;*
children: 18+ ex L.

KINGUSSIE, HIGHLAND

The Cross £ 56
Tweed Mill Brae, Ardbroilach Rd PH21 1LB (01540) 661166

*A restaurant-with-rooms in a "pleasant" location in the Cairngorms
National Park; reports, though few, all indicate all-round satisfaction.
/ **Sample dishes:** roast partridge; assiette of pork; chocolate fondant with chilli
ice cream. **Details:** www.thecross.co.uk; 8.30 pm; D only, closed Mon & Sun;
children: 9+. **Accommodation:** 8 rooms, from £100.*

KIRK DEIGHTON, WEST YORKSHIRE 5–1C

Bay Horse £ 37
Main St LS22 4DZ (01937) 580058
*A "vibrant" gastropub, consistently praised by reporters for "superb"
food (and in "Yorkshire portions" too); "no wonder it's always full".
/ **Sample dishes:** scallops wrapped in smoked bacon; sea trout; chocolate molten
cheesecake & blackberry sorbet. **Details:** 9 pm; closed Mon L & Sun D; no Amex.*

KIRKBY LONSDALE, CUMBRIA 7–4D

Avanti £ 37
57 Main St LA6 2AH (01524) 273500
*A Mediterranean bistro which makes a "welcome" find it a town
without too many competing attractions. / **Sample dishes:** smoked
salmon; lamb's liver, fillet of beef; tiramisu. **Details:** 10 pm; no Amex.*

Hipping Hall £ 58
Cowan Bridge LA6 2JJ (01524) 271187
*This "refined and luxurious" but "welcoming" country house hotel –
"a new venture of two years' standing" – is already widely acclaimed
as a "very special" experience; "nothing is too much trouble" for staff,
and Jason (Bruno) Birkbeck's "assured" food is "sensational".
/ **Sample dishes:** braised oxtail with glazed veal sweetbread; saddle of venison,
black pudding ravioli, parsnip purée, creamed cabbage, beetroot & juniper jus;
apple tarte tatin, vanilla ice cream & butterscotch sauce.
Details: www.hippinghall.com; 9.30 pm; D only, ex Sun open L & D; no Amex;
children: 10+. **Accommodation:** 6 rooms, 3 cottages rooms, from £165.*

KNIGHTWICK, WORCESTERSHIRE   2–1B

The Talbot   £ 43
WR6 5PH   (01886) 821235
Chef/patron Annie Clift's "lovely riverside inn" and microbrewery
draws feedback of the "never-a-bad-experience" variety, thanks to its
"good, traditional English cooking" and its "excellent home-brewed
ales". / **Sample dishes:** coarse pork pâté with peach chutney; courgette &
mature cheddar soufflé; apple & cider cake with home-made lemon & honey ice
cream. **Details:** www.the-talbot.co.uk; 9m from Worcester on A44; 9 pm;
no Amex. **Accommodation:** 11 rooms, from £82.

KNUTSFORD, CHESHIRE   5–2B

Belle Époque   £ 40   Ⓐ
King St WA16 6DT   (01565) 633060
The "lovely" building is genuinely Belle Époque (it "oozes character"),
and the restaurant itself has traded for over 30 years, so it's perhaps
inevitable that this "old-fashioned" dining room can seem to "trade
on its 'historic' reputation"; "on a good day", though,
fans insist "the food can be very good too". / **Sample dishes:** Bury black
pudding; beef flavoured with mushrooms, thyme, & red wine in suet pastry.
Details: www.thebelleepoque.com; 1.5m from M6, J19; 9.30 pm; closed Mon L,
Tue L, Sat L & Sun D; booking: max 6, Sat. **Accommodation:** 6 rooms,
from £89.

KYLESKU, HIGHLAND   9–1B

Kylesku Hotel   £ 38   Ⓣ
IV27 4HW   (01971) 502231
A very remote Highlands hotel overlooking a loch (actually two),
where you can eat in the restaurant or bar; it is tipped for "some of
the best seafood". / **Sample dishes:** home-smoked salmon served with
capers, lemon, brown bread & butter; wild venison fillet with a cranberry & dark
chocolate sauce. **Details:** www.kyleskuhotel.co.uk; on A894, S of Scourie, N of
loch inver; 9 pm; Closed Winter; no Amex. **Accommodation:** 8 rooms,
from £55.

LACOCK, WILTSHIRE   2–2C

At the Sign of the Angel   £ 39   Ⓐ
6 Church St SN15 2LB   (01249) 730230
No one doubts that this ancient inn in a National Trust village
provides a "fantastic" dining setting, and the welcome it offers
is "warm"; the food too has its fans, but reporters' consensus is that
it's something of a "missed opportunity". / **Sample dishes:** crab soup;
grilled lemon sole with cheese crust; home-made ice cream.
Details: www.lacock.co.uk; close to M4, J17; 9 pm; closed Mon L.
Accommodation: 10 rooms, from £105.

LANCASTER, LANCASHIRE   5–1A

Bay Horse   £ 37   ★
Bay Horse Ln LA2 0HR   (01524) 791204
"Excellent use of locally-sourced food" helps make Craig Wilkinson's
gastropub very popular (and there's now some "top-notch
accommodation" available too). / **Sample dishes:** seared scallops &
smoked salmon; mutton shank; crème brûlée with a Williams pear.
Details: www.bayhorseinn.com; 0.75m S of A6, J33 M6; 9 pm, Sun 8 pm; closed
Mon. **Accommodation:** 3 rooms, from £79.

Pizza Margherita £ 26

2 Moor Ln LA1 1QD (01524) 36333

*"An old-favourite" pizzeria, established in the late '70s by the sister of the founder of PizzaExpress — one you know this, its general style will not come as a great surprise. / **Sample dishes:** spinach & ricotta cannelloni; pizza capricciosa; dime bar crunch pie.*
Details: *www.pizza-margherita.co.uk; 10.30 pm.*

LANGAR, NOTTINGHAMSHIRE 5–3D

Langar Hall £ 50 Ⓐ⭐

Church Ln NG13 9HG (01949) 860559

"A real gem" in the Vale of Belvoir — this country house hotel is a "splendid" and "romantic" hideaway, where the food is generally "very good"; owner Imogen Skirving is a "colourful" host, and her staff "actually seem to care whether you're happy".
*/ **Sample dishes:** poached duck egg, bacon & crouton salad; char-grilled veal, crushed new potatoes & salsa verde; apple tarte Tatin.*
Details: *www.langarhall.com; off A52 between Nottingham & Grantham; 9 pm; no Amex; no jeans or trainers. **Accommodation:** 12 rooms, from £150.*

LANGHO, LANCASHIRE 5–1B

Northcote Manor £ 66 Ⓐ⭐

Northcote Rd BB6 8BE (01254) 240555

*Some say "ouch!" at the prices, but Nigel Haworth & Craig Bancroft's "classy" restaurant-with-rooms seemed to be firing on all cylinders again this year; the place "pioneered local sourcing long before it was fashionable", and the "adept" cooking puts an "honest twist" on "top-quality produce". / **Sample dishes:** steamed mutton with Jerusalem artichoke purée; saddle of venison, smoked chestnuts & cranberries; seedling apple crumble soufflé. **Details:** www.northcotemanor.com; M6, J31 then A59; 9.30 pm.*
Accommodation: *14 rooms, from £180.*

LANGSHOTT, SURREY 3–3B

Langshott Manor £ 59 Ⓣ

Ladbroke Rd RH6 9LN (01293) 786680

In implausible proximity to Gatwick airport, this Elizabethan manor house hotel attracts only positive reports on its dining.
*/ **Sample dishes:** crab & mint salad; roast duck with Victoria plums & Feta; lemon curd with barley ice cream, raspberry syrup & basil meringue.*
Details: *www.langshottmanor.com; 9.30 pm; no trainers. **Accommodation:** 22 rooms, from £190.*

LANGTON GREEN, KENT 3–4B

The Hare £ 31

Langton Rd TN3 0JA (01892) 862419

*"Smart, comfortable and spacious" — this village pub impresses most reporters with its range of "hearty English fare" (in "large portions"); a "child-friendly" place, it also benefits from a "lovely terrace". / **Details:** www.hare-tunbridgewells.co.uk; on A264 to East Grinstead; 9.30 pm; no Amex; children: 18+ at D.*

283

LAPWORTH, WARWICKSHIRE 5–4C

The Boot £ 38 Ⓐ
Old Warwick Rd B94 6JU (01564) 782464
"Overlooking one of the prettiest stretches of canal in Warwickshire",
this "attractive old inn" has natural advantages on the ambience
front; the food, if not the main point, plays an honourable supporting
rôle. / **Sample dishes:** steak tartare; char-grilled swordfish; steamed chocolate
pudding. **Details:** www.thebootatlapworth.co.uk; off A34; 10 pm.

LAVENHAM, SUFFOLK 3–1C

Angel £ 34
Market Pl CO10 9QZ (01787) 247388
"The best bet in a small town infested with tourists" – this 14th-
century inn wins praise for its "good-value" food and its "splendid"
setting; "do book". / **Sample dishes:** smoked salmon & trout; lamb & apricot
casserole; apple & almond tartlet. **Details:** www.theangelhotel-lavenham.co.uk;
on A1141 6m NE of Sudbury; 9.15 pm. **Accommodation:** 8 rooms, from £80.

Great House £ 41 Ⓐ✪✪
Market Pl CO10 9QZ (01787) 247431
"Fantastic French food in a wonderful atmosphere" –
the almost invariable verdict on the Crépy family's "very Gallic"
fixture, of over two decades' standing, housed in a "charming"
medieval building in an historic village. / **Sample dishes:** ballotine of duck
foie gras; rack of lamb with aubergine gâteau; creamy lemon & lime tart.
Details: www.greathouse.co.uk; follow directions to Guildhall; 9.30 pm; closed
Mon & Sun D; closed Jan; no Amex. **Accommodation:** 5 rooms, from £96.

LEEDS, WEST YORKSHIRE 5–1C

It's somewhat un-sung as a restaurant-destination, but Leeds
has – outside the capital – the best-balanced dining scene
in England. There is something for everyone. There's not
just a top-quality Chinese, for example (Lucky Dragon),
but also top-quality Japanese and Indian establishments (Fuji
Hero, and Aagrah and Hansa, respectively). There's also
a good Italian group (Brio) and some solid, if unremarkable,
French operations (such as Le Grillade). Towards the top end,
there's a famously big and brassy big-night-out destination
(Bibi's), and a straight-down-the-line 'gastronomic' restaurant
(No 3 York Place). And... how could we forget?... there's even
what many people would regard as one of the best and
most innovative restaurants in Britain – Anthony's.

Aagrah £ 26 Ⓐ✪
Aberford Rd LS25 2HF (0113) 287 6606
"Good quality Indian food and excellent value for money" – that's the
deal that maintains the very high popularity of this "upmarket" city-
centre spot; "though part of a chain, it has a character all of its own".
/ **Sample dishes:** chicken jalfrazi; goan machli; kulfi. **Details:** www.aagrah.com;
from A1 take A642 Aberford Rd to Garforth; 11.30 pm, 11 pm Sun; closed
Sat L & Sun L.

Akbar's £ 30 Ⓐ ⭐

16 Greek St LS1 5RU (0113) 242 5426

"Slap bang in the middle of Leeds", this "great" and "buzzy" subcontinental – a offshoot of the Bradford operation – inspires only positive reports; the food is "very good", with naans ("served on a huge hook") the highlight. / **Sample dishes:** onion bhaji; chicken Madras; rasmalai. **Details:** www.akbars.co.uk; midnight; D only.

Anthony's £ 58 ⭐⭐

19 Boar Ln LS1 6EA (0113) 245 5922

"Surely one of England's best contemporary restaurants" – Anthony Flynn's "outstandingly innovative cuisine" (in a style inspired by Spain's famous El Bulli) continues to excite adulatory feedback for this "minimalist" venture; "why he's not been awarded at least two Michelin stars" is a mystery. / **Sample dishes:** risotto of white onion espresso; poached quail; lemon chiboust. **Details:** www.anthonysrestaurant.co.uk; 9.30 pm; closed Mon, Tue L, Wed L & Sun; no Amex.

Anthony's At Flannels £ 27 ⭐

68-78 Vicar Ln LS1 7JH (0113) 242 8732

"Perfect for ladies who lunch" – Anthony Flynn's spin-off establishment occupies an "airy" space above a clothes shop; its "good-value set menu" gets a particular thumbs-up. / **Sample dishes:** goat's cheese tart & caramelised onions; grilled sea bass & crispy pancetta; lemon meringue pie. **Details:** www.anthonysatflannels.co.uk; 4.30 pm, Sun 3.30 pm; closed Mon; no Amex.

Art's £ 36 Ⓐ

42 Call Ln LS1 6DT (0113) 243 8243

"The North's original cool bistro, and still the best" – with its "great food, interesting menu and good value", this Exchange Quarter institution is "always a winner". / **Sample dishes:** haddock risotto; lamb cutlets; sticky toffee pudding. **Details:** www.artscafebar.co.uk; near Corn Exchange; 10 pm; no booking, Sat & Sun L.

Bibis £ 43 Ⓐ

Criterion Pl, Swinegate LS1 4AG (0113) 243 0905

"The room alone is worth the trip" – just as well, as the food and service "can't keep up" with the "scale and glitz" of the dining room of this "theatrical" Art Deco-style Italian institution; bills can seem "huge" too. / **Sample dishes:** air-dried beef fillet; roast corn-fed, free range guinea fowl; banana sticky toffee pudding & banoffee ice cream. **Details:** www.bibisrestaurant.com; 11.30 pm; no booking, Sat.

Brasserie Forty 4 £ 40

44 The Calls LS2 7EW (0113) 234 3232

"Pretty good food" makes this long-established contemporary brasserie, by a canal, a stand-by worth knowing about; its atmosphere, though, can seem "reserved". / **Sample dishes:** spiced fishcakes with sweet corn relish; confit leg of duck; chocolate & amaretto fondue. **Details:** www.brasserie44.com; 10pm mon-fri, 10.30 sat; closed Sun.

Brio £ 37 ⭐

40 Great George St LS1 3DL (0113) 246 5225

Food that's "very fresh, original and well presented" has made a big name for this "excellent modern Italian" (and also for its offshoot at The Light, tel 243 5533, which offers "wonderful, freshly-made pizzas"). / **Sample dishes:** pan-fried prawns; calves' liver & bacon with deep-fried fruit onions; grilled Mediterranean fruit & Mascarpone cheese. **Details:** www.brios.co.uk; 10.30 pm; closed Sun.

Bryan's £ 20

9 Weetwood Ln LS16 5LT   (0113) 278 5679

Reporters have not been impressed by the relaunch of this famous Headingley chippy – its fish 'n' chips are generally "good", but all aspects of the operation attract mixed feedback.
/ **Sample dishes:** *queen scallops; fillet of haddock; treacle sponge & custard.*
Details: *off Otterley Rd; 9.30 pm, Sun 7 pm; no Amex; need 8+ to book.*

Casa Mia Grande £ 36

33-35 Harrogate Rd LS7 3PD   (0870) 444 5154

An Italian mini-empire (with outposts at 10-12 Steinbeck Lane and Millennium Square, same tel throughout); it's "a leader for fresh fish", and you "can't beat the al fresco atmosphere" (at the original) – it's rather "pricey", though, and service often seems "disinterested" or "overstretched". / **Sample dishes:** *home-made pasta; breast of duck; bread & butter pudding.* **Details:** *www.casamiaonline.co.uk; Fri & Sat 11 pm, Sun 9:30 pm.*

Chaophraya £ 30

20a, First Floor, Blayds Ct LS2 4AG   (0113) 244 9339

"The best Thai in central Leeds"; not everyone takes to the décor, but even its critics say it's "made palatable by excellent food, good presentation and attentive service". / **Sample dishes:** *deep-fried squid in crispy batter; crispy fried sea bass fillet topped with Thai herbs; coconut ice cream.* **Details:** *www.chaophraya.co.uk; in Swinegate; 10.30 pm.*

Darbar £ 35

16-17 Kirkgate LS1 6BY   (0113) 246 0381

Entered through a "tiny doorway", this "Tardis-like" city-centre Indian occupies a large first-site of unexpected sumptuousness; the traditional cuisine is of "consistent good quality".
/ **Sample dishes:** *mixed kebab; chicken balti.* **Details:** *www.darbar.co.uk; midnight; D only, closed Sun; children: 10+.*

Flying Pizza £ 32

60 Street Ln LS8 2DQ   (0113) 266 6501

This "buzzing" Roundhay pizzeria is famous for its customers' "glitz and showing off"; foodwise its "rough patch is now history" – indeed, "the name hides the fact that other dishes are pretty good too".
/ **Sample dishes:** *mixed bruschetta; veal milanese; Italian tartufo.*
Details: *www.theflyingpizza.co.uk; just off A61, 3m N of city centre; 11 pm.*

Fourth Floor Café
Harvey Nichols £ 37

107-111 Briggate LS1 6AZ   (0113) 204 8000

"Interesting views and people-watching" help win popularity for this "comfortable" department-store venue; like many HN establishments, though, it can seem "overpriced", and service is "nothing to brag about". / **Sample dishes:** *roast quail with carrot & honey purée; sesame-crusted turbot & tempura bok choy; stem ginger mousse.*
Details: *www.harveynichols.com; 10 pm; L only, except Thu-Sat when L & D; no booking, Sat L.*

Fuji Hiro £ 23

45 Wade Ln LS2 8NJ   (0113) 243 9184

"Fresh tastes and generous helpings" win strong support for this "deservedly popular" city-centre noodle bar – an "always-buzzing" place offering "the greatest value for money".
/ **Sample dishes:** *dumplings; chilli beef.* **Details:** *10 pm; no credit cards; need 5+ to book.*

La Grillade £ 42

Wellington St LS1 4HJ (0113) 245 9707

"Lots of nooks and crannies for hushed business discussions" add to the charms of this *"buzzy"* Gallic bistro stalwart, where the food is generally *"reliable"* too; *"everyone goes"*. / **Sample dishes:** baked prawns in Gruyère; fillet steak; chocolate mousse. **Details:** www.lagrillade.co.uk; 10 pm; closed Sat L & Sun.

Hansa's £ 26 ✪✪

72-74 North St LS2 7PN (0113) 244 4408

"Astonishing clarity of flavour" distinguishes the food at Mrs Hansa-Dabhi's *"veggie heaven"* – a cramped Gujarati twenty-year-old that's *"simply great"*. / **Sample dishes:** chilli paneer; patra special; gajar halwa. **Details:** www.hansasrestaurant.com; 10.30 mon-sat 11; D only, ex Sun L only; no Amex.

Little Tokyo £ 27

24 Central Rd LS1 6DE (0113) 2439090

"Tucked-away behind Debenhams", this *"authentic"* Japanese operation has a following disproportionate to its *"tiny"* size; *"good-value"* Bento boxes come particularly recommended. / **Sample dishes:** gyoza; bento box; Japanese profiteroles. **Details:** www.littletokyo.co.uk; 10 pm, Fri & Sat 11 pm; need 8+ to book.

Livebait £ 42

The Calls LS2 7EY (0113) 2444144

"The best of a limited number of fish restaurants in the city"; it may be a chain-outlet, but even a reporter who thinks the formula is *"tired"* concedes that the food *"is always pretty good"*. / **Sample dishes:** tuna with marinated soyut, with stir-fry Asian greens; seared sea bass fillet with ginger & chilli crab, baby spinach with stir-fried noodles in hoi sin sauce. **Details:** www.livebaitleeds.5pm.co.uk; 10.30 pm, 6 pm Sun; closed Sun D.

Lucky Dragon £ 29 ✪✪

Templar Ln LS2 7LN (0113) 245 0520

"Authentic Chinese food, largely for real Chinese people" packs 'em in at this city-centre basement – *"the best oriental in Leeds by far"*; food that's of *"remarkable quality"* includes *"dim sum to die for"*. / **Sample dishes:** Lucky Dragon flamer; fillet steak Cantonese-style; lychees with ice cream. **Details:** 11.30 pm.

No 3 York Place £ 47 ✪

3 York Pl LS1 2DR (0113) 245 9922

In central Leeds, this *"classy"* establishment is very popular, and has quite a name as a *"centre of excellence"*; judged on a national basis, it's one step down from remarkable, but it's certainly a destination worth knowing about (and especially for business). / **Sample dishes:** red mullet & saffron soup; braised pig's trotter with veal sweetbreads; caramelised peanut parfait. **Details:** www.no3yorkplace.co.uk; 9.30 pm; closed Sat L & Sun.

Rico £ 29

450 Roundhay Rd LS8 2HU (0113) 2959697

A Lady Wood Italian sometimes claim as *"much better than the Flying Pizza"*; it serves *"huge portions"*. / **Sample dishes:** avocado & prawns; lasagne; fudge cake. **Details:** 10.30 pm, 11 pm Fri & Sat.

Sala Thai £ 25

13-17 Shaw Ln LS6 4DH (0113) 278 8400

*A popular local Thai; even if it has "little ambience", the food
is invariably well-rated. / **Sample dishes**: chicken spring rolls; grilled sirloin
wheeping tiger. **Details**: www.salathaileeds.co.uk; just off Otley Rd, near Arndale
Centre; 11pm; closed Sat L & Sun. **Accommodation**: rooms, from £-.*

Salvo's £ 40

115 Otley Rd LS6 3PX (0113) 275 5017

*"A Leeds institution"; "get there early or queue", at this "hugely
popular" Headingley fixture, where "interesting" Italian dishes
(and pizza) are served at "good-value" prices.
/ **Sample dishes**: deep-fried squid & king prawns; filetti di manzo; caramelised
lemon tart with fresh cream. **Details**: www.salvos.co.uk; 2m N of University
on A660; 10.30 pm; closed Sun; no Amex; no booking at D.*

Simply Heathcote's £ 42

Canal Whf, Water Ln LS11 5PS (0113) 244 6611

*"A candlelit setting overlooking the canal" adds charm to an evening
visit to (Lancastrian) chef Paul Heathcote's trans-Pennine incursion;
standards seem pretty consistent, without in any way being
remarkable. / **Sample dishes**: black pudding ploughman's; roast duck breast;
bread & butter pudding. **Details**: www.heathcotes.co.uk; off M621, J3, behind
Granary Wharf; 10pm, 11pm sat, 9pm sun.*

Sous le Nez en Ville £ 40

Quebec Hs, Quebec St LS1 2HA (0113) 244 0108

*This "relaxing" basement has long been a popular local rendezvous,
thanks not least to its famous early-bird menu; the Gallic cuisine
satisfies most reporters. / **Sample dishes**: deep-fried brie; rump steak &
chips; bread & butter pudding. **Details**: www.souslenez.com; 10 pm, Sat 11 pm;
closed Sun; no Amex.*

Sukhothai £ 27

8 Regent St LS7 4PE (0113) 237 0141

*A loyal local fan club yet again sings the virtues of this Chapel Allerton
"haven for Thai food-lovers", praising its "so friendly" staff and its
"mouthwatering" selection of "clean-tasting" dishes.
/ **Sample dishes**: chicken satay; fried banana with chopped prawn & crab,
served with sweet chilli sauce.; caramelised banana.
Details: www.thaifood4u.co.uk; 11 pm; closed Mon L; no Amex.*

Tampopo £ 28

15 South Pde LS1 5QS (0113) 245 1816

*"Better than the nearby Wagamama" – this more "authentic" Asian
joint wins praise for its "quick" and "satisfying" food, "friendly" staff
and "buzzy" atmosphere. / **Sample dishes**: chicken satay with peanut dip;
Pad Thai chicken; crème brûlée. **Details**: www.tampopo.co.uk; 11 pm,
Sun 10 pm; need 7+ to book.*

Whitelocks Luncheonette £ 28 Ⓐ
Turk's Head Yd, off Briggate LS1 6HB (0113) 245 3950
*Who cares if it's "almost a caricature of itself"? – this "traditional
city-centre pub" still "packs 'em in"; on the culinary front,
a "fine Yorkshire pudding" is the stand-out attraction.*
/ **Sample dishes:** *soup; roasts; jam roly-poly with custard.*
Details: *www.whitelocks.co.uk; 9 pm; children: 18+.*

LEICESTER, LEICESTER CITY   5–4D

Bobby's £ 21 ⭐
154-156 Belgrave Rd LE4 5AT (0116) 266 0106
*"Still a winner"; this Golden Mile veteran is "not smart", but it "can't
be beaten for authentic Gujarati food" at rock-bottom prices (and it's
"great for vegetarians").* / **Sample dishes:** *potato, aubergine & chilli fritters;
thali; kulfi.* **Details:** *www.eatatbobbys.com; 10 pm; no Amex.*

Case £ 40 Ⓐ
4-6 Hotel St LE1 5AW (0116) 251 7675
*An "old suitcase factory" provides the setting for this "lovely"-looking
"all-rounder", near St Martin's; it has quite a name as the city's
original trendy spot, but gives every impression of "resting on its
laurels".* / **Sample dishes:** *poached asparagus; fillet of beef & potato rösti;
crème brûlée.* **Details:** *www.thecase.co.uk; near the Cathedral; 10.30 pm;
closed Sun.*

Friends Tandoori £ 26 ⭐
41-43 Belgrave Rd LE4 6AR (0116) 266 8809
*"We occasionally stray, but always come back" – this smart (by local
standards) Golden Mile curry house offers "a very good standard"
of "fresh-tasting" dishes, plus "efficient" and "welcoming" service.*
/ **Sample dishes:** *chicken tikka; chicken achari with pilau rice; kulfi.*
Details: *www.friendstandoori.co.uk; 11.30 pm, 10.30 pm Sun; closed Sun L.*

The Tiffin £ 29
1 De Montfort St LE1 7GE (0116) 247 0420
*For those to whom the gritty 'Golden Mile' is too 'full on'
an experience, this civilised and "reliable", curry house near the
station represents "Indian cuisine at its very best".*
/ **Sample dishes:** *onion bhaji; chicken cooked with fresh green chillies, ginger &
garlic; vanilla ice cream.* **Details:** *www.the-tiffin.co.uk; near railway station;
10.45 pm; closed Sat L & Sun.*

LEIGH-ON-SEA, ESSEX   3–3C

Boat Yard £ 40 ❌
8-13 High St SS9 2EN (01702) 475588
*At this self-explanatory waterside veteran, "the room and the view are
amazing", but otherwise reports are fairly consistently of the view that
this potentially charming destination "still hasn't got its act together".*
/ **Sample dishes:** *figs & goat's cheese tart; roast monkfish; passion fruit mousse.*
Details: *www.theboatyardrestaurant.co.uk; near railway station; 10 pm; closed
Mon, Tue L & Sun D; no Amex.*

The Sand Bar £ 33 Ⓣ
71 Braodway SS9 1PE (01702) 480067
*"Modern but cosy" – this "great local eaterie" is an unpretentious
sort of place, with "consistently high standards".*
/ **Sample dishes:** *devilled lamb's kidneys; plaice fillet with red lentil mash.*

The Kings Head   £ 43
Ivinghoe LU7 9EB   (01296) 668388
A grand village inn, renowned for its Aylesbury duck; most reporters find it a "lovely, old-fashioned" sort of place that "cares for its patrons", but a few find it "expensive", and rather "arrogant". / **Sample dishes:** *crispy duck & watercress salad; braised & roasted belly of pork with shiitake mushrooms, cabbage & caramelised apple; French cheeses with celery, grapes & nuts.* **Details:** *www.kingsheadivinghoe.co.uk; 3m N of Tring on B489 to Dunstable; 9.30 pm; closed Sun D; jacket & tie required at D.*

Ⓐ

Auberge du Lac
Brocket Hall   £ 78
AL8 7XG   (01707) 368888
"Dare I say it? It's better than it was under Novelli" – as long as you're braced for the not-inconsiderable prices, feedback on this "idyllic" lakeside spot (with terrace) tends to confirm that it offers "special-occasion eating at its best" (particularly, lunching outside in summer); service is "extremely friendly and helpful". / **Sample dishes:** *pan-roast smoked breast of quail; smoked fillet of mullet & tiger prawns; coconut parfait & pineapple sorbet.* **Details:** *www.brocket-hall.co.uk; on B653 towards Harpenden; 9.30 pm; closed Mon & Sun D; no jeans or trainers.* **Accommodation:** *16 rooms, from £260.*

Ⓣ

Lewtrenchard Manor   £ 53
EX20 4PN   (01566) 783256
A superbly-located Elizabethan manor house hotel (now owned by the Von Essen group); it's not a great gastro-destination, but the "fantastic-value lunch menu" gets a big thumbs-up. / **Sample dishes:** *duck confit; guinea fowl boudin; crème brûlée.* **Details:** *www.lewtrenchard.co.uk; off A30 between Okehampton & Launceston; 9 pm; closed Mon L; no jeans or trainers; children: 8+ at D.* **Accommodation:** *14 rooms, from £150.*

★

Bill's   £ 24
56 Cliffe High St BN7 2AN   (01273) 476918
"There nowhere else quite like it"; Bill Collins's "absolute delight" of a deli has some claim to the title of "England's best café", thanks to its "wonderfully-presented juices and smoothies", plus "quirky recipes using exceptional local produce". / **Sample dishes:** *scrambled eggs with smoked salmon; salad of the day with focaccia.* **Details:** *www.billsproducestore.co.uk; 5 pm; closed Sun; no Amex.*

Ⓣ

Circa
Pelham House   £ 40
BN7 1UW   (01273) 471333
This townhouse hotel/conference centre attracted little coverage this year – such as there was said "service is much improved", and that the "innovative menu" for which the place is known "carries through to the plate". / **Sample dishes:** *seared scallops, sake gazpacho with chicory salad; halibut, mustard cabbage slaw & garlic spinach; cinnamon tempura with cardamom ice cream.* **Details:** *www.circacirca.com; 9.30 pm, 8 pm Sun.* **Accommodation:** *45 rooms, from £110.*

LIDGATE, SUFFOLK
3–1C

Star Inn
£ 42

The Street CB8 9PP (01638) 500275
"Spain-meets-racing country" – "flushed faces and squid stew", so to speak – at this Hispanic-owned inn of long standing, not far from Newmarket; the fare is "interesting", if perhaps "a bit pricey" for what it is. / **Sample dishes:** *paella; paella valenciana; treacle tart.* **Details:** *on B1063 6m SE of Newmarket; 10 pm; closed Sun D.*

LIFTON, DEVON
1–3C

Arundell Arms
£ 54

Fore St PL16 0AA (01566) 784666
Under the same owner for over 40 years, it's no shock that this grand anglers' hotel has settled into a groove that some find "dated"; fans, though, say it's "wonderful", and offers food that's "always sound"; the bar makes "a very fine pit stop, off the A30, for a croque-monsieur". / **Sample dishes:** *mignon of beef; casserole of scallops, turbot & sea bass; iced white chocolate mousse with raspberry sorbet.* **Details:** *www.arundellarms.com; 0.5m off A30, Lifton Down exit; 9.30 pm; no jeans or shorts.* **Accommodation:** *21 rooms, from £160.*

LIMPSFIELD, SURREY
3–3B

Alexanders at Limpsfield
The Old Lodge
£ 51

High St RH8 0DR (01883) 714365
"A bit of a find" – an ambitious new restaurant that's "trying hard"; it splits opinion, though – fans say its "clever" cooking displays "nicely restrained innovation", but doubters complain it's "priced for the ultra-rich". / **Details:** *www.alexanders-limpsfield.co.uk; 9.30 pm; closed Mon & Sun D.*

LINCOLN, LINCOLNSHIRE
6–3A

Browns Pie Shop
£ 32

33 Steep Hill LN2 1LU (01522) 527330
A "delightful" venue – occupying a characterful medieval building – whose pie-centric cuisine represents "rusticity done well"; it doesn't hit the heights it once did, though. / **Sample dishes:** *haslet; fillet of beef; Bailey's & chocolate brioche.* **Details:** *www.brownspieshop.co.uk; near the Cathedral; 10 pm; no Amex.*

Fourteen
£ 33

14 Bailgate LN1 3AE (01522) 576556
A "clean-lined" contemporary brasserie, which can make a handy town-centre stand-by. / **Sample dishes:** *goat's cheese tartlet; fillet of sea bass; chocolate hazelnut brownie.* **Details:** *10 pm.*

The Old Bakery
£ 40

26-28 Burton Rd LN1 3LB (01522) 576057
*"One of Lincoln's most talked-about eateries" – "a conversion of an historic bakery in the shadow of the castle walls" – put in an "erratic" performance this year, and was reported to be everything from "excellent" to "chaotic" and "disappointing".
/* **Sample dishes:** *double-baked cheese soufflé; Gloucester Old Spot baby pig; Mascarpone mousse.* **Details:** *www.theold-bakery.co.uk; 9.30 pm; closed Mon.* **Accommodation:** *4 rooms, from £63.*

The Wig & Mitre £ 38

30-32 Steep Hill LN2 1TL (01522) 535190

This rambling inn near the Cathedral is known for its "great buzz, and simple, well prepared food"; it has been though a rough patch of late, but supporters insist that it's "a place it has become fashionable to criticise, but it's improving". / Sample dishes: cheese *soufflé; rump of lamb; chocolate & pecan brownie.*

Details: *www.wigandmitre.com; between Cathedral & Castle; 11 pm.*

LINLITHGOW, WEST LOTHIAN 9–4C

Champany Inn £ 73

EH49 7LU (01506) 834532

Fans say it's "the best steak restaurant in the UK", and this celebrated inn (also famous for its wine list) is a destination most reporters find "expensive but worth it"; the cheaper chop-house is good too (but "you often need to queue"). / Sample dishes: smoked *salmon; char-grilled steak; cheesecake.* **Details:** *www.champany.com; 2m NE of Linlithgow on junction of A904 & A803; 10 pm; closed Sat L & Sun; no jeans or trainers; children: 8+.* **Accommodation:** *16 rooms, from £135.*

LITTLE HAVEN, PEMBROKESHIRE 4–4B

The Castle £ 28

SA62 3UG (01437) 781445

"A busy pub overlooking the spectacular harbour"; it's tipped in particular for a "good range of locally-caught fish". / Sample dishes: fresh sea bass; steak. **Details:** *www.castlelittlehaven.co.uk.*

LIVERPOOL, MERSEYSIDE 5–2A

It's difficult to avoid the conclusion that restaurants in Europe's Capital of Culture 2008 lack staying power on the culinary front. Each time the city produces a potential shooting star – first *Hope Street*, and now the *London Carriage Works* – it's not long before it seems to succumb to the power of gravity (or should that read complacency?). And even though there's a Chinatown, the ethnic restaurant scene is pretty lacklustre too. On current performance, the only place which could really be particularly recommended to a one-night visiting culture vulture is the striking *Alma De Cuba*.

Alma De Cuba
St Peter's Church £ 50

Seel St L1 4AZ (0151) 7027394

"An old church, brilliantly transformed into a restaurant"; it offers not only a "stunning" setting, but also "ambitious" and "eclectic" Caribbean food. / Details: www.alma-de-cuba.com; 11 pm, midnight Fri & Sat; *no shorts.*

Ego £ 34

Federation Hs, Hope St L1 9BW (0151) 706 0707

A "predictable all-rounder", this Mediterranean bistro is of particular interest by virtue of its location, near the Philharmonic Hall. / Sample dishes: glazed asparagus & Taleggio cheese; fillet steak with Dolcelatte; *passion fruit crème brûlée.* **Details:** *www.egorestaurants.com; 10.30 pm.*

Everyman Bistro   **£ 23**   Ⓐ⭐

5-9 Hope St L1 9BH   (0151) 708 9545

*This self-service "gem" has been a much-loved local fixture for over 35 years now; its winning formula includes a "lively" vibe and "a good selection of ales" (and wine), not to mention a "tempting" array of dishes ("veggie options are particularly good") that are "as cheap as chips!" / **Sample dishes:** sweet potato & watercress soup; Greek lamb with rice & marinated Feta; lemon syrup cake. **Details:** www.everyman.co.uk; midnight, Thu-Sat 2 am; closed Sun.*

Gulshan   **£ 26**   Ⓣ

544-548 Aigburth Rd L19 3QG   (0151) 427 2273

*Not all reporters are impressed, but fans still say this Aigburth Indian is "the only curry house in town worth mentioning". / **Sample dishes:** buttered prawns with puri; lamb pasanda; kulfi. **Details:** www.gulshan-liverpool.com; 11 pm; D only.*

Keith's Wine Bar   **£ 27**   Ⓣ

107 Lark Ln L17 8UR   (0151) 728 7688

*A Bohemian Sefton Park wine bar, with a "good selection of dishes from around the world", plus "reasonably-priced" wines. / **Sample dishes:** mussels; char-grilled cajun chicken; cakes. **Details:** 10.30 pm; need 6+ to book.*

The London Carriage Works
Hope Street Hotel   **£ 61**

40 Hope St L1 9DA   (0151) 705 2222

*"This has still got to be Liverpool's best", say fans of this modern brasserie (there's also a 'fine dining' area), in the city's trendiest boutique hotel; it started to draw flak this year, though, for getting "a bit over-ambitious" and "starting to believe its own PR". / **Sample dishes:** assiette of new season carrots; pan-fried fillet of turbot; deeply rich chocolate mousse. **Details:** www.tlcw.co.uk; 10 pm. **Accommodation:** 48 rooms, from £140.*

Malmaison   **£ 45**

William Jessop Way, Princes Dock L3 1QW   (0151) 229 5000

*"Distinctive style and an emphasis on local produce" makes this new member of the design-hotel chain a notable destination, at least by local standards. / **Sample dishes:** shrimp cocktail; cod & chips. **Details:** www.malmaison-liverpool.com; 10.30 pm. **Accommodation:** 130 rooms, from £99.*

Mei Mei   **£ 32**   Ⓣ

9-13 Berry St L1 9DF   (0151) 7072888

A Chinese operation of a few years' standing, described as a "quality" operation, and with "a few dishes out of the ordinary too".

Olive Press   **£ 35**

25-27 Castle St L2 4TA   (0151) 2272242

*Part of the Paul Heathcote empire – this "very busy" city-centre bistro impresses local reporters with its "tasty" and "good-value" Mediterranean fare. / **Sample dishes:** baked garlic mushrooms; stone-baked pizza with goat's cheese & butternut squash; orange & coffee tiramisu. **Details:** www.heathcotes.co.uk; 10 pm, Fri & Sat 11 pm.*

Puschka   £ 35

16 Rodney St L1 2TE   (0151) 708 8698

"Popular" and "unpretentious" – this "characterful venue" offers "well-sourced" dishes, realised to a very competent standard. / **Sample dishes:** grilled goat's cheese & field mushrooms; fillet of beef with blue cheese-stuffed field mushrooms on bubble & squeak; crème brûlée with tarte cassis & blackcurrant compote. **Details:** www.puschka.co.uk; 10 pm; closed Mon, Tue-Thu D only, Sun L only; no Amex; no trainers.

Sapporo Teppanyaki   £ 40   Ⓐ

134 Duke St L1 5AG   (0151) 705 3005

For "amazing theatre" – "everyone cheers as the chefs set light to the noodles, and show off their fish slice tossing skills" – you won't find a better restaurant in locally than this "hectic" and "amusing" Japanese establishment, near Chinatown; the food's not bad either. / **Sample dishes:** soup noodles; chicken fillet & noodles; ice cream, banana tempura, chocolate spring rolls. **Details:** www.sapporo.co.uk; 11 pm, Sun 10.30 pm; no shorts.

Simply Heathcote's   £ 37

Beetham Plaza 25, The Strand L2 0XL   (0151) 236 3536

"A stylish restaurant serving reliable modern British food"; near the Liver Building, it's a popular business choice. / **Sample dishes:** black pudding; roast duck breast; bread & butter pudding. **Details:** www.heathcotes.co.uk; 10 pm.

60 Hope Street   £ 43

60 Hope St L1 9BZ   (0151) 707 6060

"Still pretty good, but not quite what it was" – Liverpool's original contemporary-style restaurant offers both a "bustling" basement bistro and a "formal" restaurant on the ground floor; both, however, now strike quite a few reporters as being "expensive, for what they are". / **Sample dishes:** Garstang blue cheese soufflé with pear & walnut salad; pan-fried fillet of cod & saffron risotto cake; chocolate & vanilla cheesecake. **Details:** www.60hopestreet.com; 10.30 pm; closed Sat L & Sun.

Tai Pan   £ 26

WH Lung Bdg., Great Howard St L5 9TZ   (0151) 207 3888

"A big sprawling warehouse-like space above an oriental supermarket"; it remains "heaving with the local Chinese community" (especially for "trolley dim sum"), even though its style is "impersonal" and the food can be "average". / **Sample dishes:** dim sum; shredded beef chilli & garlic sauce; ice cream. **Details:** 11.30 pm, Sun 9.30 pm.

Yuet Ben   £ 23

1 Upper Duke St L1 9DU   (0151) 709 5772

"On the edge of Chinatown", this long-established Chinese veteran is a "true Scouse institution", and on most accounts just "as reliable as ever". / **Sample dishes:** barbecue ribs; chilli beef; glazed toffee fruit. **Details:** www.yuetben.co.uk; 11 pm; D only, closed Mon.

LLANARMON DC, DENBIGHSHIRE   5–3A

The West Arms Hotel   £ 47   Ⓣ

LL20 7LD   (01691) 600665

"A lovely intimate hotel in the heart of Wales", tipped for food that's "well cooked and reasonably priced". / **Details:** www.thewestarms.co.uk; 9 pm; no Amex. **Accommodation:** 15 rooms, from ££53.50 p/p.

LLANDEGLA, WREXHAM 5–3A

Bodidris Hall Hotel £ 32
LL11 3AL (0870) 729 2292
"Set In lovely surroundings" (an estate of 6,500 acres), a romantically medieval hall, offering *"food and service to match"*.
/ **Sample dishes:** *sirloin steak; medallions of monkfish; iced honey comb parfait*.
Details: www.bodidrishall.com; on A5104 from Wrexham; 8.45 pm; children: 14+ at D. **Accommodation:** 9 rooms, from £99.

LLANDRILLO, DENBIGHSHIRE 4–2D

Tyddyn Llan £ 55
LL21 0ST (01490) 440264

"A superb setting, exquisite food and a comprehensive wine list" – such are the virtues that win (almost) unanimous applause from reporters for Bryan & Susan Webb's *"peaceful weekend retreat"*.
/ **Sample dishes:** *asparagus; saddle of new season spring lamb; pistachio crème brûlée*. **Details:** www.tyddynllan.co.uk; on B4401 between Corwen and Bala; 9 pm; closed Mon (Tue-Thu L by prior arrangement only); no Amex; booking essential Tue L-Thu L. **Accommodation:** 13 rooms, from £110.

LLANDUDNO, CONWY 4–1D

Bodysgallen Hall £ 55
LL30 1RS (01492) 584466
"Comfortably romantic and rustic" – this *"lovely"* country house hotel stands in 200 acres of grounds, just outside the resort; the food is *"very good"* too, especially by local standards (if arguably no better than the prices demand). / **Sample dishes:** *scallops with caramelised pork belly; pan-fried beef; white chocolate & orange terrine with passion fruit syrup*.
Details: www.bodysgallen.com; 2m off A55 on A470; 9.15 Sun-Thu, 9.30 Fri; no jeans or trainers; booking: max 10; children: 8+. **Accommodation:** 35 rooms, from £175.

St Tudno Hotel £ 49
Promenade LL30 2LP (01492) 874411
The *"innovative"* kitchen of this *"calm"* and *"comfortable"* Victorian-style hotel, near the pier, comes as a bit of surprise to some reporters – all attest, however, that the dishes are *"beautifully prepared"*.
/ **Sample dishes:** *foie gras ballotine; loin of lamb; iced coconut parfait*.
Details: www.st-tudno.co.uk; 9.30 pm; no shorts; children: 6+.
Accommodation: 19 rooms, from £130.

LLANFAIR WATERDINE, SHROPSHIRE 5–4A

Waterdine **£ 42**
Llanfair Waterdine LD7 1TU (01547) 528214
*A family-run establishment offering "extraordinarily good French
cookery in a Welsh wayside inn"; it's a "comfortable" place too, "ideal
for a weekend get-away". / **Sample dishes:** breast of squab pigeon
on parsley risotto with sweet & sour beetroot sauce; fillet of Dover sole stuffed with
lightly wood smoked-salmon on crayfish sauce; gingerbread pudding.
Details: www.waterdine.com; 9.30 pm; closed Mon & Sun D; no Amex; booking
essential. **Accommodation:** 3 rooms, from £80.*

LLANFYLLIN, LLANFYLLIN 5–4A

Seeds **£ 34**
5 Penbryn Cottages SY22 5AP (01691) 648604
*"In deep mid-Wales, a very useful place in what's otherwise a culinary
wilderness"; "the food is the thing, with decent quality ingredients that
are accurately cooked and satisfying"; "quite a fair wine list too".
/ **Sample dishes:** tuna salad; roast rack of lamb with Dijon & herb crust.
Details: 8.30 pm, 9.30 pm Sat; closed Mon, Tue, Wed D & Sun D; no Amex.*

LLANGAMMARCH WELLS, POWYS 4–4D

Lake Country House **£ 59**
LD4 4BS (01591) 620202
*"A classic country house hotel, in rural mid-Wales" – a "relaxed"
place that's "well-run", and offers very good food.
/ **Sample dishes:** roast rabbit on a tart of red onions with mushroom ravioli;
Mirabelle plum doufflé with liquorice ice cream & warm compote of griottine
cherries. **Details:** www.lakecountryhouse.co.uk; off A483 at Garth, follow signs;
9.15 pm; jacket & tie required; children: 8+ at D. **Accommodation:** 19 rooms,
from £160.*

LLANGOLLEN, DENBIGHSHIRE 5–3A

Corn Mill **£ 32**
Dee Ln LL20 8PN (01978) 869555
*"It would be almost impossible to get a better location for
a restaurant", than this former mill – "complete with fully operational
water-wheel" – looking down on the turbulent waters of the Dee;
its gastropub fare, though, is "fairly average". / **Sample dishes:** smoked
haddock & salmon fishcakes; pork & apple sausage; bara birth with apricot sauce.
Details: www.brunningandprice.co.uk; 9.30 pm.*

Gales **£ 32**
18 Bridge St LL20 8PF (01978) 860089
*A "sound" wine bar, where the owner knows his vintages; the food
is simple, but it's pretty consistent. / **Sample dishes:** potted shrimps;
fisherman's pie; Bailey's bread & butter pudding.
Details: www.galesofllangollen.co.uk; 9.30 pm; closed Sun.
Accommodation: 15 rooms, from £70.*

LLANWDDYN, POWYS 4–2D

Lake Vyrnwy Hotel £ 44 (A)

Lake Vyrnwy SY10 0LY (01691) 870692

Fans of "faded elegance" will have a field day at this Baronial-style hotel (built to house the engineers who built the lake over which it now has "fantastic views"); the food is a bit of an incidental attraction, but is sometimes "delicious".

/ **Sample dishes:** roast breast of chicken; char-grilled pavé of sirloin steak; baked honey Alaska. **Details:** www.lakevyrnwy.com; on B4393 at SE end of Lake Vyrnwy; 9.15 pm; no jeans or trainers. **Accommodation:** 52 rooms, from £120.

LLANWRTYD WELLS, POWYS 4–4D

Carlton Riverside £ 49 (A)(★)

Dolecoed Rd LD5 4RA (01591) 610248

The former Carlton House hotel moved in late-2006 to new premises overlooking the River Irfon; in the locations old and new, it inspired only rapturous reports for its "good old-fashioned French-style cooking". / **Sample dishes:** home-cured Welsh beef bresaola; roast cannon of lamb; raspberry & sloe gin jelly with red fruit sorbet.

Details: www.carltonrestaurant.co.uk; 8.30 pm; closed Mon L, Sat L & Sun D; no Amex; booking: max 10. **Accommodation:** 5 rooms, from £70.

LLYSWEN, POWYS 2–1A

Llangoed Hall £ 59 (A)(★)

LD3 0YP (01874) 754525

Sir Bernard Ashley's "classic" grand country house hotel continues to inspire enthusiastic reports, which laud its "lovely setting and views", its "very good food", and its service that goes the extra mile.

/ **Sample dishes:** seared king scallops; beef fillet; chocolate mousse with Tia Maria chocolate sauce. **Details:** www.llangoedhall.com; 11m NW of Brecon on A470; 10 pm; jacket required at D; children: 8+. **Accommodation:** 23 rooms, from £210.

LOCH LOMOND, DUNBARTONSHIRE 9–4B

Lomonds
Cameron House £ 75

G83 8QZ (01389) 755565

Paul Tamburini's departure seems to have led to a collapse in standards at this "stunningly-located" (if often "quiet") lochside dining room, which this year attracted too many complaints of "appalling" service and "poorly put-together" food.

/ **Sample dishes:** ballotine of foie gras, peach, & spice bread; pan-fried red mullet with langoustines & basil; cherries, fromage blanc, & lemon curd. **Details:** www.cameronhouse.co.uk; over Erskine Bridge to A82, follow signs to Loch Lomond; 9.45 pm; D only, closed Sun & Mon; jacket & tie required; children: 14+. **Accommodation:** 100 rooms, from £208.

LOCHINVER, SUTHERLAND 9–1B

The Albannach £ 59 (A)(★)

IV27 4LP (01571) 844407

"A bit of a trek, but well worth it" – Colin Craig and Lesley Crosfield's "lovely" small hotel receives all-round praise for its "ambitious and complex" food, "good" atmosphere, and general "attention to detail".

/ **Sample dishes:** wood pigeon breast; roast turbot & champagne sabayon; caramelised apple tartlet. **Details:** www.thealbannach.co.uk; 8 pm; closed Mon; no Amex; children: 12+. **Accommodation:** 5 rooms, from £250.

LOCKSBOTTOM, KENT

3–3B

Chapter One
£ 45

Farnborough Common BR6 8NF (01689) 854848

An "expensive-looking renovation" in early-2007 has further boosted
acclaim for this now more svelte-looking establishment, where Andrew
McLeish's "surprising" and "absolutely superb" cuisine deserves to be
measured against the star names of the West End.
/ **Sample dishes:** ravioli of lobster; slow-roast belly of pork; chocolate fondant.
Details: www.chaptersrestaurants.com; just before Princess Royal Hospital;
10.30 pm; booking: max 12.

LONG CRENDON, BUCKINGHAMSHIRE   2–2D

Angel
£ 44

47 Bicester Rd HP18 9EE (01844) 208268
Trevor Bosch continues to deliver "imaginative seasonal food"
(majoring in "excellent fish") at his "reliable" and very popular ten-
year-old; it provides gastronomic cheer in a "culinarily dead bit
of Bucks". / **Sample dishes:** steamed mussels; roast fillet of sea bream;
chocolate fallen angel. **Details:** www.angelrestaurant.co.uk; 2m NW of Thames,
off B4011; 9.30 pm; closed Sun D; no Amex; booking: max 12, Fri & Sat.
Accommodation: 4 rooms, from £85.

LONG MELFORD, SUFFOLK   3–1C

Scutchers Restaurant
£ 44

Westgate St CO10 9DP (01787) 310200
"Solid", "sensible", "reliable", "pleasant" – such are the dependable
qualities which win lots of complimentary feedback for this "popular
local". / **Sample dishes:** smoked haddock mousse; slow-roast breast of ducking
with orange sauce & rösti; steamed syrup sponge pudding.
Details: www.scutchers.com; 9.30 pm; closed Mon & Sun.

LONGFRAMLINGTON, NORTHUMBERLAND 8–2B

Anglers Arms
£ 32

Weldon Bridge NE65 8AX (01665) 570271
Here's a real tip: "dine in the railway carriage", if you visit this
"reasonably-priced" establishment, where the food is praised
as "good" and "wholesome". / **Sample dishes:** steak & ale pie; cod & crab
fishcakes served on a bed of asparagus & tenderstem, drizzled with lemon & herb
Hollandaise. **Details:** www.anglersarms.com; 9.30 pm; no Amex.
Accommodation: 7 rooms, from £75.

LONGRIDGE, LANCASHIRE 5–1B

The Longridge Restaurant £ 50
104-106 Higher Rd PR3 3SY (01772) 784969
*Reports on the converted cottage where North Western bigwig Paul Heathcote kicked off his career have had their ups and – more often – downs in recent years; its current régime, however – with its "adventurous" but "down-to-earth" cuisine – is pleasing reporters more consistently. / **Sample dishes:** deep-fried Lancashire cheese fritter; breast of duck; bread & butter pudding. **Details:** www.heathcotes.co.uk; follow signs for Jeffrey Hill; 9.30 pm; closed Mon & Sat L.*

LONGSTOCK, HAMPSHIRE 2–3D

Peat Spade Inn £ 40
SO20 6DR (01264) 810612
*In its "stunning" Test Valley setting, chef/patron Andrew Clark's "friendly" two-year-old gastropub wins consistent high praise for its "delicious" cuisine. / **Sample dishes:** chicken liver & foie gras parfait; rib-eye steak; raspberry fool with shortbread. **Details:** www.peatspadeinn.co.uk; 1.25m from Stockbridge; 9 pm; closed Sun D; no Amex. **Accommodation:** 6 rooms, from £110.*

LOWER BEEDING, WEST SUSSEX 3–4A

South Lodge £ 48 Ⓐ
Brighton Rd RH13 6PS (01403) 891711
*A grand country house hotel (part of the Exclusive Hotels group), whose "lovely" restaurant is uniformly praised for its "good food and beautiful views". / **Details:** www.exclusivehotels.co.uk; opposite the Crabtree pub 1 mile up road from Leonards Lee gardens; 9.30 pm; jacket & tie; children: 12+. **Accommodation:** 39 rooms, from £195.*

LOWER ODDINGTON, GLOUCESTERSHIRE 2–1C

The Fox Inn £ 36 Ⓐ⭐
GL56 0UR (01451) 870555
*"A very English pub, offering wholesome and reliable food in the heart of the Cotswolds" – the tenor of all reports on this "busy" rural inn; prices are "sensible" too. / **Sample dishes:** gravadlax with dill & mustard dressing; confit of duck; bitter chocolate mousse cake. **Details:** www.foxinn.net; on A436 near Stow-on-the-Wold; 10 pm; no Amex. **Accommodation:** 3 rooms, from £68.*

LUDLOW, SHROPSHIRE 5–4A

La Bécasse £ 70
17 Corve St SY8 1DA (01584) 872325
*In early-2007, the celebrated Hibiscus departed for Mayfair, to be replaced a few months later by this new stablemate to L'Ortolan (from distant Shinfield); initial press reports suggest the newcomer lives up to its fine dining aims, though prices are more extravagant than its predecessor. / **Details:** www.labecasse.co.uk; 9 pm; closed Mon, Tue L & Sun.*

The Clive £ 31

SY8 2JR (01584) 856565

*This farmhouse revamped in contemporary style offers "a unique blend of old and new"; it's "well patronised", thanks to its "good" and "reliable" cooking. / **Sample dishes:** seared scallops, crisp Parma ham with avocado & red pepper salsa; seared loin of venison on sweet corn & leek mash, red cabbage, roasted courgettes & peppercorn jus; crispy meringue nest with fresh berries in Mascarpone cream, honey & raspberry sorbet.*
Details: *www.theclive.co.uk.*

Koo £ 31

127 Old St SY8 1NU (01584) 878462

*"All the more surprising (and welcome) for being tucked-away in the heart of beef and cider country" – a "charming" Japanese café where the food "is very good, on the whole". / **Sample dishes:** gyoza; tempura; green tea ice cream. **Details:** www.koo-ook.co.uk; 9 pm; D only, closed Mon & Sun.*

Mr Underhill's £ 63

Dinham Wier SY8 1EH (01584) 874431

*"The only place really keeping Ludlow's reputation going" – Chris & Judy Bradley's "delightful" restaurant-with-rooms is a standard-bearer that would do any town proud; it offers "magnificent" food that "combines excellence and wit", served in a "beautiful riverside location". / **Sample dishes:** asparagus velouté; roast rack & slow-cooked shoulder of lamb; panna cotta with fruit caviar. **Details:** www.mr-underhills.co.uk; 8.15 pm; D only, closed Mon & Tue; no Amex. **Accommodation:** 9 rooms, from £135.*

LUXBOROUGH, SOMERSET 1–2D

The Royal Oak Inn £ 37

TA23 0SH (01984) 640319

*"A lovely relaxed dining pub in pleasant surroundings"; its virtues include "restaurant-quality food", "attentive but not intrusive service" and a "very pleasant attitude to children". / **Sample dishes:** salad of wild rocket, crayfish tails & lemon with a light citrus dressing; pan-fried tail of monkfish with roasted figs wrapped in parma ham with basil oil.*
Details: *www.theroyaloakinnluxborough.co.uk; 9 pm; no Amex.*
Accommodation: *11 rooms, from £65.*

LYDFORD, DEVON 1–3C

The Dartmoor Inn £ 41

Moorside EX20 4AY (01822) 820221

*This well-known inn is "a really good all-rounder, offering great food in a relaxed setting" (and in an otherwise "barren" area too).
/ **Sample dishes:** griddled scallops with chilli & lemon grass dressing; thyme-roast duck breast; honey & rhubarb custard tart.*
Details: *www.dartmoorinn.com; 9.30 pm; closed Mon & Sun D; children: 5+ at weekends. **Accommodation:** 3 rooms, from £100.*

LYDGATE, GREATER MANCHESTER 5–2B

White Hart £ 45

51 Stockport Rd OL4 4JJ (01457) 872566

*A "likeable" operation on the edge of the Pennines, where sausages and mash, "in various forms", are the speciality of the house.
/ **Sample dishes:** pear, walnut & watercress salad; pan-fried sirloin of beef; sticky toffee pudding. **Details:** www.thewhitehart.co.uk; 2m E of Oldham on A669, then A6050; 9.30 pm. **Accommodation:** 12 rooms, from £120.*

The Broad Street Restaurant £ 41 ⭐
57-58 Broad St DT7 3QF (01297) 445 792
*A "calm" and stylish two-year-old, occupying a "well-designed and laid-out basement"; "it suits most sorts of events", thanks not least to its "creative" and "beautifully-presented" food, using "great locally-sourced ingredients". / **Sample dishes:** duck roulette; fillet of sea bass; cheeses. **Details:** 9.30 pm; D only, seasonal hours.*

Harbour Inn £ 35 ⭐
The Cobb, Marine Pde DT7 3JF (01297) 442299
*"Right on Lyme's newly refurbished seafront, in prime position" – this popular pub offers "excellent-value, very fresh fish" (and not just of the 'n' chips variety). / **Sample dishes:** fish & chips; turbot. **Details:** 9 pm.*

Egan's £ 40 ⭐
Gosport St SO41 9BE (01590) 676165
*"Always a treat" – John Egan's jolly bistro, not far from the harbour, is an excellent all-rounder; lunchtimes, in particular, offer "exceptional value". / **Sample dishes:** beef carpaccio; pan-fried sea bass with chorizo sausage; assiette of desserts. **Details:** 10 pm; closed Mon & Sun; no Amex; booking: max 6, Sat.*

Gordleton Mill £ 41 Ⓐ⭐
Silver St SO41 6DJ (01590) 682219
*"A lovely rural location, superb food and a lovely building" – such are the virtues of this "informal" restaurant-with-rooms, which pleases all of the (relatively few) reporters who comment on it. / **Sample dishes:** twice-baked salmon & dill soufflé; fillet of sea bass; chocolate & almond tart with caramelised bananas. **Details:** www.themillatgordleton.co.uk; 9 pm; closed Sun D; children: 14+ at D. **Accommodation:** 8 rooms, from £120.*

Westover Hall £ 55 Ⓣ
Park Ln SO41 0PT (01590) 643044
*"Lovely stained glass" adds to the ambience at this Victorian country house hotel, tipped for its "innovative food, attractively served". / **Sample dishes:** duck foie gras confit in a seasoned crust with fig & beetroot purée; marinated rack of lamb; griottes, tiramisu & mocha ice cream. **Details:** www.westoverhallhotel.com; 9 pm; children: 5+ after 5 pm. **Accommodation:** 12 rooms, from £200.*

Le Poussin at Parkhill £ 61
Beaulieu Rd SO43 7FZ (023) 8028 2944
*This country house hotel is still closed for refurbishment as this guide goes to press, and the Aitkens family's 'first team' is currently at their Whitley Ridge property; the re-launch here is now postponed to sometime in 2008. / **Details:** www.lepoussin.co.uk.*

LYTHAM, LANCASHIRE 5–1A

Chicory Restaurant £ 42
5-7 Henry St FY8 5LE (01253) 737111
*"What went wrong?"; this bright and modern restaurant continues
to inspire a fair number of reports – most of them, unfortunately,
to the effect that if offers "poor combinations" of food for "too much
money". / **Sample dishes:** parcel of goat's cheese, Stilton, wild mushrooms &
Brie; confit of boned lamb shank wrapped in Parma ham; baked New York vanilla
tart. **Details:** www.chicorygroup.co.uk; 9.30 pm.*

MADINGLEY, CAMBRIDGESHIRE 3–1B

Three Horseshoes £ 42
CB23 8AB (01954) 210221
*Long popular with Cambridge undergrads and their parents, this pub-
cum-restaurant in a "lovely village" features good wine and
a "comfortable conservatory"; for most reporters it's "well up to its
reputation", but doubters find it "overhyped". / **Sample dishes:** ravioli &
new potatoes; char-grilled leg of lamb; chocolate truffle cake with Devon clotted
cream. **Details:** 2m W of Cambridge, off A14 or M11; 9 pm, Sun 8.30 pm.*

MAIDENHEAD, BERKSHIRE 3–3A

Ferry £ 35
Sutton Rd SL6 9SN (01628) 525123
*"Formerly wasted as a 'Harvester'" – this riverside boozer (now under
independent ownership) is tipped by a number of reporters for its
"great views", and for food that "if not amazing, is very good of its
type".*

MAIDENS, SOUTH AYRSHIRE 7–1A

Wildings £ 32
Harbour Rd KA26 9NR (01655) 331401
*"A superb restaurant in a lovely location"; "it doesn't offer haute
cuisine, but it does offer good ingredients, well cooked".
/ **Details:** www.wildingsrestaurant.co.uk; Follow the A77 to Turnberry and turn
on to the A719 signposted Maidens.; 9 pm; no Amex. **Accommodation:** 10
rooms, from £40/person.*

MALMESBURY, WILTSHIRE 2–2C

The Old Bell Hotel £ 50
Abbey Row SN16 0BW (01666) 822344
*This grand and ancient coaching inn has a "slightly stuffy" dining
room ("part of its charm", apparently), which is "popular with local
royalty"; the cooking – contemporary in style – has been a bit up-and-
down of late. / **Sample dishes:** marinated salmon & crab; medallions of beef;
millefeuille of raspberries. **Details:** www.oldbellhotel.com; next to Abbey; 9 pm,
9.30 Fri & Sat. **Accommodation:** 30 rooms, from £125.*

MANCHESTER, GREATER MANCHESTER 5–2B

Manchester's restaurant scene – the largest provincial scene
in England – has a number of odd features.

We noted last year that the most striking feature was arguably the city's inability to sustain a top-quality, non-ethnic city-centre figurehead. Early in 2007, the two contenders for such a title (Mont and the Establishment) duly closed! If you really must dine grandly in the city-centre, the top tip nowadays (ideally on expenses) is the ultra-traditonal *French*. If you're looking for quality non-ethnic dining and paying your own way, however, it's safest to head off to the 'burbs, most obviously to West Didsbury's consistently satisfying *Lime Tree*.

Let's stay in the city-centre, though, and look at the mid-price options. This is the only city in England where the most obvious cuisine to eat is English! *Sam's Chop House* and *Mr Thomas's Chop House*, and the reviving *Market* really are 'English' restaurants! If you are not in the mood for something quite so traditional, it might be worth going Italian, and checking out the mid-level *San Carlo*, or the pizzeria-level (but very fashionable) *Croma*.

The best city-centre option, however is to eat Chinese, in which cuisine Manchester is pre-eminent outside London. The most notable name is the legendary *Yang Sing* – the city's only nationally-known restaurant – which is ably understudied by such establishments as *Little Yang Sing* and *Pacific* (and, in the city-centre, the more fashionable *Wings*).

At the fun and affordable level, Western Europe's largest student population – bolstered nowadays by a growing army of young professionals resident in the city-centre – helps to support an increasing number of places, such as *Kro*. There are lots of Indian restaurants too, mainly in the famed curry quarter of Rusholme. Some of them are very good, but they largely remain stuck in a surprisingly downmarket mould.

Akbar's £ 26
73-83 Liverpool Rd M3 4NQ (0161) 8348444
"A welcome spin-off from the Bradford stalwart", say numerous fans of this *"large"* and *"very modern-looking"* newcomer, who praise its *"massive"* and *"good-value"* dishes (*"the family naan is a theatrical event"*); critics, though, say *"it's supposed to be great but is only OK"*. / *Sample dishes*: chicken tikka masala; chicken makhani.
Details: www.akbars.co.uk; 11 pm, Fri & Sat 11.30 pm; D only; need 10+ to book.

Albert's Shed £ 34
Ⓐ
20 Castle St M3 4LZ (0161) 8399818
"A hidden gem in Castlefield", say fans of this stylish, modern, mainly-Italian joint, hailed for its *"surprisingly good"* food, its *"great location"* and its *"very friendly"* staff. / *Sample dishes*: stonebaked pizza; steaks.
Details: www.albertsshed.com; 10 pm, Fri 10.30 pm, Sat 11 pm, Sun 9.30 pm; no Amex.

Armenian Taverna £ 31
★
3-5 Princess St M2 4DF (0161) 834 9025
"No pretensions, but what it does it does well" – this old *"favourite"* basement Greek/Armenian is still a *"very reliable"* city-centre destination. / *Sample dishes*: borek; Armenian goulash.
Details: www.armeniantaverna.co.uk; 11 pm; closed Mon, Sat L & Sun L; children: 3+.

Brasserie Blanc £ 41

55 King St M2 4LQ (0161) 832 1000

Changes in format since its days as Petit Blanc ("it seems more of a squeeze than it was before") are bearing fruit at this city-centre bistro, and it's generally praised for its "genial" service and "good-value" food (especially the "astonishing set lunch").
/ ***Sample dishes:*** *deep-fried goat's cheese & tomato chutney; corn-fed guinea fowl confit; chocolate feuillantine.* ***Details:*** *www.brasserieblanc.com; 10.30 pm.*

The Bridgewater Hall £ 34

Lower Mosley St M2 3WS (0161) 950 0000

"The food's much better than you'd expect" at the home of the Hallé; the Stalls Café/Bar comes recommended for "an excellent light lunch". / ***Sample dishes:*** *pork rillette, quenelle of potted goose, confit of spiced red cabbage & beetroot; millefeuille of salmon & crayfish mousseline, baby vegetables, tomato & star anise sauce; apricot, amaretto & almond sponge.*
Details: *www.bridgewater-hall.co.uk; 7.30 pm; openings affected by concert times.*

Cedar Tree £ 25

69 Thomas St M4 1LQ (0871) 8114924

"Good-quality traditional Lebanese cooking" wins praise for this "inexpensive" Northern Quarter "gem"; service, though – "never a strong point" – seems to be "suffering from the place's popularity".
/ ***Sample dishes:*** *tabouleh; mixed grill; baklava.* ***Details:*** *10 pm; no Amex.*

Choice £ 32

Castle Quay M15 4NT (0161) 833 3400

"Consistently good" food (using "quality local ingredients") and a "great waterfront setting" are winning ever-greater acclaim for this Castlefield bar/restaurant; "if it was nearer the city-centre, it would be sold out every night!" / ***Sample dishes:*** *pan-fried scallops; rack of lamb; bread & butter pudding.* ***Details:*** *www.choicebarandrestaurant.co.uk; 9.45 pm.*

Croma £ 24

1 Clarence St M2 4DE (0161) 237 9799

Thanks to its "quick and reasonably-priced pizza" formula (featuring "unusual" toppings), this "modern", "easy" and "reliable" venue remains by far the best-known informal eatery in the city-centre (and can get "incredibly crowded"); there are also now spin-offs in Chorlton and (coming soon) Prestwich. / ***Sample dishes:*** *buffalo Mozzarella & tomato salad; crispy aromatic duck pizza; sticky toffee pudding.*
Details: *www.croma.biz; off Albert Square; 11 pm.*

Dimitri's £ 35

Campfield Arc M3 4FN (0161) 839 3319

"Sit 'outside' – in the arcade – for top atmosphere", if you visit this "busy" and "reliable" Greek spot, just off Deansgate; "it's good both for lunch and in the evening". / **Sample dishes:** seafood in tomato & wine sauce; chicken breast stuffed with Feta; bakliza. **Details:** www.dimitris.co.uk; near Museum of Science & Industry; 11.30 pm.

Evuna £ 34

277 Deansgate M3 4EW (0161) 819 2752

It's the "unrivalled" wine list (including some "fine and rare choices") which makes this "attractively-designed" Deansgate tapas bar of most interest – accounts of the food and service are mixed. / **Sample dishes:** deep-fried squid; lean duck breast served in an aged port sauce with summer fruits; Spanish cheesecake. **Details:** www.evuna.com; midnight, 10 pm Sun.

Francs £ 36

2 Goose Grn WA14 1DW (0161) 941 3954

The "steady" charms of this long-established Altrincham bistro commend it to lots of local reporters; it can, though, seem too much "like a '70s time warp" for some tastes. / **Sample dishes:** salade niçoise; stuffed pheasant with orange & peppercorn sauce. **Details:** www.francs-altrincham.com; 10 pm, Fri & Sat 10.30, Sun 9.30; no Amex.

French Restaurant
Midland Hotel £ 55

Peter St M60 2DS (0161) 236 3333

"Food that's improved in recent times" boosts the appeal – "all-round amazing", say fans – of "one of the loveliest dining rooms in the country", at the heart of this (recently revamped) city-centre grand hotel (where Mr Rolls met Mr Royce); it's "expensive for what it is", though, and feedback is still up-and-down. / **Sample dishes:** sea bass; fillet steak; white, dark & milk chocolate desserts. **Details:** www.themidland.co.uk; 10.30 pm; D only, closed Mon & Sun; no jeans or trainers. **Accommodation:** 311 rooms, from £125.

Gaucho Grill £ 50

2a St Mary's St M3 2LB (0161) 833 4333

By Kendals, a branch of the "reliable" Argentinean steak chain notable for "doing what it does very well"; the setting, in an old church, is "spectacular". / **Sample dishes:** grilled sweetbreads served with chimichurri & lemon; lobster & shrimp cured in a lime, coconut & citrus sauce with red onion, jalapeño & coriander. **Details:** www.gauchorestaurants.co.uk; 10.30 pm, 11 pm.

Great Kathmandu £ 20

140 Burton Rd M20 1JQ (0161) 434 6413

A large local fanclub hails the "amazing" Nepalese food at this West Didsbury fixture – it's "a bit rough and ready, but welcoming and always packed". / **Sample dishes:** lamb makhan chara; gulab jamun. **Details:** www.greatkathmandu.com; near Withington hospital; midnight.

305

Green's £ 35

43 Lapwing Ln M20 2NT (0161) 434 4259

This popular West Didsbury veggie again attracted mixed feedback; fans praise its "imaginative and very filling fare" – critics, though, find it "too big for its boots", with a "limited" menu, "run-of-the-mill" cooking and "cramped" seating. / Sample dishes: deep-fried oyster mushrooms; filo pastry strudel with leeks, mushrooms, tomato & ricotta; sticky toffee & Guinness pudding. Details: www.greensrestaurant.net; 4m S of city centre; 10.30 pm; closed Mon L & Sat L; no Amex.

The Greenhouse £ 21

331 Great Western St M14 4AN (0161) 224 0730

"A long-established veggie gem" – a "quirky" and "inexpensive" spot, in a Rusholme end-terrace, that's still "going strong". / Sample dishes: baby new potatoes in a spicy sauce with lime pickle & hot pita bread; bangers & mash with red onion gravy; rhubarb crumble & custard. Details: www.dineveggie.com; 11.30 pm; Mon-Sat D only, Sun L & D; no Amex.

Grinch £ 29

5-7 Chapel Walks, off Cross St M2 1HN (0161) 907 3210

Just off St Anne's Square, a "convenient" and "inexpensive" venue with a "good", vaguely Boho atmosphere; it's "ideal for a quick cheap eat". / Sample dishes: garlic bread; special fried chicken; home-made sticky toffee pudding. Details: www.grinch.co.uk; 10 pm.

Jam Street Cafe £ 15

209 Upper Chorlton Rd M16 0BH (0161) 8819944

"Friendly" and "casual", this Whalley Range café/bar is hailed by some reporters as the home of "Manchester's best breakfast"; more generally, the fare is "always fresh, and usually locally-sourced".

Jem and I £ 34

School Ln M20 6RD (0161) 445 3996

"It rivals the Lime Tree nowadays", says a fan of this "swish" Didsbury operation; overall ratings suggest it's not yet there on the service or ambience fronts, but the "brilliant" food is well up with that of the market leader. / Sample dishes: salmon fishcakes, dressed leaves & basil mayonnaise; grilled turbot with lobster ravioli; chocolate pudding & pistachio ice cream. Details: www.jemandirestaurant.co.uk; 10 pm; closed Mon L.

Juniper £ 55

21 The Downs WA14 2QD (0161) 929 4008

"Well-deserves its Michelin star", or "doesn't live up to the hype"? – the debate about Paul Kitching's "challenging" (Fat Duck-esque) cooking rages on; what is pretty clear, though, is that service at his Altrincham venture could usefully be improved. / Sample dishes: warm confit of saffron-smoked haddock; tender-cooked saddle of venison; tarte Tatin of dried fruits. Details: www.juniper-restaurant.co.uk; 9.30 pm; closed Mon, Tue L, Wed L, Thu L & Sun.

Koh Samui £ 31

16 Princess St M1 4NB (0161) 237 9511

"The decor is starting to look a little weary", at this Chinatown-fringe basement; the odd critic says the food is *"living on past glories"* too, but for the most part reporters still hail this as *"an excellent Thai eatery"*. / **Sample dishes:** duck spring rolls; stir-fried chicken with chilli & basil; Bailey's ice cream. **Details:** www.kohsamuirestaurant.co.uk; opp City Art Gallery; 11.30 pm; closed Sat L & Sun L.

Kro Bar £ 22

325 Oxford Rd M13 9PG (0161) 274 3100

Any visitor to Manchester should know about the trendy Danish-run Kro empire of bars and cafés; renowned locally for their *"good-value food and friendly service"*, they're particularly popular for breakfast. / **Sample dishes:** Caesar salad; chicken breast cooked in lemon, soy sauce, honey, garlic & thyme; banana split with toffee sauce . **Details:** www.kro.co.uk; 9 pm; no Amex; children: 18+ .

The Lime Tree £ 40

8 Lapwing Ln M20 2WS (0161) 445 1217

"We always leave happy" – typical feedback on this *"lively"* West Didsbury institution of two decades' standing; despite its low-key style, it remains Manchester's most acclaimed non-ethnic restaurant, thanks to its *"high quality"* and its *"always-reliable"* standards. / **Sample dishes:** honey & chilli roast pork belly with oriental salad; roast loin of lamb; velvet chocolate tart. **Details:** www.thelimetreerestaurant.co.uk; 10 pm; closed Mon L & Sat L.

Little Yang Sing £ 36

17 George St M1 4HE (0161) 228 7722

Often claimed by fans to be *"better than big brother"*, this Chinatown basement is the original (and now much-extended site) of the Yang Sing; it's certainly an *"ever-reliable"* choice serving a *"vast and competently-prepared"* menu. / **Sample dishes:** spare ribs; sweet & sour chicken; deep-fried ice cream. **Details:** www.littleyangsing.co.uk; 11.30 pm.

Livebait £ 42

22 Lloyd St M2 5WA (0161) 817 4110

"Consistently good" fish and seafood makes this city-centre outfit very popular, and some reporters claim that it's the *"best member"* of the (mainly London) chain of which it forms a part. / **Sample dishes:** crab gratin thermidor; seared sea bass fillets; bitter chocolate tart. **Details:** www.santeonline.co.uk; 10.30 pm.

Lounge 10 £ 49

10 Tib Ln M2 4JB (0161) 834 1331

"A real Manchester one-off" – this *"completely OTT-camp"*, *"eccentric"*, *"boudoir"*-style restaurant is the place to go if you're looking *"to woo and be wooed"*; few reports actually mention the food, but it rarely gives cause for complaint. / **Sample dishes:** tournedos of salmon, spiced lentils & sautéed lamb's liver; caramelised skate wings with pineapple & mussel curry; raspberry Alaska. **Details:** www.lounge10manchester.com; 10.30 pm, Fri & Sat 11 pm, Sun 9 pm; closed Sat L.

Love Saves The Day £ 21
345 Deansgate M3 4LG (0161) 834 2266
*"For a good coffee or a lite bite", this "brilliant" deli/café wins
a strong thumbs-up (and it's also "great for breakfasts and brunch").*
/ **Sample dishes:** *pancakes with fried bacon & maple syrup; bangers & mash.*
Details: *www.lovesavestheday.co.uk; 7 pm Mon & Tues, 8 pm Weds & Fri, 9 pm
Thurs, 6 pm, 4 pm Sun.*

The Lowry
The Lowry Centre £ 30
Pier 8, Salford Quays M50 3AZ (0161) 876 2121
*By the standards of cultural centre dining, this "modern, light and
airy" Salford dining space makes a notably "pleasant" destination;
it's "very good value at lunchtime" too. / **Sample dishes:** Bury black
pudding & Lancashire cheese hash, poached egg, English mustard dressing;
rump of lamb, pea & mint purée & bubble & squeak with caramelised shallot
dressing; poached rhubarb & ginger hazelnut oat crumble.*
Details: *www.thelowry.com; 45min prior to performance; L only, D on
performance nights only.*

The River Restaurant
Lowry Hotel £ 58
Chapel Whf M3 5LH (0161) 827 4041
*As fairly "corporate" venues go, the handily-located riverside dining
room of this five-star hotel has its uses; otherwise – despite cooking
that's "pretty good" – the whole style of the place can seem rather
"soulless". / **Sample dishes:** foie gras saute; roast sea bass; apple tart.*
Details: *www.thelowryhotel.com; 10.30 pm; booking: max 8.*
Accommodation: *165 rooms, from £230.*

Luso £ 37
63 Bridge St M3 3BQ (0161) 839 5550
*A new "modern Portuguese with an interesting selection of wines",
which everyone agrees "promises much"; fans say it delivers too with
"first class" food – to critics, though, "its heart's in the right place"
but its "inconsistent" and prone to "making compromises".*
/ **Details:** *www.lusorestaurant.co.uk .*

The Market £ 42
104 High St M4 1HQ (0161) 834 3743
*For "real character" and "that rare personal touch", it's hard to beat
this "cramped" Northern Quarter veteran of over a quarter-century's
standing; "despite the danger of getting sentimental about such
places", there's a feeling that it's "delivering strongly" at present.
/ **Sample dishes:** dried ham & asparagus baked in filo with garlic butter;
beef fillet; Manchester pavlova with custard cream, toasted coconut flakes &
raspberry sauce.* **Details:** *www.market-restaurant.com; 10 pm; closed Sun-Tue &
Sat L.*

Metropolitan £ 35
2 Lapwing Ln M20 2WS (0161) 374 9559
*In West Didsbury, a "big old pub, converted into a smart gastropub";
it enjoys a strong reputation locally for its "substantial and well-
prepared" fare. / **Sample dishes:** black pudding salad; open seafood ravioli;
treacle tart.* **Details:** *www.the-metropolitan.co.uk; near Withington hospital;
11 pm.*

Moss Nook £ 59

Ringway Rd M22 5NA (0161) 437 4778

The style "may lack inventiveness", but "friendly" service – "they do have their tongues in their cheeks when they raise the cloches with a flourish!" – and consistently good cooking make this long-established French restaurant an extremely "trustworthy" Wythenshawe destination. / *Sample dishes:* pan-fried foie gras with a red wine jus; lobster set on crab gateau; chocolate dessert.
Details: www.mossnookrestaurant.co.uk; on B5166, 1m from Manchester airport; 9.30 pm; closed Mon, Sat L & Sun; children: 12+. *Accommodation:* 1 room, at about £120.

Mr Thomas's Chop House £ 38 ⭐

52 Cross St M2 7AR (0161) 832 2245

For its fans, this "distinctive" tavern – complete with "original Victoria décor" – is "The ONLY place for lunch in the city-centre"; "classic British staples" are served in "very large portions" – "heavy on the waistline, but easy on the pocket". / *Sample dishes:* corned beef hash cake & poached egg; braised blade of beef & pan-fried fillet of beef; banana crème brûlée. *Details:* www.tomschophouse.com; 9.30 pm; closed Sun D.

Oca £ 30 ⓣ

Waterside Plaza M33 7BS (0161) 962 6666

Even if not quite living up to its initial promise, this "stylish" Sale Italian is still tipped for its "dependable" food ("especially pizza") and its "pleasant" canalside location. / *Sample dishes:* baked field mushroom with cheese & rocket; chicken Caesar salad pizza; apple crumble.
Details: www.ocarestaurant.co.uk; 11 pm, 9.30 Sun; no Amex.

Pacific £ 29 ⭐

58-60 George St M1 4HF (0161) 228 6668

"Classy food is well served" – on both the ground (Chinese) and first (Thai) floors – of this two-storey oriental, whose "smart" modern style makes it "a bit different from most of Chinatown"; "lunchtime specials are very good value". / *Sample dishes:* prawn dumplings; sweet & sour chicken; chinese custard buns. *Details:* www.pacificrestaurant.co.uk; 11.30 pm.

Palmiro £ 34 ⭐

197 Upper Chorlton Rd M16 0BH (0161) 860 7330

Standards can be "hit-and-miss", but this somewhat "austere" Whalley Range Italian still excites a good volume of praise for "simple" and "seasonal" dishes that are "occasionally sublime".
/ *Sample dishes:* Affettati; whole char-grilled seabream with salmoriglio sauce; chocolate tart. *Details:* www.palmiro.net; 10.30 pm; D only, ex Sun open L & D; no Amex.

Piccolino £ 38 Ⓐ

8 Clarence St M2 4DW (0161) 835 9860

"Busy", "lively" and "fun" – this "extremely popular" city-centre Italian (part of a national chain) is quite a local "scene" thanks not least to its "top-quality, thin-base pizzas". / *Sample dishes:* carpaccio; sea bass; chocolate fudge cake.
Details: www.individualrestaurantcompanyplc.co.uk; 11 pm, Sun 10 pm.

Punjab Tandoori £ 21 ⭐⭐

177 Wilmslow Rd M14 5AP (0161) 225 2960

"A Curry Mile restaurant that's worth going out of your way for" – if you're looking for "real Indian food" (including "legendary" dosas), this is the place. / *Details:* midnight.

Red Chilli £ 28

70-72 Portland St M1 4GU (0161) 236 2888

*"Wow it sets your taste buds tingling!" – this "impressive" and "very popular" Chinese is "a real find", even in a city with such a strong oriental restaurant tradition; "take a walk on the wild side" – "fiery" Sichuan dishes are the highpoint of its "superb and authentic" menu. / **Details:** www.redchillirestaurant.co.uk; 11 pm; need 6+ to book.*

The Restaurant Bar & Grill £ 40

14 John Dalton St M2 6JR (0161) 839 1999

*A "buzzy" vibe makes this city-centre "front-runner" an "unbeatable choice for business lunching" (or for local "celebrity spotting"); standards of its "limited" menu are usually "solid" enough. / **Sample dishes:** fried chilli squid with Thai noodle salad; crispy duck; dark chocolate brownie with Mascarpone.* **Details:** *www.individualrestaurantcompanyplc.co.uk; 11 pm; booking: max 8 at weekends.*

Rhubarb £ 42

167 Burton Rd M20 2LN (0161) 448 8887

*"The seating density can seem just too much" – otherwise there's nothing but praise for this "friendly" West Didsbury "home from home", which serves "tastefully-prepared food (with influences from around the globe)". / **Sample dishes:** porcini risotto; pan-fried fillet of sea bass; rhubarb crème brûlée.* **Details:** *www.rhubarbrestaurant.co.uk; 10 pm, Mon Tue Wed 9.30pm, Sun 8.30pm ; D only, ex Sun open L & D.*

El Rincon £ 29

Longworth St, off St John's St M3 4BQ (0161) 839 8819

*"The genuine Spanish article"; this tucked-away basement tapas bar, off Deansgate, has a "reliably fantastic" atmosphere, and the food is "tasty" too; "tapas chains take note... this is how it should be done". / **Sample dishes:** albóndigas; paella; cheesecake. **Details:** off Deansgate; 11 pm.*

Sam's Chop House £ 40

Back Pool Fold, Chapel Walks M2 1HN (0161) 834 3210

*"Traditional British dishes" – for example "huge steak 'n' kidney pies with jugs of gravy" – are served in an "un-fussy" environment at this Victorian-style city-centre basement; feedback is not entirely consistent, but mainly a hymn of praise. / **Sample dishes:** corn beef hash, steak & kidney pudding; sirloin steak; chocolate fondant.* **Details:** *www.samschophouse.com; 9.30 pm; closed Sun D.*

San Carlo £ 39

40 King Street West M3 2WY (0161) 834 6226

*Totally eclipsing its Brum and Bristol siblings, this "big bustling and modern" Italian, behind Kendals, has quite a fan club; occasionally "scatty" service notwithstanding, it's "always packed". / **Details:** www.sancarlo.co.uk; 11 pm.*

**Second Floor Restaurant
Harvey Nichols** £ 51

21 New Cathedral St M1 1AD (0161) 828 8898

*"Much-maligned in your 2007 guide", or "a pretentious place that's full of yuppies" – fans (in the ascendant) and critics hold sharply divergent views on this department-store restaurant; there's some agreement, though, that it's "good for people-watching" (and also "for breakfast or brunch"). / **Sample dishes:** asparagus; fillet of beef; three orange desserts.* **Details:** *www.harveynichols.com; 10.30 pm; closed Mon D & Sun D.*

Shimla Pinks £ 30

Dolefield, Crown Sq M3 3EN   (0161) 831 7099

This "refreshingly different" establishment – one of the few upmarket subcontinentals in town – moved to new premises during the course of our survey year; we'll have to wait for the next edition for a proper appraisal, but feedback suggests that standards are always at least "pretty good". / **Sample dishes:** tandoori salmon; murgh khas korma; kundan kaliya. **Details:** www.shimlapinksmanchester.com; opp Crown Courts; 11.30 pm, Sat & Sun 11 pm; closed Sat L & Sun L.

Simply Heathcote's £ 42 ❌

Jackson Row, Deansgate M2 5WD   (0161) 835 3536

It's very odd that the city-centre brasserie which is effectively home base for Paul Heathcote, the North West's leading chef/restaurateur, is his most disappointing operation; there are supporters, but there are too many critics to whom it's just a "dead" place, with "mediocre" food and "disinterested" staff. / **Sample dishes:** black pudding; roast duck breast; bread & butter pudding. **Details:** www.heathcotes.co.uk; near Opera House; 10 pm.

Stock £ 50

4 Norfolk St M2 1DW   (0161) 839 6644

With its "superb" setting – the old Stock Exchange – this city-centre Italian certainly makes a "stylish" rendezvous, especially for a business lunch; "service can be slow, though, and the menu is not always well-executed". / **Sample dishes:** Tuscan ham with marinated goat's cheese; rack of lamb; coffee crème brûlée with crumbled meringue. **Details:** www.stockrestaurant.co.uk; 10 pm; closed Sun.

Tai Pan £ 23

81-97 Upper Brook St M13 9TX   (0161) 273 2798

This "impersonal" but "efficient" operation – in a large shed-like structure in Longsight – is "still one of the safest bets for Chinese". / **Sample dishes:** dim sum; spare ribs; ice cream. **Details:** 11 pm, Sun 9 pm.

Tai Wu £ 25 ⭐

44 Oxford St M1 5EJ   (0161) 2366557

"The menu in English is good, but the one in Chinese is sublime", at this "busy" and "brilliant-value" central oriental; it's "the size of a work canteen, and even has a bargain buffet basement, but service is swift and pleasant". / **Sample dishes:** yang chow fried rice with pineapple; skewered chicken in blackcurrant sauce; steamed seabass & shredded pork with lemon. **Details:** www.tai-wu.co.uk; 2.45 am.

Tampopo £ 26

16 Albert Sq M2 5PF   (0161) 819 1966

For a "light", "fresh" and "interestingly different" bite at "reasonable prices", this noodle bar near the Town Hall continues to be a popular recommendation. / **Sample dishes:** prawns fried in coconut breadcrumbs; tender strips of beef; ginger crème brûlée. **Details:** www.tampopo.co.uk; 11 pm; need 7+ to book.

This & That £ 7 ⭐

3 Soap St M4 1EW   (0161) 832 4971

"A great feed for £4!"; that's the deal at this "very friendly" and "always-reliable" Northern Quarter canteen, renowned locally for its "fresh and tasty curries". / **Sample dishes:** onion bhaji; rice with three curries. **Details:** 4.30 pm, 11pm fri&sat; no credit cards.

Wing's £ 40 ⭐

1 Lincoln Sq M2 5LN (0161) 834 9000

Don't be put off by the "overwhelming aura of football celebrity" – this "consistently good" city-centre oriental is "all-round above-average". / **Sample dishes:** *salt & pepper spare ribs; quick-fried sea treasures; toffee banana with ice cream.* **Details:** *www.wingsrestaurant.co.uk; midnight, Sun 11 pm; no trainers; children: 11+ after 8 pm Mon-Fri, 21+ at D .*

Wong Chu £ 23 Ⓣ

63 Faulkner St M1 4FF (0161) 236 2346

"A good stand-by for a quick and filling meal when in a hurry or when Chinatown's more celebrated names are full up". / **Details:** *midnight; no Amex.*

Yang Sing £ 31 ⭐⭐

34 Princess St M1 4JY (0161) 236 2200

"Possibly unmatched this side of Hong Kong" – Manchester's most famous contribution to UK gastronomy remains "a beacon of excellent Cantonese fare", with banquets and "impeccable" dim sum the top menu tips (or "get the staff to decipher the Chinese menu"); a "vibrant" ambience helps offset the "rather drab" décor. / **Sample dishes:** *steamed dim sum; stir-fried monkfish & king prawns; coconut marshmallow bunny.* **Details:** *www.yang-sing.com; 11.30 pm.*

MARKET HARBOROUGH, LEICESTERSHIRE 5–4D

Han's £ 26 Ⓣ

29 St Mary's Rd LE16 7DS (01858) 462288

A well-established Chinese restaurant, that's "a culinary saviour in this thinly-served part of the world". / **Sample dishes:** *crispy aromatic duck; garlic & chilli chicken; toffee fruits.* **Details:** *11 pm; closed Sat L & Sun.*

MARLBOROUGH, WILTSHIRE 2–2C

Coles Bar & Restaurant £ 48

27 Kingsbury St SN8 1JA (01672) 515004

In a thin area, a "friendly" bar/restaurant, where the food is "simple and well presented", and where the atmosphere is usually pretty "lively". / **Sample dishes:** *baked pistachio nut tartlet; pan-fried halibut fillet on a lemon, caper & parsley risotto; chocolate nemesis with home-made short bread.* **Details:** *www.colesrestaurant.co.uk; 10 pm; closed Sun; no Amex.*

The Harrow at Little Bedwyn £ 68 A ⭐⭐

Little Bedwyn SN8 3JP (01672) 870871

*It's no inn!; with its "superb" food and its "60-page wine list", Roger and Sue Jones's establishment is a country restaurant of the highest order; let's hope its recognition by the French tyre people doesn't wreck it! / **Sample dishes:** lobster & langoustine ravioli; turbot with wild mushrooms & mash; ginger & lime brûlée.*

Details: *www.theharrowatlittlebedwyn.co.uk; 9 pm; closed Mon, Tue & Sun D; no Amex.*

MARLOW, BUCKINGHAMSHIRE   3–3A

Compleat Angler £ 61

Marlow Bridge SL7 1RG (0870) 400 8100

*This famous Thames-side dining room has traded shamelessly on its location in recent years; mid-survey it re-opened after a major reformatting, now with the name of (unchanged) chef Dean Timpson over the door; we're not hugely optimistic that much will really have changed but, in the circumstances, no rating is appropriate. / **Sample dishes:** sautéed scallops with potato, tomato & sardine terrine; fillet of beef; apricot soufflé & hazelnut ice cream.*

Details: *www.compleatangler-hotel.co.uk; 9.15 pm; no jeans or trainers.*
Accommodation: *64 rooms, from £208.*

The Oak Room ⭐⭐

Danesfield House Hotel £ 81

Henley Rd SL7 2EY (01628) 891010

*With his "original" cuisine, new chef Adam Simmonds is really putting this elegant country house hotel on the map; all early reports – including of a "superb" tasting menu – confirm that the standard of cuisine is nothing short of "excellent". / **Sample dishes:** seared scallops with Jerusalem artichoke purée, apple jelly; poached turbot, garlic leaf pannacotta & wild asparagus; poached English rhubarb with blackcurrent mousse, custard ice cream, drop scones & apple foam.*

Details: *www.danesfieldhouse.co.uk; 3m outside Marlow on the A4155; 9.30 pm; no jeans or trainers.* ***Accommodation:*** *87 rooms, from £260.*

Hand & Flowers £ 45 A ⭐

West St SL7 2BP (01628) 482277

*"When you can get in, it really is worth it!"; Tom Kerridge's "atmospheric" and "relaxed" country pub-conversion has rightly won a massive fan club thanks to his "simple" but "subtle" cooking; it's "nice to see some real English dishes on the menu too" (notes a French reporter). / **Sample dishes:** glazed omelette & smoked haddock; fillet of plaice with salt cucumber; black Provencale tarte.*

Details: *www.thehandandflowers.co.uk; 9.30 pm; closed Sun D; no Amex.*

Marlow Bar & Grill £ 41
92-94 High St SL7 1AQ (01628) 488544
A "wildly successful" ("noisy") town-centre brasserie, recommended
by reporters for all types of occasion — "with friends"… "for ladies
who lunch"… "with kids"… "as a place to be seen"; given all these
competing attractions, the food is of "surprisingly high quality" too!
/ *Sample dishes:* crispy duck spring rolls; salmon fishcakes; chocolate brownies.
Details: www.individualrestaurants.co.uk; midnight; booking essential.

Royal Oak £ 33
Frieth Rd, Bovingdon Grn SL7 2JF (01628) 488611
"It's unpretentious, but everything works", says a fans of this old pub,
just outside the town, which attracted much positive feedback;
a harsher view is that it "has all the right ingredients, but could
do more with them". / *Sample dishes:* devilled lamb's kidneys;
pan-roast lamb rump; chocolate fudge cake. *Details:* www.royaloakmarlow.co.uk;
half mile up from Marlow High Street; 10 pm.

The Vanilla Pod £ 53
31 West St SL7 2LS (01628) 898101

Fans generally find this "pretty old house" a congenial setting in which
to enjoy Michael McDonald's "light and precisely-cooked" fare;
this year saw a few disasters servicewise — hopefully put right by the
appointment of a new manager, shortly before this guide went
to press. / *Sample dishes:* scallops with vanilla; rump of lamb niçoise; bitter
chocolate fondant with liquid pistachio centre. *Details:* www.thevanillapod.co.uk;
10 pm; closed Mon & Sun.

MARTON, NORTH YORKSHIRE 8–4C

The Appletree Inn £ 40
YO62 6RD (01751) 431457
Staff who "treat all customers as if they were special" are often
praised in feedback on this olde-worlde inn; it has been substantially
revamped in recent times, and its food is uniformly well-rated.
/ *Sample dishes:* brûléed English goat's cheese with peppered tomato salad;
confit belly of pork with black pudding & gravy mustard sauce; black & blue
martin mess. *Details:* www.appletreeinn.co.uk; 9.30 pm; closed Mon & Tue.

MASHAM, NORTH YORKSHIRE 8–4B

Black Sheep Brewery Bistro £ 35 ⭐
Wellgarth HG4 4EN (01765) 680101
"A good variety of food and superb beer, brewed on the premises"
helps make this rustic brewery-annexe an all-round crowd-pleaser.
/ *Sample dishes:* Riggwelter casserole; sheepy salad; sticky toffee sponge.
Details: www.blacksheep.co.uk; 9 pm; Sun-Wed L only, Thu-Sat L & D; no Amex.

Samuel's
Swinton Park **£ 57**
HG4 4JH (01765) 680900
This "swish but not snobbish" country house hotel (set in 200 acres)
offers an "excellent", if "expensive", all-round experience; the location
is "wonderful", service "delightful", and Andy Burton's food is "light
and delicious". / **Sample dishes:** sautéed sea scallops with truffle & cauliflower
purée; fillet of sea bass with sea asparagus & tomato jelly.
Details: www.swintonpark.com; 9.30 pm; no Amex; no jeans or trainers; children:
8+ at D. **Accommodation:** 30 rooms, from £150.

MATFEN, TYNE & WEAR 8–2B

The Library and Print Room
Maften Hall **£ 42**
NE20 ORH (01661) 886500
The dining room of a rather "splendid" country house hotel (golf club
and spa), particularly tipped as "great value for Sunday lunch in the
heart of Northumberland". / **Sample dishes:** smooth game liver parfait with
pear chutney; baked halibut with crisp Parma ham, wilted pak choi & roast cherry
tomatoes; blackcurrant cheesecake with cassis syrup.
Details: www.matfenhall.com; 9.30 pm, 10 pm Sat & Sun; D only, except Sun
open L & D; no jeans or trainers; booking: max 10. **Accommodation:** 19 rooms,
from £135.

MAWGAN PORTH, CORNWALL 1–4B

Bedruthan Steps Hotel **£ 42**
TR8 4BU (01637) 860555
"Floor-to-ceiling windows overlooking the sea" – "if you're lucky,
you may even see a dolphin" – help set the scene at this family-
owned hotel; as well as very decent food there's an "excellent choice
of wines". / **Sample dishes:** quail on green bean & watercress salad with
oriental sauce & sesame seeds; pot roasted breast of chicken with shallot rosti,
sage & thyme jus; calvados parfait with cider-roasted apples.
Details: www.bedruthanstepshotel.co.uk; 9 pm; no Amex; no jeans or trainers.
Accommodation: 101 rooms, from £80.

MAWGAN, CORNWALL 1–4B

New Yard Restaurant **£ 40**
Mawgan TR12 6AF (01326) 221595
An upmarket café in the former stables of an ancient estate on the
Lizard; a small fan-club rates it very highly. / **Sample dishes:** carpaccio
of beef with cheese & cress salad; lobster thermidor; chocolate fondant & whisky
ice cream. **Details:** www.trelowarren.com; 9.15 pm; closed Sun D; no Amex.

MEDBOURNE, LEICESTERSHIRE 5–4D

Horse & Trumpet **£ 45**
12 Old Grn LE16 8DX (01858) 565000
Gary Magnani is a "passionate" chef and his three-year-old
restaurant with rooms, in a "lovely village", gathers a fair number
of reports; extras, though, can bump up the bill. / **Sample dishes:** crab
salad; hickory-smoked duck; Valrhona chocolate mousse.
Details: www.horseandtrumpet.com; 9.30 pm; closed Mon & Sun D; no Amex;
children: 12+ at D. **Accommodation:** 4 rooms, from £75.

MEIKLEOUR, PERTH & KINROSS 9–3C

Meikleour Hotel £ 30

PH2 6EB (0125) 088 3206

*"A small pub serving food, and with a separate small dining room",
tipped for its high standards across the board.* / **Sample dishes:** haggis;
smoked salmon. **Details:** www.meikleourhotel.co.uk; 9.30 pm; no Amex.
Accommodation: 5 rooms, from £120.

MELBOURN, CAMBRIDGESHIRE 3–1B

Sheene Mill £ 45

Station Rd SG8 6DX (01763) 261393

*"Perfect views of a millpond awash with swans, ducks and other
wildfowl"* create *"a fabulous setting"* at this well-known location; since
Steven Saunders's sold to Venture Inns in late-2006, however, ratings
(and feedback) have *"gone downhill"*. / **Sample dishes:** crispy-fried
soft-shelled crab; mignons of beef; dark chocolate terrine.
Details: www.sheenemill.co.uk; off A10, 10m S of Cambridge; 9 pm; closed
Sun D. **Accommodation:** 9 rooms, from £95.

MELBOURNE, DERBYSHIRE 5–3C

Bay Tree £ 46

4 Potter St DE73 8HW (01332) 863358

"Imaginative" 'New World' cuisine makes Rex Howell's
"accommodating" former coaching inn very popular with reporters;
in fact, its main problem is that it can be *"a bit of a zoo"* at peak
times. / **Sample dishes:** scallops; breast & confit of guinea fowl; coriander &
lychee sorbet. **Details:** www.baytreerestaurant.co.uk; 10 pm; closed Mon &
Sun D.

Ruskins £ 42

2 Blanchcroft DE73 1GG (01332) 864170

Penny Lee's *"fine dining BYO restaurant"* is a *"local gem"*, consistently
praised for its *"seasonal"* and *"generous"* cuisine. / **Sample dishes:** rack
of lamb; seafood linguine; confit duck leg. **Details:** 9 pm; closed Mon, Tue, Wed,
Thu L & Sun; no credit cards; booking essential.

MELMERBY, CUMBRIA 8–3A

Village Bakery £ 30

CA10 1HE (01768) 881811

The all-day café attached to the famous bakery is tipped for
a *"nice range of reasonably-priced food"*, including *"a breakfast that's
worth getting up for"*. / **Sample dishes:** vegetable soup; carrots & coriander
roulade; fruit pie of the day. **Details:** www.village-bakery.com; 10m NE of Penrith
on A686; L only; no Amex; need 6+ to book.

MILTON KEYNES, BUCKINGHAMSHIRE 3–2A

Jaipur £ 33

599 Grafton Gate East MK9 1AT (01908) 669796

"Vast" purpose-built Indian – THE place locally – with *"stunning"*
(if not especially atmospheric) décor, and *"good-quality"* food.
/ **Sample dishes:** samosas; duck masala; lemon cake. **Details:** www.jaipur.co.uk;
11.30 pm; no trainers.

MOBBERLEY, CHESHIRE 5–2B

Plough And Flail £ 36
Paddock Hill Ln WA16 7DB (01565) 873537
A "busy" but "relaxed" gastropub that sometimes seems "pricey";
generally, though, reporters feel that the food is of a "high standard".
/ **Sample dishes:** baked pork ribs in a savoury sticky sauce; corn fed chicken with
celery heart & tarragon cream; steamed ginger parkin cake with vanilla ice
cream & caramel sauce. **Details:** www.thedeckersgroup.com; 9.30 pm, 10 pm
Fri & Sat, 8 pm Sun; closed Sun L.

MOFFAT, DUMFRIES & GALLOWAY 7–1C

Well View Hotel £ 39
Ballplay Road DG10 9JU (01683) 220184
"A very small dining room" in a traditionally-styled, small Borders
hotel "providing personal service to hotel residents and others".
/ **Sample dishes:** roast rump of lamb in red wine sauce.
Details: www.wellview.co.uk; Leave M74 junction 15 into central Moffat, leave
A708 towards Celkirk and half a mile from town centre turn left onto Ballplay
Road; 7:30pm; no Amex; children: 6+. **Accommodation:** 3 rooms, from £110.

MOLD, FLINTSHIRE 5–2A

56 High St. £ 33
56 High St CH7 1BD (01352) 759225
A "modern but charming restaurant", tipped for its "interesting"
dishes from a "good choice of ingredients", and "reasonably-priced"
too. / **Sample dishes:** mixed fish grill; lobster. **Details:** www.56highst.com;
9.30 pm, Fri & Sat 10.30 pm; closed Mon & Sun; no Amex.

MONKS ELEIGH, SUFFOLK 3–1C

The Swan Inn £ 34
The St IP7 7AU (01449) 741391
"Still functioning as a village pub" – this agreeable establishment
is tipped for its "remarkably good food at the price", and a
"very fairly-priced wine list". / **Sample dishes:** crispy peking duck salad,
hoi sin sauce, finished with shredded cucumber & spring onions; roast duck
breast on a compote of aubergines, cherry tomato & basil, served with gratin
dauphinoise; iced brandy mousse. **Details:** www.monkseleigh.com; 9 pm; closed
Mon & Tue; no Amex.

MONMOUTH, MONMOUTHSHIRE 2–2B

The Stonemill £ 42
NP25 5SW (01600) 716273
An "ancient and delightful farmhouse", praised for its "sound"
cooking and its "friendly" and "effective" service.
/ **Details:** www.thestonemill.co.uk; 9 pm, Fri & Sat 9.30; no Amex.
Accommodation: 6 cottages rooms, from £40.

Morston Hall £ 62
⭐⭐

Main Coast Rd NR25 7AA (01263) 741041

*Despite Galton Blackiston's "increasing media exposure", his "consistently excellent" small country house hotel remains "a beacon of excellence in an unadventurous part of the world"; a "relaxed" place, it displays "impressive attention to detail" nonetheless. / **Sample dishes:** steamed chicken & Rocquefort mousse; roast loin of lamb; bourbon vanilla crème brûlée with blood orange sorbet. **Details:** www.morstonhall.com; between Blakeney & Wells on A149; 8 pm; D only, ex Sun open L & D. **Accommodation:** 13 rooms, from £125.*

Beetle & Wedge Boathouse £ 43

Ferry Ln OX10 9JF (01491) 651381

*For "real Wind-in-the-Willows atmosphere", it's hard to beat this Thames-side rôtisserie (which, when the adjacent hotel was still open, used to trade as 'The Boathouse'); the food – if "pricey" – is usually "enjoyable", and the arrival of a new Aussie chef seems to be raising standards. / **Sample dishes:** artichoke hearts; escalope of veal; crème brûlée. **Details:** www.beetleandwedge.co.uk; on A329 between Streatley & Wallingford, take Ferry Lane at crossroads; 9.30 pm. **Accommodation:** 1 room, at about £90.*

Black Bull £ 60

DL10 6QJ (01325) 377289

*It's still earlyish days for the new régime at this famous pub, known for its excellent fish (and for the option of dining in a "lovely, if uncomfortable" old Pullman railway carriage); most reports say it's "still a reliable performer", but they are less numerous than they were. / **Sample dishes:** smoked salmon pâté; herb-roast rack of lamb; coeur à la crème. **Details:** www.blackbullmolton.co.uk; 1m S of Scotch Corner; 9.30 pm, Fri & Sat 10 pm; closed Sun D; children: 7+.*

Cornish Range £ 39
Ⓣ

6 Chapel St TR19 6SB (01736) 731488

*Fans say "you can always count" on this small restaurant-with-rooms, a short walk from the harbour, thanks not least to its "fine, fresh seafood". / **Sample dishes:** crispy belly pork with hogs pudding, crushed new potatoes & poached egg; crab & pea risotto with flaked poached salmon & citrus crème fraîche; steamed treacle & orange sponge pudding. **Details:** www.cornishrange.co.uk; on coast road between Penzance & Lands End; 9.30 pm, 9 pm in Winter; no Amex. **Accommodation:** 3 rooms, from £80.*

Old Coastguard Hotel   **£ 39**

TR19 6PR   (01736) 731222

"A great location", "fabulous views" and a "lovely garden" are the outstanding features of this "modern" seaside hotel; the local fish, oysters and crab, however, also come recommended.

/ **Sample dishes:** *pan-fried gurnard with lemon & pinenut tabouleh & herb purée; duck breast, sarladaise potato, foie gras, poached cherries.*
Details: *www.oldcoastguardhotel.co.uk; 9.30 pm.* **Accommodation:** *20 rooms, from £90.*

MYLOR BRIDGE, CORNWALL   1–4B

The Pandora Inn   **£ 35**   Ⓐ

Restronguet Creek TR11 5ST   (01326) 372678

A "beautiful" location – on a creek, with moorings and showers for visiting yachties – helps keep this well-known inn "frenetically busy"; the food (in the bar or restaurant) is not the main event, but mostly well-rated. / **Sample dishes:** *marinated sea bass; whole roast sea bream; red wine & cinnamon poached pear.* **Details:** *www.pandorainn.co.uk; signposted off A390, between Truro & Falmouth; 9 pm, 9.30 fri sat; no Amex.*

NANT-Y-DERRY, MONMOUTHSHIRE   2–2A

The Foxhunter   **£ 48**   ★

Abergavenny NP7 9DN   (01873) 881101

A husband and wife team deliver "excellent", "Welsh/Italian" food at this former stationmaster's house; service – "attentive without being irritating" – impresses too. / **Sample dishes:** *spaghetti with crab, chilli, garlic, parsley & bisque sauce; rack of lamb, buttered spinach, peas, broad beans & mint; St Emilion au chocolat.* **Details:** *www.thefoxhunter.com; 9.30 pm; closed Mon & Sun; no Amex.* **Accommodation:** *2 cottages rooms, from £125.*

NANTGAREDIG, CARMARTHENSHIRE   4–4C

Y Polyn Bar & Restaurant   **£ 40**   Ⓣ

SA32 7LH   (0870) 042 4659

"Quality" cuisine commends this pub/restaurant run (amongst others) by ex AA-guides supremo Simon Wright and his wife – "the only downside is its popularity, which can make it hard to get a table!" / **Sample dishes:** *chicken liver parfait with plum & apple chutney; smoked salmon.* **Details:** *www.ypolyn.co.uk; 9 pm; closed Mon, Sat L & Sun D; no Amex.*

NANTWICH, CHESHIRE   5–3B

Rookery Hall   Ⓣ
Hand Picked Hotels   **£ 56**

CW5 6DQ   (01270) 610016

A country house hotel, tipped not only for its "olde worlde" surroundings, but also for its "excellent" food ("complemented by a very good wine list"). / **Sample dishes:** *asparagus with toasted crumpet, poached free range egg, truffle hollandaise sauce & crisp pancetta; rabbit loin wrapped in dried ham, braised rabbit leg, champ potatoes, apple purée & Calvados sauce; orange crème brûlée with warm madeleine orange millefeuile.*
Details: *www.rookeryhallhotel.com; 9.30 pm; closed Sat L; no jeans or trainers.* **Accommodation:** *70 rooms, from £135.*

NETHER BROUGHTON, LEICESTERSHIRE   5–3D

Red House   **£ 42**

23 Main St LE14 3HB   (01664) 822429

The "dreary" location does this gastropub no favours, but a number
of reporters tips it as a "winner", thanks not least to its
"very passable" fare (and in an area that's otherwise "not brilliantly
served"). / **Sample dishes:** black pudding & poached egg tart; rib-eye steak
with fat chips, garlic sugarsnap peas & peppercorn sauce; iced Malteser parfait
with chocolate sauce. **Details:** www.the-redhouse.co.uk; 9.30 pm; closed Sun D;
no Amex. **Accommodation:** 8 rooms, from £60.

NETTLEBED, OXFORDSHIRE   2–2D

White Hart   **£ 32**

High St RG9 5DD   (01491) 641245

"Imaginative fish specials", "good-value mid-week lunch menus" and
a "good ambience in the bistro" (as opposed to the restaurant) are
particular attractions of this country inn (nowadays revamped
in minimalist style). / **Sample dishes:** crab cake, spring onion risotto & chilli
oil; lobster fishcake, squid ragu & roast peppar coulis; sticky toffee pudding.
Details: www.whitehartnettlebed.com; Between Wallingford & Henley-on-Thames
on the A430; 9.30 pm. **Accommodation:** 12 rooms, from £95.

NEW FOREST (BEAULIEU), HAMPSHIRE   2–4D

The Terrace
Montagu Arms Hotel   **£ 53**

SO42 7ZL   (01590) 612324

The surprisingly smart (but unatmospherically-lit) dining room of a
grand village inn; food and service can be "great" (but even fans can
feel the menu is "wildly overpriced"). / **Sample dishes:** seared scallops,
lentil & coriander sauce; loin of pork with Jerusalem artichoke purée & hazelnut;
hot chocolate & orange fondant with banana ice cream.
Details: www.montaguarmshotel.co.uk.

NEW MILTON, HAMPSHIRE   2–4C

Chewton Glen   **£ 82**

Christchurch Rd BH25 6QS   (01425) 275341

This famous country house hotel – with its "wonderful" New
Forest location – often inspires reports of "faultless" cuisine and
"top quality" service in line with its "luxurious" reputation; as quite
a few reporters note, however, "boy, do you pay for it".
/ **Sample dishes:** cannon of lamb; roast scallops & truffle mash; passion fruit &
ginger crème brûlée. **Details:** www.chewtonglen.com; on A337 between New
Milton & Highcliffe; 9.30 pm; children: 5+. **Accommodation:** 58 rooms,
from £290.

NEWARK, NOTTINGHAMSHIRE 5–3D

Café Bleu £ 37 Ⓐ⭐
14 Castle Gate NG24 1BG (01636) 610141
"The best place for miles around"; this "dynamic" bistro-style
operation is "always of a good standard" and its "varied" menu
(with "Asian/French fusion" touches) has rightly won it a big local
reputation. / **Sample dishes:** *Parma ham & fig salad; baked fillet of cod;
chocolate pudding.* **Details:** *www.cafebleu.co.uk; 9.30 pm; closed Sun D;
no Amex.*

NEWBURY, BERKSHIRE 2–2D

The Crab at Chieveley £ 58 ⭐⭐
Wantage Rd RG20 8UE (01635) 247550
"David Barnard deserves a medal for his passion and originality",
says a fan of this "quirky" spot, which – "in spite of the inland
location" – has won renown for the "best fish and seafood around"
(and in "massive portions" too); service, though, can be "somewhat
offhand". / **Sample dishes:** *red mullet; roast John Dory; chocolate fondant with
Murphy's ice cream.* **Details:** *www.crabatchieveley.com; M4 J13 to B4494 –
0.5 mile on right; 9.30 pm.* **Accommodation:** *14 rooms, from £160.*

Yew Tree Inn £ 46
Hollington Cross, Andover Rd RG20 9SE (01635) 253360
*Marco Pierre White's village pub occupies a "delightful" old inn,
and mostly wins praise for "very fine, restaurant-quality food"; service,
though, is occasionally "shocking" – it's "not what you'd expect"
of such a famed chef (unless, of course, you've visited some of his
London places…). / **Sample dishes:** *croustade of quail's eggs Maintenon;
loin of venison au poivre noir; soufflé of raspberries.*
Details: *www.yewtree.tablesir.com; 9:30 pm, 9pm sun.* **Accommodation:** *6
rooms, from £60.*

NEWCASTLE UPON TYNE, TYNE & WEAR 8–2B

Although Newcastle is a famously going-out kind of place –
with most of the action centred around the Quayside – it has
not traditionally been considered a great quality restaurant
destination. It is therefore impressive that it now boats
a number of surprisingly upmarket success-stories such as the
Black Door, Brasserie Black Door, Cafe 21 (which re-located
this year), *Fisherman's Lodge* and *Jesmond Dene House.*

On the ethnic front, interest tends to be focussed
on subcontinentals, in which context *Rasa* (an import from
London) and *Vujon* stand out.

Barn Under A Wandering Star £ 41
217 Old Jesmond Rd NE1 4D9 (0191) 2211000
"The third incarnation of the 'Barn' brand, but as good as ever" –
this latest manifestation of this peripatetic "local institution" continues
to please. / **Sample dishes:** *wasabi, sake & salt-cured salmon; beef fillet with
chilli; hazelnut, caramel & dark chocolate tart.* **Details:** *10 pm; closed Sun.*

Black Door £ 58 ⭐⭐

32 Clayton Street West NE1 5DZ   (0191) 2616295

"Top-notch" – and sometimes "memorable" – food figures in many reports on the city's most commented-on restaurant, by St Mary's Cathedral; not all reporters are convinced that the service or setting quite lives up – perhaps new premises, being sought as this guide goes to press, will help provide the answer? / Sample dishes: black pudding with poached egg; assiette of lamb with aubergine, tomato confit & fondant potato; lavender parfait with caramelised almonds.
Details: *www.blackdoorgroup.co.uk; 10 pm; closed Mon & Sun.*

Blackfriars Restaurant £ 39 Ⓐ

Friars St NE1 4XN   (0191) 2615945

A 13th-century refectory provides the home for this "classy but hidden-away city-centre eatery"; fans praise its "interesting menu" and its "reliable food", but there are critics who find it "overpriced and complacent". / Sample dishes: seafood sampler; fillet steak; Belgian chocolate & lavender panna cotta. Details: www.blackfriarsrestaurant.co.uk; 10 pm; closed Sun D.

Brasserie Black Door £ 45 ⭐

Biscuit Factory, Stoddard St NE2 1AN   (0191) 260 5411

"Very good cooking" – in a "less adventurous style than the parent restaurant, which will suit many people better" – wins fans for this "minimalist" new operation in the Biscuit Factory (an art gallery); a few critics, though, complain of "small portions" and "overpricing". / Sample dishes: home-made black pudding, pear purée, toasted brioche, & pea shoots; fillet of black bream, saute potatoes, chorizo, curry vinaigrette; iced lemon parfait with strawberry soup & pistachios. Details: www.brasserieblackdoor.co.uk; 10 pm; closed Sun D.

Café 21 £ 46

Trinity Gdns NE1 2HH   (0191) 222 0755

"A consistent and reliable Quayside venue which never fails to please" – that's the gist of most of the many reports on local hero Terry Laybourne's original venture, which, for many, is "still the best place in Newcastle"; it moved post-survey to a new, bigger home down the Quay – hence we've left it un-rated. / Sample dishes: grilled tiger prawns with lemon & thyme risotto; braised fillet of sea bass; chocolate & hazelnut truffle. Details: www.cafetwentyone.co.uk; 10.30 pm.

Café Royal £ 31

8 Nelson St NE1 5AW   (0191) 231 3000

"Always too busy, but usually worth the wait" – this city-centre grand café is a "lively" place to "watch the world come and go"; its "fresh and well-prepared" fare is "always good"; it's as a brunch spot, though, that the place is a particular smash hit. / Sample dishes: wild mushroom open lasagne; glazed crab omelette with dried ham & asparagus; white chocolate & cardamom crème brûlée. Details: www.sjf.co.uk; 6pm; L only, ex Thu open L & D.

Caffe Zonzo £ 28

87-89 Goldspink Ln NE2 1NQ   (0191) 2304981

"Simple rustic cooking at incredible prices" wins (almost) invariable raves for this suburban Sardinian; a no-booking joint, it's always "busy". / Sample dishes: vegetable soup with home-baked rustic bread; rack of lamb on brown lentils; millefeuille with Strega liqueur custard.
Details: *www.caffezonzo.com; 9.15 pm; closed Sun; no Amex.*

Fisherman's Lodge £ 70 ⭐

Jesmond Dene NE7 7BQ (0191) 281 3281

*This "serene oasis", set in the parkland of Jesmond Dene, remains a "classy" venue for "occasion" dining; the food – with a strong fish emphasis – is "consistently very good" ("as it should be, at the prices"), and "good-value" lunches come particularly recommended. / **Sample dishes:** seared scallops; pan-fried sea bass with truffle gnocchi; raspberry mousse with white chocolate joconde.*
Details: www.fishermanslodge.co.uk; 2m from city centre on A1058, follow signposts to Jesmond Dene; 10 pm; closed Mon & Sun.

Francesca's £ 21 🅐⭐

Manor House Rd NE2 2NE (0191) 281 6586

*This "happy and lively cantina" – "known locally as 'The Trat'" – is quite a "Tyneside institution"; "it's nothing fancy, but offers good quality and great value". / **Sample dishes:** king prawns; sea bream; home-made tiramisu. **Details:** 9.30 pm; closed Sun; no Amex; no booking.*

Heartbreak Soup £ 34

77 The Quayside NE1 3DE (0191) 222 1701

*Some find its style "romantic" – others a bit rough and ready – but this long-established Quayside bistro remains popular for its "eclectic" and "fairly-priced" grub; window seats offer "a wonderful vista over the Tyne" too. / **Sample dishes:** sesame beef skewers; paprika-smoked lamb; white chocolate cheesecake.*
Details: www.heartbreaksoup.com; 10 pm; closed Mon & Sun; no Amex or Switch.

Jesmond Dene House £ 52 🅐⭐

Jesmond Dene Rd NE2 2EY (0191) 212 3000

*"Another triumph for Terry Laybourne"; thanks not least to the "accomplished" cuisine, most reporters hail this "stylish" yearling – in a "terrifically-located" 'Arts & Crafts' mansion – as "a great asset to Newcastle". / **Sample dishes:** ravioli of lobster with basil shellfish velouté; fillet of sea bass with sea scallops; Grand Marnier soufflé with warm chocolate sauce. **Details:** www.jesmonddenehouse.co.uk; 10.30 pm. **Accommodation:** 40 rooms, from £160.*

King Neptune £ 31

34-36 Stowell St NE1 4XQ (0191) 261 6657

*"It's standard Chinese fare, but the place is always busy", say fans of this twenty-year-old oriental; "if you want Chinese in the North East it's the only place to go" (well, nearly) – which the odd reporter feels is the only reason for its popularity. / **Sample dishes:** spring rolls; lemon chicken; caramel ice cream. **Details:** 10.45 pm.*

McCoys Rooftop at the Baltic
Baltic £ 58

South Shore Rd NE8 3BA (0191) 440 4949

*"There's been a big improvement in the cooking over the past year", at this top-floor arts-centre dining room; even so, many reporters still think prices are "outrageous", and say it has a "pleasant atmosphere and great views" but "unremarkable" food and service. / **Sample dishes:** roast scallops & slow-cooked belly pork; seared loin of venison; raspberry Alaska with raspberry jelly & white chocolate beignet.*
Details: www.mccoysbaltic.com; 9.45 pm; closed Sun D.

Open Kitchen £ 42 ⭐

Moor Court Annexe NE3 4YD (0191) 285 2909

"Dining is a personal experience," at this *"tiny but excellent"* outfit, in Gosforth, where *"a short menu of local food"* is *"done extremely well"*. / **Sample dishes:** ham & peas pudding; char-grilled calves' liver & smoky bacon dumplings; chocolate & Brazil nut torte.

Details: www.theopenkitchen.co.uk; 9.30 pm; D only, ex Sun open L & D; booking essential.

Pani's £ 28 Ⓐ

61-65 High Bridge NE1 6BX (0191) 232 4366

"There's always a warm welcome, and usually a high noise level" at this *"Italian legend"*, near Grey's Monument; the food may only be *"good"* to *"ordinary"*, but the is *"THE cheap and cheerful"* place in town. / **Sample dishes:** antipasto sardo; char-grilled venison liver; panna cotta. **Details:** www.paniscafe.co.uk; off Gray Street; 10 pm; closed Sun; no Amex; no booking at L.

Paradiso £ 36

1 Market Ln NE1 6QQ (0191) 221 1240

"A good variety of high-quality Mediterranean-style food" wins popularity for this large city-centre venue; there's some feeling, though, that the cooking *"is not as good as it used to be"*. / **Sample dishes:** tiger prawns; tuna steak; chocolate & pecan pudding with Turkish ice cream. **Details:** opp fire station; 10.30 pm, 11 pm Thu, Fri, Sat, 6 pm Sun; closed Sun D; no Amex.

Prickly Pear £ 52 Ⓐ

5-7 The Side NE1 3JE (0191) 232 5537

"Good for business, romance or a celebration"; this *"small"* Quayside fixture doesn't inspire a huge amount of feedback, but it's all very positive; look out for *"frequent good-value deals"* (and *"book ahead if you want one of the two window-seats!"*). / **Sample dishes:** charred king prawns & Asian salad; roast fillet of cod; baked rhubarb cheesecake with muesli crunch. **Details:** beneath Tyne Bridge on Quayside; 10 pm; closed Sun.

Rasa £ 33 ⭐⭐

27 Queen St NE1 3UG (0191) 232 7799

"It's so far ahead of other Newcastle curry houses, they should pack up", say fans of the *"authentically Keralan, and absolutely delicious"* food at this epic South Indian – the legendary Rasa Group's only restaurant outside London. / **Sample dishes:** malabar lamb curry; masala dosas. **Details:** www.rasarestaurants.com; 11 pm; closed Sun.

Sachins £ 26

Forth Banks NE1 3SG (0191) 261 9035

A *"popular"* Bangladeshi restaurant, praised by most – if not quite all – reporters for its *"original and different"* cuisine. / **Sample dishes:** karahi gosht; murg karahi; kulfi. **Details:** www.sachins.co.uk; behind Central Station; 11.15 pm; closed Sun.

Sale Pepe £ 25

115 St George's Ter NE2 2DN (0191) 281 1431

"Very bustling and busy" – this neighbourhood Italian pleases all reporters as a *"great, casual place to eat"*, serving *"delightfully crispy pizzas"*. / **Sample dishes:** bruschetta; ham & mushroom pizza; ice cream. **Details:** 10.30 pm; closed Sun.

Secco Ristorante Salentino £ 44 Ⓐ
86 Pilgrim St NE1 6SG (0191) 230 0444
*"It's the best Italian in town", say fans of this popular three-floor joint,
who praise its "consistent" all-round standards; the décor is "love-it-or-
hate-it", and doubters find the whole performance "average and
featureless". / Sample dishes: bocconcini di pollo; arrosto misto di carne;
crostata di prugne. Details: www.seccouk.com; 10 pm; closed Mon & Sun.*

Vujon £ 34 ★
29 Queen St NE1 3UG (0191) 221 0601
*A Quayside veteran that currently seems to be on top form, and is
undoubtedly "Newcastle's best place for a curry". / Sample dishes: kati
kebab; gustaba; rasmalai. Details: www.vujon.com; 11.30 pm; closed Sun L.*

NEWENT, GLOUCESTERSHIRE 2–1B

Three Choirs Vineyards £ 45 Ⓣ
GL18 1LS (01531) 890223
*"Idyllic" views and an "excellent" wine list win recommendations for
the dining room at this leading English vineyard; the food,
in comparison, is "fairly average", but still "enjoyable".
/ Sample dishes: loin of lamb with garlic hash brown & red wine sauce; roast rib
of beef & Yorkshire pudding; chocolate mousse with chocolate sauce.
Details: www.threechoirs.com; 9 pm; no Amex. Accommodation: 8 rooms,
from £95.*

NEWICK, EAST SUSSEX 3–4B

Ⓐ★

Newick Park
Newick Park Hotel £ 58
BN8 4SB (01825) 723633
*This privately-owned country house hotel provides a "wonderful"
setting; combine it with Chris Moore's "really delicious" cuisine,
and you have a "delightful" all-round experience.
/ Sample dishes: smoked salmon & lobster paupiette; rump of lamb; crème
brûlée with shortbread. Details: www.newickpark.co.uk; off Church Rd; 8.45 pm;
booking essential. Accommodation: 16 rooms, from £165.*

NEWPORT, NEWPORT 2–2A

The Chandlery £ 39 Ⓐ
77-78 Lower Dock St NP20 1EH (01633) 256622
*"An extremely enjoyable location in a dead-end area" – this "superb"
refit of a 19th-century commercial building wins consistent praise
from a loyal (older) fan club. / Sample dishes: slow-cooked shank of spring
lamb; duck breast; griottine cherry & frangipane tart.
Details: www.thechandleryrestaurant.com; at the foot of George St bridge on the
A48 (hospital side); 10 pm; closed Mon, Sat L & Sun.*

Cnapan Country House £ 39 Ⓣ
East St SA42 0SY (01239) 820575
*"Innovative handling of excellent local fare in wholesome dishes" –
the attraction of this "wonderfully friendly, little family-run
hotel/restaurant". / Sample dishes: grilled goat's cheese, Portobello
mushroom, & fig crostini with walnut dressing; medallions of wild venison; light
lemon surprise pudding. Details: www.cnapan.co.uk.*

Junction 28   **£ 36**

Station Approach NP10 8LD (01633) 891891

*It's not just "a must for rail enthusiasts"! – this converted station
(complete with replica dining carriage) in Bassaleg offers
an "interesting" menu of "satisfying" dishes. / **Sample dishes:** wood
pigeon breast home-cooked in hickory smoke with pickled red cabbage & creamed
celeriac; fillet of brill with a king prawn dumpling, poached in a Thai broth; bitter
chocolate tart with caramelised banana & rum ice cream.*
***Details:** www.junction28.com; off M4, J28 towards Caerphilly; 9.45 pm; closed
Sun D.*

NEWQUAY, CORNWALL   1–3B

Fistral Blu   **£ 37**   Ⓐ

Fistral Beach, Headland Rd TR7 1HY (01637) 879444

*"Delicious fish dishes eaten on the edge of the ocean" – this informal
hang-out offers a wide-ranging menu, plus "gorgeous" views of the
famous surfers' beach and beyond. / **Sample dishes:** seared Cornish
scallops served with rocket salad, saffron & lemongrass jam; timbale of prawns &
crab on a bed of mixed leaves & served with a coriander & mango coulis.
Details: www.fistral-blu.co.uk; 10 pm.*

NEWTON LONGVILLE, BUCKINGHAMSHIRE 3–2A

Crooked Billet   **£ 37**   ⭐

2 Westbrook End MK17 0DF (01908) 373936

*A "gastronomic" village pub that's "worth a detour off the M1",
thanks to its food which is "very good bordering on excellent";
a "great wine list is all available by the glass" too.
/ **Sample dishes:** cauliflower & leek soup; lamb rack with deep-friend
sweetbreads; chocolate & cardamon mousse, almond praline, poached cherries.
Details: www.thebillet.co.uk; 9.30 pm, 10 pm Fri & Sat; D only, ex Sun open
L only.*

NEWTON-ON-THE-MOOR, NORTHUMB.   8–2B

Cook & Barker   **£ 35**

NE65 9JY (01665) 575234

*Just off the A1, "a great all-rounder" – this "brilliant" and "busy" inn
is widely praised for its "excellent and wide-ranging menu"; "kids love
it" too. / **Sample dishes:** smoked salmon; beef fillet stuffed with stilton; pistachio
meringue. **Details:** www.cookandbarkerinn.co.uk; 12m N of Morpeth, just off A1;
9 pm. **Accommodation:** 19 rooms, from £70.*

NOMANSLAND, WILTSHIRE   2–3C

Les Mirabelles   **£ 37**   ⭐⭐

Forest Edge Rd SP5 2BN (01794) 390205

*"Surprisingly good food in such an out-of-the-way location";
this "charming, little provincial Gallic bistro" – in a "beautiful" New
Forest location – continues to win the highest praise for its "terrific",
"French-accented" cuisine. / **Sample dishes:** goat's cheese with spinach &
hazelnuts; fillet of cod wrapped in Parma ham; vanilla crème brûlée. **Details:** off
A36 between Southampton & Salisbury; 9.30 pm; closed Mon & Sun.*

Nutter's £ 45
Edenfield Rd OL12 7TT (01706) 650167
Fans say TV-cook Andrew Nutter is "still a great chef", and even a self-confessed competitor of this "theatrical" restaurant suggests it does what it sets out to do well; some dishes though can seem "poorly thought out" (and with "far too many ingredients").
/ ***Sample dishes:*** crispy duck confit with garlic fries; medallions of pork with ginger & soy dumplings; banana, white chocolate & toffee cheesecake.
Details: www.nuttersrestaurant.com; between Edenfield & Norden on A680; 9.30 pm; closed Mon; closed 2 weeks in Aug.

Beechwood Hotel £ 46 ⭐
Cromer Rd NR28 0HD (01692) 403231
"Wonderful locally-sourced, well-prepared food, served with a flourish" inspires a small but ardent fan club for this traditionally-styled hotel, a short drive from the coast. / ***Sample dishes:*** smoked haddock & spinach tartlet with curry ice cream; crab cakes with tzatziki dressing.
Details: www.beechwood-hotel.co.uk; 9 pm; D only, ex Sun open L & D; no Amex; children: 10+ at D. ***Accommodation:*** 17 rooms, from £120.

Betty's £ 35 ⭐
188 High St DL7 8LF (01609) 775154
A new outlet of this famous chain of "proper" tea shops, offering the "very traditional" formula that's long commended it to reporters; all the usual features are here: "it's quite pricey", and "be prepared to queue". / ***Sample dishes:*** salads; tea; cakes. ***Details:*** www.bettys.co.uk; 5. 30 pm.

McCoys at the Tontine £ 51
DL6 3JB (01609) 882 671
This "lovely old restaurant" ("oddly positioned by a dual carriageway") has been in business for over three decades, and is still "always busy"; "it has the potential to be better than it is", though, especially and there's some agreement among reporters that it's "overpriced".
/ ***Sample dishes:*** boudin noir with sauce gribiche; fillet of beef; vanilla crème brûlée & rhubarb compote. ***Details:*** www.mccoysatthetontine.co.uk; junction of A19 & A172; 9.30 pm; bistro L & D every day, restaurant Sat D only.
Accommodation: 6 rooms, from £120.

Hundred House £ 38 Ⓣ
Bridgnorth Rd TF11 9EE (01952) 730353
"A very welcome gastro-haven in a pretty barren part of the world foodwise". / ***Sample dishes:*** chicken liver pâté with brioche; pork chops; double chocolate mousse with orange anglaise. ***Details:*** www.hundredhouse.co.uk; on A442 between Bridgnorth & Telford; 9.30 pm. ***Accommodation:*** 10 rooms, from £99.

NORTON, STOCKTON ON TEES 8–3C

Cafe Lilly £ 35 (A)
83-85 Norton High St TS20 1AE (01642) 554422
"A simply-furnished café-restaurant, which is elegantly beautiful and airy, in a comfortable sort of way"; it's a "busy" place too, thanks to the quality of its "well-presented" Sardinian fare.
/ **Sample dishes:** Moroccan lamb. **Details:** 9 pm; closed Sun; no Amex.

NORWICH, NORFOLK 6–4C

Brummells £ 46 (T)
7 Magdalen St NR3 1LE (01603) 625555
A "fascinating" 17th-century building in the city-centre houses this characterful dining room; the food is of high quality, but the service can sometimes be weak. / **Sample dishes:** monkfish fritters; grilled halibut steak with wild mushrooms & basil compote; amaretto & dark chocolate pot.
Details: www.brummells.co.uk; 10.30 pm.

By Appointment £ 48 (A)(★)
25-29 St George's St NR3 1AB (01603) 630730
"Norwich's best restaurant" benefits from a "terrific" menu, "excellent" hosts and a "charmingly different" setting – "a large room and a series of smaller ones, with lots of antiques about".
/ **Sample dishes:** marinated salmon with dill vinaigrette; apricot & pistachio nut-stuffed roast loin of lamb, with a tomato, honey, garlic & thyme sauce; iced white chocolate parfait. **Details:** www.byappointmentnorwich.co.uk; in a courtyard off Colegate; 9 pm; D only, closed Mon & Sun; no Amex; children: 12+.
Accommodation: 5 rooms, from £110.

Shiki £ 34 (★)
6 Tombland NR3 1HE (01603) 619262
"Confident" Japanese cuisine and "willing" service are among the highlights commending this Tombland spot to all who report on it.
/ **Sample dishes:** agedashi tofu; noodles; Japanese pancake & rice fig.
Details: www.shiki.co.uk; 10.30 pm; closed Sun; no Amex.

Waffle House £ 20
39 St Giles St NR2 1JN (01603) 612790
"It's stuck in the '70s and looks like it's run by vegetarians" but this "cheap and cheerful" survivor is still "well worth a visit"; it's "sometimes crowded, especially during the school holidays".
/ **Sample dishes:** focaccia waffle baked with diced onion & fresh herbs with dressed olives; waffle topped with smoked bacon, sliced tomatoes, & mayonnaise; melon & home-made Italian ice cream. **Details:** www.wafflehouse.co.uk; 10 pm; no Amex; need 6+ to book.

NOSS MAYO, DEVON 1–4C

Ship Inn £ 36 (A)
PL8 1EW (01752) 872387
"A cosy setting on a creek" adds particular charm to this "fairytale" pub, which serves "a simple menu that doesn't get anything wrong".
/ **Sample dishes:** goat's cheese, apple & celery terrine; cod fillet fried in real ale batter with fries & minted mushy peas; pecan & maple syrup cheesecake.
Details: www.nossmayo.com; 9.30 pm; no Amex.

For a city which is not widely seen as a major dining destination, Nottingham harbours a surprisingly impressive core of good-quality restaurants in the middle and upper range, including the long-standing *Hart's*, *World Service*, and – at the top end of the market – *Restaurant Sat Bains*. On the ethnic front, *Mem Saab* is of note, and *Chino Latino* rates mention, despite something of a curate's egg performance.

Atlas £ 8

9 Pelham St NG1 2EH   (0115) 950 1295
"The perfect lunchtime pit stop", offering *"a fantastic range of sandwiches"*, plus *"the best coffee in the country"* (well, almost).
/ **Sample dishes:** *tuna, basil & tomato ciabatta; goat's cheese, artichoke & red pesto; home-made cakes.* **Details:** *L only.*

Cast £ 37

The Playhouse, Wellington Circus NG1 5AN   (0115) 852 3898
"Sit outside and you're in Barcelona, not Nottingham!", when you visit this bar/restaurant next door to the Playhouse; the menu is *"limited"*, though, and food and service have sometimes been surprisingly *"poor"* of late. / **Sample dishes:** *chicken liver parfait; buttered halibut; dark chocolate fondant.* **Details:** *www.castrestaurant.co.uk; 11pm, 4.30pm sun; no Amex.*

Chino Latino
Park Plaza Hotel £ 46

41 Maid Marian Way NG1 6GD   (0115) 947 7444
The *"inventive"* oriental fare *"can be wonderful"*, at this trendy *"fusion"* venue, located off an hotel foyer; it's also *"very expensive"*, though, especially *"given the noisy and non-soothing ambience"*, *"tired"* décor, and service that's *"variable, but never excellent"*.
/ **Sample dishes:** *inside-out chicken wings; beef fillet with sweet chilli jam; chocolate fondant.* **Details:** *www.chinolatino.co.uk; 10.30 pm; closed Sun.*

Crème £ 45

12 Toton Ln NG9 7HA   (0115) 939 7422
A *"spacious"* and *"airy"* establishment on the outskirts of town, tipped for cooking that's *"not overwrought, but with style and good flavours"*. / **Sample dishes:** *pepper-crusted fillet of beef on potato rosti with buttered spinach; gilt headed bream fillet with seared scallop, caviar & crème fraîche.* **Details:** *www.cremerestaurant.co.uk; 10 pm; closed Mon & Sun D; children: 14+.*

Delilahs £ 12
15 Middle Pavement NG1 7DX (0115) 948 4461

An "excellent little deli", where simple dishes are "freshly cooked
to order"; good sandwiches and coffee too. / *Sample dishes:* prosciutto &
Parmesan. *Details:* www.delilahfinefoods.co.uk; 7 pm, Sun 5 pm; no Amex.

French Living £ 32
27 King St NG1 2AY (0115) 958 5885

"Very French and very reliable" – once again the verdict on this "tiny"
and "tucked-away", candlelit city-centre cellar bistro; prices are
"competitive", especially the "very good-value lunch and early-evening
menus". / *Sample dishes:* foie gras terrine with candied plum; fillet of venison
with blueberry sauce; crème brûlée ala vanille de tahiti.
Details: www.frenchliving.co.uk; near Market Square; 10 pm; closed Mon & Sun;
no Amex; booking: max 10.

Georgetown
Colwick Hall Hotel £ 32
Racecourse Rd NG2 4BH (0870) 755 7756

Near the racecourse – "a dining room in a sympathetically-restored
18th-century mansion, offering a wide variety of Malaysian-inspired
oriental food in a colonial ambience". / *Sample dishes:* baked chicken
pieces with pepper; medallions of beef flavoured with lemon grass; small bananas
with pistachio & coconut ice cream. *Details:* www.colwick-hall.co.uk; 10.30pm.
Accommodation: 16 rooms, from £99.

Hart's £ 49
Standard Ct, Park Row NG1 6GN (0115) 911 0666

Tim Hart's "classy" modern brasserie, near the Castle, remains the
best-known place in town; an "extremely efficient" and "reliable"
operation, it "maintains a high standard of cooking"; after a revamp
a couple of years ago, it seems "warmer and less hard-edged" too.
/ *Sample dishes:* fresh crab salad with grapefruit & peashoots; beef fillet;
hot chocolate with Jersey milk ice cream. *Details:* www.hartsnottingham.co.uk;
near Castle; 10.30 pm. *Accommodation:* 32 rooms, from £120.

Iberico £ 35

The Shire Hall, High Pavement NG1 1HN (01159) 410410

A stylish bar in a crypt below the Civic Court – a new option in the ever-more-trendy Lace Market, that opened post-survey; its trendy menu is focussed on tapas, split 50/50 "Spanish-style" and "Global".

Mem Saab £ 38 ⭐⭐

12-14 Maid Marian Way NG1 6HS (0115) 957 0009

"By far the best Indian" in town – this "refined and unpretentious" curry house "reawakens the tastebuds" with an "alternative" range of dishes that are "light, carefully-spiced, and very well-presented". / **Sample dishes:** *lamb chops; Goan fish curry; pistachio kulfi.* **Details:** *www.mem-saab.co.uk; near Castle, opposite Park Plaza Hotel; 10.30 pm; D only; no shorts.*

Merchants Ⓐ
Lace Market Hotel £ 46

29-31 High Pavement NG1 1HE (0115) 958 9898

Many more "very impressive meals" are reported nowadays at this boutique-hotel dining room, with its "high design statement interior"; it's "expensive", though, and the style of service can seem "a bit formal". / **Sample dishes:** *poached egg with Parma ham & rocket leaf salad; lamb rump on braised Savoy cabbage; dark chocolate mousse with espresso ice cream surprise.* **Details:** *www.lacemarkethotel.co.uk; 10.30 pm; closed Mon L, Sat L & Sun.* **Accommodation:** *42 rooms, from £119.*

Petit Paris £ 31

2 Kings Walk NG1 2AE (0115) 947 3767

This "bright and cheerful" first-floor fixture remains a "reliable" and popular local stand-by, thanks to the "consistently high standard" of its "great-value bistro fare"; it's "speedy pre-theatre" too. / **Sample dishes:** *fish soup; duck breast; chocolate & chestnut mousse.* **Details:** *www.petitparisrestaurant.co.uk; near Theatre Royal; 10.15 pm; closed Sun.*

Restaurant Sat Bains £ 82 ⭐⭐

Old Lenton Ln NG7 2SA (0115) 986 6566

Sat Bain's "fabulous" and "very imaginative" cuisine scored top marks from reporters this year (with much praise for his "superb" tasting menus); even fans can still find it "overpriced", though (particularly on the wine front), especially as the room "lacks ambience" and staff can seem "rather young and untrained". / **Sample dishes:** *duck egg with textures of peas; Anjou pigeon, melon, feta, bitter chocolate & grapefruit; chocolate cream, sweet olive oil, toast & sea salt.* **Details:** *www.restaurantsatbains.com; 9.30 pm; D only, closed Mon & Sun; children: 8+.* **Accommodation:** *8 rooms, from £129.*

Victoria Hotel £ 28

Dovecote Ln NG9 1JG (0115) 925 4049

A former railway hotel, by Beeston Station, which is now a "busy real ale pub" (with a "superb wine list" too); its "imaginative" fare (including "good veggie options") is "well-conceived and well-prepared". / **Sample dishes:** *pâté maison; kiln-roasted salmon; Irish toffee pudding.* **Details:** *www.victoriabeeston.co.uk; by Beeston railway station; 8.45 pm; no Amex; no booking, Sun; children: 18+ after 8 pm.*

World Service **£ 49** Ⓐ✪
Newdigate Hs, Castle Gate NG1 6AF (0115) 847 5587
"Having been resting on its laurels" a few years ago, Nottingham's
'in'-crowd favourite has "picked up again in every department";
"efficient" staff serve "splendid" food, matched by a "well-thought-
out" wine list of which "buffs will approve". / **Sample dishes:** *ballotine*
of foie gras; fillet of beef with asparagus & girolle mushrooms; chocolate fondant
with salted almond ice cream. **Details:** *www.worldservicerestaurant.com; 10 pm;*
children: 12+ at D.

OAKMERE, CHESHIRE   5–2B

Nunsmere Hall **£ 58** Ⓣ
Tarporley Rd CW8 2ES (01606) 889100
A country house with a good location, largely surrounded by a lake,
and sometimes tipped as offering "the best dining for miles around";
the fare, though, is arguably on the "predictable" side.
/ **Sample dishes:** *terrine of ham hock with brioche; pan-fried fillet of sea bass;*
chocolate fondant with chocolate icing. **Details:** *www.nunsmere.co.uk; off A49,*
4m SW of Northwich; 10 pm; no jeans or trainers; children: 12+.
Accommodation: *36 rooms, from £205.*

OBAN, ARGYLL & BUTE   9–3B

Ee-Usk (Seafood Restaurant) **£ 41** Ⓐ✪✪
North Pier PA35 5QD (01631) 565666
A strikingly "stylish" spot in a building that's "all wood and glass",
and which has "terrific harbour views" – it provides the "perfect
setting" to enjoy some "terrific" seafood, and "fish that couldn't
be fresher". / **Sample dishes:** *oysters; seared king scallops; clootie dumpling.*
Details: *www.eeusk.com; 9.30 pm; no Amex; children: children 10+ at L,*
not welcome at dinner .

Manor House Hotel **£ 47** Ⓣ
Gallanach Rd PA34 4LS (01631) 562087
"A lovely hotel with sea views", tipped for its "superb food and
friendly service". / **Sample dishes:** *crabcakes with a mango, line & red pepper*
salsa; honey glazed magret of duck with creamed leeks, fondant potatoes &
orange sauce. **Details:** *www.manorhouseoban.com; 8.30 pm.*
Accommodation: *11 rooms, from £193.*

Waterfront Restaurant **£ 37** ✪
1 Railway Pier PA34 4LW (01631) 563110
All reports praise this "busy" restaurant, on the pier, for its "very fresh
and generously-portioned fish dishes"; "they'll even happily tweak
dishes to your requirements". / **Sample dishes:** *seafood chowder with*
scallops, sole, salmon & mussels; cod fillet in anchovy & oregano breadcrumbs,
on Mediterranean veg; steamed chocolate pudding.
Details: *www.waterfrontoban.co.uk; 9.30 pm; no Amex.*

OCKHAM, SURREY   3–3A

Black Swan **£ 39** Ⓣ
Old Ln KT11 1NG (01932) 862364
Fans say this new gastropub "has brought a much-needed option
to an otherwise dull area"; "on the downside, it gets very, very busy
at the weekends". / **Sample dishes:** *butternut & goat cheese cannelloni.*
Details: *www.geronimo-inns.co.uk; 10pm, 6pm on Sun; no Amex.*

OCKLEY, SURREY 3–4A

Bryce's at the Old School House £ 41 ⭐
RH5 5TH (01306) 627430
"An excellent fish-dominated restaurant" that's part of a village pub;
a "friendly" sort of operation, it's tipped for offering "particularly good
value in the bar". / **Sample dishes:** smoked haddock rarebit on toasted
brioche with poached egg & hollandaise sauce; seared king scallops & calves' liver;
cream caramel & toffee ice cream. **Details:** www.bryces.co.uk; 8m S of Dorking
on A29; 9.30 pm; closed Sun D in Nov, Jan & Feb; no Amex.

The Kings Arms £ 36 Ⓣ
Stane St RH5 5TS (01306) 711224
"A lovely old pub-restaurant, recently sympathetically refurbished",
and with a keen local following. / **Sample dishes:** king prawns in garlic
butter with warm French bread; slow-roasted honey & mustard shoulder of lamb
with vegetables; creamy lemon tart with raspberry coulis.
Details: www.thekingsarmsockley.co.uk; A29 S of Dorking; 11 pm.

ODIHAM, HAMPSHIRE 2–3D

The Grapevine £ 43 Ⓣ
121 High St RG29 1LA (01256) 701122
A pleasant village bistro-style operation which continues to impress
(not least as "a pleasant place for a tête-à-tête").
/ **Sample dishes:** grilled salmon with charred asparagus, chilli & lime butter;
barbequed tiger prawns with chilli & lime & a tzatziki dip; blueberry pie with
vinegar ice cream. **Details:** www.grapevine-gourmet.com; follow signs from M3,
J5; 10 pm; closed Sat L & Sun.

St John £ 49 Ⓣ
83 High St RG29 1LB (01256) 702697
A "small" and "cosy" restaurant where the "high-quality food" and
"inventive menus" inspired a couple of very positive reports.
/ **Sample dishes:** monkfish with potatoes, tomato compote & coriander butter;
pan-fried seabass with confit of fennel, grilled potatoes & a ratatouille jus; liquorice
crème brûlée with raspberry sorbet. **Details:** www.stjohn-restaurant.co.uk; 9 pm;
closed Sun.

OLD BURGHCLERE, BERKSHIRE 2–3D

Dew Pond £ 46 ⭐
RG20 9LH (01635) 278408
A "very enjoyable" destination all-round; Keith Marshall's country
house restaurant of nearly 20 years' standing offers "spot-on"
cooking, and the "excellent wine list won't bankrupt you either".
/ **Sample dishes:** seared scallops, pea purée, truffle oil & chorizo; roasted fillet
of turbot, tempura prawns, asparagus, mousseline potato & vermouth sauce.
Details: www.dewpond.co.uk; 6m S of Newbury, off A34; 10 pm; D only, closed
Mon & Sun; no Amex; children: 5+.

ONGAR, ESSEX 3–2B

Smiths Brasserie £ 50 ⭐
Fyfield Rd CM5 0AL (01277) 365578
"A huge selection of fish" – "well cooked and presented" – draws
many supporters to this "busy" and "bustling" establishment, smartly
decorated in contemporary style. / **Sample dishes:** Mediterranean prawns;
lobster thermidor; woodland berry Eton mess. **Details:** www.smithsbrasserie.com;
left off A414 towards Fyfield; 10.30 pm; closed Mon; no Amex; children: 12+.

ORFORD, SUFFOLK   3–1D

Butley Orford Oysterage   £ 32
Market Hill IP12 2LH   (01394) 450277
*"Touristy now, but still good" – this "basic" café has
"the plainest decor" imaginable, but remains a "fun" and highly
popular destination thanks to its "simple, fresh and tasty" fish.
/ **Sample dishes:** "angels on horseback"; skate with brown butter sauce;
chocolate trufito. **Details:** www.butleyorfordoysterage.co.uk; 9 pm;
Mon-Thu L only, closed Sun D in winter; no Amex.*

The Crown & Castle   £ 40
IP12 2LJ   (01394) 450205
*"Posh pub grub" and a "huge selection of interesting wines" help
make Ruth & David Watson's hotel, on the "beautiful Suffolk coast",
a destination that pleases pretty much all reporters (not least as a
"great place for a weekend"). / **Sample dishes:** smoked trout; sea bass with
clams; bitter chocolate mousse with Jersey cream.
Details: www.crownandcastle.co.uk; 9.15 pm; closed Sun D in winter; no Amex;
booking: max 8; children: 9+ at D. **Accommodation:** 18 rooms, from £90.*

ORPINGTON, KENT   3–3B

Xian   £ 29
324 High St BR6 0NG   (01689) 871881
*"Book ahead" if you want a table at this "excellent" and "friendly"
Chinese establishment – it has a big reputation, which is well
supported by feedback on its "sophisticated" cuisine and "thoughtful"
service. / **Sample dishes:** smoked chicken; crispy beef; toffee bananas.
Details: 11 pm; closed Sun L.*

OSMOTHERLEY, NORTH YORKSHIRE   8–4C

Golden Lion   £ 43
6 West End DL6 3AA   (01609) 883526
*This "very friendly" village pub is a destination of note in these parts;
it serves "simple food, well cooked". / **Sample dishes:** white crab with
brown crab mayonnaise; calves' liver; wine-poached pear with chocolate sauce.
Details: 9.30 pm. **Accommodation:** 3 rooms, from £80.*

OSWESTRY, SHROPSHIRE   5–3A

The Walls   £ 29
Welsh Walls SY11 1AW   (01691) 670970
*"Worth a mention" in a thin area; "the ambience is lovely", at this
"beautiful, 19th-century converted school, with high ceilings and
an open fire"; the food "comes in large portions" and "is usually
worth waiting for". / **Sample dishes:** pork schnitzel with lemon, garlic butter;
lamb steak marinated in olive oil, rosemary & garlic. **Details:** www.the-walls.co.uk;
from town centre, take Cross Street, fork right then first left; 9.30 pm; closed
Sun D.*

OUNDLE, NORTHAMPTONSHIRE   3–1A

Falcon Inn   £ 41
Fotheringay PE8 5HZ   (01832) 226254
*A "great old building" in an "ancient" village – till this year part of the
now-defunct Huntsbridge Group – where a "great wine list" is a
hallmark; generally, the food is "very good" too.
/ **Sample dishes:** chicken liver pâté; halibut; sticky toffee pudding.
Details: just off A605; 9.15pm.*

The Bush Inn
£ 33   Ⓐ

SO24 0RE   (01962) 732764

"A wonderful country pub", by a river, "with roaring fires in winter and waterside tables for the summer"; the food is "enjoyable" too. / **Sample dishes:** crab & leek tart; beef wellington; rhubarb, ginger & lemon grass crumble. **Details:** www.wadworth.co.uk; just off A31 between Winchester & Alresford; 9pm.

OXFORD, OXFORDSHIRE
2–2D

Perhaps someone once told Oxford's restaurateurs that superiority should be effortless, as they collectively seem to display complacency on an unequalled scale. Even worse than is the case in Bath, it looks like there's simply too much money chasing too few restaurants in the heart of this wonderful city. If you must eat here, going ethnic is the best advice, and *Chaing Mai* is clearly the top name.

Al Shami
£ 24

25 Walton Cr OX1 2JG   (01865) 310066

"A consistently good place to eat, unchanged after many years" – this Lebanese restaurant in Jericho inspires (almost) unanimously positive reports, especially for its "very good-value mezze". / **Sample dishes:** fried aubergines; tender lamb cubes; Arabic ice cream. **Details:** www.al-shami.co.uk; midnight. **Accommodation:** 12 rooms, from £50.

Aziz
£ 32

228-230 Cowley Rd OX4 1UH   (01865) 794945

Some reports feel the ongoing success of this long-running Bangladeshi – Oxford's best-known curry house – says more about the local culinary scene than it does about the restaurant itself; it's widely rated as a "dependable" destination, nevertheless (and now has an offshoot, on Folly Bridge). / **Sample dishes:** tandoori sheek kebab; lamb rezalla; rasmalai. **Details:** www.aziz.uk.com; 11.15 pm; closed Fri L.

Bangkok House
£ 27

42a High Bridge St OX1 2EP   (01865) 200705

A Thai restaurant, beyond the railway station; it's a "popular" place, thanks to its "tasty" and "reasonably-priced" cuisine. / **Sample dishes:** Bangkok delight; green curry; sticky rice & mango. **Details:** www.bangkokhouseoxford.co.uk; 11 pm; closed Sun.

Bar Meze
£ 32   Ⓐ

146 London Rd OX3 9ED   (01865) 761106

A Turkish restaurant, in Headington, which offers "a fun night out", and where the food is "fine" – but, as one reporter puts it: "it says a lot about Oxford that this OK-but-not-brilliant place is now one of my favourite destinations". / **Sample dishes:** baked houmous; imam bayaldi; baklava. **Details:** www.bar-meze.co.uk; 10.30 pm, 11 pm Fri & Sat.

Bombay
£ 21   ★

82 Walton St OX2 6EA   (01865) 511188

"A popular BYO Indian", in Jericho – a "friendly", "cheap" and "cheerful" sort of place, it attracts almost unanimously positive reviews. / **Sample dishes:** aloo chat; lamb rogan; banana ice cream. **Details:** 11 pm; closed Fri L; no Amex.

Branca £ 39
111 Walton St OX2 6AJ (01865) 556111
A "fun" and "noisy" Jericho Italian; it's "predictable, but it always
seems full, so they must be doing something right".
/ **Sample dishes:** king prawns & bruschetta; roast duck breast & braised lentils;
hazelnut & praline semifreddo. **Details:** www.branca-restaurants.com; 11 pm.

Brasserie Blanc £ 41
71-72 Walton St OX2 6AG (01865) 510999
Fans say there's been "improvement since it split from Loch Fyne" but,
for other reporters, this Jericho brasserie still has "too much of a
chain feel" – it serves "classic" dishes whose realisation falls
somewhere between "reliable" and "underwhelming".
/ **Sample dishes:** truffle foie gras parfait; coq au vin; lemon tart.
Details: www.brasserieblanc.com; 10 pm.

Browns £ 31 ⊗
5-11 Woodstock Rd OX2 6HA (01865) 511995
"My annual visits to this haunt of my student-days are increasingly
disappointing" – typical feedback on this once-celebrated and still-
"buzzy" English bistro, which is often simply "awful" nowadays.
/ **Sample dishes:** steak, mushroom & Guinness pie with mash potatoes & French
beans; panna cotta & caramelised oranges.
Details: www.browns-restaurants.com; 11pm, 11.30pm fri sat, 10.30pm sat;
need 5+ to book.

Café Coco £ 25
23 Cowley Rd OX4 1HP (01865) 200232
Thanks to its "great pizzas with interesting toppings", "obliging
service" and "good atmosphere", it's no surprise that this "eternally
popular" operation is indeed "always heaving". / **Sample dishes:** garlic
bread with houmous; merguez & tzatziki pizza; Belgian waffles & vanilla pot ice
cream with maple syrup. **Details:** 11pm, Sat 12.30am; no booking.

Cafe Sojo £ 18 ⊤
96 Cowley Rd OX4 1JE (01865) 724708
"A small busy place", on the Cowley Road, which – in its early days –
is tipped for "amazing" Chinese cuisine that's "very reasonably
priced". / **Details:** 11 pm; no credit cards.

Cherwell Boathouse £ 37 Ⓐ
Bardwell Rd OX2 6ST (01865) 552746
"Very atmospheric in summer or winter" – this riverside fixture boasts
a "perfect" location and a "really knowledgeable wine selection";
once again, though, there's a growing feeling that "it needs a shake-
up" – "yes you can punt there, but that doesn't make up for the
overpriced food". / **Sample dishes:** battered squid; escalope of spiced pork &
apple wood mash; lemon tart & lemon curd ice cream.
Details: www.cherwellboathouse.co.uk; 9.30 pm .

Chiang Mai £ 37 Ⓐ⭐
Kemp Hall Pas, 130a High St OX1 4DH (01865) 202233
"Thriving under new owners" – the "best restaurant in Oxford"
(by miles) serves "amazing" Thai fare in the rather bizarre but
"lovely" setting of an "atmospheric" Tudor building, just off the High;
unsurprisingly, it's "always crowded". / **Sample dishes:** satay; chicken with
cashew nuts; sticky rice. **Details:** www.chiangmaikitchen.co.uk; 10.30 pm.

Chutney's Indian Brasserie £ 26
36 St Michael's St OX1 2EB (01865) 724241
*This city-centre Indian is "a cut-above most others", and wins
consistent praise for its "wide-ranging menu" of "excellent" dishes
at "reasonable prices".* / **Sample dishes:** *kebab; chicken jafrezi; chocolate ice
cream.* **Details:** *www.chutneysindianbrasserie.co.uk; 11 pm.*

Cibo! £ 34
4 South Pde OX2 7JL (01865) 292321
*"A very jolly place" or an "overpriced local Italian"? – both schools
of thought are represented in reports on this Summertown spot,
but its "neighbourhood" charm wins it majority approval.*
/ **Sample dishes:** *mussels marinara; spaghetti allo scoglio; tiramisu.*
Details: *www.ilovecibo.co.uk; 10.30 pm; no Amex.*

La Cucina £ 29
39-40 St Clements OX4 1AB (01865) 793811
*The locals don't have a bad word to say about this "new, better-than-
average pizza 'n' pasta place" in St Clement's, whose "quick
popularity" stems from its "well-priced" staples and "welcoming"
staff.* / **Sample dishes:** *rocket leaves & roasted cherry tomatoes, with buffalo
Mozzarella, parsley & caper dressing; pizzas; rustic apple cake with vanilla ice
cream.* **Details:** *www.lacucinaoxford.co.uk.*

Edamame £ 18
15 Holywell St OX1 3SA (01865) 246916
*A "tiny Oxford treasure"; the only drawback at this "great, authentic,
Japanese cafe-style eatery", hidden-away near New College, is that it's
"much too popular" (so "you have to queue and share tables").*
/ **Sample dishes:** *baby green soy beans; pan-fried Japanese fishcakes.*
Details: *www.edamame.co.uk; opp New College; 8.30 pm; L only, ex Fri & Sat
open L & D, closed Mon; no Amex; no booking.*

Fishers £ 37
36-37 St Clements OX4 1AJ (01865) 243003
*For many locals, this "bright and basic" fish bistro is an "utterly
reliable" destination that's "the best place in town for quality fish";
as ever, though, there's a minority school of thought that it's "average
in every way".* / **Sample dishes:** *mussels; whole-baked sea bass; Bailey's &
espresso cheesecake.* **Details:** *www.fishers-restaurant.com; by Magdalen Bridge;
10.30 pm; closed Mon L; no Amex.*

Gee's £ 38
61 Banbury Rd OX2 6PE (01865) 553540

*"A beautiful but over-rated posh-nosh spot"; this "lovely" restaurant,
in a "luxurious" and "romantic" conservatory – on the northern fringe
of the city-centre – is "great for a date, but don't expect gastronomic
fireworks".* / **Sample dishes:** *pan-fried foie gras; crab, spring onion & chilli
pasta; dark chocolate mousse with orange.* **Details:** *www.gees-restaurant.co.uk;
10.30 pm.*

The Lemon Tree £ 43

268 Woodstock Rd OX2 7NW (01865) 311936

This popular North Oxford villa's has a "very pretty dining room" and a "lovely" atmosphere; the food is "uninspiring" though – "not yuk, just overpriced and disappointing". / Sample dishes: gambas with spinach basil in tempura batter; marinated steak salad; pistachio & honey semifreddo. Details: www.thelemontreeoxford.co.uk; 1.5m N of city-centre; 11 pm.

Malmaison £ 44

3 Oxford Circle OX1 1AY (01865) 268400

The old castle/prison provides the "unusual" setting for this boutique-hotel dining room; it's no culinary hotspot, but the food is usually "tasty". / Sample dishes: oysters; hamburger with bacon & Gruyère; crème brûlée. Details: www.malmaison.com; 10.30 pm. Accommodation: 94 rooms, from £140.

The Nosebag £ 22

6-8 St Michael's St OX1 2DU (01865) 721033

"Unchanged in 30 years", this no-frills veggie café remains a top tip for those in search of "hearty helpings of nourishing and healthy food". / Sample dishes: smoked mackerel pâté; fennel & Mascarpone risotto with seared prawns; carrot & walnut cake. Details: 10 pm, Fri & Sat 10.30 pm, Sun 9 pm.

The Old Parsonage £ 49

1 Banbury Rd OX2 6NN (01865) 310210

"Lovely place, shame about the food"; this medieval townhouse may have a "great setting" (and a "delightful garden"), but many reporters feel it's "vastly overpriced" and "must try harder... much harder". / Sample dishes: grilled baby artichoke, feta & roast tomato salad; grilled half lobster; chocolate soufflé. Details: www.oldparsonage-hotel.co.uk; 0.5m N of city centre; 10.30 pm. Accommodation: 30 rooms, from £160.

Pierre Victoire £ 32

Little Clarendon St OX1 2HP (01865) 316616

If you're looking for "honest and good-value French food and drink", this candlelit bistro makes an "ever-reliable stand-by". / Details: 11 pm, 10 pm Sun; no Amex.

Quod
Old Bank Hotel £ 38

92-94 High St OX1 4BN (01865) 799599

Jeremy Mogford's "crowded and popular" Italian is touted by some as a "buzzy" city-centre stand-by; as at his earlier creation Brown's, however, too many reporters find it "a shadow of its former self", offering "food that's as lousy as the service". / Sample dishes: buffalo mozzarella, roast tomato & basil salad; fillet steak & fries; chocolate pot. Details: www.oldbank-hotel.co.uk; opp All Souls College; 11 pm; no booking, Sun L. Accommodation: 42 rooms, from £165.

Shanghai 30s £ 35

82 St Aldates OX1 1RA (01865) 242230

"A super new Chinese restaurant, in a beautiful old building with Chinese lamps and furniture"; locals rave over its "beautiful" food and "excellent" service. / Details: www.shanghai30s.com.

The Talkhouse £ 39 ⭐

Wheatley Rd OX33 1EX (01865) 351648

"Marco Pierre White's input to the menu is evident", says one of the fans of this recently refurbished, thatched "gastropub/restaurant" – it offers "delicious local dishes presented with metropolitan fare".
/ **Sample dishes:** black pudding, mustard mash, poached egg; crispy belly of pork with seared sea scallops & apple purée; chocolate orange fondant with citrus crisp. **Details:** www.thetalkhouse.co.uk; 9.30 pm. **Accommodation:** 4 rooms, from £65.

Thai Orchid £ 30 Ⓣ

58a St Clements St OX4 1AH (01865) 798044

It certainly has some hot Thai competition in the city-centre, but this east-Oxford spot is tipped by some locals as an "inexpensive" alternative. / **Sample dishes:** spring rolls; green curry with chicken. **Details:** near Headington Park; 10.30 pm; closed Sat L & Sun L.

OXTON, WIRRAL 5–2A

Fraiche £ 52 ⭐⭐

11 Rose Mount CH43 5SG (0151) 652 2914

One local enthusiast hails it as "the best restaurant north of Ludlow", and – thanks to Marc Wilkinson's "imaginative, witty and precise" cuisine – this "star of the Wirral" is certainly beginning to make quite a name, notwithstanding a "cool" ambience and service some find over-attentive. / **Sample dishes:** poached red mullet; fillet of sea bass; pressed peach tonka bean parfait. **Details:** www.restaurantfraiche.com; 9.30 pm; closed Mon & Sun; no Amex.

PADSTOW, CORNWALL 1–3B

Margot's £ 37 ⭐⭐

11 Duke St PL28 8AB (01841) 533441

"A real Cornish gem"; Adrian Oliver isn't yet world-famous but, according to his numerous fans, his "tiny" bistro is "better value for money than Rick Stein's places"; "excellent local meat and fish" are served at "superb" prices. / **Sample dishes:** seared scallops with Cornish asparagus; rack of lamb; saffron poached pear with baked plums & clotted cream. **Details:** www.margots.co.uk; 9.30 pm; closed Mon L & Tue; closed Jan.

No 6 Café £ 59 ⭐

6 Middle St PL28 8AP (01841) 532093

"A really special experience", on most reports – this "very fancy", if "rather cramped", spot (where head chef Paul Ainsworth is ex-Pétrus) is rated "better than Stein" by most reporters; a small minority finds a tendency to over-elaboration.
/ **Details:** www.number6inpadstow.co.uk; 10 pm; D only Fri- Sun, except for residents.

Rick Stein's Café £ 33 ⭐

10 Middle St PL28 8AP (01841) 532700

Rick Stein's spin-off café is more casual and "fun" than his more famous HQ; even if it's not quite as highly-rated, it's certainly cheaper, and wins praise for its "simple", "lovely" dishes.
/ **Sample dishes:** mussels with chilli, tomatoes & parsley; griddled chicken breast; sunken chocolate cake. **Details:** www.rickstein.com; 9.30 pm; no Amex. **Accommodation:** 3 rooms, from £90.

Seafood Restaurant £ 73
Riverside PL28 8BY (01841) 532700

"The best fish in the UK" just *"speaks for itself"*, according to the legions of fans of TV-chef R Stein's famous, *"unstuffy"* destination, by the harbour of the town he's put on the map; as ever, some feel prices are *"a Rick-off"*, though (and *"over-salting"* of dishes was a repeated quibble this year). / **Sample dishes:** langoustines; char-grilled Dover sole; chocolate fondant. **Details:** www.rickstein.com; opp harbourmaster's car park; 10 pm; no Amex; booking: max 14; children: 3+. **Accommodation:** 14 rooms, from £125.

St Petroc's Hotel & Bistro £ 47
4 New St PL28 8EA (01841) 532700
*Standards seem to be improving at Rick Stein's "lively" bistro; it's still pretty "squashed", though, and service still has its ups and downs. / **Sample dishes:** grilled mackerel salad with sun-dried tomato & fennel seeds; wing of skate au poivre; passion fruit Pavlova. **Details:** www.rickstein.com; 10 pm; no Amex. **Accommodation:** 10 rooms, from £125.*

Stein's Fish & Chips £ 22
South Quay PL28 8BY (01841) 532700
*This "ultimate chippy" is, for some reporters, "the best of Rick Stein's Padstow establishments"; it can seem "pricey", though, and, just occasionally, is let down by its chips! / **Sample dishes:** mackerel; char-grilled monkfish. **Details:** www.rickstein.com; 9 pm, 6pm sun; no Amex.*

PARK GATE, HAMPSHIRE 2–4D

Kam's Palace £ 37
1 Bridge Rd SO31 7GD (01489) 583328
*An "impeccable" Chinese restaurant of long standing; its very loyal local fan club praises its "wide variety of dishes" and "excellent" service. / **Details:** 10.45 pm.*

PARKGATE, CHESHIRE 5–2A

Marsh Cat £ 31
1 Mostyn Sq CH64 6SL (0151) 336 1963
*"Lovely views across the Dee" (with "spectacular sunsets") set a scene for all-round satisfaction at this estuary-side bistro, where most reporters find the food "imaginative" and "well presented"; the establishment was for sale as this guide went to press. / **Sample dishes:** Caribbean trio; Louisiana red snapper with fried softshell crab; sticky ginger pudding, toffee sauce & custard. **Details:** www.marshcat.com; 10 pm.*

PAULERSPURY, NORTHANTS　　　2–1D

Vine House　　　£ 46　　　T
100 High St NN12 7NA　(01327) 811267
"Deserving more of a following" – a restaurant tipped for its
"welcoming" service and food "of high quality".
/ **Sample dishes:** smoked bacon sausage & black pudding terrine topped with
a warm poached egg & home-made ketchup; sirloin of beef with beef dripping,
chips, garlic butter & summer leaf salad; home-made elderflower jelly topped with
honey & lemon syllabub. **Details:** www.vinehousehotel.com; 2m S of Towcester
just off A5; 9.15 pm; closed Mon L-Wed L, Sat L & Sun; no Amex.
Accommodation: 6 rooms, from £95.

PAXFORD, GLOUCESTERSHIRE　　　2–1C

Churchill Arms　　　£ 36
GL55 6XH　(01386) 594000
This "good-all-round Cotswold inn-cum-restaurant" has been run
by Leo & Sonya Brooke-Little for 10 years now; reporters praise it for
its "friendly" attitude and "first-rate pub food".
/ **Sample dishes:** marinated salmon on potato pancake; blade of beef; maple &
Mascarpone cheesecake. **Details:** www.thechurchillarms.com; off Fosse Way;
9 pm; no Amex; no booking. **Accommodation:** 4 rooms, from £70.

PEEBLES, SCOTLAND　　　9–4D

Cringletie House　　　£ 54　　　A
Edinburgh Rd EH45 8PL　(01721) 725750
"In the rolling hills of the Borders", a small country house – Victorian
Baronial in style, but with a 17th-century walled garden – where the
food is "good", on most reports. / **Sample dishes:** assiette of foie gras; fillet
of beef; raspberry torte. **Details:** www.cringletie.com; 9 pm.
Accommodation: 13 rooms, from £220.

PENSHURST, KENT　　　3–3B

Spotted Dog　　　£ 33　　　A
Smarts Hill TN11 8EE　(01892) 870253
"A perfect country pub in a fantastic setting"; it's the sort of place
which does "great" Sunday lunches, and "outstanding" puddings too.
/ **Sample dishes:** pan-fried chicken liver; char-grilled tuna loin; home-made sticky
toffee pudding. **Details:** near Penshurst Place; 9.30 pm; no Amex.

PENZANCE, CORNWALL　　　1–4A

The Bay Restaurant　　　£ 38　　　T
Britons Hill TR18 3AE　(01736) 366890
A "stylish and elegant" contemporary-style operation boasting
a terrace overlooking the town and the sea; its "trying very hard
to get things right". / **Sample dishes:** pressed ham hock & wild rabbit terrine,
summer vegetable dressing; grilled Dover sole, glazed with seaweed & caper
butter; coconut & passion fruit tart with lemon grass syrup & clotted cream.
Details: www.bay-penzance.co.uk; 9.30 pm; closed Sat L & Sun L.
Accommodation: 24 rooms, from £135.

Deans At Let's Eat   £ 44
77-79 Kinnoull St PH1 5EZ   (01738) 643377
*Fans hail the relaunch of this "top-class" restaurant as an "excellent, but somewhat pricey" destination; "the old ambience is missing", though, and not all reporters are impressed. | **Sample dishes:** warm terrine of Ccomte cheese, artichokes & Savoy ham with a sweet & sour onion relish; loin of lamb on herb crushed potatoes, black olives, tomatoes, haricots verts & basil; warm gingerbread pudding, vanilla ice cream & caramel sauce. **Details:** www.letseatperth.co.uk; 9 pm; closed Mon & Sun; no Amex.*

⭐

JSW   £ 58
20 Dragon St GU31 4JJ   (01730) 262030
*Now in "larger and more atmospheric premises" (a former pub), Jake Watkins's celebrated restaurant – with its "excellent" food and its "outstanding" wine list – again seems to be firing on all cylinders. | **Sample dishes:** foie gras & shallot tarte Tatin; honey-roast duck; vanilla parfait with cinnamon beignets. **Details:** 9.30 pm; closed Mon & Sun; no Amex; children: 7+.*

Ⓣ

Roseland Inn   £ 36
TR2 5NB   (01872) 580254
*Near the King Harry Ferry, an "unchanging" pub, especially tipped for its "local seafood". | **Sample dishes:** crab & scallops salad; char-grilled polenta with gazpacho sauce, roast vegetables, & olive oil ice cubes; home-made chocolate brownie. **Details:** www.roselandinn.co.uk; near King Harry ferry; 9.30 pm; no credit cards.*

Ⓐ⭐

White Swan   £ 41
Market Pl YO18 7AA   (01751) 472288
"A town-centre gem, offering interesting food at sensible prices" and an "excellent", "by-the-glass" wine list; one reporter likens it to an "Hotel du Vin-type experience", but – as you'd hope, from an independent – standards seem rather higher.
*| **Sample dishes:** fishcakes & brown shrimp salad; roast pig belly; sticky toffee pudding. **Details:** www.white-swan.co.uk; 9 pm. **Accommodation:** 21 rooms, from £130.*

Friends   £ 44
11 High St HA5 5PJ   (020) 8866 0286
The "personal attention" of chef/patron Terry Farr helps make for a "delightful" experience, say fans of this "small" local favourite in a 16th-century building, which serves "good-value" Gallic cuisine.
*| **Sample dishes:** seared scallops; fillet of sea bass; apricot Tatin with clotted cream. **Details:** www.friendsrestaurant.co.uk; near Pinner Underground station; 9.30 pm; closed Mon & Sun D.*

La Giralda £ 28

66-68 Pinner Grn HA5 2AB (020) 8868 3429

"Quirky (not so young!) waiters" preside over this suburban Spanish veteran; even some fans concede the food is a bit "run-of-the-mill" but it's also "reasonably priced" and "utterly dependable".
/ **Sample dishes:** smoked salmon & prawns; half roast duckling; shortcake & strawberry cream. **Details:** www.lagiralda.co.uk; A404 to Cuckoo Hill Junction; 10 pm; closed Mon & Sun D.

L'Orient £ 46

Ⓐ

58 High St HA5 5PZ (020) 8429 8488

Offering "a good choice of different Asian foods" – and to a consistently high standard – this prettily-housed restaurant has an "excellent ambience" ("especially in the front part").
/ **Sample dishes:** aromatic crispy duck with pancake; coconut-flavoured lamb curry; braised tofu & seasonal vegetables. **Details:** www.lorientcuisine.com; 11 pm.

PLOCKTON, HIGHLAND 9–2B

Plockton Inn £ 28

Innes St IV52 8TW (01599) 544222

"Excellent" seafood and "good real ale too" inspire (generally) very positive reports on this "friendly" inn. / **Sample dishes:** seafood platter; salad with scallops & dill & lime crème fraîche; lemon & ginger crunch pie. **Details:** www.plocktoninn.co.uk; 9 pm; no Amex. **Accommodation:** 14 rooms, from ££84 summer, negotiable winter.

PLUMTREE, NOTTINGHAMSHIRE 5–3D

Perkins £ 35

Old Railway Station NG12 5NA (0115) 937 3695

Now run by the second generation of the Perkin family, this "converted railway station" retains the "friendly" and "good-value" charms that have long made it a popular local stand-by.
/ **Sample dishes:** seared scallops; honey & caraway-roast pork; chocolate & hazelnut torte. **Details:** www.perkinsrestaurant.co.uk; off A606 between Nottingham & Melton Mowbray; 9.30pm; closed Mon & Sun D.

PLUSH, DORSET 2–4B

Brace Of Pheasants £ 35

Ⓣ

DT2 7RT (01300) 348357

"A rural pub in deepest Dorset", tipped for its "idyllic" setting and its "'proper' home-cooked food at sensible prices".
/ **Sample dishes:** pan-fried breasts of wood pigeon on red onion confit, with a Madeira & balsamic reduction; pork & leek sausages with mustard mash & onion gravy. **Details:** www.braceofpheasants.co.uk; 9.30 pm.

PLYMOUTH, DEVON 1–3C

The Barbican Kitchen Brasserie £ 28

Ⓣ

58 Southside St, The Barbican PL1 2LA (01752) 604448

"The new place from the Tanner brothers" – a "laid-back" brasserie intriguingly located in the Plymouth Gin Distillery, tipped for its "simple, fresh local produce". / **Sample dishes:** roast salmon with pesto crushed potatoes; rib-eye steak with peppercorn sauce & skinny chips. **Details:** www.barbicankitchen.com; 9pm; no Maestro.

Chloe's
Gill Akaster House   £ 46
Princess St PL1 2EX   (01752) 201523
*Didier Franchet's two-year-old in the business district is tipped as a
"foodie oasis in the midst of a sea of mediocrity". / **Sample dishes:** foie
gras. **Details:** www.chloesrestaurant.co.uk; 10 pm; closed Mon & Sun.*

Tanners Restaurant   £ 42
Prysten Hs, Finewell St PL1 2AE   (01752) 252001
*"The best place to eat in Plymouth" – the Tanner brothers' "convivial"
fixture in an historic building has "charming" staff and "interesting"
food; the experience can be a bit "variable", though, and there's the
odd concern that the bros are "spreading themselves too thin".
/ **Sample dishes:** terrine of honey & thyme roast chicken; braised & glazed belly
pork with sage polenta; dark chocolate tart with crème fraîche.
Details: www.tannersrestaurant.com; 9.30 pm; closed Mon & Sun.*

POOL-IN-WHARFEDALE, WEST YORKSHIRE 5–1C

White Hart   £ 34
Main St LS21 1LH   (0113) 203 7862
*"Extensively refurbished in recent times", this still-"homely" boozer
is tipped for food that's "always of a high standard".
/ **Sample dishes:** coconut chicken with spinach, coriander, mango chutney & chilli
salsa; fettucine with salmon, prawns, coconut, spring onions, chilli.
Details: www.thewhitehartpool.co.uk; in Poole village 2m from Leeds & Bradford
airport; 9.30 pm, 6.30 pm Sun; closed Sun D; no booking.*

POOLE, DORSET   2–4C

Cafe Shore   £ 46
10-14 Banks Rd BH13 7QB   (01202) 707271
*A waterfront bar/restaurant tipped for its "great décor, buzzy
atmosphere and good food", and – if you're lucky – a "fantastic"
sunset too. / **Sample dishes:** tuna sashimi, cucumber & lime relish, beetroot
carpaccio; calves liver & bacon, pomme purée, caramelised onion & red wine jus;
chocolate spring roll with jelly of blood orange. **Details:** www.cafeshore.co.uk;
10.30 pm.*

Guildhall Tavern   £ 37
15 Market St BH15 1NB   (01202) 671717
*"Once a pub, now a French-owned fish restaurant"; its fan club is not
(yet) large, but all members agree that the place is "faultless".
/ **Sample dishes:** pan-fried soft herring roes on toast, with lemon & parsley; fresh
fillets of red seabream filled with mango, pineapple & plum sauce; rum & passion
fruit crème brûlée. **Details:** www.guildhalltavern.co.uk; 9.30 pm; closed Mon;
no Amex.*

Harbour Heights Hotel   £ 43
73 Haven Rd, Haven Rd BH13 7LW   (01202) 707272
*"Amazing views of Poole Harbour" are the real highlight at this
hillside hotel dining room, but most reports say the food "lives up to
the location". / **Sample dishes:** seared scallops, aioli & sea asparagus; sautéed
breast of chicken; chocolate fondant with rosewater & cherry ice cream.
Details: www.harbourheights.net; 9.15. **Accommodation:** 38 rooms,
from £120.*

Mansion House £ 40 Ⓐ ⭐

Thames St BH15 1JN   (01202) 685666

"Well patronised by business and east Dorset residents, and ideal for celebrations" – this hotel and restaurant is highly prized by more mature reporters for its *"excellent"* food and *"atmospheric"* surroundings. / **Sample dishes:** *saffron pasta with tiger prawns; scallops & salmon; banana & chocolate soufflé.* **Details:** *www.themansionhouse.co.uk; follow signs for Ferry, turn left onto quayside; 9.30 pm; closed Sat L & Sun D; no trainers; children: 5+ at D.* **Accommodation:** *32 rooms, from £96.*

Storm £ 45 ⭐⭐

16 High St BH15 1BP   (01202) 674970

"The produce changes, almost with the tide" at this cheerful bistro – owned by a local fisherman – where *"exceptional"* seafood and *"fantastic"* fish are *"wonderfully prepared"*. / **Sample dishes:** *baked fillet of halibut with Welsh rarebit topping on mash & wilted greens; baked halibut on wilted greens; ricotta & orange tart with clotted cream.* **Details:** *www.stormfish.co.uk; 9.30 pm; closed Sun L.*

PORLOCK, SOMERSET 1–2D

Andrews On The Weir £ 53

Porlock Weir TA24 8PB   (01643) 863300

"A real treat", say fans of this rather conventional-looking restaurant-with-rooms, which has a *"beautiful location"* by the sea, and offers *"good"*, *"locally-sourced and seasonal"* food; critics, however, can find it *"expensive, for what it is"*. / **Sample dishes:** *lobster salad; beef rump with braised oxtail, creamed parsnips, rösti potato, crispy tongue, capers & parsley.; strawberry cheesecake.* **Details:** *www.andrewsontheweir.co.uk; 9 pm; closed Mon & Tue; no Amex; children: 12+.* **Accommodation:** *5 rooms, from £100.*

PORT APPIN, ARGYLL & BUTE 9–3B

Airds Hotel £ 67 Ⓐ ⭐

PA38 4DF   (01631) 730236

"Paul Burns is a food-genius", says a fan of this *"beautiful, old-fashioned"* hotel, set in *"stunning surroundings"*, *"overlooking Loch Linnhe"* – *"it does seem like the back of beyond, but it's worth the trip"*. / **Sample dishes:** *monkfish with garden vegetables, trumpet mushrooms, & deep-fried leek; prime fillet of sea breem with mussels & fennel broth; roast sirloin of Scotch beef.* **Details:** *www.airds-hotel.com; 20m N of Oban; 9 pm; closed Jan. 6 - 23; no Amex; no jeans or trainers; children: 8+ at D.* **Accommodation:** *11 rooms, from £245.*

Pier House Hotel £ 46 Ⓐ ⭐

PA38 4DE   (01631) 730302

Despite new ownership (Nick & Nikki Horne), the intrinsic appeal of this remote hotel dining room (on the shores of Loch Linnhe) seems little-changed – splendid views, and *"huge platters"* of *"wonderfully fresh seafood from the loch"*. / **Sample dishes:** *deep-fried crabmeat, served with salad garnish & lime mayonnaise dip; medallions of monkfish skewered with roast capsicum topped with a chilli jam; cranachan.* **Details:** *www.pierhousehotel.co.uk; just off A828, follow signs for Port Appin & Lismore Ferry; 9.30 pm.* **Accommodation:** *12 rooms, from £90.*

PORT ISAAC, CORNWALL   1–3B

Port Gaverne Hotel   £ 38

PL29 3SQ   (01208) 880244

*In search of a "quite excellent crab sandwich"? – try the bar of this
comfy hotel in a cove, near an ultra-cute fishing village.*
/ **Sample dishes:** smoked haddock risotto; steaks.
Details: www.portgavernehotel.co.uk; N of Port Isaac on coast road (B3314);
8.30 pm; no Amex; children: 7+. **Accommodation:** 15 rooms, from £52.50.

PORT TALBOT, GLAMORGAN   1–1D

Cafe Remos   £ 25

Princess Margaret Way SA12 6QW   (01639) 882121

*Tipped for its "inexpensive menu from fresh pastas to burgers and
sandwiches" (and "the best cappuccino ever"), this "pleasing" café
also benefits from "views over Swansea Bay".* / **Sample dishes:** Thai
curry; pasta. **Details:** 9 am.

PORTAFERRY, COUNTY DOWN   10–2D

Portaferry Hotel   £ 35

10 The Strand BT22 1PE   (028) 4272 8231

*Tipped for its "beautiful location" and "delicious" dishes – a civilised
dining room, overlooking Strangford Loch.* / **Sample dishes:** crispy ham
potato cakes with mustard cream; fillet of venison; double chocolate torte.
Details: www.portaferryhotel.com; on shore front, opposite ferry slipway;
8.30 pm. **Accommodation:** 14 rooms, from £110.

PORTHGAIN, PEMBROKESHIRE   4–4B

The Shed   £ 48

SA62 5AR   (01348) 831518

*"A fish café by day, and a restaurant by night"; whatever the time,
though, the "top-quality fish and well-executed dishes" at this "first-
class" outfit are praised by all reporters.* / **Sample dishes:** pan-fried fillet
of local mackerel; lobster Newberg; walnut tart with whisky butterscotch sauce &
cream. **Details:** www.theshedporthgain.co.uk; 9 pm; closed Mon D; no Amex.

PORTHKERRY, VALE OF GLAMORGAN   2–2A

Egerton Grey   £ 43

CF62 3BZ   (01446) 711666

*"A lovely little country house hotel" that's hailed by all reporters as a
"real gem"; it's an "elegant" and "unstuffy" sort of place, and its food
is "excellent, without being over-elaborate".* / **Sample dishes:** home-cured
gravadlax of salmon, mustard & dill dressing; grilled fillet of sea bass, horseradish
pomme purée, light veal & wild mushroom jus; sticky toffee pudding, toffee sauce,
cream liquor ice cream. **Details:** www.egertongrey.co.uk; 8.30 pm.
Accommodation: 10 rooms, from £130.

PORTHMADOG, GWYNEDD 4–2C

Yr Hen Fecws £ 38 Ⓐ★
16 Lombard St LL49 9AP (01766) 514625
Thanks to the "fabulous home-made dishes at very reasonable prices", it's "hard to get a table" at this cottage-style operation in Snowdonia; the children's menu is especially commended.
/ **Sample dishes:** *pan-fried scallops with pancetta tossed salad; crispy duck breast & garlic mash, with plum & ginger sauce.; home-made bread & butter pudding.* **Details:** *www.henfecws.com; 10 pm; D only, closed Sun.* **Accommodation:** *7 rooms, from £59.*

PORTLAND, DORSET 2–4B

The Bluefish Restaurant & Cafe £ 38
15-17a, Chiswell DT5 1AN (01305) 822991
"Worth a trip" – the da Silvanos' cottage-restaurant, near Chesil Beach, is a "friendly" place, with an "interesting" menu.
/ **Sample dishes:** *pan-fried scallops with lemon & hazelnut gnocchi; roast breast of guinea fowl & ballotine of leg; chocolate & mango clafoutis & mandarin sorbet.* **Details:** *10 pm; closed Mon, Tue-Fri D only, Sat & Sun open L & D; no Amex.*

PORTMEIRION, GWYNEDD 4–2C

Portmeirion Hotel £ 50 Ⓐ
LL48 6ET (01766) 770000
For "a beautiful location and awe-inspiring views", it's hard to beat the "wonderfully atmospheric" dining room at the heart of Clough Williams-Ellis's famous Italianate village; the food too can be "first-rate" (but there was also the odd "let-down" this year).
/ **Sample dishes:** *paupiette of lemon sole & salmon; light grilled fillet of sea bass with a leek & potato blini; chocolate cappuccino cup.*
Details: *www.portmeirion-village.com; off A487 at Minffordd; 9 pm; no jeans.* **Accommodation:** *14 rooms, from £188.*

PORTPATRICK, DUMFRIES & GALLOWAY 7–2A

Knockinaam Lodge £ 55 Ⓣ
DG9 9AD (01776) 810471
The "old-fashioned but comfortable dining room" of this country house hotel not only has "wonderful sea views – it's also tipped for "imaginative, refined and exquisitely presented".
/ **Details:** *www.knockinaamlodge.com; off A77 at Colfin Smokehouse, follow signs to lodge; 9 pm; no jeans or trainers; children: at lunch only.* **Accommodation:** *9 rooms, from £230.*

PORTRUSH, COUNTY ANTRIM 10–1C

Ramore £ 32 ★
6 The Harbour BT56 8BN (028) 7082 4313
This "always-bustling wine bar, with views over the harbour" continues to win acclaim with its "really good-value dishes"; despite its recent expansion, though, "long waits" for a table can still be a hazard.
/ **Sample dishes:** *bang bang chicken, with oriental salad, peanut & garlic dips; banoffee pie.* **Details:** *www.portrushharbour.co.uk; 10 pm, Fri & Sat 10.30 pm, Sun 9 pm; no Amex; need 10+ to book.*

POULTON, GLOUCESTERSHIRE 2–2C

The Falcon Inn **£ 43**

London Rd GL7 5HN (01285) 850844
*A brightly-refurbished old inn, praised for its "good grub and good value". / **Sample dishes:** seared scallops with saffron & clam risotto; pressed terrine of ham hock & baby leeks; chocolate brownie with honeycomb ice cream.*
Details: *www.thefalconpoulton.co.uk; on A417 between Cirencester and Fairford; 9.30 pm; closed Sun D.*

PRESTBURY, CHESHIRE 5–2B

White House **£ 46**

New Rd SK10 4DG (01625) 829336
*No longer related to the hotel of a similar name, this restaurant at the heart of one of the North West's choicest villages seems to be "slipping" under its new régime – fans admittedly still find it "first-class", but there's also a feeling that you just "pay for the location" nowadays. / **Sample dishes:** sautéed tiger prawns; Cambrian fell-bred fillet of beef with chunky chips, vine roast tomatoes, fresh asparagus, & a balsamic glaze; miniature traditional puddings.*
Details: *www.thewhitehouseinprestbury.com; 2m N of Macclesfield on A538; 9 pm, 10 pm Sat; closed Mon & Sun D; no shorts.*

PRESTEIGNE, POWYS 5–4A

Hat Shop **£ 29**

7 High St LD8 2BA (01544) 260017
*"A surprise in this sleepy little border town"; "the place really was a hat shop", but nowadays offers "good cooking, friendly service and a seriously whacky ambience"; "the lunch time menu is unbelievable value". / **Sample dishes:** herb stuffed chicken wrapped in bacon with lemon sauce; plaice fillet with tartare sauce. **Details:** 9 pm; closed Sun; no credit cards.*

PRESTON BAGOT, WARWICKSHIRE 5–4C

The Crabmill **£ 39**

B95 5EE (01926) 843342
*This contemporary-style pub-conversion is "a really good rural establishment", offering "well-sourced food, cooked with flair and imagination", in "handsome surroundings"; the occasional reporter, however, fears that it risks becoming "formulaic".
/ **Sample dishes:** lamb kidney, black pudding & mushroom suet pudding; Moroccan chicken breast; chocolate jaffa truffle cake.*
Details: *www.thecrabmill.co.uk; on main road between Warwick & Henley; 9.30 pm; closed Sun D; no Amex.*

PRESTON, LANCASHIRE 5–1A

Bukhara **£ 17**

154 Preston New Rd PR5 0UP (01772) 877710
*It inspires only limited feedback, but this modern subcontinental is tipped for its "fine, authentic food" – "there's no alcohol but it's well worth the sacrifice". / **Sample dishes:** handi ghost laziz; karahi lamb.*
Details: *www.bukharasamlesbury.co.uk; 11pm; D only; no Maestro.*

Winckley Square Chophouse £ 42
23 Winckley Sq PR1 3JJ (01772) 252732
"The best bet in Preston"; this "stylish modern restaurant" – part of
the Paul Heathcote empire – is hailed by some reporters for its
"British basics cooked very well"; critics, though, say "the menu's
looking a bit tired nowadays", and service can be "slow".
/ **Sample dishes:** crispy duck confit, baby onions, smoked bacon, red wine &
balsalmic; pan-fried fillet of sea bass; bread & butter pudding, apricot compote &
clotted cream. **Details:** www.heathcotes.co.uk; 10 pm, Sat 11 pm, Sun 9 pm.

PRESTWOOD, BUCKINGHAMSHIRE   3–2A

Polecat £ 32
170 Wycombe Rd HB16 0HJ (01494) 862253
"A popular pub in a nice location" ("best in summer, when you can
use the garden"); the food is rated everything from "mediocre"
to "great-value". / **Sample dishes:** Stilton soufflé; pork tenderloin with black
pudding risotto; almond tart. **Details:** on A4128 between Great Missenden &
High Wycombe; 9 pm; closed Sun D; no Amex; need 8+ to book.

PRIORS HARDWICK, WARWICKSHIRE   2–1D

Butchers Arms £ 43
Church End CV47 7SN (01327) 260504
"A step back to the 1970s" it may be, but – in its very "traditional"
way – this "smart" Portuguese-run inn is a "good class"
of establishment, offering "consistent" cuisine; the "gargantuan and
groaning" sweet trolley is most particularly not to be missed.
/ **Sample dishes:** buffalo Mozzarella & tomato salad; grilled Dover sole; Molotov
cocktail. **Details:** www.thebutchersarms.com; 9.30 pm; closed Sat L & Sun D.

PWLLHELI, GWYNEDD   4–2C

Plas Bodegroes £ 59
Nefyn Rd LL53 5TH (01758) 612363
"It's hard to find better in Wales" than this "idyllic, and gastronomic
treat" – a "lovely restaurant-with-rooms" with a "relaxed" style,
"wonderful" food, and "a very interesting Welsh wine list!"
/ **Sample dishes:** salad of monkfish with Carmarthen ham; char-grilled rib-eye
of black beef; cinnamon biscuits with apples & plums.
Details: www.bodegroes.co.uk; on A497 1m W of Pwllheli; 9.30 pm; closed Mon,
Tue-Sat D only, closed Sun D; closed Dec-mid Feb; no Amex.
Accommodation: 11 rooms, from £110.

RAMSBOTTOM, LANCASHIRE   5–1B

Ramsons £ 37
18 Market Pl BL0 9HT (01706) 825070
"The wine list is a veritable book" (and showcases "an inspired
selection of Italian wines"), at this village spot north of Manchester,
which is presided over by "extremely attentive" owner Chris Johnson;
it's complemented by food that's sometimes "fantastic" too.
/ **Sample dishes:** grilled red bream with cauliflower mousseline; fillet of beef with
sautéed goose liver; English custard tart & nutmeg ice cream.
Details: www.ramsons.org.uk; 9.30 pm, 3.30 Sun; closed Mon, Tue & Sun D;
no Amex; booking: max 10.

Yorke Arms £ 58 ⭐

HG3 5RL (01423) 755243

"The game pie tastes as earthy as the moors you drive through on the way", say fans of Frances & Gerald Atkins's "classy", "traditional" pub, in a "lovely" Dales location; for a minority, though, it's "stiff" and "expensive", with "over-fussy" food.
/ *Sample dishes:* potted beef, ham hock & foie gras terrine; herb-crusted rack & shoulder of lamb; coconut soufflé, chocolate truffle & orange.
Details: www.yorke-arms.co.uk; 4m W of Pateley Bridge; 9 pm.
Accommodation: 14 rooms, from £120.

RAWTENSTALL, LANCASHIRE 5–1B

The Dining Room £ 47 ⭐

8-12 Burnley Rd BB4 8EW (01706) 210567

"Refined" – and often "impressive" – food ("with an emphasis on northern produce") makes Andrew Robinshaw's "unpromisingly-located" yearling popular with almost all who comment on it.
/ **Details:** www.thediningroomrestaurant.co.uk; 9.30 pm; closed Tue.

READING, BERKSHIRE 2–2D

Forbury's £ 50 ⭐

1 Forbury Sq RG1 3BB (0118) 957 4044

"The best food in Reading... but then there's not much competition!" – this ambitious Gallic outfit wins much praise for its "well cooked and imaginative" fare (although there is also a school of thought that "it isn't quite the gastro-destination it thinks it is").
/ *Sample dishes:* carpaccio of duck; fillet of venison with herb risotto; plum & Armagnac soufflé. **Details:** www.forburys.com; 9.30 pm; closed Sun.

London Street Brasserie £ 41

2-4 London St RG1 4SE (0118) 950 5036

This extremely popular "little haven of canalside good food", in the city-centre, is a "breath of fresh air in an otherwise chain-laden city"; "if you can, get a window table". / *Sample dishes:* crispy fried ham hock; chicken breast stuffed & baked with porcini mushrooms; chocolate fondant.
Details: www.londonstbrasserie.co.uk; 10.30 pm.

REED, HERTFORDSHIRE 3–2B

The Cabinet at Reed £ 43

High St SG8 8AH (01763) 848366

Some reporters still rate this "local-favourite" dining pub as a "great" destination; those who say it offers "provincial standards at London prices" are, however, becoming quite vociferous. / *Sample dishes:* apple, Cheddar & onion marmalade egg roll; fillet of beef; sticky toffee pudding with butterscotch sauce & banana ice cream. **Details:** www.thecabinetatreed.co.uk; 9.30 pm; closed Mon & Sun D.

La Barbe   £ 45
71 Bell St RH2 7AN   (01737) 241966
This "model" Gallic bistro of over two decades' standing "has upped its game in response to greater competition", and local reporters unanimously hail it as "a gem". / **Sample dishes:** *marinated king scallops; steamed sole fillet with salmon mousseline; chocolate cake with pistachio cream.* **Details:** *www.labarbe.co.uk; 9.30 pm; closed Sat L & Sun D.*

Tony Tobin @ The Dining Room   £ 62
59a High St RH2 9AE   (01737) 226650
"Outstanding" food in a "modern and attractive room" makes TV-chef Toby Tobin's town-centre fixture a "particularly good" destination for most reporters (notwithstanding the odd "hit-and-miss" experience). / **Sample dishes:** *seared scallops; seared fillet beef; chocolate fondant with pistachio ice cream.* **Details:** *www.tonytobinrestaurants.co.uk; 10 pm; closed Sat L & Sun D; booking: max 8, Fri & Sat.*

The Westerly   £ 36
2-4 London Rd RH2 9AN   (01737) 222733
Jon & Cynthia Coomb upped sticks from the Stephen Langton in Friday Street to open this new bistro in early-2007; they've made "a very good start" – service is "personal and efficient", the setting is "fresh and relaxed", and the "British with a twist" food is "imaginative, delicious and affordable". / **Sample dishes:** *beetroot & ricotta ravioli with poppyseed & mint; bouride of monkfish, red mullet & bream, prawns, mussels & clams; coquette of pig's head with beef.* **Details:** *www.thewesterly.co.uk; 10 pm; closed Mon, Tue L, Sat L & Sun.*

Fairyhill   £ 53
SA3 1BS   (01792) 390139
Often held up as "the best dining in Wales", this "intimate" Gower Pensinsula hotel is hailed by most reporters as "a lovely spot", with "unobtrusive" service, a "top-quality" wine list and "inspiring" food; the odd doubter, though feels it's "very good, but could do better". / **Sample dishes:** *king prawns, mussels & scallops, warm vegetable salad, lemon & herb butter; crème of duck with grape & honey sauce; lemon posset, fruit compote.* **Details:** *www.fairyhill.net; 20 mins from M4, J47 off B4295; 9 pm; no Amex; children: 8+ at D.* **Accommodation:** *8 rooms, from £165.*

Juboraj   £ 26
11 Heol-y-deri CF14 6HA   (029) 2062 8894
This "top-class" Indian – the "contemporary"-style HQ of a small chain – is hailed by all reporters as a "reliable" and "busy" destination. / **Details:** *www.juborajgroup.com; 10.30 pm; closed Sun.*

Fishworks   **£ 42**
13/19 The Sq, Old Mkt TW9 1EA   (020) 89485965
*This new outlet of the fishmonger/restaurant chain makes
"an interesting addition to thinly-provided Richmond"; as at the other
branches, a "fabulous range of fish" is on offer, but prices are
"surprisingly steep". / **Sample dishes:** crab salad with cucumber &
mayonnaise; Moroccan spiced grilled swordfish with tomato & parsley salad.
Details: www.fishworks.co.uk; 10.30 pm.*

Petersham Hotel   **£ 54**   Ⓐ
Nightingale Ln TW10 6UZ   (020) 8940 7471
*Especially for "a great Sunday lunch with lovely views over the
Thames", this agreeable dining room wins a big thumbs-up, thanks
to its "high-quality" cuisine and "excellent" service.
/ **Sample dishes:** seared scallops with smoked eel; potato gnocchi & smoked
salmon. **Details:** www.petershamhotel.co.uk; 9.45 pm, 8.45 pm Sun.
Accommodation: 61 rooms, from £150.*

Old Vicarage   **£ 51**
Ridgeway Moor S12 3XW   (0114) 247 5814
*Oh dear!; reports suggest that Sheffield's Only Michelin-Starred
Restaurant has let this fact go straight to its head; it's too often
damned not only as "overpriced", but "condescending" too – "we only
went for dinner, but were treated as if we were on some sort
of outing of a lifetime!" / **Sample dishes:** baked red mullet with tapenade &
Gruyère crisp; baked John Dory on crab risotto, crab bisque sauce & a crab &
mango salad; coffee pecan pudding with coffee bean sauce.
Details: www.theoldvicarage.co.uk; 10 mins SE of city centre; 9.30 pm; closed
Mon, Sat L & Sun; no Amex.*

Drakes   **£ 58**   ⭐⭐
The Clock Hs, High St GU23 6AQ   (01483) 224777
*"Probably the best in Surrey" ("even if that is damning it with faint
praise") – Stephen Drake's village-centre spot offers "innovative"
cooking, often to a truly "exquisite" standard; in best Michelin-
pleasing style, though, the atmosphere is "hushed, and slightly
boring". / **Sample dishes:** caramelised veal sweetbreads with Parma ham; Anjou
pigeon with braised red cabbage & tarragon ravioli; pistachio parfait with poached
pear & gingerbread. **Details:** www.drakesrestaurant.co.uk; 9.30 pm; closed Mon,
Sat L & Sun; no Amex; booking: max 6; children: 12+.*

Prima Pizzaria   **£ 21**   Ⓣ
33 Kirkgate HG4 1PB   (01765) 6022034
*"Intimate" and "good-value" – this self-explanatory spot "near the
cathedral" is our top tip if you find yourself dining hereabouts.
/ **Details:** www.ripon.co.uk/prima/.*

El Gato Negro Tapas   **£ 25**
1 Oldham Rd HX6 4DN   (01422) 823070
*"Sophistication comes to a rural Yorkshire"; at this increasingly-
renowned Hispanic two-year-old; in a "much improved village pub",
chef/patron Simon Shaw serves up a "superb" array of "adroitly-
prepared" tapas.* / **Sample dishes:** *tapas.*
Details: *www.elgatonegrotapas.com; 9.30 pm, 10 pm Sat; closed Mon,
Tue, Wed L, Thu L, Fri L & Sun D; no Amex.*

RISHWORTH, WEST YORKSHIRE   5–1C

Old Bore   **£ 42**
Oldham Rd HX6 4QU   (01422) 822291
*The food is "unusual" and rather "interesting" at this ancient
coaching inn; service, however, can be so-so.* / **Sample dishes:** *beef
brisket, colcannon potatoes, carrots, parsley & horseradish; beef bourguignon.*
Details: *www.oldbore.co.uk; 9.30 pm, Sun 8 pm; closed Mon & Tue.*

ROADE, NORTHAMPTONSHIRE   3–1A

Roade House   **£ 44**
16 High St NN7 2NW   (01604) 863372
*"This stalwart of Northamptonshire cuisine" continues to deliver
"simple dishes with imaginative twists"; the only drawback is its
slightly "dated" décor.* / **Sample dishes:** *salad of lightly salted cod marinated
in lemon juice; roast belly of pork; apple & almond tart with calvados syllabub.*
Details: *www.roadehousehotel.co.uk; 9.30 pm; closed Sat L & Sun; no shorts;
booking essential.* **Accommodation:** *10 rooms, from £70.*

ROCKBEARE, DEVON   1–3D

Jack in the Green Inn   **£ 42**
London Rd EX5 2EE   (01404) 822240
*A pub-cum-restaurant which attracts quite numerous, if rather mixed,
reports; still, if you're heading for Devon or Cornwall, it is just off the
A30…* / **Sample dishes:** *lemon-dressed crab; fillet of beef & mushroom duxelle;
assiette of cherry.* **Details:** *www.jackinthegreen.uk.com; 9.30 pm.*

ROMALDKIRK, COUNTY DURHAM   8–3B

The Rose & Crown   **£ 37**
DL12 9EB   (01833) 650213
*"A wonderful place to start, or finish, a country walk"; this village
coaching-inn is no place of culinary pilgrimage, but is consistently
hailed for offering "good food in gorgeous surroundings".*
/ **Sample dishes:** *wholemeal blinis with smoked salmon & crème fraîche;
roast loin of pork; crème brûlée, mango & kiwi compote.*
Details: *www.rose-and-crown.co.uk; 6m NW of Barnard Castle on B6277;
8.45 pm; D only, ex Sun open L & D; no Amex; children: 6+.*
Accommodation: *12 rooms, from £126.*

ROSSETT, WREXHAM 5–3A

The Golden Lion £ 34
Chester Rd LL12 0HN (01244) 571020
A "good all-round gastropub" – half-way between Chester and
Wrexham – tipped for its "high level of consistency".
/ **Sample dishes:** lobster thermidor; fishcakes. **Details:** 9.30 pm, 9 pm Sun;
no Amex.

ROTHERFIELD PEPPARD, OXFORDSHIRE 3–3A

The Greyhound £ 42
Gallowstree Ln RG9 5HT (0118) 9722227
Local hero Antony Worrall Thompson gets a good report from his
fellow Henley residents for this "relaxed, done-up country-pub", which
realises a "traditional hearty and meat-dominated" menu to "good"
effect. / **Sample dishes:** steak served with hand cut chunky chips, & Bearnaise
sauce or savory butter. **Details:** www.awtrestaurants.com; 9.30 pm, 10.30 pm
Sat; no Amex.

ROWDE, WILTSHIRE 2–2C

George & Dragon £ 40
High St SN10 2PN (01380) 723053
"Fantastic, fresh local food, with plenty of Cornish fish" has earned
a deserved culinary reputation for this "pleasant and rustic" pub.
/ **Sample dishes:** char-grilled scallops & black pudding brochettes; black pudding
brochette; Eton mess. **Details:** www.thegeorgeanddragonrowde.co.uk; on A342
between Devizes & Chippenham; 10 pm; closed Mon & Sun D; no Amex; booking:
max 8. **Accommodation:** 3 rooms, from £65.

ROWHOOK, WEST SUSSEX 3–4B

Chequers Inn £ 43
RH12 3PY (01403) 790480
"Simply superb cuisine" comes simply-served ("on scrubbed tables")
at this impressive country pub. / **Sample dishes:** Scottish scallops salad;
pork with buttered Savoy cabbage & thyme jus; sticky toffee pudding with vanilla
ice cream & butterscotch sauce. **Details:** www.nealsrestaurants.biz; 9 pm; closed
Sun D; no Amex.

ROYAL LEAMINGTON SPA, WARWICKSHIRE 5–4C

Thai Elephant £ 30
20 Regent St CV32 5HQ (01926) 886882
"Authentic", "friendly" and "relaxed" – this long-established oriental
attracts few, but consistently positive, reports. / **Sample dishes:** beef
satay; stir-fried duck; coconut almond cream cake.
Details: www.thaielephantrestaurant.co.uk; 10.30 pm; closed Sat L.

RUSHTON, NORTHAMPTONSHIRE 5–4D

Rushton Hall £ 51
NN14 1RR (01536) 713001
"A beautiful Jacobean hall in extensive grounds, now an hotel";
its tipped for its "fantastic public rooms, attentive service and lovely
food". / **Sample dishes:** lobster ravioli; pan-fried hake with fettucine; apricot
soufflé amaretto ice cream. **Details:** www.rushtonhall.com; 9.30 pm; children:
13+ at D. **Accommodation:** 44 rooms, from £140.

RYE, EAST SUSSEX

Webbes at the Fish Café — £ 48 ⭐

17 Tower St TN31 7AT (01797) 222210

The setting is a bit "echoey", but Paul Webb's very popular open-kitchen café, set in a former port building, offers consistent cooking of "fresh, locally-caught fish". / **Sample dishes:** char-grilled squid with bok choi, scallions & bean shoots; roast fillet of sea bass with creamed potato basil & tomato; baked apple with apple & calvados jelly. **Details:** www.thefishcafe.com; 9 pm; closed Mon L; children: 12+ at D.

Landgate Bistro — £ 27

5-6 Landgate TN31 7LH (01797) 222829

Under Martin Peacock's two-year-old régime, this long-established bistro seems again to be recognised as a useful all-rounder – reporters do not a few "rough edges", but mostly praise "simple seafood" at "very reasonable prices". / **Sample dishes:** garlic soup; venison with celeriac, carrots & Savoy cabbage; lemon tart. **Details:** www.landgatebistro.co.uk; below Landgate Arch; 9.30 pm; D only, closed Mon & Sun.

SAFFRON WALDEN, ESSEX

3–2B

The Crown And Thistle — £ 33 ⭐

High St CB10 1PL (01799) 530278

"A village gastropub with a chef who knows his stuff"; its "reasonably-priced" too, and the new landlord "has turned it into a very popular eating place". / **Sample dishes:** fillet steaks; seabass. **Details:** 9.30 pm; no Amex.

SALISBURY, WILTSHIRE

2–3C

Anokaa — £ 35

60 Fisherton St SP2 7RB (01722) 414142

"Salisbury's best restaurant of any nationality" – this Indian venture "goes from strength to strength", thanks to its "delicate" and "beautifully presented" cuisine. / **Sample dishes:** baby squid; chicken breast stuffed with avocado & green chillies lightly roasted, served with basil sauce & saffron rice; honey & lemon cheesecake. **Details:** www.anokaa.com; 10.30 pm; no shorts.

Jade — £ 30 ⓣ

109a Exeter St SP1 2SF (01722) 333355

An oriental stalwart that's still of some note locally; it's sometimes thought to be "resting on its laurels", though, and service can be "haphazard". / **Sample dishes:** steamed scallops; fillet steak; coconut ice cream. **Details:** www.jaderestaurant.co.uk; near the Cathedral; 11.30 pm; closed Sun; no Amex.

SALTAIRE, WEST YORKSHIRE

5–1C

Salts Diner — £ 29 ⓣ

Salts Mill, Victoria Rd BD18 3LB (01274) 530533

A handy complement to the Hockney gallery at this former mill – a "buzzy" place, offering "tasty pizzas, salads, burgers and so on", all from "fresh produce". / **Sample dishes:** garlic bread; grilled salmon fillet, mixed bean & roast garlic mash, rocket & lemon pesto; bread & butter pudding. **Details:** www.saltsmill.org.uk; 2m from Bradford on A650; L & afternoon tea only; no Amex.

SAPPERTON, GLOUCESTERSHIRE 2–2C

The Bell at Sapperton £ 46
GL7 6LE (01285) 760298
Reports on this contemporary-style Cotswold village inn were mixed this year; most still speak of "delicious food" and a "wonderful buzz", but a minority speak of "variable" standards, with "the only constant factor being the price…" / **Sample dishes:** belly of pork with celery braised in red wine & carrot purée; lamb with ratatouille & garlic; sticky toffee pudding with clotted cream. **Details:** www.foodatthebell.co.uk; 9.30 pm; no Amex; no booking at L; children: 10+ at D.

SAWBRIDGEWORTH, HERTFORDSHIRE 3–2B

The Straw Hat Oriental £ 29
London Rd CM21 0AJ (01279) 722434
"Excellent" sushi and a "limited range of other dishes" commend this "friendly" spot to a number of reporters.
/ **Details:** www.strawhat-oriental.co.uk.

SAWLEY, LANCASHIRE 5–1B

Spread Eagle £ 30
BB7 4NH (01200) 441202

A "comfortable" pub with a "lovely riverside location" and "beautiful views" – the food plays rather a supporting rôle.
/ **Sample dishes:** grilled medallions in black pudding; braised neck end of lamb; bread & butter pudding. **Details:** www.the-spreadeagle.co.uk; NE of Clitheroe off A59; 9 pm; closed Mon & Sun D; no Amex.

SAXMUNDHAM, SUFFOLK 3–1D

Bell Hotel £ 31
31 High St IP17 1AF (01728) 602331
"Shame about the austere setting" – on most accounts, the cooking at this small hotel can be "first-class". / **Sample dishes:** chicken, leek & lamb sweetbreads; pan-fried fillet of sea trout; steamed orange & lemon pudding with orange sorbet. **Details:** www.bellhotel-saxmundham.co.uk; 9 pm; closed Mon & Sun; no Amex. **Accommodation:** 10 rooms, from £75.

SCARBOROUGH, NORTH YORKSHIRE 8–4D

Lanterna £ 46
33 Queen St YO11 1HQ (01723) 363616
"First-rate food" – "lovely local fish" is a speciality – makes this "dependable" local one of the best Italians for miles around; fans find the interior "intimate" too, and it is enlivened by "personal" service.
/ **Sample dishes:** fish with white truffles; halibut; zabaglione.
Details: www.lanterna-ristorante.co.uk; 9.30 pm; D only, closed Sun; no Amex.

Pepper's £ 42

11 York Pl YO11 2NP (01723) 500642

Thanks to its "exciting", "wholesome" and "well-presented" fare, Jon & Kath Smith's ten-year-old venture can still seem "a real find". / **Sample dishes:** *Scarborough smoked haddock fishcake; pan-roast breast of duck; strawberry elderflower jelly with vanilla panna cotta, strawberry sorbet, & shortbread biscuits.* **Details:** *www.peppersrestaurant.co.uk; 10 pm; closed Mon, Tue-Fri D only, Sat & Sun open L & D.*

SCARISBRICK, LANCASHIRE 5–1A

Blue Elephant £ 24

Southport Road L40 8HQ (01704) 841222

"In an area devoid of quality Indian restaurants, a place worthy of more recognition"; "the menu has all the standard fare should you desire it, but is also packed with regional dishes". / **Sample dishes:** *exotic duck (for two); monk fish mackni.* **Details:** *10 mins from Ormskirk on the A570; 10.30pm, Sat 11pm; closed weekday L; no Amex.*

SEAHAM, COUNTY DURHAM 8–3C

White Room
Seaham Hall £ 65

Lord Byron's Walk SR7 7AG (0191) 516 1400

"Beautiful sea views" and Stephen Smith's "cutting-edge" food ("everything comes with foams or veloutés, which I understand you've had down south for ages") commend this "tranquil" boutique-hotel to practically all reporters — "for the area, it's certainly expensive, but probably worth it". / **Sample dishes:** *seared scallops; lamb with crushed peas; passion fruit soufflé.* **Details:** *www.seaham-hall.com; 10 pm; booking: max 8.* **Accommodation:** *19 rooms, from £225.*

SEVENOAKS, KENT 3–3B

Greggs £ 38

28-30 High St TN13 1HX (01732) 456373

Locals acclaim this family-run, town-centre spot as a "perfect neighbourhood restaurant", praising its "unrushed" style and "good-value" food. / **Sample dishes:** *pan-fried foie gras; confit of honey-glazed pork belly with apple jelly; caramelised banana layered with short bread, banana & vanilla cream.* **Details:** *www.greggsrestaurant.com; 9 pm; closed Mon & Sun D; no Amex.*

SHEFFIELD, SOUTH YORKSHIRE 5–2C

Artisan £ 44

32-34 Sandygate Rd S10 5RY (0114) 266 6096

"Much improved" in recent times, Richard Smith's premises comprise both a "reliable" ground-floor bistro and a "trendy seafood restaurant" (Catch) above; the latter — very slightly — has the edge in reporter esteem. / **Sample dishes:** *house-cured gravadlax; red wine-poached turbot & potted shrimp; raspberry panna cotta.* **Details:** *www.artisanofsheffield.com; 10 pm.*

Bahn Nah £ 29

19-21 Nile St S10 2PN (0114) 268 4900

All reports on this "excellent" oriental agree — "if you like Thai, you'll love Bahn Thai". / **Sample dishes:** *stuffed chicken wings; chilli fish; pie style custard.* **Details:** *www.bahnnah.co.uk; on A57 from Sheffield to Manchester; 11 pm; D only, closed Sun.*

Kashmir Curry Centre £ 14

123 Spital Hill S4 7LD (0114) 272 6253

"Great cooking, as long as you don't mind the bare tables" – this BYO spot occupies a school-hall type setting and is *"always reliable"*. / **Sample dishes:** *lamb chops; selection of curries; kulfi.* **Details:** *midnight; D only, closed Sun; no credit cards.*

Nirmals £ 27

189-193 Glossop Rd S10 2GW (0114) 272 4054

"The specials board has remained constant for the last twenty years", at this idiosyncratic veggie curry house... *"but I'm not complaining, because Mrs Nirmal is a very fine cook!"* / **Sample dishes:** *chicken tikka; lamb curry; home-made kulfi.* **Details:** *www.nirmals.com; near West St; midnight; closed Sun L.*

Rafters £ 47 ⭐

220 Oakbrook Rd, Nether Grn S11 7ED (0114) 230 4819

A strong local fan club hails this contemporary venture in leafy Ranmoor – with its *"reliable"* and *"distinctively-flavoured"* cooking – as *"the best restaurant in Sheffield"*. / **Sample dishes:** *dressed white crab meat; grilled fillet of seabass, with a ratatouille vinaigrette & crisp chorizo; bread & butter pudding.* **Details:** *www.raftersrestaurant.co.uk; 10 pm; D only, closed Tue & Sun; children: 5+.*

SHELLEY, WEST YORKSHIRE 5–2C

Three Acres £ 45 Ⓐ ⭐

Roydhouse HD8 8LR (01484) 602606

This *"firm-favourite"* inn (with deli attached), out on the moors, enjoys incredible popularity, thanks to its *"cosy"* buzz, its *"always-friendly"* service and its *"fantastic food"* (that's *"better than most restaurants"*). / **Sample dishes:** *home-cured bresaola; roast rack of lamb; raspberry & blueberry millefeuille.* **Details:** *www.3acres.com; near Emley Moor TV tower; 9.30 pm.* **Accommodation:** *20 rooms, from £100.*

SHEPTON MALLET, SOMERSET 2–3B

Charlton House £ 82

Charlton Rd BA4 4PR (01749) 342008

This Mulberry-owned (and decorated) country house hotel is still a *"wow!"* destination for some reporters; since last year's change of chef, however, some feel the style of cooking has become *"too fancy"* (and it's *"very pricey, for what you get"*). / **Sample dishes:** *fillet of brill; cannon of pork in ham-roast sweetbreads; dark chocolate & cherries & vanilla Mascarpone.* **Details:** *www.charltonhouse.com; on A361 towards Frome; 9.30 pm.* **Accommodation:** *25 rooms, from £165.*

SHERBORNE, DORSET 2–3B

The Green £ 43 Ⓣ

The Green DT9 3HY (01935) 813821

"Quality food in a lovely setting" using *"fresh, local ingredients"* wins enthusiastic, more-than-local recommendations for this little-known four-year-old, run by chef/patron Michael Rust. / **Sample dishes:** *duck with peaches & redcurrant; monkfish with red wine & herbs.* **Details:** *9 pm.*

Kinghams   £ 47   Ⓐ

Gomshall Ln GU5 9HE (01483) 202168
Paul Baker's "pretty" Tudor cottage has an "idyllic" (if "suburban") location "in a charming village", and its dining room has a "snug" atmosphere; the menu is arguably "predictable", but the food is "well put together". / **Sample dishes:** carpaccio of venison; loin of lamb; pear, blackberry & almond tart. **Details:** www.kinghams-restaurant.co.uk; off A25 between Dorking & Guildford; 9 pm; closed Mon & Sun D.

L'Ortolan   £ 78   Ⓐ ⭐

Church Ln RG2 9BY (0118) 988 8500

Alan Murchison's cuisine provides a "luxurious, expensive, but fantastic adventure for the senses", at this well-known restaurant; with its "relaxed but very professional" service and "unstuffy" ambience, reporters find it a "wonderful" all-round experience; let's hope La Bécasse, the new Ludlow spin-off, doesn't distract. / **Sample dishes:** tomato consomme with poached lobster & crème fraîche; braised shoulder & roast saddle of rabbit; orange & elderflower parfait with orange cake & jelly. **Details:** www.lortolan.com; J11 off M4, take A33 towards Basingstoke, at first roundabout restaurant signposted; 9.30 pm; closed Mon & Sun.

The Chaser Inn   £ 35

Stumble Hill TN11 9PE (01732) 810360
A Georgian inn that's a "popular" culinary destination for which it's "best to book ahead"; the cooking – on most accounts – is "hearty and wholesome". / **Sample dishes:** baked field mushrooms; braised half shoulder of lamb; Bailey's cheesecake. **Details:** www.thechaser.co.uk; 9.30 pm; no Amex.

Aagrah   £ 28   ⭐

4 Saltaire Rd BD18 3HN (01274) 530880
"Good food and service by people who really know their business" have won enduring success for this "above-average" Indian – part of a well-known Yorkshire chain. / **Sample dishes:** tandoori mix; murgh hyderabadi; kulfi. **Details:** www.aagrah.com; 11.30 pm; closed Sat L & Sun L.

SHREWSBURY, SHROPSHIRE

5–3A

Cromwells Hotel

£ 32 ⭐

11 Dogpole SY1 1EN   (01743) 361440

"Interesting food in generous portions" makes this "friendly small hotel", in the town-centre, worth seeking out; on a warm day, you can sit outside too. / **Sample dishes:** mussels; lamb shank; sticky toffee pudding. **Details:** www.cromwellsinn.com; opp Guildhall; 10 pm. **Accommodation:** 6 rooms, from £60.

SKENFRITH, MONMOUTHSHIRE

2–1B

Bell

£ 41

NP7 8UH   (01600) 750235

An old riverside inn with a big reputation for its "good" and "intelligently-presented" food, its "eclectic" wine list and its "idyllic" setting; this year, though, it sometimes seemed rather "ordinary". / **Sample dishes:** asparagus with poached hen's egg, hollandaise & Parmesan shavings; marinated loin of lamb; hot chocolate fondant, coconut ice cream, griottine compote. **Details:** www.skenfrith.co.uk; on B4521, 10m NE of Abergavenny; 9.30 pm, Sun 9 pm; closed Mon (Nov-Mar only); booking essential; children: 8+ at D. **Accommodation:** 8 rooms, from £105.

SNAPE, SUFFOLK

3–1D

The Crown Inn

£ 35

Bridge Rd IP17 1SL   (01728) 688324

"Handy for the Maltings", this "nice old pub" ("really more of a restaurant now") is a "cosy" sort of place, which most reporters continue to rate as an all-round "joy". / **Sample dishes:** crayfish tails in Thai mayonnaise; confit of duck; treacle tart with stem ginger ice cream. **Details:** off A12 towards Aldeburgh; 9 pm; no Amex; children: 14+. **Accommodation:** 3 rooms, from £80.

SNETTISHAM, NORFOLK

6–4B

Rose & Crown

£ 32

Old Church Rd PE31 7LX   (01485) 541382

"Surprisingly good food for a small Norfolk village inn" inspires consistently upbeat feedback on this "great" pub. / **Sample dishes:** smoked chicken, apple & walnut salad; char-grilled Holkham ribeye steak, onion rings, bearnaise sauce on side; pecan pie. **Details:** www.roseandcrownsnettisham.co.uk; 9 pm; no Amex. **Accommodation:** 16 rooms, from £90.

SOLIHULL, WEST MIDLANDS

5–4C

Beau Thai

£ 30 ⭐

761 Old Lode Ln B92 8JE   (0121) 743 5355

In the second year of its new ownership (by Ronnachai 'Joe' Khotsombati), this Thai restaurant – long eminent locally – is "still as good as ever". / **Sample dishes:** chicken satay; deep-fried red snapper; ice cream. **Details:** www.beauthairestaurant.co.uk; 10.30 pm, 11 pm Fri & Sat ; closed Mon L, Sat L & Sun L.

Metro Bar & Grill

£ 40 ⓣ

680-684 Warwick Rd B91 3DX   (0121) 705 9495

An "efficient and reliable operation", tipped as "especially good for fish and beer". / **Sample dishes:** smoked haddock fishcake, lemon mayonnaise; marinated lamb kebabs, tomato, red onion & coriander salad, tzatziki; blueberry & white chocolate trifle. **Details:** www.metrobarandgrill.co.uk; 10 pm; closed Sun.

Rajnagar £ 32

256 Lyndon Rd B92 7QW (0121) 7424842

A twenty-year-old, rather grand Bangladeshi, tipped for its high-quality cuisine and service. / **Sample dishes:** marinated king prawn; lamb tikka. **Details:** www.rajnagar.com.

SONNING-ON-THAMES, WOKINGHAM 2–2D

The French Horn £ 75

RG4 6TN (0118) 969 2204

"A real gem" – this stalwart spot (est. 1971) has an "amazing setting" on the Thames, and offers "traditional" fare that's "well worth the highish prices" (not least its famous and "phenomenal" spit-roasted duck); perhaps unsurprisingly, though, its approach can seem "old-fashioned". / **Sample dishes:** foie gras terrine; roast duck; chocolate marquise. **Details:** www.thefrenchhorn.co.uk; M4, J8 or J9, then A4; 9.30 pm; booking: max 10. **Accommodation:** 21 rooms, from £160.

SORN, EAST AYRSHIRE 7–1B

The Sorn Inn £ 35

35 Main St KA5 6HU (01290) 551305

"In the middle of rolling green hills, a great place to stop for a country lunch"; a "restaurant and chophouse" where the "good honest food" stands out. / **Sample dishes:** rillette of duck, beetroot, & puy lentil dressing; roast chump of lamb with bubble & squeak, char-grilled vegetables, & roast cherry tomato purée; warm waffle with butterscotch sauce & vanilla ice cream. **Details:** www.sorninn.com; 9 pm; closed Mon & Sun D; no Amex. **Accommodation:** 4 rooms, from £50.

SOUTH BRENT, DEVON 1–3D

Turtley Corn Mill £ 35

Avonwick TQ10 9ES (01364) 646100

Some reporters prefer its sibling (The Ship at Noss Mayo), but this "comfortable" rural gastropub wins consistent praise nonetheless for its all-day provision of a "wide choice" of "good-value" fare. / **Sample dishes:** smoked haddock topped with poached egg & Hollandaise sauce; sticky toffee pudding. **Details:** www.avonwick.net; bear left before you rejoin the A38 westbound, towards Totnes. We are 100m on the left.; 9:30pm.

SOUTH CROYDON, SURREY 3–3B

Tinkers £ 37

299 High St CR0 1QL (0208) 6865624

This "small" and "welcoming" family-run operation is an "intimate" little place, serving food that's "reasonably-priced" and "well-presented". / **Sample dishes:** fillet of bream on new potato, cherry tomatoes & mange tout, dressed with black olives. **Details:** www.tinkersrestaurant.co.uk; 10 pm; closed Mon, Sat L & Sun.

SOUTHAMPTON, SOUTHAMPTON 2–3D

Kuti's £ 34

37-39 Oxford St SO14 3DP (023) 8022 1585

A local reputation for "unsurpassable Indian cuisine" has made a big name for this "booming" spot – by far the city's best-known restaurant (and with a growing number of local spin-offs); in a city with so little competition, though, it can seem "overrated". / **Sample dishes:** paneer kebab; chicken malabari. **Details:** www.kutis.co.uk; near Stanley Casino; 11 pm.

SOUTHEND-ON-SEA, ESSEX 3–3C

Pipe of Port £ 33
84 High St SS1 1JN (01702) 614606
"Sawdust-strewn and gloomy" – this long-established basement wine
bar has a style that's "unique" ("well, in Essex anyway"), and its
"filling" food – "such as pies and traditional puds" – is "consistently
good". / **Sample dishes:** large Mediterranean prawns; roasted rump of lamb
with redcurrent & mint jus with wild potato; lemon meringue pie.
Details: www.pipeofport.com; basement just off High Street; 10.30 pm; closed
Sun; no Amex; children: 16+.

SOUTHPORT, MERSEYSIDE 5–1A

Michael's £ 32
47 Liverpool Rd PR8 4AG (01704) 550886
In Birkdale Village, this neighbourhood two-year-old wins rave-reviews
from a tiny local fan club, who say it benefits from "friendly" service
and "outstanding" food.

Warehouse Brasserie £ 35
30 West St PR8 1QN (01704) 544662
A "buzzing" spot of over ten years' standing, that, for most reporters,
remains "the best restaurant in town", thanks to its "innovative"
cooking (of "big-city standard"). / **Sample dishes:** seared scallops;
roast duck breast, potato & duck hash cake; ginger & lime crème brûlée.
Details: www.warehousebrasserie.co.uk; 10.30 pm; closed Sun; no Amex.

SOUTHROP, GLOUCESTERSHIRE 2–2C

The Swan £ 40
GL7 3NU (01367) 850205
"For a country pub, the food is outstanding" at this family-owned,
"traditional-feeling" hostelry – "THE place to eat in Gloucestershire".
/ **Sample dishes:** Thai pork & squid salad; fillet of sea bass; chocolate fondant.
Details: www.theswanatsouthrop.co.uk; 9.30, Sun 9; no Amex or Maestro.

SOUTHWOLD, SUFFOLK 3–1D

The Crown
Adnams Hotel £ 39
High St IP18 6DP (01502) 722275
This well-known Adnam's inn "at the heart of the town" is now
an exclusively no-bookings operation (and "they've extended the bar
to where the restaurant was"); "simple and elegant" food
(and "excellent" beers and wines too) are served in a large and
"buzzy" setting. / **Sample dishes:** chilli-fried squid with char-grilled fennel,
radish & orange salad; seared salmon with crème fraîche; chocolate fondant.
Details: www.adnamshotels.co.uk; 9.30 pm; no Amex. **Accommodation:** 14
rooms, from £120.

The Swan £ 48
The Market Pl IP18 6EG (01502) 722186
With its "hushed" style, the dining room of this "really atmospheric
old hotel" has seemed "a bit of a dying duck in recent years";
reporters haven't given up on it yet though – it has "such undelivered
potential" (not to mention the "excellent Admans wine list"),
and "could be superb". / **Sample dishes:** smoked mackerel fillet; lemon &
herb breast of chicken; sorbet with summer berry compote & nut biscotti.
Details: www.adnams.co.uk; 9.30 pm; no Amex; children: 5+ at
D. **Accommodation:** 42 rooms, from £156.

Gimbals   £ 38   🅐⭐
Wharf St HX6 2AF   (01422) 839329
Local fans of this "eclectic" bistro – "run by a husband and wife team with love and care" – claim it's "probably the best restaurant in West Yorkshire" ("and that includes Leeds"); even if that's overdoing it, it's still "a real find". / **Sample dishes:** *seared king scallops wrapped in prosciutto; monkfish & rice stew with lobster broth; sticky toffee pudding.* **Details:** *9.15 pm; D only, closed Sun; no Amex.*

The Millbank   £ 38
Millbank HX6 3DY   (01422) 825588

"Up a precipitous Pennine lane" – "in a beautiful rural location" – nestles this "modern dining pub"; a good number of reporters say it's "highly recommendable" and "worth finding", but the year's feedback also included a few very mediocre experiences.
/ **Sample dishes:** *roast scallops with crab samosa & chilli sauce; beef Wellington; lemon grass crème brûlée with raspberry sorbet.* **Details:** *www.themillbank.com; 9.30 pm, Sun 8 pm; closed Mon L; no Amex.*

The Old Plow   £ 45
Flowers Bottom Ln HP27 0PZ   (01494) 488300
Commentary on the Cowans' former Chilterns pub – complete with "oak beams and log fires" – was more diverse this year; fans still say it's "worth finding for its value-for-money food and excellent service" (especially in the bistro), but even fans can find it "overpriced".
/ **Sample dishes:** *salt & pepper chilli tiger prawns & scallops; lamb rump steaks; lemon & orange crème brûlée.* **Details:** *www.yeoldplow.co.uk; 20 mins from M40, J4 towards Princes Risborough; 9 pm; closed Mon, Sat L & Sun D.*

Asia   £ 32   🅐
2 Beaconsfield Rd AL1 3RD   (01727) 800002
A new "contemporary" Thai/Indian that's been "an instant hit" with the locals, who find it "chic, cool and trendy" (and "reasonably-priced" too); the odd naysayer, though, feels it's "trying too hard".
/ **Sample dishes:** *prawn & mango puri; monkfish curry; hot chocolate samosa.* **Details:** *www.asia-dining.co.uk; 11 pm, 11.30 pm Fri & Sat.*

Barissimo   £ 13   🅣
28 St Peter St AL1 3NA   (01727) 869999
"The best place in St Albans to while your time away for a coffee and more" – this award-winning Italian café is particularly tipped for its "good range of hot and cold snacks". / **Details:** *5.30pm, Sun 4pm; L only; only Maestro.*

La Cosa Nostra £ 34
62 Lattimore Rd AL1 3XR (01727) 832658
"Cheap, cheerful and always a fun night out" – this *"family-friendly"* Italian has long been a favourite local destination, thanks to its *"buzzy"* feel and its reliable pizza and other fare.
/ **Sample dishes:** pepperoni arrostiti; filetto Rossini; crème brûlée. **Details:** near railway station; 11 pm; closed Sat L & Sun; no Amex.

Darcy's £ 38
2 Hatfield Rd AL1 3RP (01727) 730777
It remains the majority view that this *"calm"* town-centre restaurant is *"St Alban's best"*, and that its Antipodean-based cuisine is *"head and shoulders above the oppo"*; there's an ever-growing faction, though, which says: *"it's amazing how many people take this place at its own (inflated) estimation"*. / **Sample dishes:** kangaroo spring roll with dipping sauces; lamb rump; lemon parfait with blueberry madelin. **Details:** www.darcysrestaurant.co.uk; 9.45 pm.

Lussmans £ 29
Waxhouse Gate, High Street AL3 4EW (01727) 851941
A *"lively"* bistro, near the Abbey; fans say the food is *"of consistent quality"*, and *"well presented"* too – a small band of critics, though, just find standards *"deeply average"*. / **Sample dishes:** bruschetta al funghi; yellow fin tuna; organic vanilla & blueberry cheesecake. **Details:** www.lussmans.com; 10 pm, 9 pm Sun.

Mumtaj £ 23
115 London Rd AL1 1LR (01727) 843691
Near the Old Cinema Hall, this may look like *"the most uninspiring of venues"*, but this Indian fixture is tipped as being *"extraordinarily good"*. / **Details:** midnight.

St Michael's Manor £ 51
Fishpool St AL3 4RY (01727) 864444
"Nice building… expected the food to be better" – once again the verdict on this potentially *"splendid"* venue, *"hidden away in the small streets"*; fans say it *"gets everything right"*, but critics find it *"bland"* or *"tired"*. / **Sample dishes:** coconut-coated tiger prawns; poached halibut; lemon panna cotta. **Details:** www.stmichaelsmanor.com; near Cathedral; 9 pm. **Accommodation:** 30 rooms, from £180.

The Waffle House
Kingsbury Water Mill £ 18
St Michael's St AL3 4SJ (01727) 853502
"A nice range of waffles, both sweet and savoury" makes this '80s survivor, near the river, a very popular destination – they don't take bookings, though, and the queues can be *"unbearable"*.
/ **Sample dishes:** houmous & avocado waffle; pecan nut waffle with butterscotch sauce. **Details:** www.wafflehouse.co.uk; near Roman Museum; 6 pm; L only; no Amex; no booking.

Seafood Restaurant   £ 61

The Scores KY16 9AB   (01334) 479475
A "futuristic" glass box – with a "superb" clifftop setting and
"fabulous" views – houses this "excellent" seafood restaurant (sibling
to the one in St Monan's); prices can seem on the "hilarious" side,
though, and service can sometimes let the side down.
/ **Sample dishes:** salmon ballotine; grilled fillet of halibut, seafood, mussel &
pancetta chowder; fig & frangipane tart. **Details:** www.theseafoodrestaurant.com;
10 pm, Sun 9.30 pm; no shorts; children: 12+ at D.

Vine Leaf   £ 38

131 South St KY16 9UN   (01334) 477497
"Every course is a work of art", say fans of this "fabulous" bistro,
which continues to be a "favourite" for some reporters.
/ **Sample dishes:** Thai fishcakes; eight-hour lamb; baked apricot & almond tartlet
with amaretto cream anglaise. **Details:** www.vineleafstandrews.co.uk; 9.30 pm;
D only, closed Mon & Sun. **Accommodation:** 3 guest apartments rooms,
from £80.

Lawtons at No 16   £ 51

16 Nun St SA62 6NS   (01437) 729220
Steve & Kim Lawton's "charming" venture of over 25 years' standing
continues to inspire all-round applause for its "lovely" food and
"attentive" service. / **Sample dishes:** lobster ravioli; fillet of beef on a
horseradish suet pudding; dark chocolate & Kahlua crème brulée.
Details: www.lawtonsatno16.co.uk; 9.30 pm; D only, closed Sun; no Amex.

Alba Restaurant   £ 41

The Old Lifeboat Hs, Wharf Rd TR26 1LF   (01736) 797222
"Great views" (from the top floor) and "delicious and subtle" fish
dishes have made quite a name for Grant Nethercott's "lively"
harbourside restaurant; the whole of the carefully-chosen wine
list is available by the glass too. / **Sample dishes:** sautéed scallops with
black pudding; casserole of monkfish; chocolate taster plate.
Details: www.thealbarestaurant.com; 10 pm.

Blue Fish   £ 42

Norway Ln TR26 1LZ   (01736) 794204
"Great", "fresh" fish and seafood – consumed while "overlooking
St Ives" – is the draw to this agreeable arts-centre restaurant, which
comes complete with panoramic terrace. / **Sample dishes:** moules
marinière; scallops wrapped in Parma ham; raspberry crème brûlée.
Details: behind the Sloop Inn; 10 pm; no Amex.

Peppers   £ 24

22 Fore St TR26 1HE   (01736) 794014
A family restaurant that uses the best suppliers, and offers affordable
quality dining (including "excellent pizza"). / **Sample dishes:** stuffed
mushrooms; pizza calzone. **Details:** www.peppers-stives.co.uk.

Porthgwidden Beach Café £ 34
TR26 1SL   (01736) 796791
"Sit in your flip-flops eating fabulous food, overlooking the sea" –
that's the deal at this *"very friendly"* café, near the beach.
/ **Sample dishes:** herb pancakes with seafood filling; mackerel fillets with red
onion jam; strawberry & Cointreau brûlée. **Details:** www.porthgwiddencafe.co.uk;
10 pm; closed end of Oct - mid December; no Amex; booking: max 10.

Porthminster Café £ 42
Porthminster Beach TR26 2EB   (01736) 795352

"Can there be a lovelier spot" than this *"perfectly-located"* beach-
front café, which enjoys *"stunning views over the bay"*? – *"mouth-
watering"* seafood dishes crown a *"truly memorable"* all-round
experience. / **Sample dishes:** crisp-fried chilli squid; grilled turbot; poached
tamarillo. **Details:** www.porthminstercafe.co.uk; near railway station; 10 pm;
closed Nov-Mar; no Amex.

Tate Cafe
Tate Gallery £ 29
Porthmeor Beach TR26 1TG   (01736) 796226
The café *"on top of the art gallery"* is of most note for its
"outstanding views", but the food generally seems to be pretty good
too. / **Sample dishes:** smoked haddock & salmon fishcake with tartare sauce;
chicken breast with spice, lentils & rocket; Seville orange & pecan bread with
butter pudding. **Details:** www.tate.org.uk; 7 pm; closed Mon D, Tue D, Wed D,
Sat D & Sun D; no Amex.

ST MARY'S, ISLES OF SCILLY

Juliet's Garden £ 35
TR21 0NF   (01720) 422228
"What must be one of the best views in the British Isles" (*"across the
harbour and neighbouring islands, and with amazing sunsets"*) helps
win a 'tip' for this remote establishment, above Porthloo Beach.
/ **Sample dishes:** home-cured fillet of mackerel; seafood thermidor; panna cotta
with port & plum compote. **Details:** www.julietsgardenrestaurant.co.uk; 8.30 pm;
no Amex.

ST MAWES, CORNWALL 1–4B

Hotel Tresanton £ 53
27 Lower Castle Rd TR2 5DR   (01326) 270055
"A fantastic setting overlooking the harbour" sets the scene at Olga
Polizzi's rewnowned seaside hotel dining room (and terrace); foodwise,
"excellent fresh fish" is a highlight, but the odd reporter does feel the
place is *"trading on its reputation"*. / **Sample dishes:** seared scallops with
crab cakes; cod & langoustines; apple & rhubarb crumble.
Details: www.tresanton.com; near Castle; 9.30 pm; booking: max 10; children:
6+ at dinner. **Accommodation:** 29 rooms, from £230.

Rising Sun £ 44

The Square TR2 5DJ (01326) 270233

You get "a great view" and "super people-watching too", on the terrace of this harbourside hotel; it's also unanimously praised by reporters for its "enjoyable" food. / **Sample dishes:** *grilled sea bass; ballotine of duck; orange & passion fruit tart with greek yoghurt & black pepper lemongrass ice cream.* **Details:** *www.risingsunstmawes.com; 9 pm; D only, ex Sun open L & D; no Amex.* **Accommodation:** *8 rooms, from £100.*

ST MERRYN, CORNWALL   1–3B

Ripleys £ 48   ⭐

PL28 8NQ (01841) 520179

"Rick Stein-quality food at half the price" – that's the prospect at Paul Ripley's "first-rate" venture, near Newquay Airport, where dishes are "unfussy" but "delicious". / **Sample dishes:** *pan-fried monkfish livers with creamed leeks & sweet & sour dressing; roast rump of spring lamb; cherry & almond tart.* **Details:** *9.30 pm; closed Sun & Mon, D only Tue-Sat; no Amex; booking: max 8; children: 6.*

ST MONANS, FIFE   9–4D

Seafood Restaurant £ 50   ⭐

16 West End KY10 2BX (01333) 730327

"You can't help but fall in love with this place", say fans of this "excellent" seafood restaurant, near St Andrew's, which wins praise for its "superb" view, "great" cooking and "all-round attention to detail". / **Sample dishes:** *crab & leek tart; fillet of halibut; dark chocolate tarte with carmelised orange & chantilly cream.* **Details:** *www.theseafoodrestaurant.com; 9.30 pm; closed Mon & Tues D Oct - March.*

STADHAMPTON, OXFORDSHIRE   2–2D

The Crazy Bear £ 49   Ⓐ⭐

Bear Ln OX44 7UR (01865) 890714

A "quirky" venture that's "an all-time favourite" for some reporters, on account of its "lively" mix of "bizarre décor" with very "decent" food – be it Thai (downstairs) or British (upstairs). / **Sample dishes:** *asparagus spears; char-grilled calves' liver; iced passion fruit parfait.* **Details:** *www.crazybeargroup.co.uk; 10 pm.* **Accommodation:** *17 rooms, from £115.*

STAITHES, NORTH YORKSHIRE   8–3C

Endeavour £ 39   ⭐⭐

1 High St TS13 5BH (01947) 840825

"In the most picturesque little fishing village you could wish for", this "cosy and romantic" restaurant-with-rooms serves a seafood menu that's "interesting without being way-out"; those who stay over get "consistently excellent cooked breakfasts" too. / **Sample dishes:** *king scallops, dusted in oven-dried coral, seared & served on a rich risotto; roast halibut fillet crusted in sesame seeds, with a lime & cumin sauce; crème brûlée with spiced plums.* **Details:** *www.endeavour-restaurant.co.uk; 10m N of Whitby, off A174; 9 pm; closed Mon, Tue L, Wed L & Sun; no Amex.* **Accommodation:** *4 rooms, from £80.*

Fratellis   **£ 34**   **T**

13 St Mary's Hill PE9 2DP   (01780) 754333

*The best-known branch of a small Lincolnshire chain – an efficient
Italian, with "decent" fare. / Sample dishes: king prawns, white wine, chilli,
tomato & garlic; chicken & pancetta pasta parcel, with a cream & rosemary
sauce. Details: www.fratellis.co.uk; 9.30 pm.*

The George Hotel   **£ 54**   **A**

71 St Martins PE9 2LB   (01780) 750750

*This grand and famous coaching inn is a "comfortable"
establishment, with a dining room which is a "quiet haven", and a
"beautiful" courtyard in summer; the food is variable, but the wine
list is "interesting"; for a cheaper option, choose the "more relaxed"
Garden Room. / Sample dishes: pan-fried scallops with veal sweetbreads;
sirloin of beef & Yorkshire pudding; sherry trifle.
Details: www.georgehotelofstamford.com; off A1, 14m N of Peterborough,
onto B1081; 10 pm; jacket & tie required; children: 8+ at
D. Accommodation: 47 rooms, from £125.*

Leaping Hare Vineyard   **£ 39**   **A**

Wyken Vineyards IP31 2DW   (01359) 250287

*Fans say it's a "delightful" and "unexpected" experience to dine
in this former barn, with its "fresh" food and "their own very good
wines"; reports are not entirely consistent, though, and "amateurish"
service is a perennial bugbear. / Sample dishes: goat's cheese, leek &
tarragon risotto; slow-roast barbary duck; crème brûlée.
Details: www.wykenvineyards.co.uk; 9m NE of Bury St Edmunds; follow
tourist signs off A143; 9 pm; L only, ex Fri & Sat open L & D; no Amex.*

The Grinling Gibbons Restaurant   **A**
Stapleford Park   **£ 71**

LE14 2EF   (01572) 787522

*This location – a gorgeously grand hotel and country club –
is certainly "special"; whether the food lives up to it (or the prices
charged) is more moot. / Sample dishes: marinated salmon; roast John Dory;
chocolate & raspberry cheesecake. Details: www.stapleford.co.uk; 4m from
Melton Mowbray on B676; 9 pm; D only, ex Sun open L & D; jacket; children:
12+. Accommodation: 55 rooms, from £250.*

STATHERN, LEICESTERSHIRE   5–3D

Red Lion Inn   £ 36

2 Red Lion St LE14 4HS   (01949) 860868

This "exceptional" gastropub – sibling to the Olive Branch
at Clipsham, "in the wilds of rural Leicestershire" – is widely hailed for
its "very good food" (and its "good choice of beers and wines");
service, however, can be a bit "iffy". / **Sample dishes:** chicken liver pâté
with apple & grape chutney; sautéed calf's liver; vanilla crème brûlée & Kahlua ice
cream. **Details:** www.theredlioninn.co.uk; 9.30 pm; closed Sun D; no Amex.

STOCKBRIDGE, HAMPSHIRE   2–3D

Clos du Marquis   £ 44

London Rd SO20 6DE   (01264) 810738

"Genial" South African chef/patron, Germain Marquis "continues
to delight" with his "French provincial" cooking, at this highly popular
pub-conversion. / **Sample dishes:** scallops; fillet of beef; carmelised foie gras.
Details: www.closdumarquis.co.uk; 2m E on A30 from Stockbridge; 9 pm; closed
Mon & Sun D.

Greyhound   £ 51

31 High St SO20 6EY   (01264) 810833

"Food of a consistently high standard" helps win much praise for this
"excellent gastropub"; service can be "irritating", though, and there's
a feeling in some quarters that the place is "overrated".
/ **Sample dishes:** fishcake, poached egg & chive butter; pan-fried halibut with
wild mushrooms; chocolate fondant with hazelnut ice cream.
Details: www.thegreyhoundatstockbridge.co.uk; 9 pm; closed Sun D; no Amex;
booking: max 12. **Accommodation:** 8 rooms, from £75.

STOCKCROSS, BERKSHIRE   2–2D

Vineyard at Stockcross   £ 90

RG20 8JU   (01635) 528770

Sir Peter Michael's "modern" country house hotel is still of most note
for a wine list "like two telephone directories" ("including the
best Californian selection outside California"); its setting can seem
rather "business-like", and the bill "requires a second mortgage",
but John Campbell's "clever" cuisine "continues to improve".
/ **Sample dishes:** salmon & spiced lentil; John Dory with gnocchi; hazelnut
treacle & muscatel. **Details:** www.the-vineyard.co.uk; from M4, J13 take A34
towards Hungerford; 9.30 pm; no jeans or trainers. **Accommodation:** 49 rooms,
from £270.

STOKE HOLY CROSS, NORFOLK 6–4C

Wildebeest Arms £ 34
82-86 Norwich Rd NR14 8QJ (01508) 492497
*"A little oasis in a good-food desert" – this "quirkily-decorated" inn
was generally rated a "reliable" place this year, with "interesting"
food. / **Sample dishes:** pan-fried scallops; pan-fried fillet of salmon; raspberry
Bakewell tart. **Details:** www.animalinns.co.uk; from A140, turn left at Dunston
Hall, left at T-junction; 9 pm.*

STOKE ROW, OXFORDSHIRE 2–2D

The Crooked Billet £ 43 Ⓐ ★
Newlands Ln RG9 5PU (01491) 681048
*This "hard-to-find, old country inn" has a particularly "snug" and
"lovely" ambience; its "hearty" menu ranges from fish to game
to "rib-sticking local meat dishes" – numerous reports suggest that
"after a dip in standards in recent years, the place is now back
on song". / **Sample dishes:** mushroom & Mozzarella risotto cakes; pan-fried
sea bass; white chocolate & raspberry cheesecake.*
***Details:** www.thecrookedbillet.co.uk; off the A4130; 10 pm; no Amex.*

STOKE-BY-NAYLAND, SUFFOLK 3–2C

Angel Inn £ 34
Polstead St CO6 4SA (01206) 263245
*The style can seem "a little fussy", but "consistent quality" and
"huge portions" win more bouquets than brickbats for this popular
16th-century coaching inn. / **Sample dishes:** baked goat's cheese; grilled
skate wing; sticky toffee pudding. **Details:** www.theangelinn.net; 5m W of A12,
on B1068; 9.30 pm. **Accommodation:** 6 rooms, from £65.*

The Crown £ 39
CO6 4SE (01206) 262346
*A "huge" and "popular" pub (sometimes "too busy"), serving "good"
food from a "varied" and "well-presented" menu (as well
as "excellent" wines); it's "not always easy to get a table".
/ **Sample dishes:** caramelised skate; roasted wood pigeon; English custard &
nutmeg tart. **Details:** www.eoinns.co.uk; 9.30 pm, Fri & Sat10 pm, Sun 9 pm;
no Amex.*

STON EASTON, SOMERSET 2–3B

Ston Easton Park £ 62
Ston Easton BA3 4DF (01761) 241631
*"You can place bets on how many Bentleys will be parked outside...
and there's usually a helicopter on the lawn", at this "stunning"
(but perhaps "soulless") Palladian pile (now part of the Von Essen
empire); it's a treat for "afternoon tea, and lots of it" –
more substantial fare is "good, but not great". / **Sample dishes:** pavé
of marinated duck breast & confit duck leg with ham roulette; roast fillet of sea
bass. **Details:** www.stoneaston.co.uk; 11m SW of Bath on A39; 9.30 pm;
no jeans. **Accommodation:** 23 rooms, from £175.*

STONEHAVEN, ABERDEEN　　　　　　　9–3D

Carron　　　　　　　　　**£ 35**

Cameron St AB39 2HS　(01569) 760460

*"A restored Art Deco tearoom that offers an interesting selection
of snacks and more serious meals"; it has a "lovely" terrace too,
which "looks out onto a well-kept garden".* / **Sample dishes:** white &
brown crab meat, layered on avocado & served on crisp leaves drizzled with
parsley oil; pot-roasted haunch of venison served in a rich port & orange sauce.
Details: www.carron-restaurant.co.uk; 9.30 pm; closed Mon & Sun; no Amex.

Lairhillock Inn　　　　　　　**£ 35**

Netherley AB39 3QS　(01569) 730001

*"A nice pub in the middle of nowhere, where the ale is real, and so
is the food"* – the *"great traditional Sunday lunch"*, served in the
restaurant, is particularly worth seeking out; (NB It changed hands
in May 2007, but the chef remains the same). / **Sample dishes:** cullen
skink; grilled venison escalopes; sticky toffee pudding.
Details: www.lairhillock.co.uk; 7m S of Aberdeen; 9.30 pm.

STOURBRIDGE, WORCESTERSHIRE　　　5–4B

French Connection　　　　　**£ 33**

3 Coventry St DY8 1EP　(01384) 390940

*Celebrating its 20th year – a bistro worth knowing about for its
"good French food at reasonable prices".* / **Sample dishes:** pear &
Roquefort tartlet; boeuf bourguignon; chocolate & pear crèpes.
Details: www.frenchconnectionbistro.com; 9.30 pm; closed Mon, Tue D & Sun.

STOW-ON-THE-WOLD, GLOUCESTERSHIRE 2–1C

The King's Arms　　　　　　**£ 38**

Market Sq GL54 1AF　(01451) 830364

*It can seem a tad "pricey" for what it is, but this 500-year old
Cotswold coaching inn wins praise for its "innovative and tasty food,
and its relaxing and comfortable atmosphere".*
/ **Sample dishes:** poached halibut fillet; grilled fillet of sea bass with leeks,
cherizo, & sunblushed tomato; strawberry & Pimm's terrine.
Details: www.thekingsarmsstow.co.uk; 9.30 pm, 10 pm Sat.
Accommodation: 10 rooms, from £80.

The Old Butchers　　　　　　**£ 38**

7 Park St GL54 1AQ　(01451) 831700

*Fans hail the "wonderful food and value" (and "the best fish") at this
modern bistro; reports have become a little mixed, though – one fan
feels the place "is trying to be both everyday and upmarket,
and falling to do either properly".* / **Sample dishes:** brandade de morue
with poached egg; rump of lamb & chopped aubergine salad; pain perdu with
spiced plums. **Details:** www.theoldbutchers.com; 9 pm.

STRATFORD-UPON-AVON, WARWICKSHIRE 2–1C

Café Chutney　　　　　　　**£ 32**

Beaconwood Bordon Hill CV37 9RX　(01789) 204427

*"Great food that's reasonably priced" makes this "friendly" curry
house a stand-by worth knowing about.*

Lambs   **£ 39**

12 Sheep St CV37 6EF   (01789) 292554

"Numerous nooks" and *"cosy alcoves"* add to the charms of this old
Tudor House – an *"efficient"* operation that's the best-known place
in this touristy town (and *"perfect pre-theatre"*).
/ **Sample dishes:** *carpaccio of beef; calves' liver; dark chocolate truffle cake.*
Details: *www.lambsrestaurant.co.uk; 9.45 pm; closed Mon L; no Amex; booking:
max 12.*

The Oppo   **£ 37**

13 Sheep St CV37 6EF   (01789) 269980

"Another reliable bistro" (rated very similarly to the somewhat better-
known Lambs), which is tipped by some for *"the best pre-theatre
meal"* in town. / **Sample dishes:** *fine chicken liver pâté; roast chicken with
banana; sticky toffee pudding.* **Details:** *www.theoppo.co.uk; 10 pm; no Amex;
booking: max 12.*

Thai Kingdom   **£ 31**

11 Warwick Rd CV37 6YW   (01789) 261103

*"The food is delicious, light and spicy, and service is always
charming"*, at this *"good-value"* townhouse Thai, near the town-
centre; *"it's excellent pre-theatre"*. / **Sample dishes:** *squid stir-fried with
red pepper, onion, garlic & black pepper; beef in a red wine sauce with vegetables.*
Details: *www.thaikingdom.co.uk; 10.45 pm.*

The Vintner   **£ 35**   Ⓐ ⭐

4-5 Sheep St CV37 6EF   (01789) 297259

*Emerging as the town's highest-rated destination – this "beautiful
black and white building" is uniformly praised by reporters for its
"good brasserie-style food".* / **Sample dishes:** *carpaccio of beef with
rocket & parmesan; pan-fried lemon sole with caper butter.*
Details: *www.the-vintner.co.uk; 11 pm, 9.30 Sun; no Amex.*

STRONTIAN, ARGYLL   9–3B

Kilcamb Lodge Hotel   **£ 58**   Ⓣ

PH36 4HY   (01967) 402257

*"A fantastic small hotel perched on the edge of the village,
overlooking the Loch, where the great view from the restaurant
is even better when a deer wanders by"*; the menu is *"limited"*,
but the overall experience very satisfactory. / **Sample dishes:** *tortellini
of brown crab & langoustine, lobster consume with seared scallops; slow-roasted
pork belly with Szechuan spiced pork loin; five textures of summer berries, jelly,
sorbet, mousse, extraction, leather.* **Details:** *www.kilcamblodge.co.uk; 9.30 pm;
no jeans or trainers; booking essential; children: 12+.* **Accommodation:** *10
rooms, from £130.*

STUCKTON, HAMPSHIRE   2–3C

Three Lions   **£ 51**   ⭐

Stuckton Rd SP6 2HF   (01425) 652489

"You always leave with a warm glow", says one of the fans of the
Womersley family's New Forest restaurant-with-rooms, where the
cooking is *"more complex than it might at first sight appear"*;
some reporters, though, find the décor *"rather '80s"*.
/ **Sample dishes:** *galette of smoked haddock; loin of lamb; chocolate pudding.*
Details: *www.thethreelionsrestaurant.co.uk; 1m E of Fordingbridge off B3078;
9 pm, Fri & Sat 9.30 pm; closed Mon & Sun D; no Amex.* **Accommodation:** *7
rooms, from £75.*

STUDLAND, DORSET   2–4C

Shell Bay Seafood   £ 37   Ⓐ
Ferry Rd BH19 3BA   (01929) 450363
*"If you want to impress Australians with a view and great fish", there's
"no finer setting" than this "delightfully-located" spot ("looking
towards Brownsea Island"), where the "simple" seafood dishes
almost invariably satisfy. / **Sample dishes:** prawn & crayfish in a spring roll;
sea bass; chocolate brownie & white chocolate ice cream.*
Details: *www.shellbay.net; just near the Sandbanks to Swanage ferry; 9 pm;
closed Mon Sept - May; children: 12+ at dinner.*

STURMINSTER NEWTON, DORSET   2–3B

Plumber Manor   £ 39   ✪
DT10 2AF   (01258) 472507
*"Like being welcomed into a family home in grand style" –
this comfortable hotel (run by the Prideaux family since the '70s)
pleased all reporters with its "very good English cooking";
a "good Sunday lunch" is a highlight. / **Sample dishes:** wild mushroom
millefeuille; guinea fowl; chocolate torte.* ***Details:*** *www.plumbermanor.com;
off A357 towards Hazelbury Bryan; 9.30 pm; D only, ex Sun open L &
D.* ***Accommodation:*** *16 rooms, from £110.*

SUNDERLAND, TYNE & WEAR   8–2C

ThrowingStones
National Glass Centre   £ 26
Liberty Way SR6 0GL   (0191) 565 3939
*"In an area without much to offer", this "interesting"-looking café –
"with views over the river" – is a "pleasant surprise", serving "simple,
good-value meals" ("especially for lunch"). / **Sample dishes:** chicken liver
pâté; pot-roast beef; toffee & apple meringue.*
Details: *www.nationalglasscentre.com; A19 to Sunderland, follow signs for
National Glass Centre; 11.30 pm; Mon-Thu L only, closed Sun D; no Amex.*

SUNNINGDALE, BERKSHIRE   3–3A

Fego Caffe   £ 26   ✪
Chobham Rd SL5 0DU   (01344) 876464
*"Fabulous breakfasts", a "lazy coffee" or a "quick bite of lunch" –
the sort of occasions when this "friendly" café hits the spot.
/ **Sample dishes:** Cajun grilled chicken salad with avocado & feta; vanilla ice
cream topped with espresso.* ***Details:*** *www.fegocaffe-intheuk.com; 5 pm; L only;
no Amex.*

SURBITON, SURREY   3–3B

                                                      ✪✪
The French Table   £ 44
85 Maple Rd KT6 4AW   (020) 8399 2365
*"Superlative" cooking combines with "personal" service to make Eric
& Sarah Guignard's "top-notch" restaurant an "ever-popular"
suburban "oasis" (albeit a sometimes "crowded" one) – it enjoys
a huge fan club among reporters. / **Sample dishes:** foie gras & chicken
liver pâté; goat's cheese gnocchi; assiette gourmande of chocolate.*
Details: *www.thefrenchtable.co.uk; 10.30 pm; closed Mon & Sun D, Sat D only;
booking: max 10, Fri & Sat.*

Joy £ 34 ⭐

37 Brighton Rd KT6 5LR   (020) 8390 3988

"A light and airy" modern Indian restaurant in the 'burbs which gets *"very busy"*, thanks to its *"unusual"* menu and its *"good-quality"* cuisine. / **Sample dishes:** *crab bujni; lamb banjara; gajar halwa.*
Details: *www.joy-restaurant.co.uk; 11.30 pm.*

SUTTON GAULT, CAMBRIDGESHIRE   3–1B

Anchor £ 40 Ⓐ

Bury Ln CB6 2BD   (01353) 778537

"Built as a hostel for the men draining the fens", this old inn (in the middle of nowhere) retains a *"lovely and traditional"* atmosphere; it has sometimes suffered from *"distinctly average"* food and service, but some regulars sense the possibility of *"improvement under new management"*. / **Sample dishes:** *rillette of smoked eel; roast loin of lamb; cinnamon panna cotta with spiced panetone & apple sorbet.*
Details: *www.anchorsuttongault.co.uk; 7m W of Ely, signposted off B1381 in Sutton; 9pm, Sat 9.30 pm.* **Accommodation:** *4 rooms, from £65.*

SUTTON GREEN, SURREY   3–3A

Olive Tree £ 40 ⭐

Sutton Green Rd GU4 7QD   (01483) 729999

"Simple food is done very well", at this agreeable venue – it's still *"more pub than restaurant, but with quality poised between the two"*. / **Sample dishes:** *crab & avocado; roasted monkfish, mustard & tarragon sauce; bread & butter pudding.* **Details:** *www.theolivetree.us; 9.30 pm; closed Mon D & Sun D; no Amex.*

SWANSEA, SWANSEA   1–1D

Bouchon De Rossi £ 35 Ⓣ

217 Oxford St SA1 3BG   (01792) 655780

A recent arrival tipped by one reporter for a *"reasonably-priced and interesting menu"* that's *"consistently well cooked"*; fans say it's *"perfect before the theatre"* too. / **Sample dishes:** *saffron risotto; lobster thermidor; lisse fermier.* **Details:** *10 pm; closed Mon & Sun.*

La Braseria £ 39 Ⓐ

28 Wind St SA1 1DZ   (01792) 469683

This *"predictable"* Spanish-style stalwart – where, like Cardiff's Champers, you choose it, and they grill it – is *"a fairly boisterous venue of particular interest in a city not exactly brimming with decent restaurants"*; *"now they also have a branch by the docks, it's easier to get a table"*. / **Sample dishes:** *gravadlax; bass on rock salt; raspberry cheesecake.* **Details:** *www.labraseria.com; 11.30 pm; closed Sun; need 6+ to book; children: 6+.*

Patricks £ 35

638 Mumbles Rd SA3 4EA (01792) 360199

A "crowded" brasserie-with-rooms, on the Mumbles, where "the style
and service are a little in advance of the actual content"; even so,
it's "a very useful place for a pleasing meal in a poorly-served area".
/ *Sample dishes:* char-grilled asparagus & tomato bruschetta; fillet of sea bass;
champagne & summer fruit jelly with clotted cream ice cream.
Details: www.patrickswithrooms.com; in Mumbles, 1m before pier; 9.50 pm;
closed Sun D. *Accommodation:* 8 rooms, from £110.

SWINTON, SCOTTISH BORDERS 8–1A

Wheatsheaf Inn £ 36

Main St TD11 3JJ (01890) 860257

In "a bit of a culinary dessert" – "for 50 miles in all directions!" –
this "pricey" pub pleases most reporters; it can seem a touch
"pretentious", though, and the service can sometimes
be "overwhelmed by the demand". / *Sample dishes:* sautéed Paris brown
mushrooms; roast rack of lamb; sticky ginger & pear pudding.
Details: www.wheatsheaf-swinton.co.uk; between Kelso & Berwick-upon-Tweed,
by village green; 9 pm; Closed Sun D Jan & Feb; no Amex; children: 10+ at D.
Accommodation: 10 rooms, from £102.

TADCASTER, NORTH YORKSHIRE 5–1D

Aagrah £ 26 ⭐

York Rd LS24 8EG (01937) 530888

"It deserves its reputation", say fans of this useful outpost of the
eminent Yorkshire curry chain, which serves "an excellent range
of dishes". / *Sample dishes:* bahrain kebab; murgh hyderabadi; kulfi.
Details: www.aagrah.com; 7m from York on A64; 11.30 pm, 11 pm Sun; closed
Sat L & Sun L.

TAPLOW, BERKSHIRE 3–3A

Ⓐ

Terrace
Cliveden House £ 81

Cliveden Rd SL6 0JF (01628) 668561

A "priceless" view rewards visitors to the Astor family's former
palazzo (now a Von Essen establishment), which stands in a great
estate, and the menu ("interesting twists on luxury staples")
is generally pleasing too; there are critics, though, who dismiss it as
a place with "metropolitan aspirations, but provincial habits".
/ *Sample dishes:* asparagus soup with roast langoustines; pan-roast fillet
of turbot; banoffee tart with rich vanilla ice cream.
Details: www.clivedenhouse.co.uk; 9.30 pm; jacket. *Accommodation:* 39
rooms, from £360.

Ⓐ

Waldo's
Cliveden House £ 98

Berry Hill SL6 0JF (01628) 668561

"Perfect for a special celebration" – this grand basement dining room
is "notably more inventive than the Terrace, upstairs"; Daniel
Galmiche's food is consistently good, but it's the outstanding service
and "indulgent", "romantic" ambience that are really "wonderful".
/ *Sample dishes:* carpaccio of beef, served with celery granite & lime oil; corn-fed
Anjou pigeon; apricot Tatin scented with camomile, served on a caramel almond
base with vanilla ice cream & almond wafers. *Details:* www.clivedenhouse.co.uk;
M4, J7 then follow National Trust signs; 9.30 pm; D only, closed Mon & Sun;
jacket & tie required; booking: max 6; children: 12+. *Accommodation:* 39
rooms, from £360.

The Castle Hotel   **£ 61**   A ☆

Castle Grn TA1 1NF (01823) 272671
*This once-celebrated "old-school dining room" – part of a landmark
hotel – continues its fight back to prominence; the style may
be slightly "Agatha Christie", but the place was generally reckoned
to offer a "superb" all-round experience this year.*
/ **Sample dishes:** *home-smoked salmon; slow-roast duck; bitter chocolate tart.*
Details: *www.the-castle-hotel.com; follow tourist information signs; 9.30 pm;
closed Sun D.* **Accommodation:** *44 rooms, from £185.*

Browns Hotel   **£ 49**   T

80 West St PL19 8AQ (01822) 618686
*Fans tip this as "a wonderful hotel brasserie" – a "smart" place that's
"great for a light lunch".* / **Sample dishes:** *braised lamb; swordfish.*
Details: *www.brownsdevon.co.uk; 10 pm.* **Accommodation:** *20 rooms,
from £99.*

Hotel Endsleigh   **£ 55**   A

PL19 0PQ (01822) 870 000
*Ogla Polizzi's "stunningly-restored house, in beautiful grounds" wins
nothing but praise for its "most romantic" setting (on the edge
of Dartmoor), and its very good food "to match"; it also has
"a delightful summer terrace", with "marvellous views".*
/ **Sample dishes:** *roast quail with roasted figs, denhay ham, celeriac tarte fine, &
sherry vinegar jus; seabass with pea purée, pea & ham tortellini & tomato batter;
iced mango & passion fruit parfait with coconut panacotta & ginger doughnut.*
Details: *www.hotelendsleigh.com; Right outside of Milton Abbot ; 10.30 pm.*
Accommodation: *16 rooms, from £200.*

Jersey Farm   **£ 28**   T

Darlington Rd DJ12 8TA (01833) 638223
*Tasty and varied food – including "exceptional Sunday roasts" –
wins praise for this contemporary country hotel (and in a part of the
world not flush with competing options).* / **Sample dishes:** *fanned paw
paw with compote of kiwi & strawberry dressed with melon & ginger coulis;
game & venison stew with herb dumplings & thyme roasted potatoes.*
Details: *www.jerseyfarm.co.uk; 9 pm.*

Howards House Hotel   **£ 58**   T

SP3 5RJ (01722) 716392
*"A very welcoming hotel", in a pretty village house; as a place to eat,
it attracts relatively few, but consistently positive, reports.*
/ **Sample dishes:** *roast foie gras, pickled plums & cherry vinegar caramel;
pan-fried halibut, butternut squash gnocchi & deep-fried oysters; orange blossom
crème caramel with an orange terrine.* **Details:** *www.howardshousehotel.com;
9m W of Stonehenge off A303; 9 pm; closed Mon L & Fri L.*
Accommodation: *9 rooms, from £155.*

Calcot Manor £ 47 Ⓐ
GL8 8YJ (01666) 890391
As it "gets bigger every year", this famously "child-friendly" hotel
(and spa) inspires ever more reports on its dining room, which
is competent without itself quite reaching 'destination' status;
this year's reports on dining at the in-house boozer, the Gumstool Inn,
were very positive. / **Sample dishes:** fresh langoustine tails; grilled sausages
with rich onion gravy & mashed potatoes; vanilla crème brûlée.
Details: www.calcotmanor.co.uk; junction of A46 & A4135; 9.30 pm.
Accommodation: 35 rooms, from £205.

Priory Inn £ 38 Ⓐ ✪
London Rd GL8 8JJ (01666) 502251
"Proper" pizza is the highlight of the "surprisingly good"
(if "not elaborate") food that makes this "attractive beamed inn"
quite a "local asset". / **Sample dishes:** roast beetroot soup with crème
fraîche; baked chicken with apricot & plum stuffing; caramelised rice pudding with
whisky sauce. **Details:** www.theprioryinn.co.uk; 10 pm. **Accommodation:** 14
rooms, from £99.

Trouble House Inn £ 46
Cirencester Rd GL8 8SG (01666) 502206
"A quaint country boozer, simply-decorated, and with an outstanding
menu for a pub"; the kitchen can get "overstretched", though, leading
to "hit-and-miss" results. / **Sample dishes:** foie gras & apple with pickled
grapes; grilled belly of pork & black pudding; strawberry meringue with strawberry
sorbet. **Details:** www.troublehouse.co.uk; 1.5m from Tetbury on A433 towards
Cirencester; 9.30 pm; closed Mon; closed 2 weeks in Jan; booking: max 8; children:
14+ in bar.

Abbey Refectory Ⓣ
Tewkesbury Abbey £ 18
Church St GL20 5RZ (01684) 273736
"Good quality and value" ("specials" in particular) make this
centuries-old dining space still of interest to today's diners.
/ **Details:** www.tewkesburyabbey.org.uk; M5 motorway, exit junction number
9; L only; no Amex.

Carpenters Arms £ 34 Ⓣ
YO7 2DP (01845) 537369
A pretty inn (converted from a row of miners' cottages) said to offer
"wonderful pub food in a lovely setting". / **Sample dishes:** braised shank
of lamb with cider; duck with oriental vegetable stir fry.
Details: www.carpentersarmsfelixkirk.co.uk; 9 pm; closed Mon & Sun D;
no Amex.

THORNHAM, NORFOLK　　　　　　　6–3B

Lifeboat Inn　　　　　　　　**£ 38**
Ship Ln　PE36 6LT　(01485) 512236
"A pretty solid pub-cum-restaurant that's always heaving"
(and "service can fail when they are busy"); for most reporters,
though, "after a long day on the beach, you can't go wrong here".
/ **Sample dishes:** smoked salmon platter with crevettes; fish pie; sticky toffee
pudding. **Details:** www.lifeboatinn.co.uk; 20m from Kings Lynn on A149
coast road; 9.30 pm; D only, ex Sun open L & D; no Amex.
Accommodation: 13 rooms, from £96.

THORPE LANGTON, LEICESTERSHIRE　　　5–4D

Bakers Arms　　　　　　　　**£ 36**　　🅐
Main St　LE16 7TS　(01858) 545201
"Friendly service, and good fresh food" – that's the deal at this classic,
olde-worlde village pub, which fans say "never disappoints".
/ **Sample dishes:** scallops & black pudding; chump of lamb with creamed
leeks & bacon; sticky toffee pudding. **Details:** www.thebakersarms.co.uk;
near Market Harborough off A6; 9.30 pm; D only, ex Sat open L & D & Sun open
L only, closed Mon; children: 12+.

THURSFORD, NORFOLK　　　　　　　6–4C

Crawfish　　　　　　　　　**£ 28**　　⭐
Holt Rd　NR21 0BJ　(01328) 878313
"A rare find in a boozer, especially round here" – this pub-cum-Thai
is "the best oriental in Norfolk", say fans, and offers "very good and
authentic" dishes. / **Details:** www.realthaifood.co.uk; 10.30 pm; closed Mon;
no Amex.

TITLEY, HEREFORDSHIRE　　　　　　2–1A

Stagg Inn　　　　　　　　　**£ 41**　　⭐⭐
HR5 3RL　(01544) 230221
Ex-Gavroche chef Steve Reynolds's "continuing commitment to local
organic food" contributes to some "original" and "perfectly judged"
results at this "unpretentious" and "rustic" inn. / **Sample dishes:** seared
scallops with lentils & mint; duck breast; caramelised passion fruit tart.
Details: www.thestagg.co.uk; on B4355, NE of Kington; 9 pm; closed Mon &
Sun D; no Amex. **Accommodation:** 6 rooms, from £85.

TOLWORTH, SURREY　　　　　　　3–3B

Superfish　　　　　　　　　**£ 16**　　⭐⭐
25 The Broadway　KT6 7DJ　(020) 83902868
"Unbeatable for grilled fish" – a member of a small chain
of upmarket Surrey chippies, all of which get a massive thumbs-up
from reporters; see website for further branches.
/ **Sample dishes:** fish & chips; cherry flan. **Details:** www.superfishuk.co.uk;
10 pm; closed Sun.

Darts Farm Café   £ 24   ⓣ
Clyst St George EX3 0QH   (01392) 875587
*"A great meeting place"; this "noisy" dining area of a rural retail
complex has quite a reputation locally for its "wholesome" food
(in particular "the freshest of fish"). / **Sample dishes:** chicken liver pâté;
grilled chicken breast; raspberry & rhubarb crumble with clotted cream.
Details: www.dartsfarm.co.uk; L only; no Amex.*

The Galley   £ 52   Ⓐ★
41 Fore St EX3 0HU   (01392) 876078
*The "camp but elegant" style of this "small and friendly" restaurant-
with-rooms is a big hit with most reporters – it can sometimes seem
"over-priced", but those in search of "top seafood" rarely seem
disappointed. / **Sample dishes:** crab-filled avocado with armagnac seafood
sauce; fillets of turbot in tempura beer batter with Yorkshire caviar & vinegar cut
chips; milk organic chocolate sweet orange, nutmeg & chilli.
Details: www.galleyrestaurant.co.uk; 9.30; closed Mon & Sun; booking essential;
children: 12+. **Accommodation:** 4 rooms, from £125.*

Start Bay Inn   £ 26   ★
TQ7 2TQ   (01548) 580553
*A beachfront pub with a big name for its "excellent fish dishes" and
"extraordinary value for money"; in fact, that's the main problem –
"you can't book", and if it's "busy" (often), waits can be "hideous".
/ **Sample dishes:** prawn cocktail; cod & chips; chocolate sponge pudding.
Details: www.startbayinn.co.uk; on beach front (take A379 coastal road
to Dartmouth); 10 pm; no Amex; no booking.*

Elephant Bar & Restaurant   £ 40   ★
3-4 Beacon Ter, Harbourside TQ1 2BH   (01803) 200044
*Now divided into a casual brasserie and an "eclectic" (Michelin-
blessed) first-floor fine dining room, this "popular" establishment is,
say fans, "not to be missed", as its food is "superb"; given the
"top prices", though, the performance can sometimes seem rather
"average". / **Sample dishes:** crab with avocado, mango, & mint salsa, & warm
crab beignet; loin of venison with vanilla-roasted butternut & baby beetroot jus;
almond tansy pudding with sweet pumpkin & vanilla ice cream.
Details: www.elephantrestaurant.co.uk; 9.30 pm; closed Mon & Sun D; children:
14+ at bar.*

No 7 Fish Bistro   £ 40   ⓣ
Beacon Ter TQ1 2BH   (01803) 295055
*A "busy" and "bustling" restaurant, tipped for its "consistently good
fresh fish". / **Sample dishes:** creamy-curried prawns; fillet of fish with tempura
batter; home-made crème brûlée. **Details:** www.no7-fish.com; 9.30 pm; D only
Sun-Tue, closed Sun & Mon in Winter.*

Orchid Restaurant
Corbyn Head Hotel   **£ 50**   Ⓐ ★
Seafront TQ2 6RH   (01803) 296366
"Lovely sea-views, and notably good food and service" create all-round
satisfaction with this seaside hotel dining room, where the cuisine
is much more ambitious than is the norm. / **Sample dishes:** *goat's cheese
spring roll, beetroot sorbet & beetroot tartar; saddle of venison, braised red
cabbage, garlic mash, hazelnut butter & liquorice; dark chocolate & lime fondant,
coconut sorbet.* **Details:** *www.orchidrestaurant.net; 9.30 pm; closed Mon & Sun;
no jeans or shorts.* **Accommodation:** *45 rooms, from £120.*

TOTNES, DEVON   I–3D

Kingsbridge Inn   **£ 34**   Ⓣ
9 Leechwell St TQ9 5SY   (01803) 863324
*New ownership seems to have pepped up this "lovely old pub",
recommended for its "good atmosphere, comfy surroundings and
great food using local produce".* / **Sample dishes:** *beetroot &
juniper-infused gravadlax with gin & tonic lime granita; fillet of beef with scampi &
thermidor sauce; warm chocolate mousse cake with cherries & vanilla ice cream.*
Details: *9.30 pm.*

TREEN, CORNWALL   I–4A

Gurnards Head   **£ 38**   Ⓣ
TR26 3DE   (01736) 796928
"A great dining pub" – with a wonderful coastal location – on the way
to Land's End from St Ives. / **Sample dishes:** *sirloin beef; poached skate.*
Details: *www.gurnardshead.co.uk; on coastal road between Land's End & St Ives,
near Zennor B3306; 9.30 pm; no Amex.* **Accommodation:** *7 rooms,
from £72.50.*

TROUTBECK, CUMBRIA   7–3D

Queen's Head   **£ 33**   Ⓐ ★
Townhead LA23 1PW   (01539) 432174
*"You have to time your visit wisely", if you wish to avoid a wait at this
"idyllically located", "traditional" pub, which has "spectacular views"
and which serves "a well-cooked tasty menu"; fortunately, though,
"that's no problem at all if you fancy an hour getting stuck into the
local ales".* / **Sample dishes:** *confit of duck lick; grilled Cumberland sausage
served in a bean & chorizo casserole; sticky toffee pudding.*
Details: *www.queensheadhotel.com; A592 on Kirkstone Pass; 9 pm; no Amex;
booking: max 8, Fri & Sat.* **Accommodation:** *16 rooms, from £100.*

TUNBRIDGE WELLS, KENT   3–4B

Hotel du Vin et Bistro   **£ 45**
Crescent Rd TN1 2LY   (01892) 526455
"An excellent choice of wines" and an *"attractive"* location continue
to win praise for this boutique-hotel as an *"enjoyable"* location; service
"could be improved", however, and the *"solid"* food – never the
greatest – seems increasingly incidental. / **Sample dishes:** *chicken & foie
gras parfait with pear chutney; pan-fried calves' liver; sticky toffee pudding.*
Details: *www.hotelduvin.com; 9.45 pm; booking: max 10.* **Accommodation:** *34
rooms, from £95.*

380

Indochina   **£ 26** ⭐

54 London Rd TN1 1DS   (01892) 618861

A contemporary town-centre restaurant, whose "beautifully-cooked" Malaysian fare and notably "personable" service win support from all who comment on it. / Details: 11 pm; closed Sun L.

Thackeray's   **£ 52** ⭐

85 London Rd TN1 1EA   (01892) 511921

Richard Phillips's "stunning" food (that's often "beautiful to look at" too) is winning ever more "dependable" acclaim for this contemporary-style restaurant, in a pretty old villa; the set lunch, in particular, offers "outstanding value". / Sample dishes: pan-fried escalope of duck foie gras; roast fillet of beef; white chocolate & raspberry mouse & dark chocolate tart. Details: www.thackerays-restaurant.co.uk; near Kent and Sussex hospital; 10.30 pm; closed Mon & Sun D.

TUNSTALL, LANCASHIRE   7–4D

Lunesdale Arms   **£ 33** ⭐

LA6 2QN   (01524) 274203

"A bit off the beaten track, but well worth a visit"; Emma Gillibrand's "friendly" gastropub won consistent praise this year for its "imaginative blackboard menu" – realised "with flair" – and its "cheerful" and "efficient" service. / Sample dishes: twice-baked tomato & goat's cheese soufflé; slow-roast shoulder of lamb; chocolate brownie. Details: www.thelunesdale.co.uk; 15 min from J34 on M6 onto A683; 9 pm; closed Mon.

TURNERS HILL, WEST SUSSEX   3–4B

Alexander House Hotel   **£ 56** Ⓐ

East St RH10 4QD   (01342) 714914

"Stunning", "brilliant" and "faultless"… or "pretentious", "abysmal" and "outrageously expensive" – this "attractive" Jacobean country house, set in 170 acres, attracts feedback which can be characterised only as 'Jekyll and Hyde'. / Sample dishes: orange-scented scallops; fillet of beef with foie gras; chocolate fondant with blood orange ice cream. Details: www.alexanderhouse.co.uk; off M23 J10, follow signs to E. Grinstead and Turners Hill, on B2110; 10pm; no jeans. Accommodation: 38 rooms, from £175.

TWICKENHAM, MIDDLESEX   3–3B

Arthur's   **£ 37** ⭐

The Green TW2 5AB   (020) 88933995

"Known to the locals as 'The Bog on The Green'", Tony Row's former public WC – overlooking the aforementioned public space – is quite a local hit, thanks to his "lovely, reasonably-priced" food. / Sample dishes: fishcakes; fillet of beef with pepper sauce. Details: 10 pm; no Amex.

TYN-Y-GROES, CONWY   4–1D

Groes Inn   **£ 38** Ⓐ

LL32 8TN   (01492) 650545

"A fine example of a traditional pub at its best" – Wales's oldest inn still pleases most (if not quite all) reporters with its "satisfying" fare. / Sample dishes: creamy smoked haddock; poached salmon & grilled plaice; bread & butter pudding. Details: www.groesinn.com; on B5106 between Conwy & Betws-y-coed, 2m from Conwy; 9 pm. Accommodation: 14 rooms, from £103.

Sidney's   £ 39

3-5 Percy Park Rd NE30 4LZ   (0191) 257 8500

A "local-favourite" bistro, praised by most reporters for its "good" food, including some "excellent fish and seafood". / **Sample dishes:** baked queen scallops; crispy duck & watercress salad; sticky toffee pudding. **Details:** www.sidneys.co.uk; 9.30 pm; closed Sun.

ULLINGSWICK, HEREFORDSHIRE   2–1B

The Three Crowns Inn   £ 38

HR1 3JQ   (01432) 820279

A half-timbered inn, that's worth knowing about for its "reliable" food and "friendly" style. / **Sample dishes:** dry-spiced mackerel; fried veal; chocolate fondant with cherries. **Details:** www.threecrownsinn.com; 1.5m from A417; 9.30 pm; closed Mon; no Amex. **Accommodation:** 1 room, at about £95.

ULLSWATER, CUMBRIA   7–3D

Sharrow Bay   £ 67

CA10 2LZ   (01768) 486301

A "magnificent" Lakeland location, "pampering" service, "superb" food (though there's "too much of it") and "magisterial" wine list still add up to a "splendid" experience at the UK's original country house hotel; it's now part of the Von Essen stable, and one or two long-term fans felt that quality had "fallen slightly" this year. / **Sample dishes:** dressed crab & terrine of lobster; best end of lamb; tropical fruit salad & passion fruit. **Details:** www.sharrowbay.co.uk; on Pooley Bridge Rd towards Howtown; 8 pm; children: 13+. **Accommodation:** 24 rooms, from £350.

ULVERSTON, CUMBRIA   7–4D

Bay Horse   £ 46

Canal Foot LA12 9EL   (01229) 583972

"An oasis in an area not known for great food"; this lovely old inn (overlooking Morecambe Bay) is currently "on top form", and notable for its "excellent" all-round standards. / **Sample dishes:** potted shrimps; pan-fried strips of fillet steak; brandy pudding with cream. **Details:** www.thebayhorsehotel.co.uk; after Canal Foot sign, turn left & pass Glaxo factory; 8 pm; closed Mon L; children: 12+ evening. **Accommodation:** 9 rooms, from £90.

UPPER BOROUGH WALLS, BATH   5–4C

Raphael   £ 39

Gascoyne Hs, Upper Borough Walls BA1 1RN
(01225) 480042

A "stylish" brasserie, with "slick" cooking and "friendly" service. / **Sample dishes:** vodka & beetroot infused organic salmon gravadlax served on pesto pancakes with horseradish crème fraîche; char-grilled lamb cutlets infused with cumin & paprika. **Details:** www.raphaelrestaurant.co.uk; late.

UPPER SLAUGHTER, GLOUCESTERSHIRE   2–1C

Lords of the Manor   £ 75   ⭐
GL54 2JD   (01451) 820243
"Really improved" food is helping re-establish the fame of this
potentially very charming dining room in a prime Cotswold village;
now they could usefully set to work on the service, which *"has an
element of Fawlty Towers about it"*. / **Sample dishes:** cheese & gaufrette
potatoes; monkfish with crispy polenta; chocolate fondant with five-spice jelly.
Details: www.lordsofthemanor.com; 2m W of Stow on the Wold; 9.30 pm;
no jeans or trainers; children: 7+ at D. **Accommodation:** 27 rooms, from £170.

UPPINGHAM, RUTLAND   5–4D

The Lake Isle   £ 39   Ⓐ
16 High Street East LE15 9PZ   (01572) 822951
"Careful use of good fresh materials" and a *"good wine list"* make
this *"lovely"* restaurant-with-rooms worth seeking out; it has
a *"delightful location in a small market town"*. / **Sample dishes:** supreme
of baked halibut; hot chocolate fondant with home-made vanilla ice cream.
Details: www.lakeislehotel.com; 9 pm; closed Mon L & Sun D.
Accommodation: 12 rooms, from £75.

URMSTON, GREATER MANCHESTER   5–2B

Isinglass   £ 36   Ⓣ
46 Flixton Rd M41 5AB   (0161) 749 8400
This *"excellent suburban brasserie"* in Urmston is a smash hit with
the locals — they say *"it's a delight to have a decent modern British
restaurant here at last"*, and that *"it should be more widely reported"*.
/ **Sample dishes:** blue cheese brulée with tomato & sorrel scone, exotic cresses;
peppered fillet steak. **Details:** www.isinglassrestaurant.co.uk; 10 pm; closed Mon.

UTTOXETER, STAFFORDSHIRE   5–3C

Restaurant Gilmore   £ 47   ⭐
Strine's Farm ST14 5DZ   (01889) 507100
The Gilmores made quite a name with their eponymous Brum
restaurant — now they've converted a farmhouse in a *"pleasant rural
setting"*, where they offer *"consistently excellent food"* of a standard
that *"really stands out in the area"*. / **Sample dishes:** slow-roasted crispy
belly of pork with glazed apple tart & calvados gravy; lemon & lime mousse cake,
sesame nut brittle & vanilla raspberries. **Details:** www.restaurantgilmore.com;
9 pm; closed Mon, Tue, Wed L, Sat L & Sun D.

VIRGINSTOW, DEVON   1–3C

Percy's   £ 53   Ⓐ⭐
EX21 5EA   (01409) 211236
*"A very good restaurant with comfortable rooms, close to Dartmoor
and the North Devon coast"*; reports all attest to its all-round charms,
not least its *"excellent and imaginative"* cuisine. / **Sample dishes:** warm
salad of squid & scallops dill, honey & mustard dressing; oven roast home-reared
lamb cooked pink, rosemary jus. **Details:** www.percys.co.uk; 9.30 pm; D only;
no Amex; children: 12+. **Accommodation:** 8 rooms, from £110.

WADDESDON, BUCKINGHAMSHIRE 3–2A

Five Arrows £ 40
High St HP18 0JE (01296) 651727
"A touch of old world charm, and good food too" – an enduringly
popular formula (if a pricey one), at Lord Rothschild's grand inn;
"there are some well-priced wines on the list", though ("as well as the
posh ones"). / *Sample dishes:* braised shoulder of lamb with turnip
dauphinoise, shallot tarte tatin & Quince Jus; roast fillet & slow braised venison
with sauce grand veneur & fondant potato; chocolate & ginger cake.
Details: www.thefivearrows.co.uk; on A41; 9.30 pm, Sun 7 pm.
Accommodation: 11 rooms, from £85.

WAKEFIELD, WEST YORKSHIRE 5–1C

Aagrah £ 26
Barnsley Rd WF1 5NX (01924) 242222
"Always coming up trumps" – this branch of the excellent Yorkshire
curry house chain wins the usual acclaim for its "patently fresh"
dishes. / *Sample dishes:* bahrain kebab; murgh hyderabadi; kulfi.
Details: www.aagrah.com; from M1, J39 follow Barnsley Rd to A61; 11.30 pm,
11 pm Sun; closed Sat L & Sun L. *Accommodation:* 13 rooms, from £40.

WALBERSWICK, SUFFOLK 3–1D

Anchor £ 32
Main St IP18 6UA (01502) 722112
Londoners may find this rural yearling of most interest as an offshoot
of Fulham's famous White Horse – it offers "great grub in a great
setting", but is sometimes let down by a "chaotic front-of-house".
/ *Sample dishes:* moules marinières with home-made bread; confit of duck
on root mash & red cabbage with an orange sauce; hot chocolate pudding.
Details: www.anchoratwalberswick.com; 10 pm. *Accommodation:* 8 rooms,
from £45/person.

Bell Inn £ 35
Ferry Rd IP18 6TN (01502) 723109
"Very olde worlde charm" makes this ancient inn, on the village green,
a popular destination, especially in summer; the food, though
secondary, rarely gives cause for much dissatisfaction.
/ *Sample dishes:* pan-fried herring; Cumberland sausage with mash & peas.
Details: www.blythweb.co.uk/bellinn; off A12 on B1387 (no access from
Southwold); 9 pm, 10.30 pm Sun; no Amex. *Accommodation:* 6 rooms,
from £90.

WARMINSTER, WILTSHIRE 2–3B

Angel Inn £ 37
Upton Scudamore BA12 0AG (01985) 213225
A cosy inn that offers "tasty" food in "agreeable" surroundings, and is
"well above the average for the area". / *Sample dishes:* mussels in white
wine & cream sauce; pan-fried sea bass fillet with pesto mash potato, basil &
tomato butter; sticky toffee pudding & home-made vanilla ice cream.
Details: www.theangelinn.co.uk; 9.30 pm; no Amex. *Accommodation:* 10
rooms, from £88.

WARWICK, WARWICKSHIRE 5–4C

The Art Kitchen £ 44
7 Swan St CV34 4BJ (01926) 494303
"An unusual Thai restaurant which is a bar at the front and
a restaurant at the back" – a "great little place", where the food
is "usually excellent". / *Details:* www.theartkitchen.com; 10 pm.

Saffron £ 25

Unit 1 Westgate Hs, Market St CV34 4DE (01926) 402061
"The location – inside a shopping centre – isn't the most attractive",
but this friendly Indian is praised as *"a fantastic curry house"* by its
small fan club. / **Sample dishes:** *seekh kebab; chicken tikka masala.*
Details: *www.saffronwarwick.co.uk; 11.30 pm; D only.*

WATERGATE BAY, CORNWALL 1–3C

The Beach Hut
Watergate Bay Hotel £ 39

On The Beach TR8 4AA (01637) 860543
*If you don't go for the idea of Fifteen, this nearby casual beach hang-
out is tipped for its "fresh fish" and other "simple fare".*
/ **Sample dishes:** *vegetable salad with grilled goat's cheese & citrus dressing;
sage-roast chicken breast with bacon, leek & peas; lemon posit with pear
compote & biscuit crumble.* **Details:** *www.watergatebay.co.uk; 9 pm; no Amex.*

Fifteen Cornwall £ 60

Watergate Bay Hotel TR8 4AA (01637) 861000
*It may have a "stunning" location – as well as lofty ideals – but Jamie
Oliver's "modern and funky" Cornish spin-off bears many hallmarks
of the Hoxton original, including "slow and amateur" service and
"slapdash" food, and all at "West End prices"; if you do go,
breakfast is the best bet.* / **Sample dishes:** *potato gnocchi, lamb ragu,
orange & rosemary gremolata; fillet of brill, young borlotti beans, courgettes, cherry
tomato brodo & saffron aioli; vanilla bean panna cotta, with blackcurrant
compote & shortbread.* **Details:** *www.fifteencornwall.co.uk; on the Atlantic
coast between Padstow and Newquay; 9.45 pm; children: Age 7-12 welcome for
6.30 sitting only.*

WATERMILLOCK, CUMBRIA 7–3D

Leeming House Hotel £ 55

Ullswater CA11 0JJ (01768) 486674
*With its "extremely good-value" cooking, "cheerful" service,
and "extensive" wine list, reporters find nothing to fault in the dining
room of this country house hotel, which overlooks the lake.*
/ **Sample dishes:** *seared smoked salmon; roast venison; chocolate tart.*
Details: *www.macdonald-hotels.co.uk; near A592; 9 pm; no jeans or trainers.*
Accommodation: *41 rooms, from £180.*

WATERNISH, ISLE OF SKYE 9–2A

Lochbay £ 38

IV55 8GA (01470) 592235
*"On the shore of one of Skye's more spectacular lochs", a tiny venture
offering "the freshest of fish", "sensitively cooked", and "fabulous
views".* / **Sample dishes:** *scallops with lime curry; halibut with vegetables.*
Details: *www.lochbay-seafood-restaurant.co.uk; 8:30pm; closed Mon & Sun.*

Stein Inn £ 26

IV55 8GA (01470) 592362
*A shore-side pub which serves "local real ales and good-quality food"
in a "stunning" setting; crab sandwiches a speciality.*
/ **Sample dishes:** *breast of duck with garlic cider cream sauce; pork chop with
walnut & blue cheese butter.* **Details:** *www.stein-inn.co.uk; 9.30 pm; no Amex.*
Accommodation: *5 rooms, from £26.*

WATH-IN-NIDDERDALE, NORTH YORKSHIRE 8–4B

Sportsman's Arms £ 39 **A**
HG3 5PP (01423) 711306
*"You'd have to have a heart of stone not to find it romantic", says a
fan of Ray Carter's beautifully-located and "well-run" Dales inn;
fortunately the food "matches up".* / **Sample dishes:** feuilleté of crab &
avocado; roast best end of lamb; summer pudding.
Details: www.sportsmans-arms.co.uk; take Wath Road from Pateley Bridge; 9.30,
Sun 8; no Amex. **Accommodation:** 11 rooms, from £60/person.

WATLINGTON, OXFORDSHIRE 2–2D

Fox & Hounds £ 39 **A**
Christmas Common OX49 5HL (01491) 612599
"Everything you expect from a pub, but often don't get" –
this "characterful inn" (plus "updated" dining annex) offers a "short
but good" menu (and wine list), nice outside seats, and "a roaring fire
on miserable days".* / **Sample dishes:** cauliflower & Taleggio cheese soup;
slow-cooked cushion of veal; rose & vanilla panna cotta.
Details: www.thefoxandhounds.org; 10 pm; no shorts.

WELLS, SOMERSET 2–3B

Goodfellows £ 52 ★
5 Sadler St BA5 2RR (01749) 673866
*"Consistently high-quality fish and pâtisserie" – masterminded by Mr
and Mrs Fellows, respectively – ensure that this "fine" three-year-old
venture is highly popular with reporters; "good-value" lunches come
especially recommended.* / **Sample dishes:** seared tuna carpaccio; pan-fried
scallops; fig tart with mandarin sorbet. **Details:** www.goodfellowswells.co.uk; 9.30;
closed Mon, Tue D, Wed D & Sun. **Accommodation:** 0 rooms, from £0.

Old Spot £ 39 ★
12 Sadler St BA5 2SE (01749) 689099
*"A newly-opened restaurant that's well worth a visit"; its "simple but
precise" cooking of "impeccable seasonal ingredients"
is almost invariably proclaimed a "delight" – chef/patron Ian Bates
"used to work at Bibendum, and it shows".* / **Sample dishes:** pork terrine;
rare grilled tuna. **Details:** 10.30 pm; closed Mon, Tue L & Sun D.

WELSH HOOK, PEMBROKESHIRE 4–4B

Stone Hall Mansion £ 40 **T**
SA62 SA62 (01348) 840212
*A small country house hotel tipped for its "excellent food" and "brief
but carefully-selected wine list".* / **Details:** www.stonehall-mansion.co.uk;
9 pm; D only, closed Mon & Sun; no shorts. **Accommodation:** 4 rooms,
from £95.

WELWYN, HERTFORDSHIRE 3–2B

Wellington £ 38
1 High St AL6 9LZ (01438) 714036
*With its "modern-bistro" menu and its "extensive selection of wines
by the glass", this attractive gastropub is a handy destination; the food
didn't totally impress all reporters this year, but is usually "tasty and
well-prepared".* / **Sample dishes:** shredded chicken with Jersey potatoes;
cod & chips; chocolate & Malteser mousse.
Details: www.wellingtonatwelwyn.co.uk; 10 pm; no Amex.

WEST BYFLEET, SURREY
3–3A

Chu Chin Chow   **£ 34**   Ⓣ
63 Old Woking Rd KT14 6LF (01932) 349581
*Locals tip this long-established Chinese restaurant as a "smart and good-value" destination. / **Details:** 11 pm.*

WEST CLANDON, SURREY
3–3A

L' Auberge
Onslow Arms   **£ 42**   Ⓣ
The Street GU4 7TE (01483) 222447
*"Surprisingly good for a chain outlet" – this annexe to a "traditional beamed pub" offers "really good French cuisine in a proper restaurant setting" (and a "ridiculously cheap" lunchtime menu too). / **Sample dishes:** salad of marinated baby squid; tomato & aubergine caviar tian. **Details:** www.massivepub.com; 9.30 pm, Fri 10 pm.*

WEST MERSEA, ESSEX
3–2C

The Company Shed   **£ 16**   ✪✪
129 Coast Rd CO5 8PA (01206) 382700
*"Fantastic seafood, next to the fishing boats on the quay" draws legions of visitors to this "remote" and rather "bizarre" shed; "arrive very early to ensure a table", and don't forget to "bring your own wine, salad, bread and so on". / **Sample dishes:** seafood platter; oysters. **Details:** L only, closed Mon; no credit cards; no booking.*

WEST WITTON, NORTH YORKSHIRE
8–4B

Wensleydale Heifer   **£ 43**   ✪
Main St DL8 4LS (01969) 622322
*"Weird – in the middle of the Yorkshire Dales, a fish-restaurant"; but while this "opposite-of-terroir" approach bothers the occasional reporter, most find the food "lovely". / **Sample dishes:** maple roast lobster salad; fish & chips. **Details:** www.wensleydaleheifer.co.uk; 9.30 pm. **Accommodation:** 9 rooms, from £110.*

WESTCLIFF-ON-SEA, ESSEX
3–3C

Paris   **£ 44**   Ⓐ✪
719 London Rd SS0 9ST (01702) 344077
*"Matthew is a first-class host", at this "consistently good" operation near Chalkwell Park, and his theme nights "can transport you on an exploratory culinary fantasy"! / **Sample dishes:** monkfish wrapped in bacon; beef Wellington; lobster bisque. **Details:** www.parisrestaurant.net; on A13 into Southend; 10 pm; closed Mon, Sat L & Sun D.*

WESTERHAM, KENT
3–3B

Kinara   Ⓐ✪
Pitts Cottage   **£ 29**
High St TN16 1RQ (01959) 562125
*"What a find!"; the "very different" subcontinental fare served in this "charmingly-located" and very ancient cottage – once the country retreat of William Pitt – can come as something of a surprise. / **Sample dishes:** chunks of lamb cooked with spinach, garam massala & finished with coriander. **Details:** www.pittscottage.co.uk; 11.30 pm.*

Napoli E   **£ 25**
18a-18b, Market Sq TN16 1AR (01959) 561688
"A great family Italian, with good portions and good food".

WESTFIELD, EAST SUSSEX   3–4C

Wild Mushroom   **£ 42**
Westfield Ln TN35 4SB (01424) 751137
"Not the most prepossessing of places from the outside but the food and service are very good"; reports are not very numerous, but all confirm that this former boozer is a notably *"consistent"* operation.
/ **Sample dishes:** grilled fillet of wild sea bass with saffron cream potato & samphire & Indian spiced prawns; fillet of beef; praline mousse with pistachio sauce & hazelnut caramel. **Details:** www.wildmushroom.co.uk; 9.30 pm; closed Mon & Sun D; closed 2 weeks in Jan; children: 8+ at D.

WEYBRIDGE, SURREY   3–3A

Colony   **£ 35**
3 Balfour Rd KT13 8HE (01932) 842766
"Fabulous meals every time" are the gist of almost all reports on this long-established Chinese restaurant, which *"seems to have weathered its change of ownership well"*. / **Sample dishes:** prawns with sesame seeds; deep-fried chilli beef; toffee apples & bananas. **Details:** on A317; 10.30 pm.

WEYMOUTH, DORSET   2–4B

Crab House Café   **£ 38**
Ferrybridge Rd DT4 9YU (01305) 788867
If you're looking for "seafood by the sea", you won't do much better than the "fresh, simple and properly cooked" dishes at this "casual" and "eclectic" place, overlooking Chesil Beach. / **Sample dishes:** fillet of bass with citrus fruit; skate with chorizo. **Details:** www.crabhousecafe.co.uk; 9 pm; closed Tue; no Amex.

Perry's   **£ 38**
4 Trinity Rd, The Old Harbour DT4 8TJ (01305) 785799
A "lovely setting with harbour views" is the high point at this well-established fixture in Old Weymouth (under new ownership this year); one regular fears its "getting worse", but for the most part it wins consistent praise for its "pleasant" food and "friendly" service.
/ **Sample dishes:** pan-fried scallops; roast fillet of cod on potato & crab cake; passion fruit meringue pie with Cointreau syrup.
Details: www.perrysrestaurant.co.uk; 9.30 pm; closed Mon in winter; no Amex; children: 7+.

WHALLEY, LANCASHIRE   5–1B

Three Fishes   **£ 32**
Mitton Rd BB7 9PQ (01254) 826888
"Achieving the same high standards as Northcote Manor, but with less cost and formality"; this *"fine"* gastropub spin-off – *"decorated with the pictures of its suppliers"* – delivers *"simple, great British food at a price everyone can afford"*; a further NM-offshoot, the Highwayman, has recently opened in Kirkby Lonsdale.
/ **Sample dishes:** shrimps; Lancashire hotpot; Lancashire curd tart.
Details: www.thethreefishes.com; 9 pm.

Greens   £ 33   ⭐

13 Bridge St YO22 4BG   (01947) 600284

*Rob & Emma Green's "small and crowded" bistro is well-rated by all who comment on it, particularly as regards its "excellent", "local" fish. / **Sample dishes:** grilled fillet of wild sea bass with smoked potato purée, baby beets & red wine dressing; rack of lamb with confit of shoulder, provençale vegetables, white bean purée & rosemary pesto.*
Details: www.greensofwhitby.com; 9.30 pm; no Amex.

Magpie Café   £ 26   ⭐⭐

14 Pier Rd YO21 3PU   (01947) 602058

*"The only problem is the queue", at this "unfailing", "old-fashioned" legend, whose "faultless and enormous fish 'n' chips" – served up "in view of the harbour" – have made it one of the UK's best-known eateries. / **Sample dishes:** mussels; lemon sole, salmon & scallops; spotted dick & custard.* **Details:** www.magpiecafe.co.uk; opp Fish Market; 9 pm; no Amex; no booking at L.

Trenchers   £ 36   ⭐⭐

New Quay Rd YO21 1DH   (01947) 603212

*"Forget the crowded Magpie!" ("and AA Gill's prejudices!"), say fans – this "cheery" and "upmarket" chippy is "much loved by locals and tourists alike" and serves equally "fantastic" fish 'n' chips. / **Sample dishes:** prawns, mussels & smoked salmon; fish & chips; home-made sticky toffee pudding.* **Details:** www.trenchersrestaurant.co.uk; opp railway station, near marina; 8.30 pm; no Amex; need 7+ to book.

The Crown at Whitebrook   £ 63   Ⓐ⭐

NP25 4TX   (01600) 860254

*It's "in the back of beyond", but this beautifully-located restaurant-with-rooms generally wins raves from reporters for its "outstanding" cooking, and there's certainly nothing remotely rustic about its "manicured" presentation! / **Sample dishes:** salad of asparagus, Jersey royals, mushrooms & bleu cheese; corn-fed chicken supreme, caramelised shallots, smoked bacon ravioli & tarragon juice; open lemon tart with lavender & honey parfait.* **Details:** www.crownatwhitebrook.co.uk; 2m W of A466, 5m S of Monmouth; 9 pm; closed Mon & Tue; no Amex; children: 12+.
Accommodation: 8 rooms, from £110.

The Pear Tree Inn £ 44 🅐⭐
Top Ln SN12 8QX (01225) 709131

"Once a country pub, now a sought-out restaurant" – this *"Wiltshire hide-away"* gets a strong thumbs-up from most reporters, who praise its *"varied"* and *"interesting"* food and its *"stylish"* and *"romantic"* setting. / **Sample dishes:** *hand-picked Cornish crab; new seasoned lamb with braised shoulder; chocolate & macadamia brownie.* **Details:** *9.30 pm, 10 sat, 9 sun; no Amex.* **Accommodation:** *8 rooms, from £90.*

Crab & Winkle £ 48
South Quay, Whitstable Harbour CT5 1AB (01227) 779377

Fans praise the "excellent fish and seafood" and the "romantic" harbour-view setting of this restaurant over the fish market; others find it merely "good" and "popular". / **Sample dishes:** *battered haddock, cod, sea bass; smoked haddock with poached egg; sticky toffee pudding.* **Details:** *www.crab-winkle.co.uk; 9.30 pm; no Amex.*

JoJo £ 20 ⭐
209 Tankerton Rd CT5 2AT (01227) 274591

"A quirky little place that's well worth a visit" – an *"affordable"* (BYO) and *"friendly"* establishment hailed by some as offering *"the best tapas in Kent".* / **Details:** *www.jojosrestaurant.co.uk; 10.30 pm; closed Mon, Tue & Sun D; no credit cards.*

Sportsman £ 37 ⭐⭐
Faversham Rd, Seasalter CT5 4BP (01227) 273370

It's "well worth the trek to the edge of the North Sea", to visit this "wonderful and relaxed" inn, which has a "beautiful" coastal location; Stephen Harris's "exciting" cooking just "gets better and better", and delivers "big butch flavours from very fine ingredients". / **Sample dishes:** *lobster risotto; roast lamb; rhubarb sorbet & burnt cream.* **Details:** *www.thesportsmanseasalter.co.uk; 8.45 pm; closed Mon & Sun D; no Amex; children: 18+ in main bar.*

Wheeler's Oyster Bar £ 33 🅐⭐⭐
8 High St CT5 1BQ (01227) 273311

This "quirky", "tiny parlour" inspires adulation for its "knowledgeable" service, "out-of-this-world" seafood (not least "quiveringly fresh" oysters), and "oustanding" fish; "the ability to BYO is a bonus". / **Sample dishes:** *roast monkfish with a baked pistou tart; panna cotta with cherries.* **Details:** *www.whitstable-shellfish.co.uk; 7.30 pm; closed Wed; no credit cards.*

Whitstable Oyster Fishery Co. £ 48 ⭐
Horsebridge CT5 1BU (01227) 276856

"Just what eating by the seaside should be"; this famous institution – with a "lovely setting right on the beach" – may charge "London prices", but it serves up "the freshest of fish in an informal, simple and cheery atmosphere"; "service seems to have tightened up of late". / **Sample dishes:** *deep-fried squid; roast sea bass with garlic & rosemary; peach apricot & raspberry crumble.* **Details:** *www.oysterfishery.co.uk; on the seafront; 9 pm, Sun 8.15 pm; closed Mon .*

WILLIAN, HERTFORDSHIRE 3–2B

The Fox £ 40 ⭐
SG6 2AE (01462) 480233
Food "of consistently high quality" makes this "light", "airy" and "friendly" modern gastropub popular with all who comment on it. / **Sample dishes:** beetroot & artichoke salad with toasted cashew nuts & spiced lemongrass vinaigrette; cumin & maple glazed duck breast on wilted oriental leaves with peanuts & coriander. **Details:** www.foxatwillian.co.uk; 9.15 pm; closed Sun D; no Amex.

WILMSLOW, CHESHIRE 5–2B

Heddy's £ 30 ⓣ
100-102 Water Ln SK9 5BB (01625) 526855
"A great all-round experience" in this (surprisingly) under-provided town; it's tipped for its "good standard of Middle Eastern/European cuisine" and "excellent value". / **Sample dishes:** vine leaves filled with vegetables & rice; spicy minced lamb with vegetables & parsley, skewered & charcoal grilled; baklava. **Details:** www.heddys.com; 10.30 pm; closed Mon L, Sat L & Sun.

WINCHCOMBE, GLOUCESTERSHIRE 2–1C

5 North Street £ 46 ⭐
5 North St GL54 5LH (01242) 604566
"Standards remain high", at Marcus and Kate Ashenford's "lovely and cosy" little restaurant, where the "innovative" cooking seems to have benefitted from a "simpler" style of late, and where a meal can be truly "memorable". / **Sample dishes:** half lobster with pasta, ginger vegetables, & a champagne lemon grass sauce; duck breast, lentils & smoked bacon with celeriac purée; chocolate tart with caramelised banana. **Details:** 9 pm; closed Mon, Tue L & Sun D.

Wesley House £ 55 ⓐ
High St GL54 5LJ (01242) 602366
A "delightful" inn which has a widespread fan club among reporters, thanks to its "friendly, country service" and its "enjoyable, well-presented" food. / **Sample dishes:** pasta; grilled quail; lemon parfait & passion fruit jelly. **Details:** www.wesleyhouse.co.uk; next to Sudeley Castle; 9 pm; closed Sun D. **Accommodation:** 5 rooms, from £80.

WINCHESTER, HAMPSHIRE 2–3D

Chestnut Horse £ 44 ⓐ⭐
Easton Village SO21 1EG (01962) 779257
"A lovely pub in a lovely Itchen Valley village"; it's a "popular" destination, where – on most reports – the food measures up to the setting. / **Sample dishes:** avocado & bacon salad; fish & chips; cherry & almond clafoutis. **Details:** 9.30 pm, 8pm Sun; no Amex.

Hotel du Vin et Bistro £ 46
14 Southgate St SO23 9EF (01962) 841414
The food is "sound", the dining room is always "buzzy", and "the whole package is still very enjoyable", at the original branch of the boutique-hotel chain that's famous nowadays of its "exceptional wine list"; enthusiasm for the experience, though, is slowly ebbing. / **Sample dishes:** pigeon terrine with beetroot carpaccio; monkfish wrapped in Parma ham; sticky toffee pudding. **Details:** www.hotelduvin.com; 9.45 pm; booking: max 10. **Accommodation:** 24 rooms, from £130.

Lainston House Hotel £ 75 ★

SO21 2LT   (01962) 863588

*The word "expensive" crops up in numerous reports on this "romantic" country house hotel dining room; most reporters, though, think the "pure class" of the experience is justification enough. / **Sample dishes:** smoked duck breast with confit leg ballotine & brulée; twice-baked rosemary goat's cheese soufflé; banana split parfait.* **Details:** www.lainstonhouse.com; 9.30 pm, 10 pm Fri & Sat. **Accommodation:** 50 rooms, from £225.

Wykeham Arms £ 36 Ⓐ

75 Kingsgate St SO23 9PE   (01962) 853834

*"Dependable, always crowded and reasonably-priced" – this "quirky", "old-school" boozer remains extremely popular, thanks to its "high-quality" food and its "good wine list" (with many choices by the glass). / **Sample dishes:** chicken liver parfait; roast rack of lamb; pear cheesecake with home-made apple & brandy sorbet.* **Details:** between Cathedral and College; 8.45 pm; closed Sun D; booking: max 8; children: 14+. **Accommodation:** 14 rooms, from £90.

WINCLE, CHESHIRE 5–2B

The Ship Inn £ 36 Ⓐ★

Barlow Hill SK11 0QE   (01260) 227217

*"A beautiful old pub, tastefully restored and doing top-notch pub food"; all reports confirm it as an "exemplary" place, which "does everything right". / **Sample dishes:** field mushrooms & brie bruschetta; sirloin steak; sticky toffee pudding.* **Details:** 11 pm; closed Mon.

WINDERMERE, CUMBRIA 7–3D

First Floor Café
Lakeland Limited £ 29 ★

Alexandra Buildings LA23 1BQ   (015394) 47116

*"Surprisingly good" food (from an ex-head chef of Le Gavroche) makes it well worth seeking out the smart café above this famous kitchenware retailer's flagship store; service is notably "friendly" and "helpful" too. / **Sample dishes:** mixed leaf salad; crab cocktail with cherry tomato & new potato salad; orange & almond cake.* **Details:** www.firstfloorcafe.co.uk; 6 pm, Sat 5pm, Sun 4 pm; no Amex.

Gilpin Lodge £ 65 Ⓐ★

Crook Rd LA23 3NE   (01539) 488818

*For a "Relais & Châteaux-style" experience, you won't fare much better than at this "inviting", family-run, hotel – an Edwardian country house set in "beautiful" grounds; Chris Meredith's food is "very good", and it's backed up by a "superb" wine list. / **Sample dishes:** cream of langoustine soup; pheasant confit with root vegetable casserole; pear & frangipane tart.* **Details:** www.gilpinlodge.co.uk; 9.15 pm; children: 7+. **Accommodation:** 20 rooms, from £210.

Holbeck Ghyll £ 68 Ⓐ★

Holbeck Ln LA23 1LU   (01539) 432375

*A celebrated country house hotel, offering "excellent food in a delightful setting" (and "amazing" views of Windermere too); you undoubtedly "pay for it", though, and, for some tastes, the style is a little "formal". / **Sample dishes:** roast scallops with celeriac & balsamic dressing; best end of lamb with shallot purée; chocolate plate.* **Details:** www.holbeckghyll.com; 3m N of Windermere, towards Troutbeck; 9.30 pm; booking essential; children: 8+ at D. **Accommodation:** 23 rooms, from £220.

Jerichos £ 44 Ⓐ ✪

Birch St LA23 1EG (01539) 442522

Chris Blaydes "continues to amaze with the consistency and quality" of his town-centre restaurant – tipped by a couple of reporters as "the Lakes' best place to eat". / **Sample dishes:** char-grilled beef fillet & chips; butterscotch panna cotta with poached rhubarb.
Details: www.jerichos.co.uk; 9.30 pm; D only, closed Mon; no Amex; children: 12+.

Samling £ 78 Ⓐ

Ambleside Rd LA23 1LR (01539) 431922

This contemporary country house hotel, with "superb views" over Windermere was rebranded under the 'Treacle Moon' banner as we went to press; some "fantastic" meals are recorded but there's also quite a feeling that the place is "over-priced" and "trying too hard". / **Sample dishes:** roast scallops; fillet of beef with braised rib; poached pear with white chocolate. **Details:** www.thesamling.com; take A591 from town; 9.30 pm. **Accommodation:** 11 rooms, from £195.

WINDSOR, WINDSOR & MAIDENHEAD 3–3A

Al Fassia £ 31 ✪

27 St Leonards Rd SL4 3BP (01753) 855370

"Marvellous Moroccan food" and "welcoming" service is the gist of most reports on the Chab family's "value-for-money" restaurant; it's open all day, and can get "very busy in the evenings". / **Sample dishes:** pastellilos; tajine with chicken; home-made pastry.
Details: 10.30 pm, Fri & Sat 11 pm.

The Greene Oak £ 35 Ⓣ

SL4 5UW (01753) 864294

"An absolute gem of a gastropub", say early-days fans of this new establishment; they laud its "superb" food, "reasonable" prices and "efficient" service, and its "bright and modern surroundings". / **Sample dishes:** smoked salmon, lemon, capers & brown bread; crab with cucumber & dill; champagne-poached strawberries.
Details: www.thegreeneoak.co.uk; 9.30 pm; no Amex.

Spice Route £ 39 Ⓣ

18a, Thames St, Boots Pas SL4 1PL (01753) 860720

"Inventive" food (with fusion twists) makes it worth remembering this "innovative" Indian (even if "it doesn't have much of a buzz"). / **Sample dishes:** butter chicken; lamb brochettes; orange & Cointreau brûlée.
Details: www.spice-route.co.uk; 11 pm; D only.

WINKFIELD, BERKSHIRE 3–3A

Cottage Inn £ 48 Ⓐ

Winkfield St SL4 4SW (01344) 882242

Its "full of atmosphere and fun" – this buzzy village inn wins consistent praise for its "homely" style and its reliable scoff. / **Sample dishes:** sausage & mash with onion gravy.
Details: www.cottage-inn.co.uk; 9 pm; closed Sun D. **Accommodation:** 10 rooms, from £87.50.

Winteringham Fields £101

DN15 9PF (01724) 733096

Colin & Bex McGurran had a tough act to follow when they bought this well-known country house hotel from the Schwabs in 2005; some reports do gripe about "gross" prices and "lack of attention to detail", but on most accounts this remains a "wonderful place to eat", with "divine" food from chef Robert Thompson.
/ **Sample dishes:** *seared scallops; rump of new season lamb; assiette of miniature desserts.* **Details:** *www.winteringhamfields.com; 4m SW of Humber Bridge; 9.30 pm; closed Mon & Sun; booking: max 8.* **Accommodation:** *10 rooms, from £145.*

Freemasons Arms £ 38

8 Vicarage Fold BB7 9DF (01254) 822218

"A great country pub with smashing food"; it's "the enthusiasts wine list", though – "built up over the years by chef-owner Ian Martin" – that makes the place of real note. / **Sample dishes:** *chicken liver pate; corn-fed chicken; damson crumble.* **Details:** *www.freemasonswiswell.co.uk; 9.30 pm; closed Mon & Tue; no Amex.*

Spooners Restaurant £ 40

61 High St MK17 8QY (01908) 584385

"Always a pleasant experience" – this "small and cosy" family-run fixture is tipped by locals as a "very popular" place, thanks not least to its "reliable" standards. / **Sample dishes:** *black hickory ham with celeriac remoulade & caper berries; fillet steak baked with blue cheese butter sauce; pink champagne & raspberry jelly with ice cream.*
Details: *www.spooners.co.uk; 2m from J13 on the M1; 9.45 pm; closed Mon & Sun.*

Birch £ 42

20 Newport Rd MK17 9HX (01525) 290295

"Consistently great food" is making quite a name for this "relaxed" country pub, which comes from the same stable as Black Horse in Ireland. / **Sample dishes:** *home-cured & smoked salmon; lamb with baton carrots & creamed cauliflower; apple & pear crumble with anglaise sauce.*
Details: *www.birchwoburn.com; 10 pm; closed Sun D; booking: max 12, Fri & Sat.*

Paris House £ 70

Woburn Pk MK17 9QP (01525) 290692

The "glorious" setting in "gentle English parkland" has long been the major attraction at this "time warp" establishment in a Tudor-style building; this year, though, a good number of reports confirmed that its Gallic cuisine "couldn't be faulted". / **Sample dishes:** *flambe king prawns in Pernod & garlic butter; roast rack of lamb; prune & armagnac cheesecake.* **Details:** *www.parishouse.co.uk; on A4012; 9.30 pm; closed Mon & Sun D.*

Peters Palace **£ 21** Ⓣ
48 Chertsey Rd GU21 5BG (01483) 770605
"A great buffet for not much money" – that's the main attraction
at this *"cheap 'n' cheerful"* Chinese of long standing.
/ **Sample dishes:** *sweet & sour pork; beef with green pepper & black bean
sauce.* **Details:** *11 pm.*

Saracen's Head **£ 34** Ⓐ
NR11 7LX (01263) 768909
*"Worth the trip down the dark lanes to find it"; this "magnificent old
inn" is a "friendly" and "unpretentious" place, serving "good local
food".* / **Sample dishes:** *mussels with cider & cream; crispy fried brie with
apricot sauce.* **Details:** *www.saracenshead-norfolk.co.uk; 2m W of A140 through
Erpingham; 9 pm; booking essential.* **Accommodation:** *6 rooms, from £85.*

Bilash **£ 42** ★
2 Cheapside WV1 1TU (01902) 427762
"Great food" – plus an *"enthusiastic owner who seems genuinely
concerned that diners are enjoying the experience"* – make this
"innovative" Indian *"Wolverhampton's saving grace, restaurant-wise".*
/ **Sample dishes:** *kebab; murgh dalchini; cinnamon saffron kulfi.*
Details: *www.thebilash.co.uk; opp Civic Centre; 10.30 pm; closed Sun.*

Captain's Table **£ 35**
3 Quay St IP12 1BX (01394) 383145
*On most accounts, Pascal Pommier's village-restaurant offers
"consistently good food and unpretentious service at moderate
prices"; in season, there's the prospect of courtyard-dining too.*
/ **Sample dishes:** *goat's cheese soufflé; slow-roast duck leg confit; toffee pudding
with toffee sauce.* **Details:** *www.captainstable.co.uk; 100 yds from theatre;
9.30 pm, Fri & Sat 10 pm; closed Mon & Sun D; closed 2 weeks in Jan; no Amex.*

Riverside **£ 36** ★
Quayside IP12 1BH (01394) 382587
*"A slightly odd set-up – a large conservatory attached to a Suffolk
cinema"; "this may not sound promising", but standards are "highly
professional" – "the joint film-and-eating ticket comes recommended".*
/ **Sample dishes:** *pan-fried sea bass with saffron mash & citrus dressing;
pan-fried sea bass & saffron mash; gooseberry strudel with crème anglaise.*
Details: *www.theriverside.co.uk; next to Woodbridge train station; 9.30 pm;
closed Sun D.*

Seckford Hall Hotel £ 41

IP13 6NU   (01394) 385678

This "exceptional" Elizabethan country house hotel has been in the same ownership for more than 55 years; even a reporter who finds its culinary style "pretentious" says the food is "good".
/ **Sample dishes:** lobster & linguine; banana panna cotta.
Details: www.seckford.co.uk; off the A12, signposted from last Woodbridge roundabout; 9.30 pm; closed Mon L; no jeans or trainers. **Accommodation:** 32 rooms, from £140.

The Waterfront Cafe £ 37

The Granary, Tide Mill Way IP12 1BY   (01394) 610333
"Right on the waterfront, and ideal for a summer's day" – this all-day establishment is praised for its "simple local foods" ("such as fresh dressed crab", and even "game, in season"); "pet and child-friendly" too. / **Sample dishes:** fresh local lobster; fresh dressed crab.
Details: www.thewaterfrontcafe.co.uk; 5 pm.

WOODSTOCK, OXFORDSHIRE 2–1D

The Feathers Hotel £ 48

Market St OX20 1SX   (01993) 812291
It's disappointing that this chichi boutique-hotel, near the gates of Blenheim – potentially such a charming destination – generates such mixed feedback; too much of it is to the effect that it's "grossly overrated" and "seriously overpriced". / **Sample dishes:** seared scallops with salsify & watercress; roast rump of lamb & salsa verde; lemon posset & sweet pesto. **Details:** www.feathers.co.uk; 8m N of Oxford on A44; 9 pm; closed Mon L & Sun D; no jeans or trainers. **Accommodation:** 20 rooms, from £165.

WOOLSTHORPE-BY-BELVOIR, LINCOLNSHIRE 5–3D

Chequers Inn £ 39

Main St NG32 1LU   (01476) 870701
In a "picturesque" location near Belvoir Castle, a pub tipped by a number of reporters for its "above-average" food.
/ **Sample dishes:** clam, squid & salmon risotto with parmesan; lemon sole, wilted spinach, saute new potatoes & cherry tomatoes; chocolate tart with bitter orange sorbet. **Details:** www.chequers-inn.net; 9.30 pm, 8.30 pm Sun.
Accommodation: 4 rooms, from £59.

Brown's £ 48 Ⓐ

24 Quay St WR1 2JJ (01905) 26263
"A nice location" – by the Severn, in a "former grain mill" –
and "a good menu" help win popularity for this "London-style"
venture (even if "service could do with some kinks ironing out");
as this guide goes to press, it's closed for a refurb, following the floods
of mid-2007. / **Sample dishes:** smoked salmon; fillet of beef; crème brûlée.
Details: www.brownsrestaurant.co.uk; near the Cathedral on riverside; 9.45 pm;
closed Mon & Sun D.

Glasshouse £ 43 ★

Danesbury Hs, Sidbury WR1 2HU (01905) 611120
"Shaun Hill is a master of cooking – his food is so simple, but the
flavours are outstanding"; this "ultra-modern" town-centre brasserie –
his new co-venture – is rated "one to watch" by quite a few reporters.
/ **Details:** www.theglasshouse.co.uk; 10 pm, Sun 3pm.

Loftsome Bridge Coaching House £ 34 Ⓣ

YO8 6EN (01757) 630070
The menu "doesn't change very much", but the dining room of this
ancient bridge-side inn is tipped as "the best in the area" nonetheless.
/ **Sample dishes:** country pâté with Madeira, with spiced apple & tomato
chutney; breast of chicken gratiné, baked with sun-dried tomatoes, Parma ham &
white wine; lemon tart with raspberries. **Details:** www.loftsomebridge-hotel.co.uk;
9 pm; D only, ex Sun L only; no jeans. **Accommodation:** 17 rooms, from £65.

Pant-yr-Ochain £ 34 Ⓐ

Old Wrexham Rd LL12 8TY (01978) 853525
Located by a small lake, this "very pleasant" and popular gastropub
"feels more like a country club"; it serves a "big menu" of "tasty"
fare. / **Sample dishes:** chicken & red pepper terrine; lamb shank with garlic &
mint gravy; bread & butter pudding with apricots.
Details: www.pantyrochain-gresford.co.uk; 1m N of Wrexham; 9.30 pm,
Sun 9 pm; children: 13+.

High Moor £ 32 Ⓐ

8 High Moor Ln WN6 9QA (01257) 252364
It has "wonderful views over the Lancashire plain", but this
"upmarket" venture suffered from mixed reviews this year –
even some fans said the food "can be indifferent" and foes now see
it as "a place to be seen, but disappointing". / **Sample dishes:** pan-fried
chicken livers; belly of pork with gravy & apple sauce; double chocolate pudding.
Details: 9.30 pm; closed Mon; no Amex.

Mulberry Tree £ 42

9 Wood Ln WN6 9SE (01257) 451400
Even a reporter who found the interior of this pub-conversion "truly
dreadful" conceded that the food is "technically competent"; fans say
it's "excellent", but there is a feeling that "the bar is better value than
the restaurant"; just off the M6. / **Sample dishes:** black pudding on English
muffin & soft-poached egg; glazed lamb shank; vanilla crème brûlée.
Details: info@themulberrytree.info; 2m along Mossy Lea Rd, off M6,
J27; 9.30 pm; no Amex; children: 14+.

WRIGHTINGTON, LANCASHIRE 5–1A

Simply Heathcote's
The Wrightington Country Club Hotel £ 42

Moss Ln WN6 9PB (01257) 424500
"Tucked-away in an hotel in a sleepy Lancashire village",
this outpost of the Paul Heathcote empire wins praise for its
"straightforward English fare in a large, modern dining room,
overlooking field and forest". / Sample dishes: braised pork cheek; seared
trout. Details: www.heathcotes.co.uk; 10 pm, 11 pm Sat.

WYTHAM, OXFORDSHIRE 2–2D

White Hart £ 40
OX2 8QA (01865) 244372
"Just off the A34, but just outside the Oxford tourist honeypot zone"
– this is, on all reports, a "jolly good place to eat and drink",
especially on days you can enjoy the "stunning" terrace.
/ Sample dishes: free range chicken & foie-gras terrine, with apricot chutney;
rump of lamb with herb crust, wilted spinach, potato fondant & redcurrant jus;
chocolate & hazelnut fondant. Details: www.thewhitehartoxford.co.uk; midnight;
no Amex. Accommodation: 0 rooms, from £-.

YARM, CLEVELAND 8–3C

D P Chadwicks £ 37
104b High St TS15 9AU (01642) 788558
This "bright, busy and noisy" bistro is a "consistent" destination,
which – according to its small but loyal fan club – is "the place to go
in Teeside". / Sample dishes: gambas in chilli & garlic; smoked haddock; crème
brûlée. Details: just after Yarm Bridge; 9.30 pm; closed Sun; booking: max 12.

YARMOUTH, ISLE OF WIGHT 2–4D

George Hotel £ 50
Quay St PO41 0PE (01983) 760331
It's been a very unsettled year at this popular hotel, long well known
for quality dining; as this guide goes to press, the former brasserie
space is set to re-emerge as the new restaurant (and this will
henceforth be the only major dining option available).
/ Sample dishes: grilled goat's cheese with red pepper, almond & balsamic salad;
fish stew in a langoustine sauce; chestnut parfait with chocolate sorbet.
Details: www.thegeorge.co.uk; 9.30 pm; D only, closed Mon & Sun; children: 12+
at D. Accommodation: 17 rooms, from £180.

YARPOLE, NR LEOMINSTER, HEREFORDSHIRE 2–1B

Bell Inn £ 35
Green Ln HR6 0BD (01568) 780359
"Great local ingredients and excellent French staff" combine to make
this "black and white pub in a sleepy village" – owned by the Bosis,
of Hibiscus fame – popular with most reporters; "the cooking and
delivery are not always-note perfect, though". / Sample dishes: smoked
salmon rillettes, mixed leaves, caper & shallot dressing; Hereford rare beef salad,
shavings of parmesan, black olive & anchovy, thyme dressing.
Details: www.thebellinnyarpole.co.uk; 9.30 pm; closed Mon; no Amex.

Pot Kiln £ 45 ⭐

Frilsham RG18 0XX (01635) 201366

It's "the pub of dreams", say fans of Mike Robinson's "absolutely brilliant" but "hard-to-find" inn – the "very rustic" food is of "exceptionally high quality" (as is the "wonderful" local beer). / **Sample dishes:** breast of wood pigeon, crispy bacon & black pudding; pavé of deer; sticky toffee pudding. **Details:** www.potkiln.co.uk; between J12 and J13 of the M4; 9 pm; closed Sun D.

Royal Oak Hotel £ 45 ⓣ

The Square RG18 0UG (01635) 201325

It's not the destination it once was, but this pretty town-centre inn still offers "good food at a fair price". / **Sample dishes:** carpaccio; calves' liver; meringue. **Details:** www.royaloakyattendon.com; 5m W of Pangbourne, off B4009; 9.30 pm, 9 pm Sun. **Accommodation:** 5 rooms, from £130.

Abbey Inn £ 39 ⓣ

Byland Abbey YO61 4BD (01347) 868204

"On those long hot afternoons" ("rare in Yorkshire", admittedly), this English Heritage-run inn – with its views of Byland Abbey – is a top tip for an "all-round experience". / **Sample dishes:** pan-fried scallops; cannon of lamb; plum tomato & basil tart with parmesan shavings & balsamic jus. **Details:** www.bylandabbeyinn.com; 9 pm; closed Mon L & Sun D; no Amex. **Accommodation:** 3 rooms, from £95.

Bettys £ 37 Ⓐ⭐

6-8 St Helen's Sq Y01 8QP (01904) 659142

In spite of the inevitable queue, this "efficient and quaint tea house" continues to please most reporters with its "lovely traditional fayre". / **Sample dishes:** smoked salmon fishcakes; Florentine rosti; rhubarb crumble tartlet. **Details:** www.bettysandtaylors.com; down Blake St from York Minster; 9 pm; no Amex; no booking.

The Blackwell Ox Inn £ 35 ⓣ

Huby Rd YO61 1DT (01347) 810328

A "very cosy village pub", "five minutes' drive from York"; it has no great culinary aspirations, but it does offer "good consistent simple food, done very well". / **Sample dishes:** foie gras & chicken liver parfair with toast & chutney; smoked haddock, bubble 'n' squeak, poached egg & mustard cream; warm chocolate pudding. **Details:** www.blackwelloxinn.co.uk; 9.30 pm; closed Sun D; no Amex. **Accommodation:** 6 rooms, from £95.

Blue Bicycle £ 48
34 Fossgate YO1 9TA (01904) 673990
"The downstairs bordello booths" are the ones to bag at this *"cramped"* and *"busy"* bistro; fans hail its *"inventive"* cooking, but overall reports are notably up-and-down. / **Sample dishes:** *wild mushroom risotto; baked sea bass on crayfish & thyme risotto; iced-lemon curd parfait with mascarpone sorbet.* **Details:** *www.thebluebicycle.com; 9.30 pm, Sun 9 pm; no Amex; booking: max 8.* **Accommodation:** *4 rooms, from £150.*

Café Concerto £ 36
21 High Petergate YO1 7EN (01904) 610478
"Have a hearty lunch, read the papers and chill out" – that's the vibe at this *"long-term-favourite"* café, by the Minster; be prepared for *"long queues"*. / **Sample dishes:** *duck breast salad; pan-fried calves' liver with bacon; frozen mango & passion fruit parfait.* **Details:** *www.cafeconcerto.biz; by the W entrance of York Minster; 9.30 pm; no Amex; booking: max 6.*

City Screen Café Bar
City Screen Picturehouse £ 24
Coney St YO1 9QL (01904) 612 940
You may *"wait ages"*, but this cinema café (with a lovely terrace overlooking the river) rewards your patience with *"good food"* and *"good value"*. / **Sample dishes:** *Mexican-style tortillas & salsa; burger & chips; cakes.* **Details:** *www.picturehouses.co.uk; 9 pm; no booking.*

Four High Petergate £ 39
4 High Petergate YO1 7EH (01904) 658516
"At last, York is getting the restaurants it deserves!", says one reporter, and all agree that this *"friendly"* hotel bistro (*"with views onto one of York's oldest streets"*) is one of them; it offers *"fine"*, *"simple"* and *"robust"* dishes in a *"cosy"* setting.
/ **Sample dishes:** *slow-braised pork cheeks in sweet potato purée; cinnamon-scented duck breast; dark chocolate pistachio truffle torte.* **Details:** *www.fourhighpetergate.co.uk; 9.30 pm.* **Accommodation:** *14 rooms, from £95.*

J Baker's Bistro Moderne £ 39
7 Fossgate YO1 9TA (01904) 622688
The *"really different"* and *"eclectic"* approach of Jeff Baker's new venture – where a 'grazing' menu is a feature – has quickly won it acclaim as a true *"culinary delight"* (even if, perhaps inevitably, it strikes the occasional reporter as *"pretentious"*).
/ **Sample dishes:** *crab trifle; galloway steak & crunchy duck egg; lemon tops with curd ice cream, jelly & biscuits.* **Details:** *www.jbakers.co.uk; 10 pm; closed Mon & Sun.*

Masons Bistro £ 40
13 Fossgate YO1 9TA (01904) 611919
"High standards" are maintained at this *"boudoir-ish"* venture – a converted pub with *"a mish-mash of furniture"*, where the menu proposes *"classic bistro fare"*. / **Sample dishes:** *kleftiko; featherblade of beef slow-cooked with red wine; raspberry brûlée tart.* **Details:** *www.masons-bistro.co.uk; 9.30 pm; closed Mon L; children: 14+ at D.*

Melton's £ 42 ⭐

7 Scarcroft Rd YO23 1ND (01904) 634 341

*With its "consistently solid" standards, this "reliable", "front-room"
style venture ("in a terraced house between the city-centre and the
race course") is often tipped as "the best restaurant in York".*
/ ***Sample dishes:*** *goat's cheese soufflé with pine-nut dressing; roast beef;
chocolate indulgence with Grand Marnier sabayon.*
Details: *www.meltonsrestaurant.co.uk; 10 mins walk from Castle Museum;
10 pm; closed Mon L & Sun; no Amex.*

Melton's Too £ 30 ❌

25 Walmgate YO1 9TX (01904) 629 222

*Reports (many) on this all-day eatery have again become very mixed
– fans say it's "good for any occasion", but others have found recent
visits simply "very disappointing". / **Sample dishes:** Cheddar & watercress
tart; confit of duck; sticky toffee pudding. **Details:** www.meltonstoo.co.uk;
10.30 pm, Sun 9.30 pm; no Amex; need 8+ to book.*

Middlethorpe Hall £ 57 Ⓐ

Bishopthorpe Rd YO23 2GB (01904) 641241

*"A beautiful country house", on the outskirts of the city, complete
with a "wonderful, panelled dining room"; though not a great foodie
destination, it's cooking is consistently praised. / **Sample dishes:** seared
diver scallops; roast monkfish tail; chocolate fondue.*
Details: *www.middlethorpe.com; next to racecourse; 9.30 pm; children: 6+.*
Accommodation: *29 rooms, from £185.*

Tasting Room £ 41 ⭐

13 Swinegate Court East YO1 8AJ (01904) 627879

*Thanks to Nigel Stacey's "interesting" and "imaginative" menu (and a
"good wine list" too), this "very friendly" city-centre restaurant
is beginning to make quite a name for itself. / **Sample dishes:** salad
of Parma ham & asparagus; loin of lamb with creamed cabbage, apple &
horseradish; custard crème brûlée with shortbread biscuits.*
Details: *www.thetastingroom.co.uk; 9 pm; closed Sun; no Amex; children: 4+.*

Vanilla Black £ 34 ⭐

26 Swinegate YO1 8AZ (01904) 676750

*"The best veggie in the North of England"? – there's the occasional
report of "variability", but otherwise feedback on this "classy", "calm"
and "spacious" spot is quite a hymn of praise. / **Sample dishes:** crispy
cinnamon apple & walnut parfait with blackberry vinaigrette; hickory-smoked
duchesse potatoes & Wensleydale cheese pudding with pineapple pickle &
softboiled quail egg; express crème brulée. **Details:** www.vanillablack.co.uk;
9.15 pm; closed Mon, Tue L & Sun; no Amex.*

MAPS

Map 1

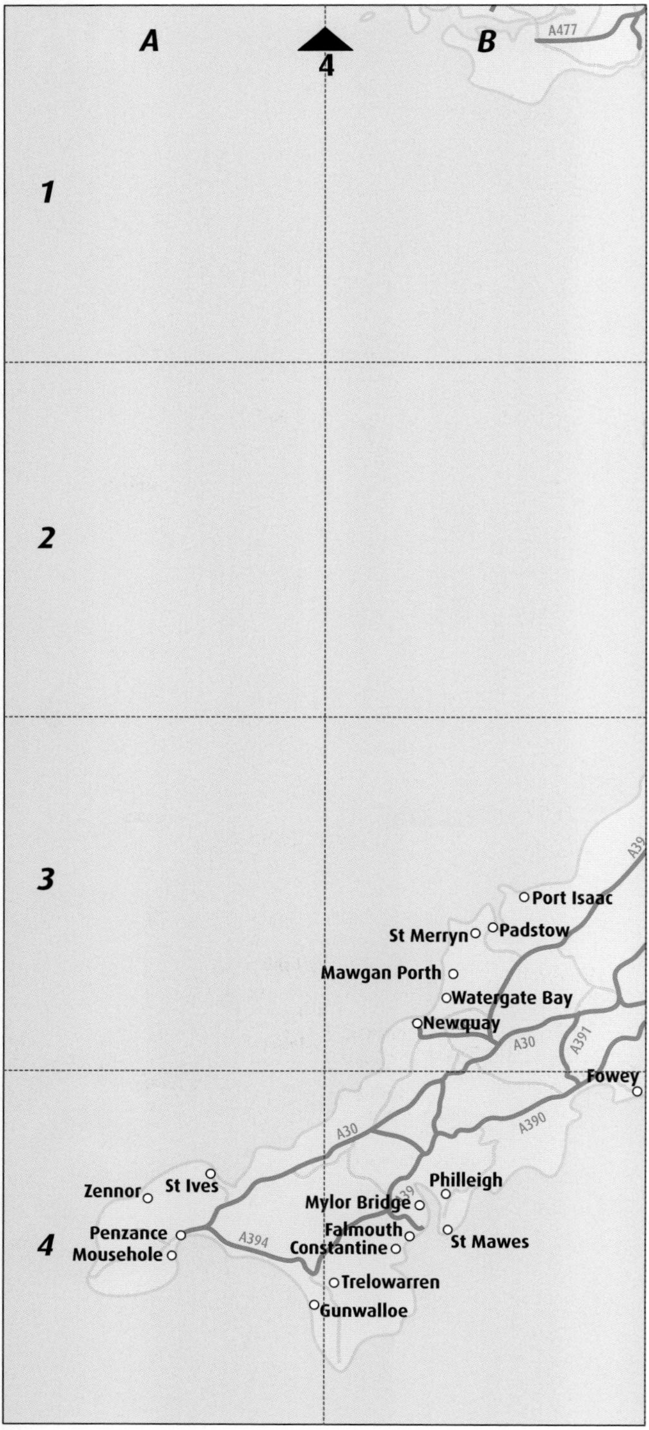

A   ▲4   B   A477

1

2

3
○Port Isaac
St Merryn○ ○Padstow
Mawgan Porth ○
○Watergate Bay
○Newquay
A30   A391
■Fowey

4
Zennor○ St Ives○
Philleigh○
Mylor Bridge○
Falmouth○ ○St Mawes
Penzance○   A394
Mousehole○   Constantine○
○Trelowarren
○Gunwalloe

Map 1

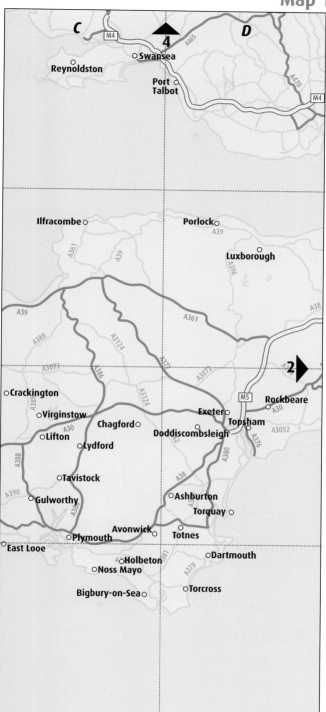

Map 1

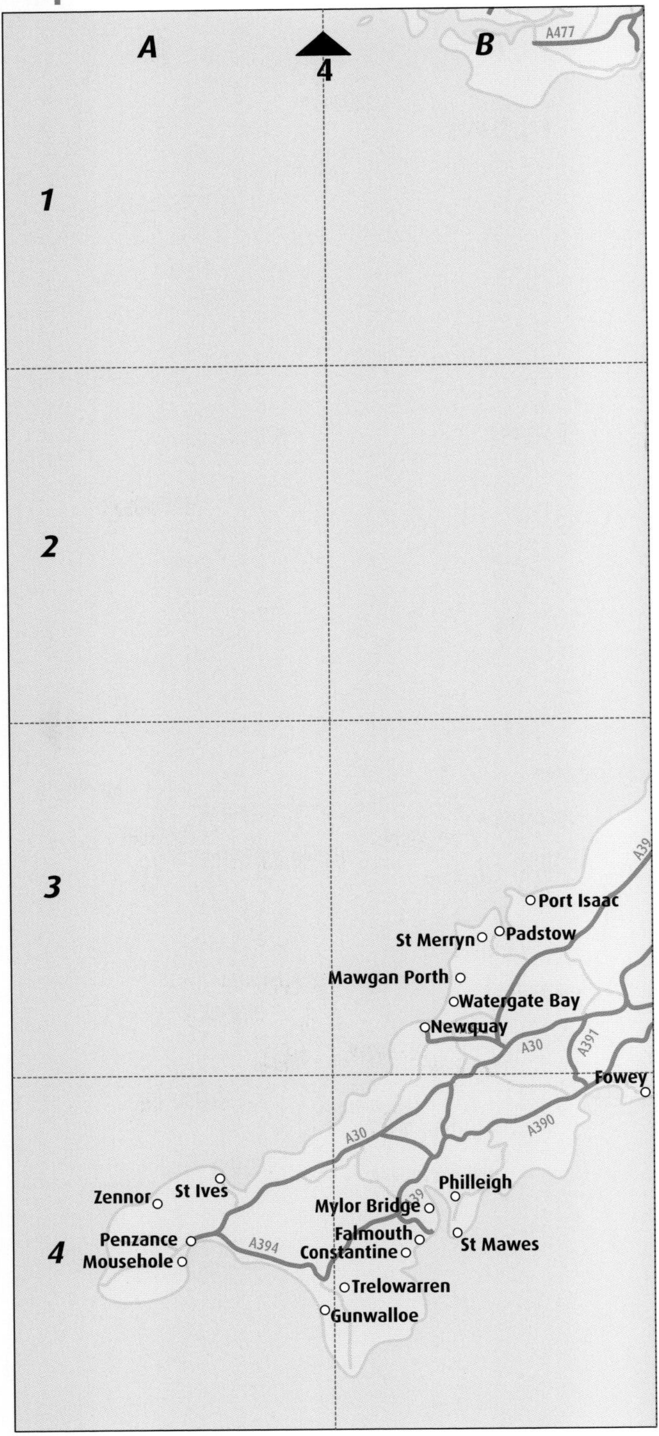

A   ▲4   B

1

2

3

○ Port Isaac
St Merryn ○ ○ Padstow
Mawgan Porth ○
○ Watergate Bay
○ Newquay
A30

Fowey ○

4

A30   A390

Zennor ○ St Ives ○
Mylor Bridge ○ Philleigh
Penzance ○ A394 Falmouth ○ St Mawes ○
Mousehole ○ Constantine ○
○ Trelowarren
○ Gunwalloe

Map 1

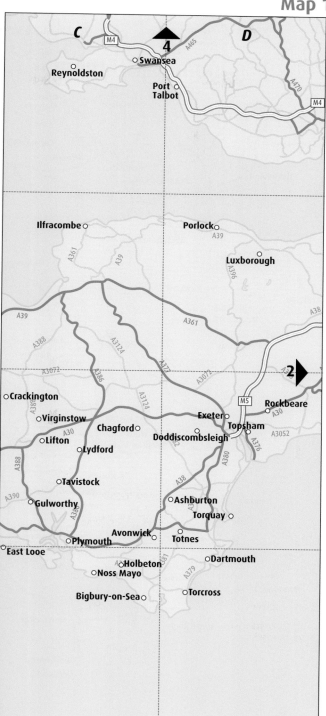

Map 2

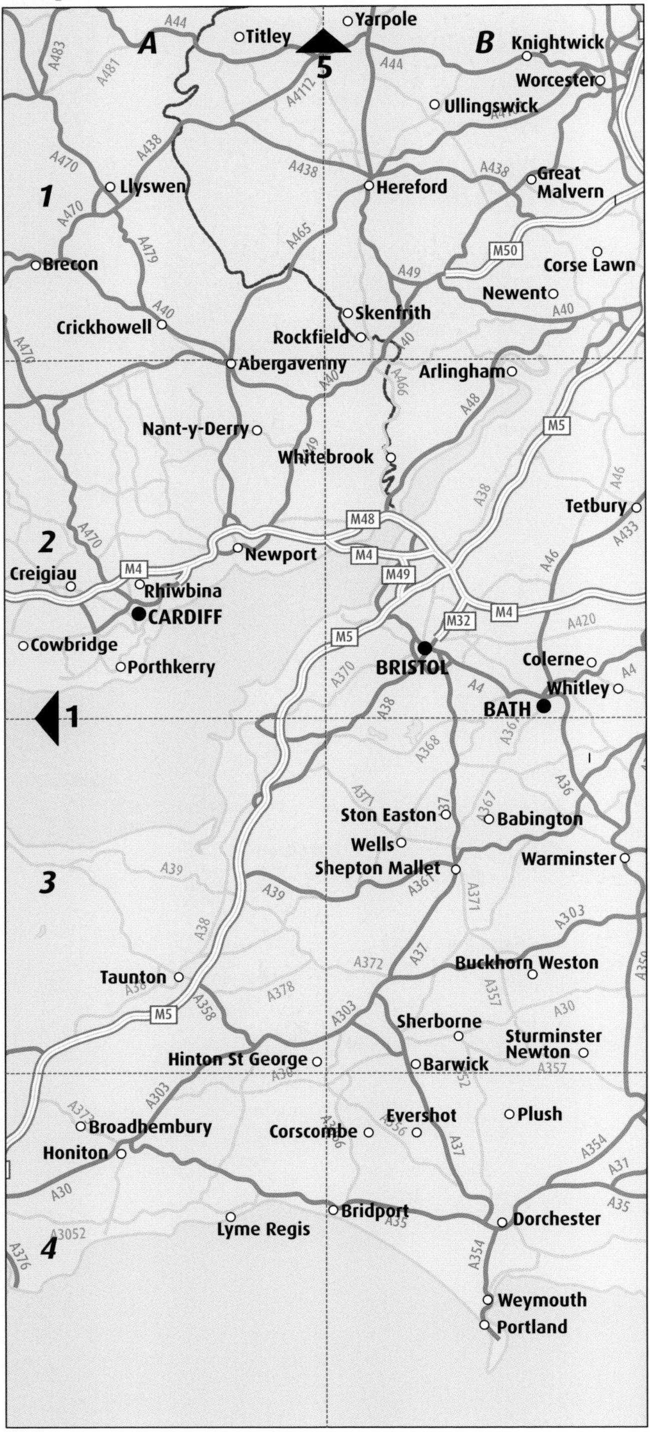

A

Titley   Yarpole

5

B   Knightwick

Worcester

Ullingswick

1

Llyswen

Hereford

Great Malvern

Brecon

Corse Lawn

Newent

Crickhowell

Skenfrith

Rockfield

Abergavenny

Arlingham

Nant-y-Derry

Whitebrook

Tetbury

2

Newport

Creigiau

Rhiwbina

CARDIFF

Cowbridge

Porthkerry

BRISTOL

Colerne

Whitley

BATH

1

Ston Easton

Babington

Wells

Shepton Mallet

Warminster

3

Taunton

Buckhorn Weston

Sherborne

Sturminster Newton

Hinton St George

Barwick

Broadhembury

Corscombe

Evershot

Plush

Honiton

Bridport

Dorchester

Lyme Regis

Weymouth

Portland

Map 2

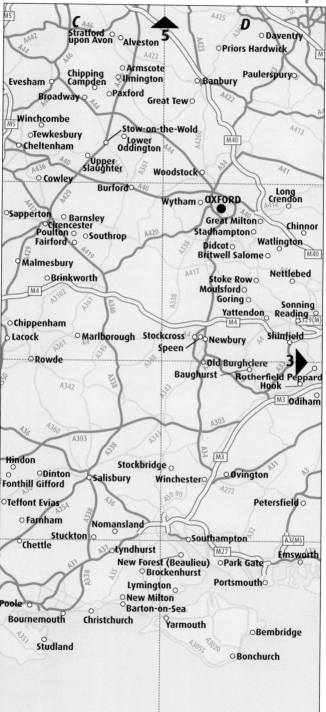

Map 3

Map 3

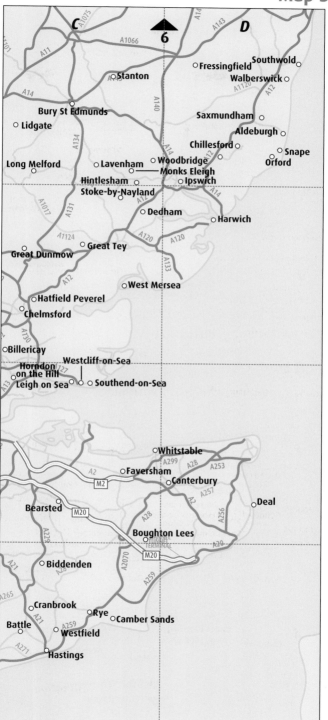

Map 4

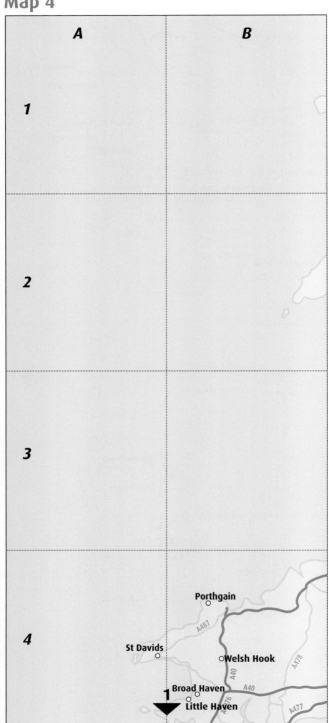

Map 4

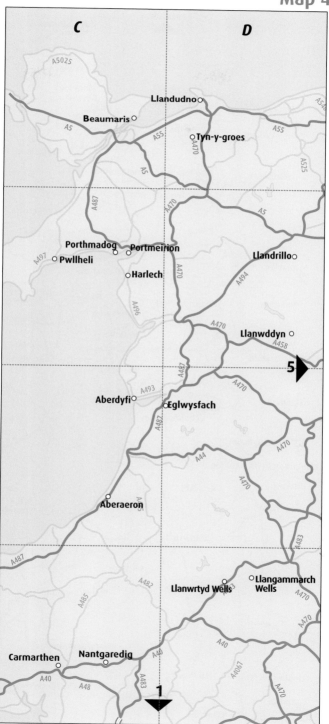

Map 5

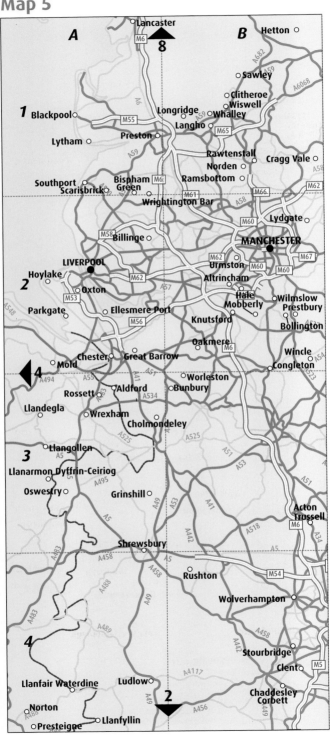

Map 5

Map 6

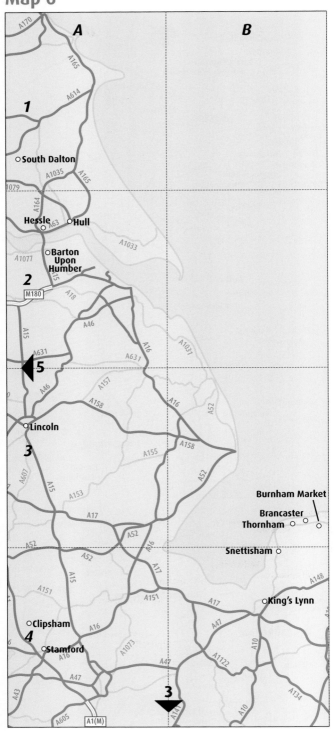

Map 6

C

D

Holkham
○   ○ ○**Blakeney**
A149   **Morston**

Holt ○ A148

Wolterton ○

Fakenham ○

○ **Itteringham**

A140

○**North Walsham**

A1067

A47

Norwich ○   **Brundall**
○   A47

Stoke Holy Cross ○

A11

A146

A143

3 ▼

A140

Map 7

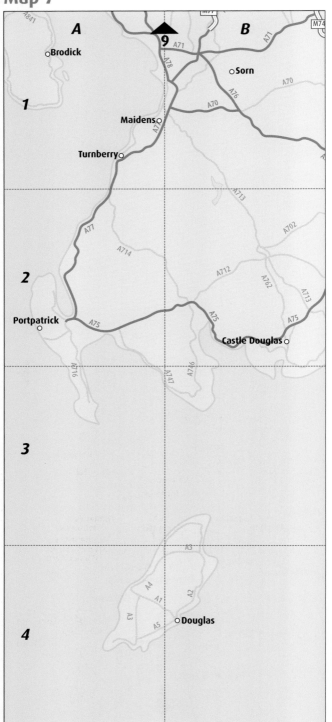

Map 7

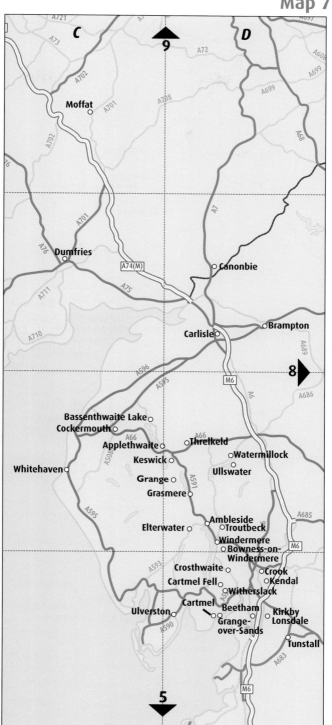

Map 8

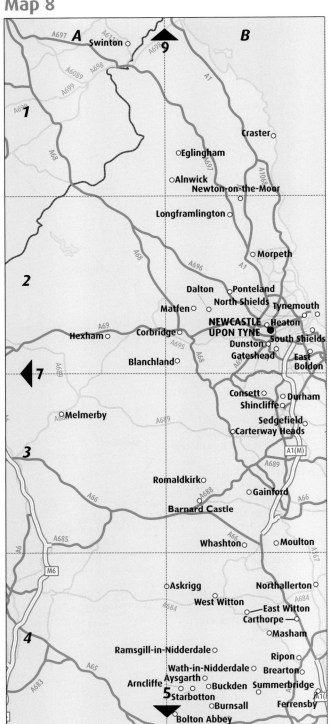

Map 8

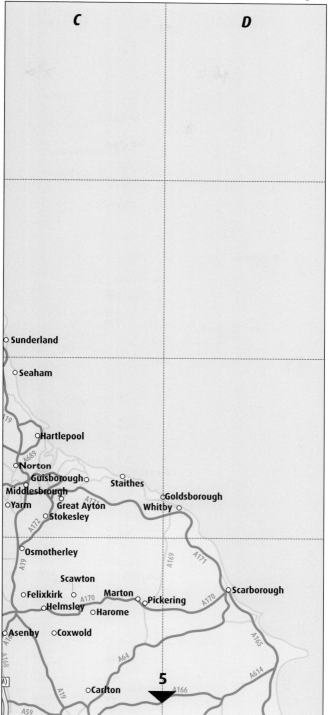

C

D

Sunderland

Seaham

A19

Hartlepool

A689
Norton
Guisborough
Middlesbrough
Yarm
Great Ayton
Stokesley
A172

Staithes

Goldsborough
Whitby

A172

A19
Osmotherley

Scawton

A169
A171

Felixkirk
A170
Marton
Helmsley
Harome

Pickering

A170
Scarborough

Asenby
Coxwold

A168
A64

A165

A168

A19

Carlton

5

A166

A614

A59

Map 9

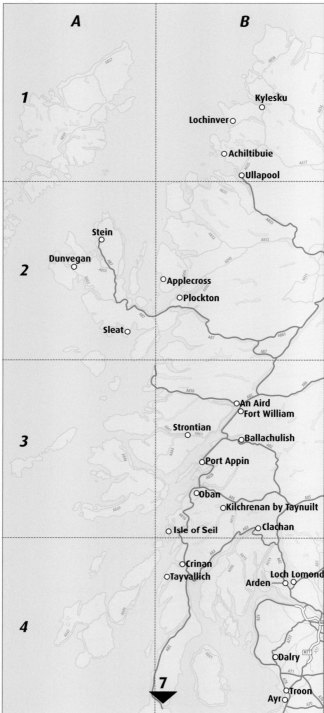

A

B

1

Kylesku

Lochinver○

○Achiltibuie

○Ullapool

2

Stein○

Dunvegan○

○Applecross

○Plockton

Sleat○

3

○An Aird
○Fort William

Strontian○

○Ballachulish

○Port Appin

○Oban

○Kilchrenan by Taynuilt

○Isle of Seil

○Clachan

○Crinan

○Tayvallich

Loch Lomond○

Arden○

○Dalry

○Troon

Ayr○

7

Map 9

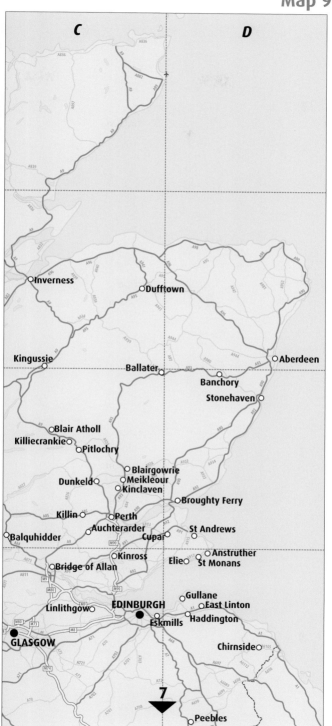

C

D

Inverness

Dufftown

Kingussie

Ballater

Aberdeen

Banchory

Stonehaven

Blair Atholl

Killiecrankie

Pitlochry

Blairgowrie

Dunkeld

Meikleour

Kinclaven

Broughty Ferry

Killin

Perth

Balquhidder

Auchterarder

Cupar

St Andrews

Anstruther

Elie

St Monans

Kinross

Bridge of Allan

Gullane

East Linton

Linlithgow

EDINBURGH

Eskmills

Haddington

GLASGOW

Chirnside

7

Peebles

Map 10

Map 10

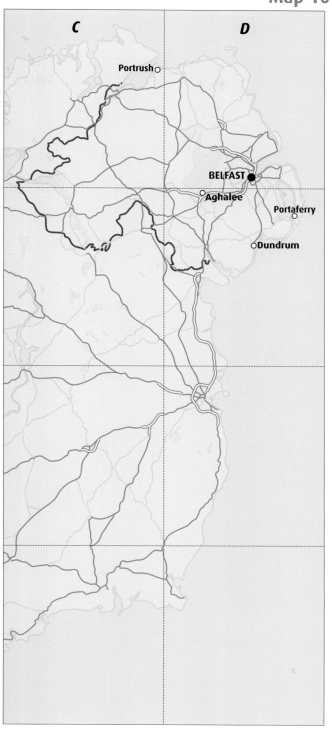

C

D

Portrush

BELFAST

Aghalee

Portaferry

Dundrum

ALPHABETICAL INDEX

ALPHABETICAL INDEX

ALPHABETICAL INDEX